Civil Drafting & Introduction to GIS
Revised Third Custom Edition

D1320531

Taken from:

Civil Drafting Technology, Seventh Edition
by David A. Madsen, Terence M. Shumaker, and David P. Madsen

AutoCAD® Civil 3D® 2010: Procedures and Applications
by Harry O. Ward and Nancy S. Orem

Learning Solutions

New York   Boston   San Francisco
London   Toronto   Sydney   Tokyo   Singapore   Madrid
Mexico City   Munich   Paris   Cape Town   Hong Kong   Montreal

Cover Art: Courtesy of PhotoDisc/Getty Images, Untitled 5, Barry Cronin.

Taken from:

Civil Drafting Technology, Seventh Edition
by David A. Madsen, Terence M. Shumaker, and David. P. Madsen
Copyright © 2010, 2007, 2004, 2001, 1998, 1994, 1983 by Pearson Education, Inc.
Published by Prentice Hall
Upper Saddle River, New Jersey 07458

AutoCAD® Civil 3D® 2010: Procedures and Applications
by Harry O. Ward and Nancy S. Orem
Copyright © 2010 by Pearson Education, Inc.
Published by Prentice Hall

All rights reserved. No part of this book may be reproduced, in any form or by any means, without permission in writing from the publisher.

This special edition published in cooperation with Pearson Learning Solutions.

All trademarks, service marks, registered trademarks, and registered service marks are the property of their respective owners and are used herein for identification purposes only.

Pearson Learning Solutions, 501 Boylston Street, Suite 900, Boston, MA 02116
A Pearson Education Company
www.pearsoned.com

Printed in the United States of America

4 5 6 7 8 9 10 V0CR 15 14 13 12 11

000200010270594887

ST

ISBN 10: 0-558-79674-5
ISBN 13: 978-0-558-79674-7

Brief Contents

To access all student data files for this section of the textbook, go to www. pearsondesigncentral.com

Part I

Taken from: AutoCAD® Civil 3D® 2010: Procedures and Applications by Harry O. Ward and Nancy S. Orem

To access all student files and figures for this section of the textbook, go to the companion website, http://ups.prenhall/chet_madsen_civildrafting_7

Part II

Taken from: Civil Drafting Technology, Seventh Edition by David A. Madsen, Terence M. Shumaker, and David P. Madsen

To access all student data files for this section of the textbook, go to www. pearsondesigncentral.com

Part I Contents

Chapter 6   Civil 3D—The Modern Curvilinead   157

Chapter 7   Advanced 3D Surface Modeling   211

Chapter 8   Advanced Profiles and Sections   231

Chapter 9   Advanced Corridor Development   257

Chapter 10   Advanced Site Grading and Virtual Site Design™   293

The Components and Interface of Civil 3D

1

Chapter Objectives

- Understand the field of civil engineering and its relationship with Computer Aided Design and Drafting.
- Be familiar with the applications embedded within the Civil 3D offering.
- Realize that Civil 3D is not a program; rather it is a cross-pollination of several programs integrated into a single engineering solution.
- Understand why Civil 3D is creating a paradigm shift in the civil engineering business.
- Understand the software's new philosophies, interfaces, and capabilities.

INTRODUCTION

Chapter 1 introduces Civil 3D, its philosophies, what it is composed of, and its interface. The philosophies are causing a ***paradigm shift*** in the civil engineering business because the software is an application with entirely new methods, interfaces, and capabilities. These will be described in concept so that the reader, upon beginning the procedurized tutorials and exercises, will at least have an impression of what to expect the software to accomplish.

paradigm shift: A fundamental change in how processes are performed.ggp

This chapter also discusses the contents of the Civil 3D suite of software because many solutions come with its install and its adjunct installs. It describes the applications embedded within Civil 3D's capabilities.

Unlike the help system that accompanies the software, this chapter provides detailed illustrations and explanations of the interface and related icons in a single location. This will ease learning these items and undoubtedly save the reader time and reduce frustration in the use of the software. The icons have an enormous number of subtle variations that the user must be aware of in order to stay in complete control of the project data.

REVIEW OF FUNCTIONS AND FEATURES TO BE USED

The features being introduced in this chapter include what the software offers, an explanation of AutoCAD MAP 3D, what the interface tools are, and what the icons mean. This chapter explains how the software is style- and data-driven, how it uses objects for design, and the fact that it offers DOT-level highway design capabilities.

THE COMPONENTS OF AUTODESK CIVIL 3D

Civil 3D consists of the integration of several programs including AutoCAD as the foundation graphics engine. Although the full set of commands is available, only the **File**, **Window**, **Help**, and **Insert** pull-down menus are shown when the software initially launches. Augmenting AutoCAD

Figure 1-1   Civil 3D and MAP 3D pull-down menus

is the MAP 3D software, which adds GIS, important utilities, and drafting cleanup tools to the user's toolkit (see Figure 1-1). The civil engineering component of the software adds on the heavy civil engineering design software. A visualization tool completes the offering by allowing for the development of some of the industry's highest-quality visualizations.

Visualization was included in the 2006 version, but the entire AutoCAD version has been updated to include major rendering tools. This provides users with benefits in that the AutoCAD data is now directly renderable (if that is indeed a word). This textbook will describe rendering only briefly because that function is deserving of a text in itself.

Civil 3D includes a native visualization tool. It uses some of the core technology developed in Autodesk VIZ, including much of the photometric lighting and rendering technology. Civil 3D has optimized methodology to render and animate data from Civil 3D more effectively. Its user interface has been simplified. The guiding principle is that Civil 3D is the model building and organization application, whereas AutoCAD is used for visualization.

For the purposes of this text, AutoCAD knowledge is assumed to be a prerequisite, as there are many sources and textbooks available from which AutoCAD can be learned. Appendix E offers a brief discussion of visualization.

pull-down menus, icons, toolbars, pop-downs, and dialog boxes: Interface items.

Some of the conventions to be used in this text include references to ***pull-down menus, icons, toolbars, pop-downs,*** and ***dialog boxes***. An example of the pull-down menu is shown in Figure 1-2. In fact, ellipses within the pull-down menu indicate that a dialog box will display to complete the information gathering needed to fulfill the command request.

An example of a toolbar is shown in Figure 1-3; this one has three icons. Toolbars are configurable; that is, the user can reshape them by dragging one corner. Toolbars are also customizable in that commands can be added to or deleted from them.

A pop-down menu is shown in Figure 1-4, and there are usually choices to be made within them.

Dialog boxes are used frequently and might appear similar to that shown in Figure 1-5.

Note:
Some add-in software available for Civil 3D that is important to know about includes Trimble Link™, Carlson Connect™, and Leica Exchange. These supplements allow for data exchange with manufacturers' equipment and provide Civil 3D with the ability to send data directly to 3D/GPS Machine Control devices.

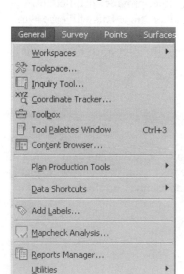

Figure 1-2   Menus and submenus

Figure 1-3   Example toolbar

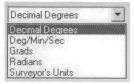

Figure 1-4   Pop-down menu

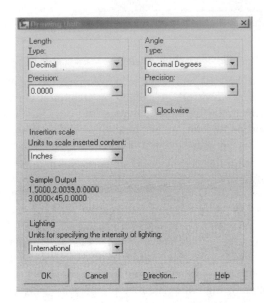

Figure 1-5   Dialog box

INTRODUCTION TO AUTOCAD MAP 3D

MAP 3D is a required and foundational aspect of Civil 3D, yet it is one of the more misunderstood and underutilized software packages. This software was an independent solution sold as an adjunct to AutoCAD for many years. It has been available for over ten years; however, it was not always sold under the name MAP. Years ago, part of it was called the Autodesk Data Extension (ADE). This software, introduced in 1993, possessed many drafting-oriented features that were missing in the main AutoCAD solution.

Together with AutoCAD, MAP 3D made for a great set of tools. Unfortunately, it was not a big seller, although those with very advanced needs probably purchased it. For those who have had a history with AutoCAD products, this was one of their business models; that is, selling "extensions" to AutoCAD. There were at least two other extensions as well: the Autodesk Modeling Extension (AME) and the Autodesk SQL Extension (ASE). SQL stands for Structured Query Language used to extend database functionality.

The Autodesk Modeling Extension was included in the base AutoCAD software in Release 14. The Data Extension and SQL Extension, combined into a new product in 1996 called AutoCAD MAP, became fairly popular, especially for civil engineering and surveying users. By combining the graphics tools with the database tools, MAP created an environment that GIS users could benefit from. The ASE toolset allowed users to attach to external databases and create links to the AutoCAD graphical entities, perform sophisticated queries, and generate robust reports and results using AutoCAD.

AutoCAD MAP 3D, introduced in 2004, added surface modeling, surface analysis, and ***point groups*** to the software. These functions are part of the Civil 3D package and as such are removed from the MAP 3D menus. Because of MAP 3D's importance as part of the software, a discussion of its capabilities follows.

point groups: A Civil 3D object representing a collection of points grouped by a relationship such as utility points, property points, and terrain points.

AutoCAD MAP 3D augments AutoCAD and enhances the creation, maintenance, and presentation of mapping information. With MAP 3D, users can do the following:

* Open and link AutoCAD drawings to associated databases.
* Develop new data or edit data to maps to make them more intelligent.
* Use many unique features to assist in cleaning up "noise" in maps.
* Use a "batch" plotting facility for easy and flexible map plotting.
* Produce basic thematic maps with legends.
* Perform geodetic transformations on graphical objects in a file. This allows for moving or rotating data from one geodetic zone to another.

- Access map data in other formats, such as Oracle, MicroStation, Mapinfo, Arcview, and ArcInfo.
- Link any external documents to objects in their maps.

MAP 3D is the foundation for Civil 3D and helps in developing and managing complex design projects. MAP 3D can increase teamwork efficiency by creating a comprehensive and cost-effective project database. It integrates multiple drawings into one seamless environment providing access, editing, and reporting of drawing, attribute, and related database information within a single AutoCAD session. You can view and edit objects from multiple source drawings in a single work session.

The basis of this product is a robust query engine designed to assist AutoCAD users working with large or complex data sets. MAP 3D lets you query AutoCAD drawings based on any combination of drawing properties, object location, or information stored in related databases. This flexibility speeds up work by allowing you to focus on just the pertinent information. The query engine enables "super cross-references" because you can access several drawings simultaneously yet limit the reference to precisely the geographic area of the drawing you want. You also have full editing access to all of these queried drawings so edits can be made concurrently.

AutoCAD MAP 3D's multiple-drawing edit capability provides a secure environment for multiple MAP users who may be sharing their data or drawings. Project teams can efficiently and safely share drawings and data. By providing simultaneous access to interrelated drawings, teams can work concurrently from the same source drawings, increasing project team flexibility and efficiency and reducing total process time.

AutoCAD MAP 3D's management tools include routines to automate linking graphic objects to database records, a system to link documents to graphic objects thereby allowing easy access to those documents from your drawings, and an object data structure for storing and accessing data within your AutoCAD drawings.

Features of MAP 3D

AutoCAD MAP 3D allows users to access and modify graphic and nongraphic data stored in multiple AutoCAD drawing (.DWG) files. Users perform these modifications from within their current "active" AutoCAD file, and the user's environment acts as a single database of information.

One of the most popular features within the package allows multiple users to access central AutoCAD drawings and perform an advanced query for objects and data within those drawings. Once queried, the user can decide where the objects should finally reside; that is, back in the source drawings, with a new drawing, or remain in the current drawing. This awesome power has now been augmented with strong SQL features, import/export capabilities, and geodetic transformations.

The ability to perform graphic data accessing is selective and can occur through multiple drawings, whereas nongraphic accessing uses the AutoCAD extended entity data (or object data). The MAP 3D module provides direct access from within AutoCAD to external database management systems (DBMS). Examples of these are Microsoft Access, dBASE, INFORMIX, ORACLE, and PARADOX. Using Extended entity data (EED), a user can also link the AutoCAD data with other applications such as word processing and spreadsheets.

The nongraphic link provides the same command set regardless of the database in use. MAP 3D has drivers for the most popular databases systems. Open DataBase Connectivity (ODBC) is supported for general databases as well.

An Application for MAP 3D

An example of a MAP 3D application is that it can be used to input and/or modify data on a large engineering project in which the data are distributed among many large AutoCAD (.dwg) files. With MAP 3D, you can establish connections between entities or symbols in the various drawings with your current drawing, without carrying the overhead associated with the unwanted data that may exist in those files.

The method of accessing the geographic limits of the data in the drawings is the use of spatial databases. Augmenting this is the ability to access the data via property selection. In other words, you can identify the boundary of the data search and bring over only the data on the Road-Centerline layer to the current working session.

For an engineering project, a key map outlining the project's boundaries may be advantageous, so that users can select data from geographic locations without becoming overwhelmed by the total volume of data. A little forethought should easily identify anticipated "subboundaries."

Main Features of MAP 3D

1. Information can be isolated and analyzed by
   - Viewing selected features and statistics
   - Exporting data to external files and accessing EED
2. Data editing. After the data are extracted, they can be
   - Changed or deleted
   - Moved to another drawing or saved back to the original drawing
   - Saved to a new drawing
3. Data Selection Enhancements exist for more effective queries, such as
   - Boolean constructs (AND, OR, XOR)
   - Transform data from one coordinate system to another
   - Match features across edges of different drawings
4. MAP 3D has unique editing features to assist in cleaning up mathematical noise in maps. This noise consists of sloppy drafting, errors where entities cross one another or are duplicated, and so on. These features help prepare maps for accurate analysis and the creation of map topologies. They comprise
   - ***Rubber sheeting*** stretches objects from one set of points to a new set of points, often used to correct scans and to compensate for map distortions
   - Boundary clipping
   - Map-edge cutting tools that create clean breaks between linear objects
   - Precisely aligned map-sheet edges
   - Neatly cut and created spaces for annotations
5. The ability exists to import/export other formats including MicroStation (DGN), Mapinfo (MIF), Arcview, Oracle, and ArcInfo file formats.
6. Basic thematic maps with legends can be produced. Create thematic maps while allowing for automatic altering of color, linetype, text, and other parameters to show correlation in database information. Thematic maps can be based on object properties such as layer and linetype, object data you define in the drawing, or SQL data linked to external databases. As well as limiting objects in the thematic display to a certain area, users can also limit objects based on specific layers or particular block names.

> **rubber sheeting:** Stretches objects from one set of points to a new set of points, often used to correct scans and to compensate for map distortions.

AutoCAD MAP 3D also supports topologies. A Topology in GIS describes the relationship of connecting adjacent features and adds a level of "intelligence" to the data set. A user can create, modify, and delete topologies; create buffers around points, lines, and polygons; analyze maps with point, line, and polygon overlays using **INTERSECT**, **UNION**, **IDENTITY**, **ERASE**, **CLIP**, and **PASTE** operations; use "shortest path trace" to find the shortest distance between two locations, useful for emergency services; and use "flood trace" to trace out from a point a specific distance in all directions, useful, for example, for analyzing demographic data and comparing alternative retail locations based on driving or walking times. You can also use flood trace to trace out to blocks that have specific attribute, object data, or external database record value, useful, for example, for finding all valves that need to be turned off in a water network.

Security

A newly installed copy of MAP 3D contains no prebuilt securities, except one for the superuser. The superuser must set these. Login as the superuser by using SUPERUSER as the login name and SUPERUSER as the password (note all caps). To establish security, follow this procedure:

1. Use the **EDIT-USER** command to set up at least one superuser.
2. Using the **EDIT-USER** command, the superuser sets the privileges.
3. Using the **CONFIGURE** command, the superuser enables the FORCELOG variable. After this is set, users must log into MAP 3D with the **SET USER** command.

The Spatial Database

In a CAD environment, a spatial database is a set of internal and external databases for one or more related drawings. Part of the description defines a CAD drawing. The remainder itemizes nongraphic characteristics such as databases or other documents.

You can think of drawing files as part of a spatial database. MAP 3D evaluates the data that define the graphics and their associated data, and the data linked to it from external databases. A CAD drawing becomes visible only in a drawing editor, such as AutoCAD, which is really a special kind of database manager; it both writes and interprets data that represent graphic elements, called *entities*.

Thus, a spatial database describes anything that you can represent in part or completely by one or more drawings. For example, a spatial database could describe a treatment plant, a city, an oil refinery, a geographical region, and so forth. Moreover, a spatial database can represent not only shapes but also names, materials, part numbers, suppliers, dates, and the like. *The primary requirement is that all entities share a common coordinate system.*

An AutoCAD spatial database has up to three parts:

1. The Graphic database, which is a data file that contains the definitions of all the geometric entities in a drawing such as lines, circles, arcs, and so on.
2. The Extended entity data (EED) or Object data. These data define additional, nongraphic aspects of an entity. Normally unseen, they are part of the drawing file and are stored with individual entities.
3. The External database(s) contains data files that you can read with a database manager. Like the EED database, it also contains nongraphic data. However, it can be linked to entities in one or many drawings.

All of these databases are within the scope of basic AutoCAD. However, the power of MAP 3D lies in that it can take advantage of these databases in several drawings simultaneously.

The power of MAP 3D is its ability to open a working session using a *current drawing*, attaching other AutoCAD files to the working session, performing queries of external information, and importing the results of queries into the current drawing. After the data have been added, deleted, or modified, they can then be saved to a new drawing, to the current drawing, or back to the drawings from whence the data came.

Source drawings are AutoCAD drawings and any data files linked to them that contain all of a project's data (both graphic and nongraphic) on which you want to run queries. Different source files categorize a project's data in different ways. For example, they can categorize data by location— as for a set of adjacent maps—or by content—for example, by water, gas, electricity, and so on— or by any mix of these and other criteria. When you use the AutoCAD **OPEN** command, the entire drawing is loaded. All of the drawing's entities, or as many as the current view allows, appear. When MAP 3D "opens" (or attaches) one or more source drawings, no part of them appears. Instead, "attach" means that the contents of those drawings are available for querying and bringing into the current drawing. MAP 3D supports several query strategies.

Queries

Querying, as the central activity of MAP 3D, is how MAP 3D selects information from one or more drawing files. Several strategies exist for defining query criteria and for handling the entities resulting from the query. Queries range from simple to complex and can be saved for reusing, editing, and supplementing them with AutoLISP expressions. Queries access one or more source drawing files. Usually, MAP 3D queries bring entities directly into the current drawing.

A MAP 3D query has several levels of complexity that are primarily determined by query definition criteria, query mode, and method of saving queried entities.

Query Definitions.   A query definition sets the criteria for selecting entities. The definition can include graphics; Boolean operators such as AND, OR, and XOR; SQL expressions; and AutoLISP expressions. Query definitions use three types of criteria:

1. **Location.**   Selects entities based on their location in the source drawing. The location can be relative to a specific point or feature or within a window. For example, you can search for entities that lie within a given radius of a specified point or within a given distance on either side of a specified line.

2. **Properties.**   Selects entities based on properties that relate to graphic or Extended entity data (EED) in the drawing file, such as length, layer, material, part number, and so on.

3. **SQL.**   Selects entities based on data in linked SQL database tables, such as supplier, owner, cost, and so on.

Query Access Modes.   MAP 3D queries entities in source drawings in one of several query modes including Preview, Draw, and Report modes.

The modes are distinguished by how permanent the query entities in the current and source drawings will be. The Preview and Draw modes display entities in the current drawing with different degrees of completeness, with different consequences for the source drawing, and for different purposes. The Report mode exports data to a file without displaying it. While querying, MAP 3D locks the source drawing file so other users cannot access that drawing. After all the entities retrieved from the source drawings appear in the current drawing, all source drawing files are unlocked so other MAP users can have access. After data are edited, a record-locking mechanism kicks in and locks only that entity so that others cannot edit it at the same time. This prevents users from "stepping on each other's toes."

Preview Mode.   If you execute a Preview mode query, objects that match the query criteria appear on-screen but are not actually copied from the source drawings. Use the **REDRAW** command on the **View** menu to clear the screen. It displays the queried entities on the screen in the current drawing without affecting either the current or the source drawings. These queried entities typically have an entity type of ADEXXXXXXX if listed; however, this will disappear on redraw. Show mode displays queried entities in the current drawing only temporarily; however, **ZOOM** and **PAN** will work until a **REDRAW** operation occurs that causes the queried entities to disappear. Use Preview mode for a quick view of a query and to see whether you are on the right track.

Draw Mode.   If you execute a Draw mode query, objects that match the query criteria are copied into the work session, provided they have not already been copied in by a previous query. The original objects remain unchanged in the source drawings. AutoCAD MAP 3D will not place duplicate copies of an object in the work session. If a previous query copied an object into the work session, the new query will not copy it in again. If you retrieve an object that is on a locked layer, you cannot save changes back to the source drawing. To save changes back, you must open the source drawing and unlock the layer before performing the query. Draw mode copies the queried entities into the current drawing, displays the queried entities on-screen, and leaves the source drawings unchanged. Because the queried entities are copied into the current drawing, using **REDRAW** does not make the entities disappear. After data are modified, MAP 3D locks the entities in the source file. No other MAP 3D user can edit until they are saved back or released. When an object is locked, other users can view it, but they cannot edit it.

Report Mode.   If you execute a Report mode query, AutoCAD MAP 3D creates the specified text file. Use a text editor, such as Windows Notepad, to view the report file.

Additional tools that make MAP 3D a worthwhile foundation item for Civil 3D include the Drawing Cleanup commands, **TRANSFORM** and **RUBBER SHEETING**, and mass editing commands such as **BOUNDARY BREAK** and **BOUNDARY TRIM**. GIS professionals need these tools to ensure that their linework is accurate and clean, as do engineers and surveyors.

Editing and Graphical Cleanup Tools

The Drawing Cleanup commands correct linear object and node errors to create a clean topology. The commands include these abilities: **Delete Duplicates**, **Erase Short Objects**, **Break Crossing Objects**, **Extend Undershoots**, **Apparent Intersection**, **Snap Clustered Nodes**,

Dissolve Pseudo-Nodes, **Erase Dangling Objects**, **Simplify Objects**, **Zero-Length Objects**, and **Weed Polylines**. The **TRANSFORM** command scales, offsets, and rotates selected objects. The **RUBBER SHEETING** command stretches objects from one set of points to a new set of points and is often used to correct scans that were made from stretched hard copies. The **BOUNDARY BREAK** command cleans map edges by cutting lines, *2D* polylines, arcs, and circles that cross a specified edge. The **BOUNDARY TRIM** command trims objects to a selected or defined boundary.

The MAP 3D menu tools for performing data cleanup can solve problems that have vexed users for years—further evidence of why a land development professional should be using AutoCAD MAP 3D for everyday operations. The following describe several common scenarios that can wreak havoc on engineering projects.

Scenario 1.   On a site where existing surface data are defined by mass points and *breaklines*, the surveyor must process these data and build an *existing ground* surface. Engineers using AutoCAD Land Development Desktop points and faults, on the other hand, might develop the proposed site. In either case, various situations could lead to crossing breaklines or vertical faces. Of course, surface processing does not tolerate vertical faces because the *slope* is infinity, owing to a divide by zero in the calculation.

The software, however, can locate all the invalid crossings and, depending on the type of crossing, will trim, break, or otherwise fix such incidents. Previously, users spent large amounts of time performing these tasks manually.

Scenario 2.   The traditional AutoCAD user might trim and erase feverishly to clip data to specific locations or boundaries. Now, the software can break all of the objects so that their properties may be altered and can perform the trimming to boundaries. Users can easily trim data to open or close polylines.

Scenario 3.   If a user inadvertently copied AutoCAD drawing data on top of itself, such an error would double not only the file size but also the plot stroking, thereby affecting the quality of the plot. MAP 3D can help users avoid such a nightmare by deleting duplicate objects while preserving the integrity of the original file data.

Each of these scenarios demonstrates how the software can perform sophisticated drawing cleanup operations in a simple, common-sense fashion.

Among other features of the cleanup tools are the following:

- MAP 3D can automatically eliminate the speckling inherent in scanned images and can automatically extend or trim property lines that do not close, according to user-specified tolerances. It can weed out densely populated vertices in polyline data.
- The conversion utilities will redefine lines, arcs, 3D polylines, and circles into polylines.
- After editing, the **Mapping** commands provide the ability to modify the original entities, create new entities but retain the original ones, or create new entities and delete the original ones.
- Users can perform object selection for editing by using automatic algorithms or by simply selecting objects using traditional AutoCAD methods.
- Rubber sheeting of data is supported in a user-friendly way. Paper stretch can cause inherent errors in data that have been scanned and converted to vector data. The software tools allow users to correct this situation.

Geodetic Transformations

One of the most powerful commands in MAP 3D's repertoire for a surveyor is the ability to assign a geodetic coordinate system (Global Coordinate System) and transform data from one geodetic coordinate system to another.

2D: Two dimensions, characterized by the use of the *X*- and *Y*-axes in the Cartesian coordinate system resulting in planar material.

breaklines: 3D polylines representing breaks in the planar slopes of the terrain. A breakline causes the mathematics of the terrain modeling to avoid building triangles that would cross a breakline. The triangle thus has a side adjacent to the breakline but does not cross it.

existing ground: Natural ground

slope: A change in elevation over a horizontal distance, usually described by a ratio (3:1).

Note: You will need to configure the database to use with MAP 3D and that is out of the scope of this text. The addition of GIS into CADD software has become increasingly powerful. The reader is advised to seek additional resources to learn MAP 3D because this text is dedicated to Civil 3D.

CIVIL 3D—A CIVIL ENGINEERING DESIGN APPLICATION WITH NEW PHILOSOPHIES

Civil 3D continues to provide a unique software solution that offers a revolutionary approach to civil engineering design and drafting. It consists of the fusion of several Autodesk solutions including AutoCAD, MAP 3D, and the Civil 3D toolset along with Trimble Link™, Carlson Connect™, and Leica Exchange. Trimble, Carlson, and Leica are independent companies that provide links into Civil 3D so their users can use this product within their respective software solutions. They typically supply these add-ons after Civil 3D is released and they will probably do so again for the 2010 version. All of the traditional AutoCAD commands exist and can be accessed through the usual toolbars, pull-down menus, Custom User Interface, or type-in commands.

The new philosophies included within this software are data-driven design, reactive object technology, "ripple-through effectiveness," state-of-the-art interface enhancements, and an interactive and dynamic library of settings. The data-driven design refers to how objects will design themselves based on how the settings data are established. For instance, the horizontal curves for a road can be established such that they always meet a minimum standard allowable curve for the state or county in which they are being designed. Reactive object technology refers to items such as annotation automatically updating itself and reorienting itself when objects change or when the view is altered or rotated. The ***ripple-through effect*** refers to the impact that modifying an alignment has on the corridor's profiles, sections, and assemblies, whereas they automatically recompute their new values attributable to the modification. The interactive and dynamic library of settings refers to how the objects developed will take on aesthetic and visual characteristics based on how their display settings have been configured. The objects will change their appearance based on any changes to these settings automatically as well.

> **ripple-through effect:** A term coined to describe the dynamic modeling characteristics of Civil 3D in performing automatic updates to data.

What Civil 3D Introduces

In addition to Civil 3D's fundamentally sound and traditional routines, it introduces profoundly new capabilities to civil engineering users of CADD. These include the following:

- New interface tools, support for ribbons
- New objects specifically developed for civil design
- Dynamic, model-based design, data-driven methods, and the ripple-through effect
- Data-driven, object style libraries that control graphics appearances and text
- DOT-level highway design capabilities
- Rehabilitation and reconstruction design tools

> **Note:**
> Ribbons, which were introduced in Office 2007 by Microsoft as an interface enhancement. They consist of a bar across the top of your program window that shows the functions that can be performed from a single location. Ribbons try to consolidate the program's functions into a familiar place so that the user does not need to pick through multiple levels of menus, toolbars, or task panes.

Interface Tools.   The Civil 3D interface tools are evident in the **Tool Palettes** and **Toolspace**, as the software is launched, as shown in Figure 1-6. The interface for 2010 fully supports the ribbons found in Vista and Microsoft Office products. In the figure ribbons are shown for the menu command Modify. Note that the Modify tab is selected. Civil 3D commands can be selected likewise. (We will leave it to the readers to investigate the ribbons on their own. This text will continue to refer to the commands from the pull-down menus.) Autodesk has gone to great lengths to place more functionality at the user's fingertips, and the invention of the hide-away **Toolspace** and **Tool Palettes** provides excellent examples. For this book it is much easier for us to refer to commands by pull-down menu rather than to try to describe which icon picture to select when choosing commands. Therefore, it is recommended that you set up your workspace for production as it is in Figure 1-10. Notice that the Civil 3D program is not maximized. In order to set your system up so that it is conducive with the textbook references and descriptions perform the following exercise.

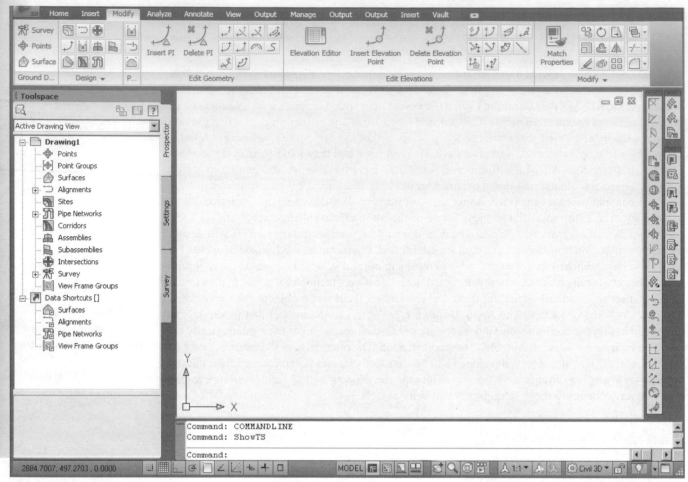

Figure 1-6   Interface with ribbons

Exercise 1-1: Ribbons and Menus

1. In the small toolbar at the upper left corner of the screen, click on the down arrow. Select the command to **Show Menu Bar** as shown in Figure 1-7. This will bring up the normal menu commands that we will use to choose our routines from.
2. Then right click to the right of the ribbons and the menu shown in Figure 1-8 will display. Select **Close** to terminate the ribbon display.
3. In the bottom right corner of the system, click on the **Workspace Switching** button shown in Figure 1-9 and select the Civil 3D workspace. This should place Civil 3D menus at the top of the screen. If not, select it again and you should see the display shown in Figure 1-10.

Figure 1-7   Show menu bar

Figure 1-8   Terminate the ribbon display

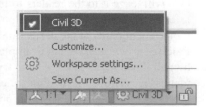

Figure 1-9   Workspace switching

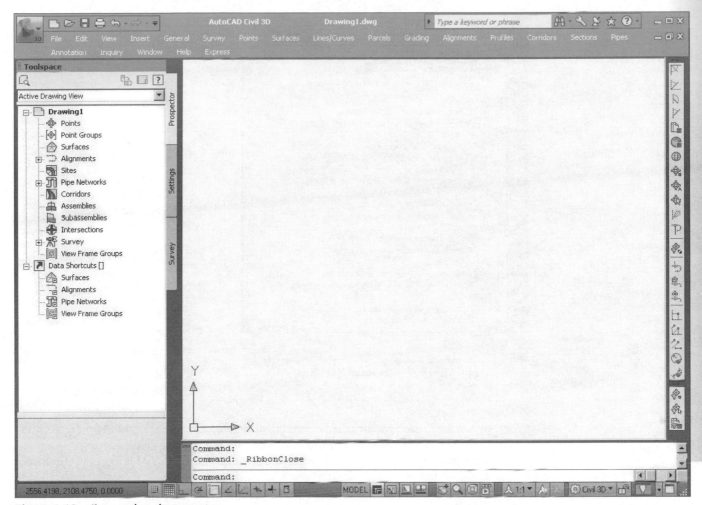

Figure 1-10   Proposed workspace setup

An entire set of Survey-related tools exists in the software as evidenced by the **Survey** pull-down menu.

The following procedure shows you how to accomplish this user workspace. Note that it is not required for the use of the software; it simply places the maximum amount of power at your fingertips without sacrificing design space. The advantage is that you have maximized the working area for design but have left the **Tool Palettes** and **Toolspace** available. Simply passing the mouse over these palettes opens them. When you finish making a selection from one of them, the palettes automatically close up.

Exercise 1-2: Set Up Production Workspace

1. Launch the Civil 3D software by double-clicking the icon on the desktop.
2. The system may appear similar to that shown in Figure 1-10.

An Inquiry Toolspace, with instantaneous readouts of many types of data, is included as part of the interface and can be found under the **General** menu. See Figure 1-11.

3. If the **Palettes** and **Toolspaces** are not displayed, select **Toolspace...** and **Tool Palettes Window** from the **General** pull-down menu.
4. Right-click on the spine of each palette and select **Auto-hide** (Figure 1-12).

You can hold the <**Ctrl**> key down when moving palettes to prevent them from docking or uncheck the **Allow Docking** option in the shortcut menu.

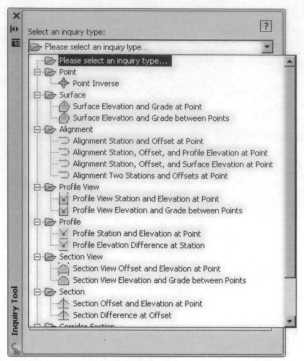

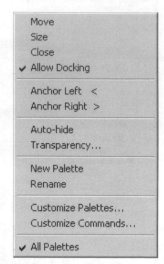

Figure 1-11   The Inquiry Toolspace

Figure 1-12   Right-click menu on palettes

5. When done, each palette collapses and floats in the workspace, as shown in Figure 1-13.
6. Size the Civil 3D window to about two-thirds of your desktop size.
7. Drag the **Tool Palettes** to the far right side of the desktop and drop it. Drag the **Toolspace** to the far left side of the desktop and drop it and click on the minus sign. They will both contract.

Figure 1-13   Collapsed palettes

8. Resize the Civil 3D window from the upper left and lower right corners to fit completely between the contracted palettes. You have now maximized your functionality without sacrificing drawing space.
9. Trying to set this up without using a procedure similar to this will cause the palettes to "dock," thereby reducing your overall drawing area. See Figure 1-14.

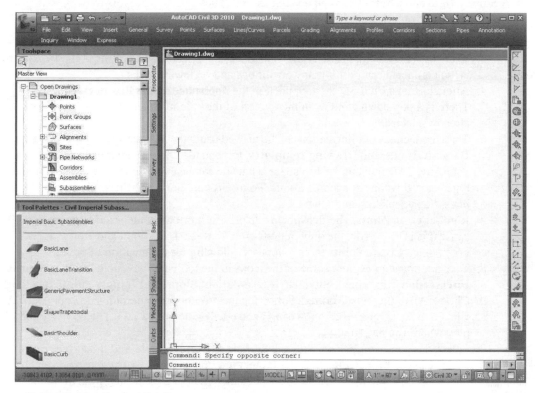

Figure 1-14   Docked Palettes

Panorama Palette.   The **Panorama** window is a multipurpose palette with the primary purpose of displaying data such as points, alignment entities, and description keys. The **Panorama** is also a **Tool Palette** that provides users with an **Event Viewer** to view messages that are logged during an Autodesk Civil 3D session. For example, if a surface is being created, you will read about the breaklines that may have been imported into the AutoCAD file.

If there are crossing breaklines (where one breakline physically crosses over or under another), that breakline is not added into the data set for surface modeling. The **Event Viewer** informs you of this occurrence. See Figure 1-15.

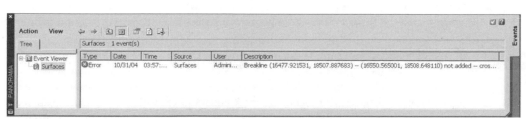

Figure 1-15   Panorama

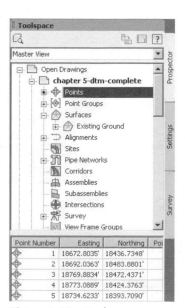

Figure 1-16   Toolspace Prospector

Toolspace Palette.   The Civil 3D environment includes the **Toolspace**, shown in Figure 1-16. The **Toolspace** has two panels: one called a **Prospector** for data and the other for **Settings**. The **Toolspace** allows the user to view project data and status at any time and updates itself dynamically to show the status of all design data within the drawing.

Figure 1-12 shows that when Points exist, they are displayed when the cursor is on the **Points** item. Observe also that the **Surfaces** item is expanded and shows one surface in existence.

Exercise 1-3: Investigate Toolspace

This exercise investigates the **Toolspace** more closely.

1. Make sure that you are in Civil 3D and that your **Toolspace** is displayed. If it is not, select **General >> Toolspace….**

A **Survey Item** and a **Survey** tab can be seen as well. These allow surveyors to work with graphical and dynamic objects in the same way as designers can in their part of the **Toolspace**.

2. Save your drawing to Toolspace.dwg in your project location.
3. There are two essential parts to the **Toolspace: Prospector** and **Settings**. The **Prospector** is the command central for many operations and reviewing tasks.
4. After starting a Civil 3D session, click in the **Toolspace** on the **Prospector** tab.
5. There is a pop-down window in the top left of the palette. Select **Master View** if it is not already selected.
6. Three collections of information can be viewed using the **Master View: Open Drawings**, **Data Shortcuts**, and **Drawing Templates**. Expand the **Open Drawings** item, and you see your AutoCAD filename of Toolspace. That file can be expanded to see the potential data types stored within it, such as Points, Point Groups, Surfaces, Sites, Corridors, Assemblies, Subassemblies, and others.
7. Right-click on **Points**. The **Prospector** displays a shortcut menu pertaining to points. Because this is a new file, the only options are **Create…**, **Transfer…**, and **Refresh**. Hit **Create…**, and a **Create Points** toolbar appears, allowing for the creation of points.
8. Take a moment to explore some of the icons in the toolbar. They include **Miscellaneous**, **Intersection**, **Alignment**, **Surface**, **Interpolation**, **Slope**, and **Import Points** functions.
9. Choose **Miscellaneous Manual**. Following the prompts, set a point inside your AutoCAD file. Give the point a description of **FG** and an elevation of **112.33**. The point should display where you placed it.
10. Select the point you placed with a left-click; then right-click, and a shortcut menu appears. Choose **Edit Points…**, and a **Panorama** box appears. Notice that you can change the elevation value from 112.33 to 113.22, and when you close the **Panorama**, the point is updated.
11. Close the **Create Points Creation** toolbar.

These were just some very basic examples of using some of the new interface tools. As the text progresses, you will use these tools in detail.

New Objects for Design and Drafting.   A wide variety of objects is available to use in designing. Many of these objects were introduced in Land Desktop; however, they are now more fully implemented. But what are objects? Specifically, we are referring to Intelligent Objects, which are Autodesk data types that provide a programming structure for a variety of design items that contain data, functions, and allowable behaviors while interacting with the design and other objects.

A **Networks** Item and a **Figures** Item can be observed as Object types. These are found under the **Survey** item in the **Prospector**. These items will populate as the surveyor imports or creates traverse networks or linework defined as a figure.

The concept of object relationships is not new to Autodesk users. Land Desktop introduced this in a much more primitive form. Land Desktop contours were objects because they tried to act more like contours than traditional polylines did. What this meant is that the contour label would slide along a contour object when it was moved. It brought the break under the text with it and healed up the location from which it came. Civil 3D takes this to the next logical level. Contours are no longer objects because they are a part of the bigger picture, but they are now treated as a display option for the Surface Object. The Surface Object contains all the surface data within it, and the user uses style libraries to display the surface in a variety of analytical ways; for example, as contours, as slope shaded analyses, as a rendered object, and so forth. The Surface Object itself is affected by changes to its source data; that is, the points, the breaklines, or other surface data that were used to develop the surface.

The novel and revolutionary aspect of Civil 3D objects is that, because they are style-based and dynamic, they react and interact with other Civil 3D objects. Introducing links between design objects that react dynamically minimized the need for many manual tasks, such as ensuring that modifications are enacted between linework and labels, alignments and profiles, and the like. This process creates a ripple-through effect of actions and reactions and updates the data within the design automatically. Changes in one object can be passed automatically to objects associated to it at the user's option. For instance, if a curve within an alignment is altered, any grading using that alignment as a baseline can be consequently updated. Furthermore, all related alignment stationing, linework labels, and other alignment-related data are likewise updated.

These relationships are quite extensive, and you should have a feel for which objects update other objects. Some rules of thumb are listed here.

- When Points are modified, they can directly influence Surfaces.
- When Surfaces are modified, they can directly influence Grading Objects and Profiles.
- When Parcels are modified, they can directly influence Grading Objects and Corridors.
- When Alignments are modified, they can directly influence Grading, Corridors, Profiles, and Sections.
- When Grading Objects are modified, they can directly influence Surfaces and Corridors.
- When Subassemblies are modified, they can directly influence Assemblies and Corridors.
- When Assemblies are modified, they can directly influence Corridors.

A relationship exists among design objects, the styles that control their display, and the labels that control their annotation. These styles and labels are also managed as objects within Autodesk Civil 3D.

Objects are the basic working mechanism of the engineering design workflow. The underlying methodology for Civil 3D uses an object-oriented architecture. Therefore, design components such as points, surfaces, and alignments are intelligent and maintain relationships with other objects. The classic example is a horizontal alignment that has associated profiles and cross sections. If the alignment is manipulated, the profiles and sections linked to that alignment are automatically updated accordingly.

The major object types in Civil 3D are represented as follows.

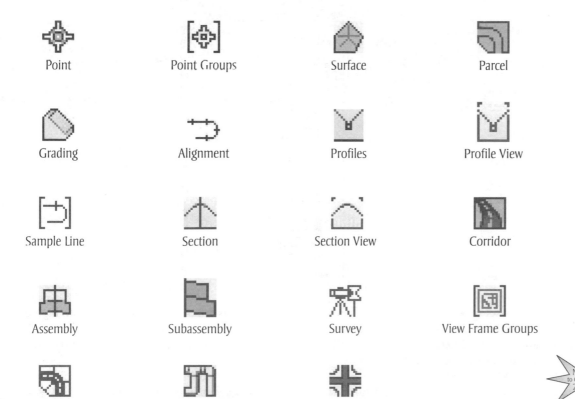

Point	Point Groups	Surface	Parcel
Grading	Alignment	Profiles	Profile View
Sample Line	Section	Section View	Corridor
Assembly	Subassembly	Survey	View Frame Groups
Sites	Pipe Networks	Intersections	

Civil 3D software is the first version of AutoCAD for civil engineering users in which lines, arcs, and polylines will *not* be the predominant data types for design and drafting. Rather, surface, roadway, parcel, and point objects will be the predominant design objects that are created and modified. Although other civil-oriented software solutions are on the market, none have taken this reactive technology as far as Civil 3D has. The ability to perform storm sewer drafting and compute watershed locations is also available in Civil 3D.

Dynamic, Model-Based Design, Data-Driven Methods, and the Ripple-Through Effect.   The concept of a live, dynamic model is new to the civil engineering field and consists of the ability to make changes to integral design components and have those changes update any related project components. The classic example is a horizontal alignment that has associated profiles and cross sections. If the alignment is modified, the alignment annotation, the profiles, and the sections linked to that alignment are updated automatically. Another example could be parcels with associated distance, bearing, and area labels that are updated automatically when the parcel geometry is altered.

Survey networks and figures are dynamic parts of the software. This means that changes to setups or backsights can be automatically recalculated in the network object.

Data-Driven, Object Style Libraries.   Object style libraries are very important to the use of the software in that they control the appearance and design characteristics of the object. When a new object is created, a predefined style can be applied to control how it displays. Styles can be modified on the fly and are retroactive. For example, if contours appear red and the user would like them to appear blue, a style modification can occur and be applied to the contours. They will then inherit the property of displaying blue. If the style definition is modified, the changes are immediately applied to all objects using that style, similar to Text Styles or Dimension Styles.

The styles are managed on the **Toolspace Settings** tab shown in Figure 1-17. All Civil 3D objects have a Standard style that can be used as is, or new ones can be created as needed. The best approach would be to have someone in the organization predevelop all of the styles needed as part of the implementation of the software. Styles can be organized and stored in a drawing template (.dwt) file.

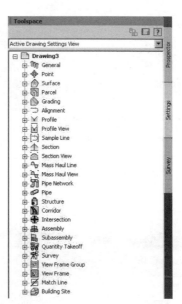

Figure 1-17   Toolspace Settings

A set of Survey settings exists in the **Settings** tab. This tab allows the user to create Figure Prefix Libraries for defining linework or figures and Equipment Databases where settings for ambient conditions and other equipment parameters are contained. The management of the Survey databases occurs here as well.

When developing a style for an object, the object will be physically placed on a main layer. However, component objects can reside on supplemental layers in order to control the display of those components. So an alignment object can reside on the CL layer, but the lines can reside on the CL-Lines layer while the arcs reside on the CL-Arc layer. The user can issue this instruction by using an * to denote using the object's layer as a prefix or suffix. It becomes an interesting visual when the user would like to inspect the arcs within an alignment separate from the linear components.

DOT-Level Highway Design Capabilities.   Civil 3D offers Autodesk users high-end highway design tools that allow for multiple baseline designs and multiple regions with each baseline. Baselines are centerlines for adjacent roadway occurrences. Regions are areas within those baselines where different things might be happening, such as *superelevations* or different assemblies.

Rehabilitation and Reconstruction Design Tools.   Civil 3D provides a highly customized and very specific toolset for designers who are working in the area of roadway rehabilitation and maintenance design. These tools include subassemblies and routines for sidewalk replacement, curb replacement, and several variations on milling and overlaying pavements. The initial installation of Civil 3D may not import these into the **Tool Palettes**, but they can be accessed through the Catalogs and dragged and dropped into a **Tool** palette of your making.

User control functions exist in the very useful user-defined boundaries as well as the ability to add station-based assembly insertions.

Trench Pipes and Retaining Wall Sub-assemblies add to the rehabilitation tools.

Figures 1-18 and 1-19 indicate the rehabilitation capabilities of Civil 3D.

superelevations: Refers to the cross slope introduced into a cross section of a roadway in order to compensate for the centrifugal forces created by horizontal curves. According to the laws of mechanics, when a vehicle travels on a curve it is forced outward by centrifugal force. On a superelevated roadway, this force is resisted by the vehicle weight component parallel to the superelevated surface and the side friction between the tires and pavement. The pavement is essentially tilted to counter the forces described above.

Page (1 of 2) **1** 2   Next

OverlayBrokenBackBetweenEdges
Overlays a four lane crowned corridor between gutter flange points

OverlayBrokenBackOverGutters
Overlays a four lane crowned corridor over gutter.

OverlayCrownBetweenEdges
Overlays a simple crowned roadway between two known edge-of-pavement points.

OverlayMedianAsymmetrical
Widens an existing divided highway inward over a depressed median, with an asymmetrical barrier.

OverlayMedianSymmetrical
Widens an existing divided highway inward over a depressed median, with a symmetrical barrier.

OverlayMillAndLevel1
Overlay with milling or leveling on an uncrowned roadway.

OverlayMillAndLevel2
Overlay with milling or leveling on a crowned roadway.

OverlayParabolic
Inserts parabolic travel lanes between know flange points.

OverlayWidenFromCurb
The OverlayWidenFromCurb subassembly is used to overlay one side of an existing road, and add one

OverlayWidenMatchSlope1
Overlay and widening, matching existing slope on a crowned roadway.

Figure 1-18   Rehabilitation tools, page 1

Page (2 of 2) **1** 2   Prev

OverlayWidenMatchSlope2
Overlay and widening, matching existing slope on an uncrowned roadway.

OverlayWidenWithSuper1
Overlay and widening of a roadway using Outside Lane superelevation.

Figure 1-19   Rehabilitation tools, page 2

TIP   In addition to these fine tools, Autodesk has also developed the ability for designers to create designs where the old roadway will be repaired. This is in contrast to prior solutions in which the assumption was that all roads were new roads. An enormous amount of roadway repair occurs throughout the world, and these abilities allow for milling, overlaying, sidewalk, or curb and gutter replacements on existing roadways.

Engineers, drafters, and roadway repair workers will benefit not only from the ability to design DOT-level roadways but from the roadway rehabilitation tools as well. Many regions in the country or in the world do not have a lot of new growth; however, they do perform a large amount of roadway maintenance. These skills will provide new productivity for that staff.

Understanding Civil 3D Icons

The following information offers the user a description of the icons in Civil 3D. Although Civil 3D Help provides this information, it is scattered around and sometimes difficult to locate. This text places all of these items in this single location for easy reference.

The icons at the top of the **Prospector** palette control the display of icons within the **Prospector** panel, display the **Panorama** window, and provide access to **Help.** The icons and their respective meanings are outlined next, as found in Civil 3D Help.

 Toggles the display of **Project Item State** icons in the **Prospector. The Project Item State** icon indicates its status with respect to the project, such as whether it is checked in or out. Details for these icons are shown.

If no icon is displayed, then the drawing has been added to the project, but you do not have a local copy.

 The drawing is available to be checked out, the **Vault** copy matches your local copy.

 The drawing is available to be checked out, but your local copy is newer than the **Vault** copy.

 The drawing is available to be checked out, the **Vault** copy is newer than your local copy.

 The drawing is checked out to you, but you do not have a local copy.

 The drawing is checked out to you, the **Vault** copy matches the local copy.

 The drawing is checked out to you, your local copy is newer than the **Vault** copy.

 The drawing is checked out to you, the **Vault** copy is newer than your local copy.

 The drawing is checked out to someone else, and you do not have a local copy.

 The drawing is checked out to someone elsc, and your local copy matches the **Vault copy**.

 The drawing is checked out to someone else, and your local copy is newer than the **Vault copy**.

The drawing is checked out to someone else, and your local copy is older than the **Vault copy**.

 This icon is displayed next to the drawing name in the **Prospector** when the local copy becomes out-of-date.

 Toggles the display of **Drawing Item State** icons in the **Prospector.** The **Drawing Item State** icon indicates the state of an object within a drawing, including whether or not it is locked.

The following icons describe the possible states of information.

 The object is locked.

 The object is referenced by another object.

 The object is a reference to an object in another drawing.

 Toggles the display of **Drawing Item Modifier** icons at the top of the **Prospector**. The **Drawing Item Modifier** icon indicates the status of the item relative to the project or the drawing. A description of the **Drawing Item Modifier** icons is provided here.

No icon means the object is **Not** out of date and **Does Not** violate constraints, the Local copy of the object **Is** more recent than the Project copy, and the Local copy of the object has **Not** been edited relative to the Project object.

 The object **Is** out of date or **Does** violate constraints, the Project copy of the object **Is** more recent than the Local copy, and the Local copy of the object **Has** been edited relative to the Project object.

 The object is **Not** out of date and **Does Not** violate constraints, the Project copy of the object **Is** more recent than the Local copy, and the Local copy of the object **Has** been edited relative to the Project object.

 The object **Is** out of date or **Does** violate constraints, the Project copy of the object is **Not** more recent than the Local copy, and the Local copy of the object **Has** been edited relative to the Project object.

 The object is **Not** out of date and **Does Not** violate constraints, the Project copy of the object is **Not** more recent than the Local copy, and the Local copy of the object **Has** been edited relative to the Project object.

 The object **Is** out of date or **Does** violate constraints, the Project copy of the object **Is** more recent than the Local copy, and the Local copy of the object **Has Not** been edited relative to the Project object.

 The object is **Not** out of date and **Does Not** violate constraints, the Project copy of the object **Is** more recent than the Local copy, and the Local copy of the object **Has Not** been edited relative to the Project object.

 The object **Is** out of date or **Does** violate constraints, the Project copy of the object is **Not** more recent than the Local copy, and the Local copy of the object **Has Not** been edited relative to the Project object.

 Toggles the display of the **Panorama** window, if the **Panorama** window contains active vistas.

 Indicates that data do exist in this area.

The view in the **Prospector** might appear similar to Figure 1-20. The name of the drawing is EG Drawing. Points do exist, and Point Groups exist. When the tree for a drawing is expanded, AutoCAD icons are displayed in front of each drawing name. If the icon is blue, it means that the drawing is in the project. If the icon is red, then the drawing is currently open.

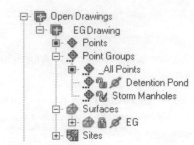

Figure 1-20   Data and Project icons

The **Toolspace** has Windows Explorer style expansion and contraction facilities that are called Trees. They display items in a hierarchical structure. Any item containing other items below it is called a Collection. In Figure 1-20, Open Drawings, EG Drawing, Point Groups, and Surfaces, are Collections. A symbol may be shown to the far left of each Collection name; this is called a Tree Node. Its intent is to provide information about the display of the items in the Collection. The following list describes these Tree Node symbols:

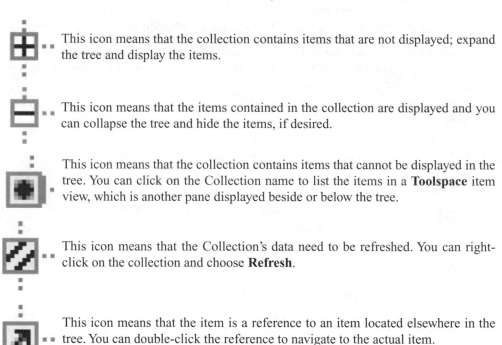

This icon means that the collection contains items that are not displayed; expand the tree and display the items.

This icon means that the items contained in the collection are displayed and you can collapse the tree and hide the items, if desired.

This icon means that the collection contains items that cannot be displayed in the tree. You can click on the Collection name to list the items in a **Toolspace** item view, which is another pane displayed beside or below the tree.

This icon means that the Collection's data need to be refreshed. You can right-click on the collection and choose **Refresh**.

This icon means that the item is a reference to an item located elsewhere in the tree. You can double-click the reference to navigate to the actual item.

This icon means that the Collection contains no items.

Other icons exist for Survey items that include Control Points, Non-Control Points, Directions, Setups, and Traverses, and can be seen in the **Toolspace** under Survey.

Pipe Utilities Grips

Several grips that allow for modifying pipe and components are described here.

> **The Endpoint Free Grip.** Clicking the endpoint free grip in the **Plan** view moves that endpoint of the pipe to a new point. The midpoint and opposite endpoint of the pipe are maintained during this edit so the length does not change. Curved pipes behave identically to an AutoCAD arc.

The Midpoint Free Grip. Clicking the midpoint free grip moves the whole pipe to a new, specified point. Curved pipes behave identically to an AutoCAD arc.

The Length Constraint Grip. Pipe length can be increased or decreased by gripping the end of the pipe, and only that end shortens or lengthens. The direction of the pipe does not change in this mode of operation.

The Midpoint Resize Constraint Grip. This grip allows you to reset the pipe's width based on the pipe sizes available in the parts list and part catalog. When the midpoint resize grip is used on a pipe, a series of parallel lines display next to the pipe, whereby each set of parallel lines represents an available pipe width. A tooltip displays the pipe width, and you can snap to any of the parallel lines to select a new pipe width on the fly.

Sheet Set Manager Palette

Another interface item in Civil 3D is the **Sheet Set Manager**, an AutoCAD 2005 enhancement that is included in the Civil 3D product. Sheet sets organize, create, and publish multiple drawing layouts into a single set of plans. Before the **Sheet Manager** existed, a set of drawings was organized using manual procedures. The individual drawings in the set may have emanated from several different AutoCAD files, and the process of ensuring that they were properly maintained, ordered, and correctly numbered was very time consuming. Open the **Sheet Set Manager** by typing **Sheetset**. The **New Sheet Set...** option in the **Sheet Set Manager** palette opens a Wizard that guides you through the process of creating a sheet set. Once a **.dst** file is chosen, you can right-click in the **Sheet Set Manager,** you can also right-click in the **Sheet Set Manager** window and obtain the menu shown in Figure 1-21.

Once in the Wizard, there are two ways to create a sheet set. You can use a sample sheet set provided by Autodesk or use an existing drawing set of your own. The sample sheet set option works like a template and provides the organization and default settings for the new sheet set. After the setup is complete, you can compose individual sheets within the set by importing layouts and placing saved views as needed. The individual sheets created using this method are saved as separate drawing files, in which the original drawing files are linked as referenced drawings. The sheet set is saved as a separate file with the extension of .DST.

If you have already created layouts for the desired drawings and now need to assemble them together into a plan set, you would use the second option. You can specify one or more folders that contain drawing files, and the layouts can be imported into the sheet set. In this case, no new drawing files are created. Keep in mind, though, that this option will not fully utilize the capabilities of the sheet set feature to manage and organize such items as sheet numbers, callouts, and such because the title blocks and views have already been defined.

The **Sheet Set Manager** palette performs the management of the sheets. The user can create new sheet sets, open existing ones, list the sheets, and observe the views within a particular sheet. The sheets can also be arranged into individual groups to assist in navigation and organization. Figure 1-22 shows that a variety of details are available as well as a thumbnail preview if so desired.

The sheet file can be opened by double-clicking on it. If the sheet set was created using the **Sample Sheet Set** option, you must specify the folder location of the AutoCAD files whose views are to be used. These become support drawings and are displayed in the **Sheet Set Manager** dialog box along with their saved views, which can be chosen and placed on a sheet. The sheets and their views are routinely numbered and update dynamically when changes are made to a name or a number. After the sheet set has been developed, the complete set or just certain selected sheets can be published (or plotted). Publishing is a term now used for outputting the data to an external source. Not all plots are printed to hard copy anymore; some outputs go to the .DWF format for viewing in the Express Viewer or on the Internet. Of course, outputting to a plotter is still a normal function for creating hard copies. The **Sheet Set Manager** has made plotting drawings individually an obsolete endeavor. Other enhancements include the **eTransmit** option, which allows for the creation of a transmittal package formatted in the Zip format, and the **Archive** option, which creates a compressed archive of the entire sheet set.

Figure 1-21   Sheet Set Manager menu

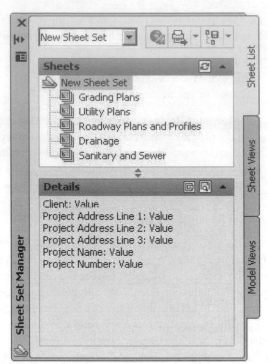

Figure 1-22   Sheet Set Manager palette

Chapter Summary

This chapter introduced Civil 3D and its capabilities for model building and organization. It also gave an explanation of MAP 3D, a foundational aspect of Civil 3D that adds GIS, important utilities, and drafting cleanup tools to the user's toolkit. Now that we've covered the basics, we move into a design project in Chapter 2.

Chapter Test Questions

Multiple Choice

1. The Civil 3D user must know which of the following in order to use Civil 3D for typical subdivision design?

   a. AutoCAD
   b. Geometry concepts
   c. Surface or DTM concepts
   d. All of the above

2. A user must understand which Civil 3D interface items in order to negotiate through the data effectively?

   a. **Tear-off** palettes
   b. **Toolspace**
   c. Slide Sorter
   d. **Kiosk** tools

3. Which of the components allows users to access all of the Properties of project data?

   a. **Settings** tab
   b. **Preview** window
   c. Right-clicking on the **Surfaces** item
   d. All of the above

4. Some of the add-in software available for Civil 3D includes which of the following?

   a. Trimble Link
   b. Carlson Connect
   c. Leica X-Change
   d. All of the above

5. MAP 3D can connect and provide read/write access to which of the following?

a. Microstation files
b. Photoshop files
c. Microsoft Access
d. None of the above

6. One user can use MAP 3D to access many AutoCAD drawings simultaneously. How many users can attach to the same AutoCAD drawing simultaneously?

a. One
b. None
c. An unlimited number
d. Two

7. Which components consist of the AutoCAD spatial database for MAP 3D?

a. Graphic database
b. Extended entity data (EED) or Object data
c. External database(s)
d. All of the above

8. Drafting technicians should know how to use MAP 3D in conjunction with Civil 3D in which of the following ways?

a. Attaching multiple drawings to a working session
b. Performing drawing cleanup operations
c. Importing/exporting data to other manufacturers' programs
d. All of the above

9. Drawing Cleanup tools allow for which of the following?

a. Deleting Duplicate Objects, Erasing Short Objects, and Breaking Crossing Objects
b. Raster and pixel-based photo editing
c. OLE cleanup and editing
d. Altering audio sounds from MP3 and WAV files

10. The **Panorama** performs which of the following functions?

a. Road design
b. Site grading
c. Utility piping layout
d. None of the above

True or False

1. True or False: GIS capabilities are not part of the Civil 3D solution.

2. True or False: All Civil 3D data can be reformatted into 3D/GPS Machine Control data.

3. True or False: 3D surfaces can be formatted to 3D/GPS Machine Control data.

4. True or False: MAP 3D can link AutoCAD graphics to external databases such as Microsoft Access and Oracle.

5. True or False: Rubber sheeting can allow the user to correct the inherent errors in data that has been scanned in and converted to vector data.

6. True or False: Civil 3D cannot use the AutoCAD **Sheet Set Manager** because it can open only one drawing at a time.

7. True or False: Every icon in the Civil 3D **Toolspace** will invoke an engineering command.

8. True or False: Some icons appear in the **Prospector** when project objects are out of date.

9. True or False: The **Prospector** shows when project items are populated with data.

10. True or False: Users can access project data in various ways through the **Prospector**.

CHAPTER EXERCISES

1. What are the major object types Civil 3D uses? Why would we use them?

2. What would be some examples of uses for object technology? How does this compare to parametric technology?

3. What is GIS? Explain what it is used for and how it differs from CAD.

4. What is GPS? Explain what it is used for and how the future of engineering and surveying will be changed by the advances in this area.

5. What is a spatial database as related to GIS?

6. Civil 3D is comprised of what software components?

7. Do you think the cost of designing engineering projects is more than, less than, or the same as it was 30 years ago? Explain your answer.

8. Explain the uses for alignments; provide examples of their use and the benefits they provide to designers.

9. Explain the uses for Corridor Profiles; provide examples of their use and the benefits to designers.

10. If you were provided a series of stations, offsets, and elevations relative to an alignment, explain what this means and what usefulness it might present. What can be accomplished with this information?

11. Write a few paragraphs on how visualizations (or renderings) can be used in the civil engineering industry.

12. If engineers work in two dimensions, what limitations do they have compared with someone working in three dimensions? Explain your response.

13. How can laser-guided machine control be used in conjunction with GPS-guided machine control to automate earth-moving tasks?

A Civil 3D JumpStart Project

2

Chapter Objectives

- Perform basic functions of Civil 3D on all facets of a project because the chapter goes through an entire project from start to finish.
- Prepare an existing ground surface from actual 3D project data, create contours, and label them.
- Develop a property parcel for a shopping center and prepare the labeling required for its drafting.
- Develop an alignment for an access road to the shopping center.
- Develop a finished ground profile and a corridor to put the road into 3D.
- Design the grading for the shopping center and the parking facility.

INTRODUCTION

This chapter commences immediately with a design project. The details and advanced usage of the commands are reserved until subsequent chapters; however, this chapter takes you through an entire project from start to finish, with only a minimal amount of settings manipulations. You prepare an existing ground surface from actual 3D project data, create contours, and label them. You develop a property parcel for a shopping center and prepare the labeling required for its drafting. Then you develop an alignment for an access road to the shopping center, and a *finished ground* profile and a corridor to put the road into 3D. The next step is to design the grading for the shopping center and the parking facility.

REVIEW OF FUNCTIONS AND FEATURES TO BE USED

This chapter uses engineering functions to create a terrain or surface model and shows you how to use this "Object," display it in different ways, and label it. The project creates a Parcel object from primitive geometry entities and displays it to show directional and distance labels as well as parcel areas. It also develops an alignment from primitive geometry and defines it as an object. Styles will be used to control its appearance as well as that of the other objects. You will create a *profile view* with an *existing ground profile* and then develop a finished ground profile for the access road again. Assemblies are created from subassemblies, and a corridor object is designed using assemblies. Grading objects are also developed for the site of the shopping center.

finished ground: The improved conditions for the site.

profile view: A Civil 3D term for the location in Civil 3D where profiles are displayed. Each profile view displays new or existing profiles and offsets for one horizontal alignment. Although you can create profiles without displaying them on a profile view, when a profile view is created, the complete list of profiles for the alignment is displayed so that a profile can be selected for display in the profile view.

existing ground profile: The vertical alignment for the roadway as defined by the location of the horizontal alignment draped onto the existing ground terrain model.

You will benefit from the ability to see rapidly what Civil 3D can do from a broad-brush approach. This chapter and its accompanying procedures start with existing ground data and end with a completed (albeit, simple) design project.

Job Skills

PROJECT DESIGN APPLICATION—

Part One: Project Design Application

To begin, you create an Existing Ground surface. You also select some basic settings to make the surface react and display the way you wish. Your first task is to open a drawing with raw data in it and inspect the contents of the data.

Note:
These data were prepared without the benefit of a Civil 3D template and, as a result, have few to no settings predeveloped within them. Here some of the important ones will be set. For actual projects, you are strongly advised to configure the product to adhere to your organization's CADD standards.

Exercise 2-1: Open Drawing and Inspect Data

To access student data files, go to www.pearsondesigncentral.com.

1. Launch Civil 3D and close the Drawing.dwg that initially opens.
2. Select **File** from the pull-down menu, then **Open**, and choose the Chapter-2a.dwg in your student data files.
3. Notice that there are breaklines and mass points in the file, which together represent the existing ground conditions.
4. On inspection of the data, notice that there is a road running east to west. Zoom in and you will see a cul-de-sac heading toward the south from the road.
5. Click on a breakline somewhere in the file and notice the grips. Place your cursor in one of the grips, but do not click it. Simply look at the lower left corner of the screen and observe that the *X*, *Y*, *Z* coordinates are shown for the grip. Notice that the *Z* coordinate or elevation has a value representing the elevation of the surface at that location.

Note:
The mass points are actually Auto-CAD blocks floating at the correct elevation. An aerial photogram-metist developed the breaklines using stereodigitizing techniques. The three-dimensional breaklines have elevations at each vertex. The mass points are placed in the data set to densify the surface data.

After having observed the data set, you can prepare a Civil 3D surface for Existing Ground. Before doing that, inspect some important surface-related settings. The first one to change is the Precision of the Contour label. Because we are labeling even contours that are multiples of 2, there is no need to have thousandths-place precision on the annotation when whole numbers will suffice. The precision is unneeded, and the extra decimal places tend to clutter up the drawing. Additionally you need to create a layer on which the annotation will reside.

Exercise 2-2: Develop Settings

1. Go to the **General** pull-down menu and choose **Toolspace...** or type **Showts** to display the **Toolspace** palette if it is not already there. Click on the **Settings** tab.
2. In the **Master View**, expand **Surface**. Then expand **Label Styles**.
3. Choose the **Contour** label style, and note that one exists called **Standard**.
4. Click on the **Standard** label style, right-click the mouse, and choose **Edit....**
5. The **Label Style Composer** dialog box displays. Click on the **Information** tab and observe the contents of the panel. Click on the **General** tab and observe the contents of the panel.
6. Click the **Layout** tab. Several properties exist in the **Property** column.
7. Click on **Text**; expand text. Choose **Contents** and then refer to the **Value** column. Click on the value for **Contents**. Choose the button with the three dots called ellipses **(...)**.
8. This brings up the **Text Component Editor—Contents** dialog box.
9. Click into the **Preview** window on the right side of the dialog box, highlight the data there, and erase them so that the window is blank.
10. Click on **Precision** in the **Modifier** column.
11. The value for the Precision is 0.001, which is not appropriate for your contour label because you do not wish to have decimal points on even contours. Click on 0.001 and select **1** from the pop-down window in the **Value** column.

12. Then click the **gray arrow** at the top of the dialog box to populate the **Preview** window with the new data settings.
13. Look on the **Preview** window, and you will see some code indicating that new settings exist. Hit **OK**.
14. In the **General** tab, for the **Layer** property, click on the **Value** where it shows Layer 0 and notice that a button with ellipses (…) exists. Choose the button, and a **Layer Selection** dialog box appears. Choose **New**. In the **Create Layer** dialog box, click on the value for **Layer** property where it says **Layer1**, and type in a new layer name of **C-Topo-Labl**.
15. Hit **OK** until you've terminated the command.

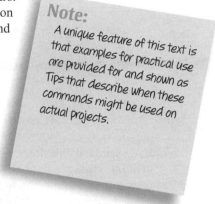

Note:
A unique feature of this text is that examples for practical use are provided for and shown as Tips that describe when these commands might be used on actual projects.

Exercise 2-3: Set Up a Surface

1. Choose **Surfaces** from the pull-down menu.
2. Select **Create surface….**
3. The **Create Surface** dialog box appears.
4. Several types of surfaces can be created: a TIN surface, a Grid surface, and two types of Volume surfaces.

TIP The Volume surfaces are created during earthwork take-off computations. The Grid surface is used when a surface of evenly spaced rectangular data whose elevations are interpolated from the data is desired.

5. We want a *TIN* surface. In the window below is the informational item that includes the name of the surface. Click on the **Value** column for the Surface name.
6. The Surface name is incremental, so the first surface is **Surface1**, the second surface is **Surface2**, and so on. Click in this field and type **Existing Ground** as your name. Hit **OK**.
7. To the right of the **Type** is the **Layer** field. Pick on the button on the right side of the dialog box for **Surface** layer. An **Object Layer** dialog box appears. Where it says **Base Layer Name**, choose the button on the right for **Layer**, and the **Layer Selection** dialog box opens.
8. Hit the button for **New** layer and enter **C-Topo** in the field for **Layer1**. Hit **OK** twice. Then where it says **Modifier Value**, select **Suffix** from the pop-down window.
9. When the **Modifier Value** field to the right becomes available, type in a dash and an asterisk **(-*)**. This will create a layer with the name of the surface as a suffix to the layer name. You should get a layer called **C-Topo-Existing Ground**, as can be seen in the **Preview** window.
10. Type **Existing Ground** for the **Description** also.
11. Leave all else as default and click **OK**.
12. Next go to the **Toolspace** and choose the **Prospector** tab.
13. Look under **Open Drawings** for your drawing. Expand **Surfaces** to show the new surface you just created for Existing Ground.

The next step is to identify the 3D surface data and build the surface.

TIN: Triangulated Irregular Network representing the surface.

Exercise 2-4: Build Surface

1. Expand the **Existing Ground Surface** item. You see an item for **Definition**.
2. Expand **Definition**, and you see all the data types that can go into the preparation of the surface. These include **Breaklines**, **Contours**, **DEM files**, **Drawing Objects**, and other data types.
3. Our data set contains breaklines and blocks, as discussed earlier. Therefore, use the commands for adding **Breaklines** and use **Drawing Objects** to add the blocks.
4. Begin by clicking on **Breaklines**, then right-click on **Breaklines** and select **Add….**
5. A dialog box for **Add Breaklines** displays. Add a **Description** of **EG**.

TIP

The choices allow for **Proximity breaklines**, **Wall breaklines**, and **Breaklines from a fil**e. Proximity breaklines are 2D polylines that have points with elevations at each vertex in the polyline. The point elevations will be used by the software in creating 3D breaklines from the 2D polylines. The Wall breakline option is used to represent vertical components of surfaces. In actuality, they are not truly vertical because this would cause issues in the software relating to a divide by zero in the denominator for various slope computations. Therefore, the software allows for Wall breaklines that contain wall height data, but the top of the wall is slightly offset from the bottom of the wall so as to avoid the vertical computational issue. The last choice is to bring in breaklines from an external text file.

6. Use **Standard** breaklines as the type of breakline but notice that other choices exist in the pop-down list.
7. Use **Standard** breaklines, which are the 3D polylines in the file. The last setting is a **Mid-ordinate distance** field, which is available for creating 3D breaklines from 2D polylines that have curves in them. In this case if you use the default of 1′, a 3D polyline would be created such that small chords simulate the curve but do not deviate from the arc by more than 1′.
8. Hit **OK**. When you are prompted to `Select objects:`, place a window around the data. Do not worry if there are points mixed in with the selection set of breaklines because the software filters anything that is not a breakline.
9. A **Panorama** dialog box may appear that indicates that there are two crossing breaklines. Coordinates are displayed so you can check the severity of the issue. In this case, it has been determined that this will not harm your surface integrity, and so continue on. Click the green check mark in the top right of the **Panorama** dialog box to continue. Upon completion of this function, the software creates the surface, as shown by a yellow boundary.
    Crossing breaklines can be found using the **Zoom to** option in the **Panorama**.
10. Now in the **Prospector**, choose **Drawing Objects** under the **Definitions** area of the **Exiting Ground Surface**. Right-click and choose **Add....**
11. For the **Object type**, choose **blocks**.
12. Type **EG** as the **Description** field in the dialog box and hit **OK**.
13. When you are prompted to `Select objects:`, place a window around the data. Do not worry if breaklines are mixed in with the selection set of points because the software filters out the data it does not need.
14. On completion, the yellow surface boundary is updated to include the blocks.

Now that the surface is created, you typically want to view contours representing the surface.

Exercise 2-5: Develop Contours for Surface
_____

1. In the **Toolspace**, choose the **Settings** tab. Choose **Surface >> Surface Styles >> Standard**. Right-click on **Standard** and choose **Edit....**
2. In the **Surface Style** dialog box, choose the **Display** tab.
3. With the view direction in the pop-down window set to **Plan**, click on the lightbulb to turn on the **Major** and **Minor** contours and turn off the lightbulb for **Border**. Note the colors are preset and can be changed here, if so desired.
4. On leaving the dialog box, the contours in Civil 3D are automatically updated to show the contours as defined in the Style.
5. The next step is to create **Contour** labels on the **Contours**. Choose **Surfaces >>Add Surface Labels >> Add Surface Labels . . . Contour-Multiple at Interval** from the pull-down menu.
6. When prompted to `Select a surface:`, select the surface. Then you are prompted to `Pick first point:` in order to identify a start point for the labeling to begin. Place a point at the top of the site and place a second point to the bottom and outside the site. When you are prompted `Interval along contour <100.000>:` type **500′**.

7. Hit **<Enter>**. On completion of the command, zoom in and inspect the data and the contour labels every 500' across the site.
8. Save your file to a name with your initials as the suffix of the name, Chapter-2-a-hw.dwg.

Part Two: Project Design Application

Part Two of this exercise is to develop a property parcel. It consists of a fairly simple four-sided shape that is 500' wide by 500' long. Please note that the software is certainly not limited to this simplicity; rather, this introductory exercise is planned to keep it simple in order to make several conceptual points clear.

You will open the drawing Chapter 2-b.dwg from the student data files, a file that contains the completed surface data from the previous set of exercises. The next objective is to develop a parcel boundary in which you design a commercial shopping center. The first step is to create the primitive geometry for the boundary lines. Following that using the Civil 3D functionality will create Parcel objects from the primitive linework.

Exercise 2-6: Develop Geometry for Parcel Boundary

1. Open the drawing called Chapter 2-b.dwg.
2. Begin by creating a layer called **C-Prop-Bndy**; set the color to **yellow**, and set it to be the current layer. Draw a polyline as described next. Select the icon for **Polyline** in AutoCAD or type **PL <Enter>**. The system responds as shown:

    ```
    Command: PLINE
    Specify start point: <Polar off> 15600,18540
    Current line-width is 0.0000
    Specify next point or [Arc/Halfwidth/Length/Undo/Width]: <Coords
    off> <Coords on> @500<0
    Specify next point or [Arc/Close/Halfwidth/Length/Undo/Width]: @500<90
    Specify next point or [Arc/Close/Halfwidth/Length/Undo/Width]: @500<180
    Specify next point or [Arc/Close/Halfwidth/Length/Undo/Width]: CL
    ```

To access student data files, go to www.pearsondesigncentral.com.

3. Next you will address the settings for the boundary to place the Civil 3D parcel on the **C-Prop-Bndy** layer.
4. From the **Parcels** pull-down menu, choose the **CREATE PARCEL FROM OBJECTS** command. When you are prompted with Select lines, arcs, or polylines to convert into parcels or [Xref]:, select the polyline you just drew, hit **<Enter>**.
5. The **Create Parcels—From objects** dialog box opens (Figure 2-1). Accept the default Site name and Parcel style.
6. Now select an existing layer for the Parcel layer. In the area for **Layers**, click on the button to the right of **Parcel layer:** This opens the **Object Layer** dialog box. For the parameter called **Base Layer Name:**, click on the button to the right for **Layers**. Click on the layer **C-Prop-Bndy**. Hit **OK**.
7. In this example, you create a layer to use for the Parcel segment layer. Click on the **Layer** button to the right of the **Parcel segment layer:** This opens the **Object Layer** dialog box. For the parameter called **Base Layer Name**, click on the button to the right for **Layers**. Click on the button for **New....** In the **Value** column for **Layer Name**, type in **C-Prop-Bndy-Line** and then hit the value for Color and select **red**. Hit **OK** until you return to the **Create Parcels—From objects** dialog box.
8. Turn on the **Automatically add segment labels** option at the bottom of the dialog box. Use **Standard** for all of the settings. Ensure that the check mark is **On** for **Erase existing entities**. Hit **OK** to exit and execute.
9. The Parcel object should be created in AutoCAD. Check in the **Toolspace** and click on the **Prospector**. Under **Open Drawings**, expand your current drawing named Chapter-2b.dwg. Expand the **Sites**, and you see **Site 1**, which was created when you created the parcel. Expand **Site 1** and you see **Parcels**; expand **Parcels** to see your parcel, called **Standard_100**. Make sure that the previews symbol at the top left of the **Toolspace** is selected. Select the **Parcels** item, then right-click and check the **Show Preview** option. If you click on the parcel that was just created, you will see it in the preview window. Figures 2-2 and 2-3 show the **Prospector** panel and the AutoCAD data.
10. Save and close your drawing.

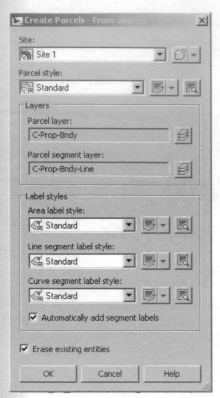

Figure 2-1   Create Parcels—From objects

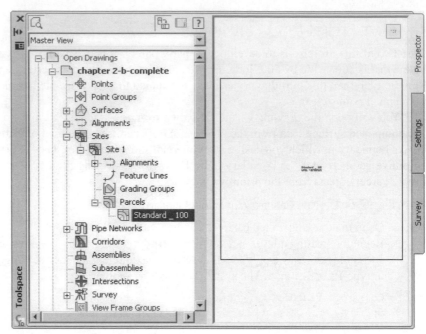

Figure 2-2   Parcel Preview

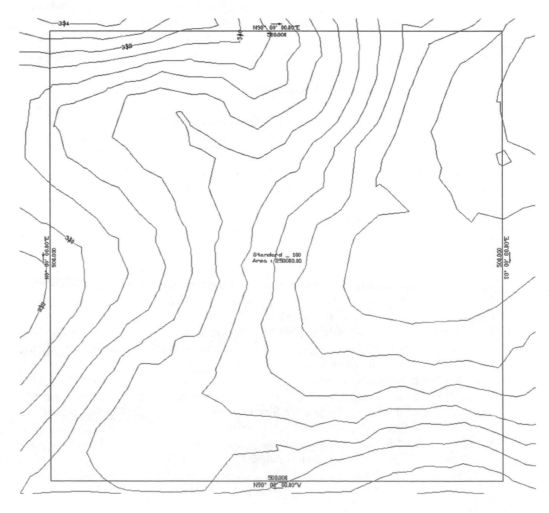

Figure 2-3   Parcel in AutoCAD

Now that there is a parcel boundary for the property, continue on with the design. The next step is to develop an entrance road to the shopping mall. You will reconfigure the road that runs east to west just south of our parcel boundary. First, draw the primitive geometry for the roadway centerline alignment.

Exercise 2-7: Develop a Horizontal Alignment for Access to the Parking Lot

1. Open the drawing called Chapter-2c.dwg. It contains the surface you developed and the parcel boundary.

2. Create a layer called **C-Road-Cntr**, set the color to **green**, and set the layer current.

3. Type **L** for **Line** in AutoCAD. When prompted for the start point, type **15925,18543 <Enter>**.

4. Then type **@330<S <Enter>**.

5. Then type **@500<N55dE <Enter>**.

6. Then type **@600<E <Enter>**.

7. Next you place curves into the linework using the **FILLET** command by typing **F** for **Fillet**. Type **R** for **Radius** and set the first radius to **100**. Then pick the first two *tangents* that you drew, and a 100′ radius curve will be drawn. Type **F** for **Fillet** again. Type **R** for **Radius** and set the radius to **500**. Then pick the second and third tangents that you drew, and a 500′ radius curve will be drawn.

8. Type **PE** for **PolyEdit**. Select the first polyline drawn. When you are prompted with: Do you want to turn it into one? <Y>, hit **<Enter>**. The software responds with Enter an option [Close/Join/Width/Edit vertex/Fit/Spline/Decurve/Ltypegen/Undo] :. Type **J <Enter>**. You will be asked to Select objects. Select the first tangent, the first curve, the second tangent, the second curve, and finally the third tangent. Hit **<Enter>** when done. The geometry for the center of the road is now a polyline.

9. From the *Alignments* pull-down menu, choose **Create Alignment from Polyline**. When you are prompted to Select the first line/arc/polyline or [Xref] :, select the polyline for your roadway. You are prompted to Select lines/arcs or polylines to create alignment: Press enter to accept alignment direction or [Reverse]: **<Enter>**. The **Create Alignment from Objects** dialog box appears. Select the following: Alignment (<[Next Counter (CP)]>), Type: Centerline, Site 1 for the site, and the Alignment style of Standard. Now click on the **Layer** button to the right of **Alignment layer**. This opens the **Object Layer** dialog box. For the parameter called **Base layer name:**, click on the button to the right for **Layers**. Click on the button for **New....** In the **Values** column for **Layer name**, type in **C-Road-Cntr**, hit the value for Color, and select **green**. Hit **OK** until you return to the **Create Alignment from Objects** dialog box.

10. Use the default for **Alignment label set** of **Standard**. Click the **down arrow** next to the button to the right of **Alignment label set**. Click on **Edit Current Selection** (a check mark may already be set here, which is fine). The **Alignment Label Set—Standard** dialog box appears.

11. At the top of the dialog box in the **Labels** tab, shown in Figure 2-4, are pop-down windows for the **Type:** of label and the **Major Station Label Style:**. Make sure that the **Type:** is **Major** *Stations* and the **Major Station Label Style:** is **Standard**. Then, click on the **down arrow** next to the button to the right of the **Major Station Label Style:** pop-down menu. Select **Edit Current Selection**. The **Label Style Composer—Standard** dialog box displays. Choose the **General** tab.
    Under the **Property** column is a **Label** item. A subitem for the **Label** is **Layer**. Select the **Value** column for the **Layer Property**, and see the **Layer** button with ellipses (...). Select that button to change the layer for labels. Choose the **C-Road-Cntr** layer for the labels. Hit **OK**. Hit **Apply** and **OK** for the **Label Style Composer—Standard** dialog box.

12. Next, change the **Type:** to **Minor Stations** and ensure that the **Minor Station Label Style:** is **Standard**. Click on the **down arrow** next to the button to the right of the **Minor Station Label Style:** pop-down menu. Select **Edit Current Selection**. The **Label Style Composer—Standard** dialog box displays. Choose the **General** tab. Under the **Property** column is a **Label** item. A subitem for the **Label** is **Layer**. Select in the **Value** column for the **Layer Property**, and see a button with ellipses (...). Select that button to change the layer for labels. Choose the **C-Road-Cntr** layer for the labels. Hit **OK**. Hit **Apply** and **OK** for the **Label Style Composer—Standard** dialog box.

To access student data files, go to www.pearsondesigncentral.com.

tangent: Intersects a circle once. A tangent line is perpendicular to the radius drawn to the point of tangency (or point of contact with the arc or circle). If a line is perpendicular to a radius at its outer endpoint, then it is tangent to the circle.

alignment: A series of two-dimensional curvilinear geometry elements, used to represent features such as road centerlines where it is beneficial to understand the relationship that these elements have to each other.

stations: A distance along a horizontal alignment that is usually divided by 100′. Therefore 12 stations is 1200′. In metric, this might represent kilometers such that station 10 is 10 kilometers.

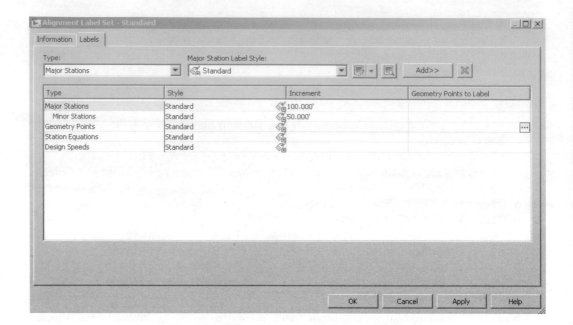

Figure 2-4   Alignment Label Set—Standard

13. Next, change the **Type:** to **Geometry Points** and ensure that the **Geometry Points Label Style:** is **Standard**. Click on the **down arrow** next to the button to the right of the **Geometry Points Label Style:** pop-down menu. Select **Edit Current Selection**. The **Label Style Composer—Standard** dialog box displays. Choose the **General** tab. Under the **Property** column is a **Label** item. A subitem for the **Label** is **Layer**. Select in the **Value** column for the **Layer Property**, and see a button with ellipses (…). Select that button to change the layer for labels. Choose the **C-Road-Cntr** layer for the labels. Hit **OK**. Hit **Apply** and **OK** for the **Label Style Composer—Standard** dialog box.

14. Hit **Apply** and **OK** to exit the **Alignment Label Set— Standard** dialog box.

15. In the area for **Conversion Options**, turn off the toggle for **Add curves between tangents,** because you have already added them using the **FILLET** command. Hit **OK**.

16. You should see a roadway alignment, fully labeled on the **C-Road-Cntr** layer. Observe in the **Prospector** that Alignment-(1) exists under the **Sites, Site 1, Alignments, Centerline Alignments** item. If you click on **Alignment-(1)**, a preview of the alignment shows up in the preview panel. If it does not, ensure that the button at the top left of the dialog box is toggled on. Right-click on **Alignments** and check the **Show Preview** option. Then click on **Alignment-(1)**.

17. Save and close your drawing.

> **Note:**
> Chapters 8 and 9 on road design go into detail about road design works, whereas the intent of this exercise is to prototype a site rapidly.

Now there is a horizontal alignment for the access road into the shopping area. The next task is to develop a vertical profile for the roadway you just created. To accomplish this, develop a Profile along the alignment and computed from the **Existing Ground** surface. It will be placed inside a Profile View, which is the Civil 3D object that displays profiles. Chapter 8 on Profiles discusses this in more detail, but in summary, the Profile View is a Civil 3D concept that contains the grid that profiles are drawn in. The Horizontal Axis of the grid reflects the *stationing*, or linear distance along the horizontal alignment, and the Vertical Axis represents elevational data. The Profile View will include the existing ground profile with annotation. The settings in the **Toolspace** that control the Profile View are in the Profile View Style, which sets the display and spacing of gridlines, profile titling, and the annotation of stations and elevations within the grid. The **Profile View Label Styles** control the display of text and annotation. Once you develop the Profile View and the Existing Ground profile, then you develop a finished *grade* profile for your road.

stationing: Distance along a baseline. It is measured in units of 100 feet in Imperial units and, typically, 1000 meters in metric. Therefore, 1 station = 100′ and is illustrated as 1 + 00.

grade: A change in elevation over a horizontal distance, usually described in percent (%).

Exercise 2-8: Develop a Profile View

1. Open the drawing called Chapter-2d.dwg. It contains the surface you developed, the parcel boundary, and the roadway centerline.
2. From the *Profiles* pull-down menu, click **Create Profile from Surface...**, and the **Create Profile from Surface** dialog box appears. In the **Alignment** pop-down, **Alignment-(1)(1)** should already be there from the alignment creation performed earlier.
3. Click on the **Existing Ground** surface in the window on the right. Click the **Add>>** button to send it to the bottom window for calculation. The station range should be correct from the alignment computations.
4. Now click on the **Draw in profile view** button.

If you hit **OK**, the computation is active but has no place to display the results because the Profile View has not been established.

5. The **Create Profile View** dialog box appears (see Figure 2-5). In the **Profile view name:** field, type **Access Road**, and from the **Select Alignment:** pop-down window, select **Alignment-(1)(1)**. It should already be in the window. Accept the default layer name of **C-Road-Prof**. In the center of the dialog box is a pop-down window called **Profile view style:**. Choose the style called **Major Grids**. You can edit this style if changes to the display of the Profile View are needed. Accept the defaults.

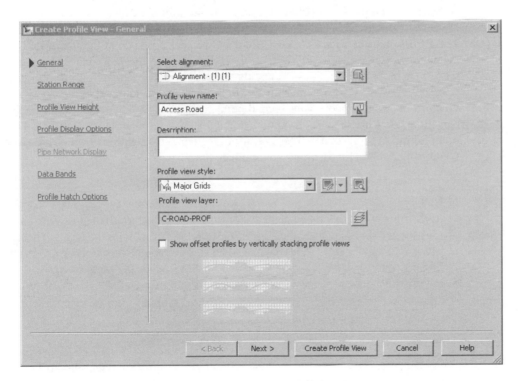

Figure 2-5   Create a Profile View

6. For the **Station Range** and the **Profile View Height**, accept the defaults. Click **Create Profile View**.
7. When you are prompted to `Select profile view origin:`, type **18000,21000** as the coordinate for the location of the Profile View. This is up and to the right of the Plan View. Zoom into the grid representing the Profile View. The evenly spaced horizontal and vertical lines are the grid lines with spacing inherited from the **Major Grids** settings. Vertical blue lines are drawn wherever keypoints for the alignment's horizontal geometry exist, such as *PCs* and *PTs*.
8. Save and close your drawing.

To access student data files, go to www.pearsondesigncentral.com.

profiles: An object containing elevation data that is related to a horizontal alignment. It can apply to existing conditions or proposed conditions. The information within the profile is typically referred to by stations and elevations.

PC: Point of Curvature.

PT: Point of Tangency.

vertical tangents: Linear objects in the profile representing a grade between PVIs. These are linear three-dimensional components of the vertical alignment denoted with a grade usually in percentage (%).

PVI: The Point of Vertical Intersection of the incoming and outgoing vertical tangents.

vertical curves: Parabolic curves located around a PVI to smooth the road as it transitions from one tangent grade to another. These curvilinear three-dimensional components of the vertical alignment denoted by a PVI and a length of curve are typically parabolic with an ever-changing radius.

To access student data files, go to www.pearsondesigncentral.com.

Draw the Existing Ground Profile in the Profile View

The Profile View displays surface profiles and also provides the grid on which you can develop a layout profile or finished grade profile. Each Profile View displays new and/or existing profiles and offset profiles for a single horizontal alignment. Profiles can be created without choosing to display them in the Profile View. When a Profile View is developed, a complete list of profiles for the alignment in question is available so that it can be selected for inclusion in the view.

We have succeeded in developing a Profile View and the Existing Ground profile for the Access Road [or Alignment-(1)(1)]. The next task is to create a finished ground profile in the Profile View. Begin with the *vertical tangents*, which are primitive geometry elements for the profile. At the Points of Vertical Intersection (or *PVIs*), you add vertical curves. These curves differ from the horizontal alignments in that they are not simple arcs; rather, they are parabolic curves. The curve on a hill is known as a *crest curve*, whereas the curve in a depression is known as a *sag curve*. The mathematics behind *vertical curves* will be discussed in Chapter 8 on profiles.

Exercise 2-9: Add Vertical Tangents

1. Open the drawing called Chapter-2e.dwg.
2. From the **Profiles** pull-down menu, choose the command **CREATE PROFILE BY LAYOUT....** When you are prompted to `Select profile view to create profile:`, pick the text box above the profile. The **Create Profile-Draw New** dialog box appears.
3. Notice that it knows you are dealing with Alignment-(1)(1). In the **Name** field, type **Access Road FG**. Type **Access Road FG** in the **Description** field as well.
4. At the bottom of the dialog box in the pop-down window for **Profile label set**, choose the style called **Complete Label Set**. Accept the default for the **Profile layer** option. Accept the default **Design Style** for the **Profile style** option. Hit **OK**.
5. The **Profile Layout Tools—Access Road FG** toolbar opens up at the top of the screen. When you are prompted to `Select a command from the Layout tools:`, choose the first icon button for **Draw Tangents without Curves**. When you are prompted to `Specify start point:`, pick an **Endpoint** snap on the leftmost end of the **Existing Ground** linework. Choose your second point when prompted at about station 3+50 and elevation 320. Choose your third point at about station 7+00 and elevation 345. The last point for the **Access Road** will be an **Endpoint** snap to the rightmost part of the **Existing Ground** linework. Hit **<Enter>** to terminate the sequence.

TIP — When estimating the location of the stations and elevations at which to place these points, use the tooltips that pop up when the cursor is paused. Do not allow the cursor to be snapping, or it tells the snap being computed. Rather, just place the cursor near a line but not on it, and the tooltip will pop up to tell you what the station and elevation is. Use this to estimate the station and elevation requested in the procedure.

Exercise 2-10: Add Vertical Curves

Now add vertical curves to the profile tangents. Although the software does support both symmetrical as well as asymmetrical vertical curves, you use symmetrical at this point.

The software has the concept of Fixed, Free and Floating Vertical curves. This concept is similar to the earlier philosophy for horizontal curves and lines and is discussed in Chapter 6 on geometry. Basically, the concept involves constraint-based commands and the creation of Fixed, Floating, and Free vertical tangents and vertical curves. These objects can be edited dynamically and retain their tangencies.

A Fixed entity is fixed in its position and is defined by criteria such as a radius or located points. It is not dependent on other entities for geometry development or tangency. A Floating entity is always tangent to one entity and is defined by the parameters provided or is dependent on one entity to define its geometry. A Free entity is always tangent to an entity before and after it and must have at least two other entities to attach to which define its geometry.

1. From the **Profile** pull-down menu, choose the command **EDIT PROFILE GEOMETRY....**
2. When prompted to `Select the profile;` click on the finished ground profile tangents just drawn, and the **Profile Layout Tools** toolbar appears. Click on the sixth button from the left; the tooltip should say **Draw fixed parabola by three points**.

    This prompt will change as do others in the software, depending on the choice last selected by the user. From the pop-down menu, choose the option for **Free Vertical Curve (Parameter)**. When you are prompted to `Select first entity:`, click near the first incoming tangent to the PVI. When you are prompted to `Select next entity:`, click near the outgoing tangent.
3. When you are prompted to `Specify curve length or [Radius/K]:`, type **300 <Enter>**.
4. The software then assumes you will continue with additional PVIs and prompts you to `Specify first entity:` again. Click near the second PVI and you are prompted again to `Select next entity;`, Click near the outgoing tangent. When you are prompted to `Specify curve length or [Radius/K]`, type **300 <Enter>**. **<Enter>** terminates the routine.
5. You see two vertical curves now added where the PVIs are.
6. Save and close the file.

Exercise 2-11: Create a Corridor for the Access Road

Now develop the remaining part of the road, that is, the finished ground *cross section* conditions for the pavement. Civil 3D introduces a corridor design capability that completes the road design cycle. It builds on the horizontal and vertical alignments that you have worked on so far. A *corridor* is a Civil 3D object and as such is linked to the horizontal and vertical alignments, surfaces, and assemblies that were used to create it. If one of these components is altered, the corridor is correspondingly modified. The next step is to modify subassembly properties for your design criteria, create an *assembly* from the *subassemblies*, and create the corridor model.

For our Access Road, we have the following design requirements: The road will be a crowned section with a pavement width of **12'**. The cross slope of the lane is **–2.08%** from the crown to allow for drainage off the roadway when it rains. A shoulder for this road will be **4'** wide with a cross slope of **–4%** from the edge of pavement. The side sloping from the shoulder will be **3:1** until it hits existing ground.

Note:
Subassemblies are the primitive components of assemblies, and they instruct the software in how to handle lanes, curbs, guardrails, or shoulders and related side sloping. Autodesk provides many subassemblies to begin with, and you can access them from **Tool Palettes**. The assemblies, on the other hand, are stored in the drawing and can be accessed from the **Project Toolspace** under **Assemblies**. They contain the definition of the typical section being designed and are developed by piecing together subassemblies.

Note:
A 3:1 side slope is a condition describing an elevation rise of 1' for every 3' horizontally and is usually denoted by this ratio.

cross section: A transverse view of the surface.

corridor: A structure that allows passage or conveyance of people or things.

assembly: Objects that manage collections of subassemblies; used for the basic structure of a corridor object.

subassemblies: The fundamental building blocks used to create assemblies. It defines the geometry of a component used in a corridor section and includes predeveloped components for such things as travel lanes, curbs, side slopes, and ditches. It has intelligent behavior built into it and can automatically adapt to design conditions comprising superelevations and cut or fill requirements.

TIP These subassemblies are some of the first examples of parametric technology being introduced to the civil engineering community. Once these objects are created, the parameters within them can be changed on the fly. The dynamic modeling abilities of the software then can cause a ripple-through effect as the changes are applied to all related objects in the corridor.

To access student data
files, go to
www.pearsondesigncentral.com.

Exercise 2-12: Create the Assembly

1. Open the drawing called Chapter-2f.dwg.
2. Type **Z** for **Zoom** at the command prompt, then type **C** for **Center** and type **17000,20000**. When asked for a height, type **50**.
3. This places you in a location where the assembly can be created. There is nothing special about this location; it is simply out of the way and zoomed to a height of **50′**.
4. From the **Corridors** pull-down menu, select **Create Assembly...**. The **Create Assembly** dialog box opens.
5. Enter the name as **Access Road**. Leave the remaining settings as default and hit **OK**.
6. When you are prompted to `Specify assembly baseline location:`, pick a point in the middle of the screen. A small symbol with a red line will show up. This indicates the assembly location to which you will attach subassemblies.

If you look in the **Prospector** and expand the tree for **Assemblies**, you see the assembly name. Now you will attach the subassemblies to both the left and the right sides of the assembly location.

Exercise 2-13: Attach Subassemblies to the Assembly Marker

1. Go to the **General** pull-down menu and choose the **Tool Palettes Window**. From the **Civil 3D Imperial Subassemblies** palette, click the **BasicLane** subassembly and the **Properties** dialog box appears.
2. Look under the **Advanced** menu parameters at the bottom of the **Properties** palette.
3. Set the **Side** to **Right** and notice the lane width is **12′**. Change the parameter **%Slope** to **-2.08**. Set the depth to **1.0**.
4. In the drawing, pick the assembly baseline location, which is the circular symbol in the middle of the assembly that you created. Hit **Enter** twice. The lane should show up on the right side of the assembly marker.
5. From the **Civil 3D Imperial Subassemblies** palette, click the **BasicShoulder** subassembly. Look in the **Properties** palette and set the parameter for **Side** to **Right**. Set the depth to **0.67**. Ensure that the width is set to **4.0** and the **% Slope** is **-4.00**. When you are prompted to `Select marker point within assembly or [RETURN for Detached]:` pick the perimeter edge of the circle symbol located at the top right corner of the **BasicLane** subassembly. Hit **Esc**. The shoulder should extend to the right of the lane.
6. From the **Civil 3D Imperial-Basic** palette, click the **BasicGuardrail** subassembly. Look in the **Properties** window and select **Right** side from the pop-down parameter for **Side**. When you are prompted to `Select marker point within assembly or [RETURN for Detached]:` pick the perimeter edge of the circle symbol located at the top right of the shoulder. Hit **Esc**.
7. At this point you can mirror the subassemblies to create the left side of the road. Select the three subassemblies that you created. Right-click, then click mirror. You are prompted to `Select marker point within assembly:`, pick on the center point of the assembly.
8. Right-clicking at the bottom of the tabs on the **Tool Palette** brings up a list of the tabs. From the **Imperial-Generic** palette, click the **LinkOffsetAndSlope** subassembly. Again, the **Properties** dialog box opens each time a subassembly is picked. In this case, ensure that the **%Slope** is set to **–2**. Also set the **Offset from Baseline** to **22.0** (which produces a **6′** area past the guardrail before sidesloping kicks in). A positive number for the offset indicates that it heads off to the right, whereas a negative offset indicates to the left.
9. Then pick inside the drawing and then pick the perimeter edge of the circle symbol located at the right, center **BasicGuardrail** subassembly. The **Link** should extend to the right of the guardrail.
10. Look back into the **Properties** palette and set the **Offset from Baseline** parameter to **–22.0**, so it will be applied to the left.
11. Then pick the perimeter edge of the circle symbol located at the left, center **BasicGuardrail** subassembly. The **Link** should extend to the left of the guardrail.
12. From the **Imperial-Basic** palette, click the **BasicSideSlopeCutDitch** subassembly. Review the settings for the parameters in the **Properties** palette and accept the defaults. Set the **Side** to **Right**.
13. Then pick the perimeter edge of the circle symbol located at the right, center **LinkOffsetAndSlope** subassembly. The **Link** should extend to the right.

Figure 2-6   Access Road Assembly

14. Go back to the **Properties** palette and set the **Side** to **Left**.
15. Then pick the perimeter edge of the circle symbol located at the left, center **LinkOffsetAndSlope** subassembly. The **Link** should extend to the left.
16. Press **<Enter>** twice or hit **Esc** to finish the command. Save the file.

You have now created the assembly. Figure 2-6 shows how it should appear. Keep in mind that the designer can build the right side independently of the left if desired. The assembly does not have to be symmetrical, and on actual projects, it often may not be symmetrical. If a developer is developing a project on the east side of the road, it may proffer to improve that side of the road while allowing a future developer to improve the west side of the road.

Now move forward to creating the roadway. In this task, the pieces to the Corridor puzzle come together. You have all the components for the Corridor. To summarize, you developed the primitive geometry for the alignment and developed a completed alignment. You then computed and drew an Existing Ground profile inside a Profile View. From there you designed a finished ground profile for the Access Road. You then set the settings for some subassemblies and created an assembly. Now create the Corridor and the finished design surface.

Exercise 2-14: Create a Corridor

To access student data files, go to www.pearsondesigncentral.com.

1. Open the drawing called Chapter-2g.dwg.
2. We will restore a pre-saved view to place our view around the centerline.
3. Type **V<Enter>** for **View** at the command prompt to obtain the **View Manager** dialog box. Choose the **Access Road Plan View**, hit **Set Current**, then hit **OK**. You are at the centerline of the Access Road. There is also a view setup for the profile should you need it.
4. From the **Corridors** pull-down menu, select **Create Simple Corridor....**
5. The **Create Simple Corridor** dialog box appears. Enter **Access Road** for the name and hit **OK**.
6. When you are prompted to `Select a baseline alignment <or press enter key to select from list>:`, pick the green centerline in the view.
7. You are prompted to `Select a profile <or press enter key to select from list>:`.
8. The **Select a Profile** dialog box appears. Choose the **Access Road FG** and hit **OK** (Figure 2-7).
9. You are prompted to `Select an assembly <or press enter key to select from list>:` hit **<Enter>** and the **Select an Assembly** dialog box appears. Select **Assembly-1** from the list and hit **OK** (Figure 2-8).
10. A large window of data will display for **Target Mapping**, as in Figure 2-9. Do not close this box yet.

Figure 2-7   Select a Profile

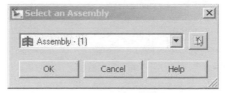

Figure 2-8   Select an Assembly

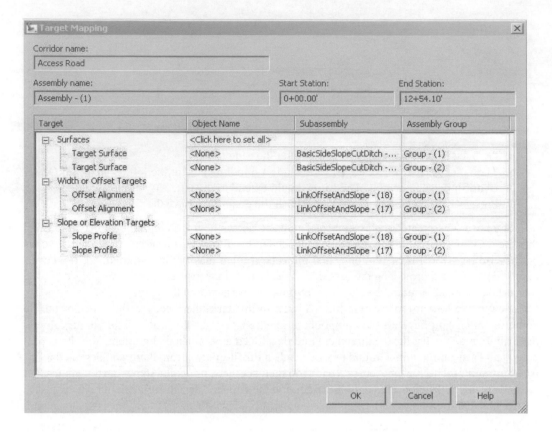

Figure 2-9 Target Mapping

Exercise 2-15: Target Mapping

Target Mapping is a technical way of assigning the particular alignments, profiles, and surfaces required by the subassemblies to create the complete assembly. For instance, the **BasicSideSlopeCutDitch** subassembly needs to know which surface it will be computing to, and so the **Target Map** for this would be the Existing Ground surface.

1. In the second column and in the row for **Surfaces** is a cell that says <Click here to set all>.
2. When you click on the cell, a dialog box called **Pick a Surface** displays. Choose the **Existing Ground** and click **OK**. You will see the Target Surface is now Existing Ground. Click **OK**, and the corridor will generate, as shown in Figure 2-10.
3. Close the **Panorama** if it appears and inspect the results of the processing. A Corridor model will be evident in the drawing.
4. Restore a pre-saved view to place your model in a bird's-eye perspective with shading to help see the road better. Type **V<Enter>** for **View** at the command prompt to obtain the **View Manager** dialog box. Click the **ISO View**, hit **Set Current**, then hit **OK**.
5. You see the road is 3D, complete with representation of the guardrails, as shown in Figure 2-11.

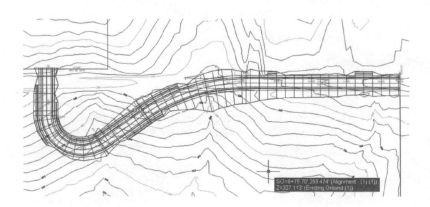

Figure 2-10 Corridor Created

Figure 2-11   Corridor ISO

6. Type **ZP <Enter>** to return to the previous view when you are finished viewing.
7. Save and close the file.

Exercise 2-16: Viewing Additional Results of the Corridor Design

The Corridor model is now built, but it is necessary to discuss a few methods that exist to review the model. One is to investigate what the finished sections look like. Follow this procedure to observe the section conditions.

1. Open the drawing called Chapter-2h.dwg. The previously created corridor is shown.
2. Under the **Corridors** pull-down menu, choose **View/Edit Corridor Section**. When you are prompted to `Select a Corridor <or press enter to select from list>:`, pick any part of the corridor that you can.
3. Once the corridor is selected, the first station of the section displays along with a **Section Editor** toolbar that allows you to move up and down the alignment, viewing any section desired. This is displayed in Figure 2-12.
4. Take a few moments to zoom in and out and review the section that appeared. Notice where the lanes, the ditch, and the tie-out slopes are.
5. Then move forward to the next station and observe the display.
6. Continue observing and when you are ready, close the toolbar; the normal view will return as it was before you entered this facility.

To access student data files, go to www.pearsondesigncentral.com.

Many aspects of the Corridor model can be manipulated and many of them will be in Chapter 9 on corridors. However, here is a brief example of the powers. You follow a procedure that identifies some basic *feature lines* of the corridor, such as the centerline, the edge of the pavement (or EP), the bottom of the ditch, and the daylight cut and fill lines. These will be inspected for quality control purposes, but they serve a purpose later in establishing construction information because they can also be exported as alignments or grading feature lines. Grading feature lines are discussed in Chapter 10 on site grading.

feature line: An object that the grading commands can work with. It represents breaks in the surface features. For example, the edges of pavement, ditches, or daylighting could be feature lines. Their appearance is controlled by feature line styles.

Exercise 2-17: Corridor Feature Lines

1. Select the Corridor model by picking it, and it will highlight. Right-click and select **Corridor Properties...** from the shortcut menu.
2. The **Corridor Properties** dialog box displays. Select the tab for **Feature Lines** (Figure 2-13).
3. By default, all of the feature lines are assigned to the **Standard** feature line style. In order to see some of the objects within the corridor better, assign **Feature Line Styles** to the **Daylight_Cut**, the **Daylight_Fill**, and the **Edge of Travel Way** (ETW) feature lines. When you return to Civil 3D, they will appear differently as a result of this style modification.
4. In the **Code** column, pick the **Daylight_Cut** code and look in the **Feature Line Style** column. Pick the **blue** icon in this column, and a dialog box called **Pick Feature Line Style** will display. In the pop-down window, select the style called **Daylight Line—Cut**, and hit **OK**.
5. In the **Code** column, pick the **Daylight_Fill** code and look in the **Feature Line Style** column. Pick the **blue** icon in this column, and a dialog box called **Pick Feature Line**

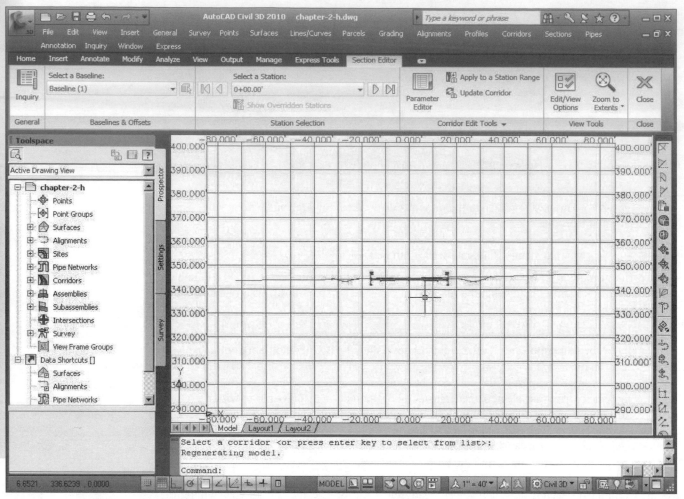

Figure 2-12   Corridor Section Editor

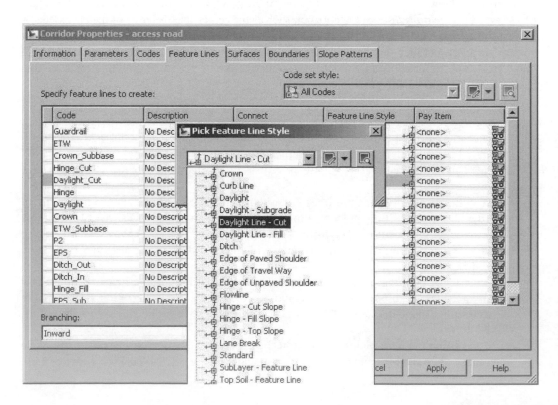

Figure 2-13   Feature Lines

Style will display. In the pop-down window, select the style called **Daylight Line—Fill**, and hit **OK**.

6. In the **Code** column, pick the **ETW** code and look in the **Feature Line Style** column. Pick the **blue** icon in this column, and a dialog box called **Pick Feature Line Style** will display. In the pop-down window, select the style called **Edge of Travel Way**.

7. Then click the **down arrow** button on the right side of the pop-down window. Choose **Edit Current Selection** from the options (Figure 2-14).

Figure 2-14   Edit Current Selection

8. The **Feature Line Style** dialog box will display. Choose the **Display** tab. Change the **Feature Line Color** to **Yellow** and change the **Lineweight** to **0.80 mm**. Hit **OK**.

9. Hit **OK**. Hit **OK** one more time to exit the main **Corridor Properties** dialog box. The system will regenerate the Corridor. If you do not see the alterations, click the **LWT** button, the ninth from the left, at the bottom of the screen to **On**.

10. The corridor should appear as shown in the graphic. The cut is red and fill is green per the alterations just made to the display of the corridor. The edge of pavement is yellow and a heavy lineweight. If the **Panorama** displays, close it.

11. Save the file and close the drawing.

At this point in the project, you have created the terrain model, a parcel for the design of our site, an alignment, a profile, an assembly, and a corridor that provides access to the commercial shopping center being designed. Refer to Figure 2-15. Some basic adjustments to the display of our data have been made along the way.

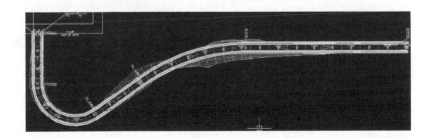

Figure 2-15   Cut and Fill Colored

Site Design

The next task is to create some building pads for the stores and a parking lot for the commercial site being designed. The design criteria for the site are as follows:

- A Building Restriction Line *(BRL)* of 25′ prevents any structures from being within 25′ of the property line.

- The finished floor of the stores will be at 350′.

- The parking lot slope is indicated with callouts in the drawing or with points placed at various critical locations in the file. You will draw 3D Polylines to help guide the drainage over the parking lot.

- The parking lot ties into the access road edges of pavement at 344.58′. The crown of the Access Road is at 344.78′.

BRL: Building Restriction Lines indicate the limits for construction of structures inside a property. They ensure that structures are not built too close to other structures.

- A 6′ wide sidewalk with a –2% grade exists around the stores except on the north and west sides.

- The majority of the drainage flow will be directed toward the Access Road, where it will be conveyed until station 3 + 56, at which a drain inlet will be placed to divert it offsite.

- The site ties out to natural ground at a 3:1 side slope.

- A layer in the drawing called **Site Geometry** contains the buildings for the shopping center.

- A layer called **Site Drainage Criteria** indicates where the Feature Lines will go that will guide the drainage and become Feature Lines.

Exercise 2-18: Design the Shopping Center Building Finished Floor Slabs and the Parking Lot

To access student data files, go to www.pearsondesigncentral.com.

1. Open the drawing called Chapter-2i.dwg. The previously created corridor is shown with the visual adjustments that were made to it. There are buildings in the file with their elevation set to **0.0** and an accompanying **6′** wide sidewalk.
2. Change the properties of the buildings to place them on the **3D-Data** layer. To do this, type **Properties** to invoke the **Properties** dialog box. Select the polyline and change the elevation parameter to **350.0**. Hit **Enter** and **Esc** to end the task.
3. Repeat this for the sidewalk, but make the elevation **349.88**, which represents a –2% drop over 6′.
4. Then offset the edge of sidewalk away from the buildings using the **OFFSET** command and a distance of **0.4′**. This represents the Top of Curb of the sidewalk.
5. Then offset the Top of Curb again, away from the building, a distance of **0.1′**. This now represents the Flowline of the Curb.
6. With the **Properties** dialog box open, select the Flowline of Curb, and change the elevation to **349.38**, which is a 0.5′ drop from the Top of Curb.
7. You will see that this coincides with two points (Points 1 and 2) placed in the file at the same elevations, that is, 349.38. These two points represent the start of our flow divide, and now you can see how they were determined.
8. Ensure that your current layer is set to **3D-Data**.
9. Type in **3P** at the command prompt to invoke the **3DPOLY** command. Use a **Node** snap and snap to Point 1 for the first point. Use a **Node** snap and pick Point 8. Continue by picking another **Node** snap and selecting Point 9. Hit **<Enter>** to terminate. You might notice that the 3D Polyline is now set to 3D due to snapping to the nodes that had elevations.
10. Type in **3P** or hit **<Enter>** at the command prompt to invoke the **3DPOLY** command again. Use a **Node** snap and snap to Point 2 for the first point. Use a **Node** snap and pick Point 8. Hit **<Enter>** to terminate.
11. Type in **3P** or hit **<Enter>** at the command prompt to invoke the **3DPOLY** command again. Use a **Node** snap each time to snap to Points 4, 5, 6, and 7. Hit **<Enter>** to terminate.

At the north end of the site, notice that Point 3 has been placed at an elevation of 349.6. This represents a –2% cross-slope over that pavement distance. This pavement area is for the loading and unloading of trucks and supply vehicles. The asphalt pavement flows away from the buildings at –2% and then at –1% to the east and west of Point 3. Now you will create grading for the perimeter of the site and parking lot.

12. In the **Grading** pull-down menu, select the **CREATE FEATURE LINES FROM OBJECTS** command. Choose the two cyan-colored lines touching Point 3, representing the perimeter of the parking lot.
      When the dialog displays click the **Style** field **On** and select **Edge of Travelway** for the feature lines. Hit **OK**.
13. All of these are grading feature lines. Click on the **West** feature line. Select the Edit Elevations then select the **Elevation Editor**.
14. Refer to Figure 2-16 and set the first elevation to **349.6** if it is not already set. Then establish all the grades for jump segments at **–0.5%**, except for the last segment. Set the last segment to **–1%**, which should set the last elevation to **344.56**.

Station	Elevation	Length	Grade Ahead	Grade Back
0+00.00	349.600'	280.998'	-0.500%	0.500%
2+81.00	348.195'	292.753'	-0.500%	0.500%
5+73.75	346.731'	98.251'	-0.500%	0.500%
6+72.00	346.240'	171.349'	-0.500%	0.500%
8+43.35	345.383'	82.006'	-1.000%	1.000%
9+25.36	344.563'			

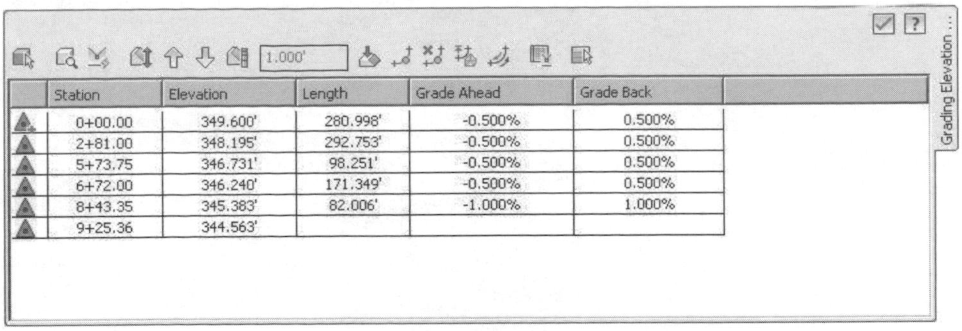

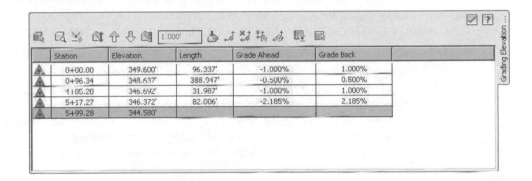

Figure 2-16 Elevation Editor

15. Click on the **Eastern** feature line and right-click. Select the **Elevation Editor....**
16. Refer to Figure 2-17 and set the first elevation to **349.6** if it is not already set.
17. Then in the **Grade** column, set the first segment's grade to **–1.0%**.
18. Set the next segment to **–0.5%**.
19. Set the next segment to **–1.0%**.
20. Set the last segment to **–2.185%**, which should set the last elevation to **344.58**.

The 3D linework should now all reside on the **3D-Data** and the **C-Topo-Grad-Flin** layers for easy selection later. Next set the grading for the perimeter of the site as it ties out to natural ground.

Station	Elevation	Length	Grade Ahead	Grade Back
0+00.00	349.600'	96.337'	-1.000%	1.000%
0+96.34	348.637'	388.947'	-0.500%	0.500%
4+85.20	346.692'	31.987'	-1.000%	1.000%
5+17.27	346.372'	82.006'	-2.185%	2.185%
5+99.28	344.580'			

Figure 2-17 Elevation Editor Data

Exercise 2-19: Establish a 3D Grading Perimeter

1. From the **Grading** pull-down menu, select **Create Grading....** These are called **Grading Creation Tools**. A toolbar called **Grading Creation Tools** will display, shown in Figure 2-18.

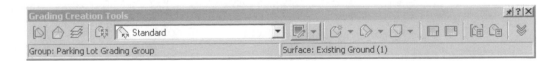

Figure 2-18 Grading Creation Tools

Use of this tool is detailed in Chapter 10 on site grading; however, it is necessary to set some of the parameters now in order to move forward with this exercise. The first button from the left sets the **Grading Group**. The second button sets the **Target Surface**. The third button sets the **Grading Layers**.

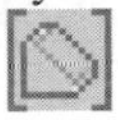

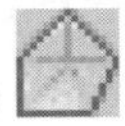

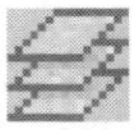

2. Select the first icon button from the left of the toolbar. This invokes the **Select Grading Group** dialog box (Figure 2-19) to allow you to name the Grading Group. Under **Group name:**, type **Parking Lot Grading Group**. Then hit **OK**. You may note that this creates a **Parking Lot Grading Group** in the **Prospector** under **Sites**, **Site 1**, **Grading Groups**.

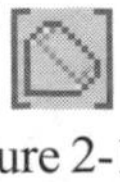

Figure 2-19   Select Grading Group

3. Select the second icon button 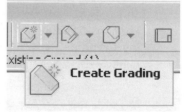 from the left of the toolbar. This invokes the **Select surface** dialog box to allow you to select the surface to which you are going to tie out. Choose **Existing Ground** when the dialog box displays, hit **OK**.

4. Select the third icon button from the left of the toolbar. This invokes the **Set Grading Layers** dialog box to allow you to develop layers for the grading feature lines. The default should be **C-TOPO-GRAD** for the Grading. Hit **OK**.

5. Now select the fourth button item ⟨ Standard ⟩ from the left to **Select a Criteria Set**. This opens a dialog box that might default to **Standard**. Open the pop-down window and choose the **Basic Set**. Hit **OK**. The pop-down window now has several options available. Choose the option called **Surface @ 3-1 Slope** (Figure 2-20).

6. Now hit the second button just to the right of the pop-down window in the **Grading Creation Tools** toolbar. It should have a tooltip called **Create Grading** if you pause your cursor over the button. If not, click the **down arrow** and select **Create Grading** (Figure 2-21).

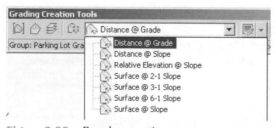

Figure 2-20   Pop-down options

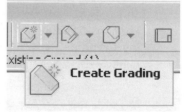

Figure 2-21   Create Grading

7. When this command is invoked, the command prompt will ask you to select the feature. Click on the Western perimeter feature line.

8. When prompted to `Apply to entire length? [ Yes/No] <Yes>`, hit **<Enter>** for Yes.

9. Without leaving the command, when prompted to `Select the feature:`, select the Eastern perimeter line and pick a point to the East of the site for the direction. Hit **<Enter>** then **<Esc>** to terminate.

10. When complete, close the toolbar. You should see the perimeter graded out to the Existing Ground. The red indicates Cut activity and the green indicates Fill. The perimeter is the Daylight where the proposed ties into the existing.

11. Save and close the file.

The next step is to create a finished ground surface representing the Access Road and the grading for the parking lot and the commercial shopping center.

Exercise 2-20: Create a Finished Ground Surface

1. Open the drawing called Chapter-2j.dwg. The previously created corridor and parking lot grading are shown in Figure 2-22.
2. Go to the **Prospector** and expand the **Open Drawings** collection. Then expand Chapter-2j.dwg.

To access student data files, go to www.pearsondesigncentral.com.

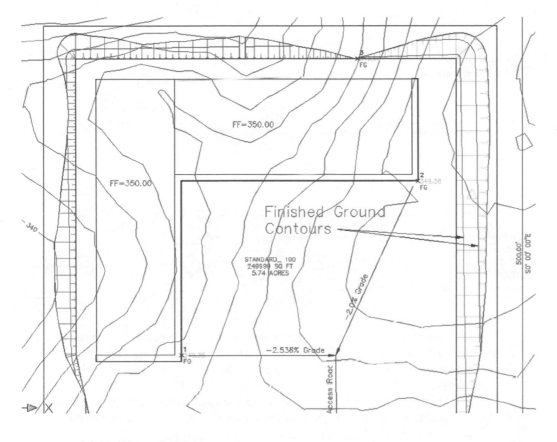

Figure 2-22   Corridor and parking lot grading

3. Then expand **Surfaces**, right-click on **Existing Ground**, and choose **Surface Proper-ties....** Set the **Surface Style** to **Contours (Background)** and choose the button to the right to get the pop-down menu. Choose **Edit Current Selection**, choose the **Contours** tab, and set the **Contour Interval** to **2′** and **10′** (see Figure 2-23). Hit **OK** twice.
4. Then expand **Sites**, **Site 1**, and **Grading Groups**. You see the **Parking Lot Grading Group**. Left-click on the **Parking Lot Grading Group**, and you will see a preview of the group in the right pane if the **Show Preview** is checked under **Grading Groups**. Right-click on the **Parking Lot Grading Group** and choose **Properties....** The **Grading Group Properties** dialog box will open.
5. In the **Information** tab, turn **On** the toggle for **Automatic Surface Creation**. This will invoke the **Create Surface** dialog box.
6. The **Type** will be a **TIN surface**, which is the default. The layer will default to **C-TOPO**.
7. Ensure that the name **Parking Lot Grading Group** is in the **Name** field under **Information**.
8. Provide the **Description** of **Parking Lot Grading Group**.
9. Under the **Properties**, **Style**, click on the name **Standard** to invoke the ellipses (...), choose **Border and Contours**. Hit **OK**. Hit **OK** twice to execute.

Notice that contours now exist for the finished ground around the parking lot. Figure 2-22 shows some leaders pointing to the finished ground contours. The next step is to add in the fea-ture lines for the drainage vectors, the sidewalks, and the buildings.

Exercise 2-21: Creating Feature Lines

1. In the **Prospector**, expand the **Surfaces** collection and then expand the **Parking Lot Grading Group** item. Expand the **Definition** item, and you see **Breaklines**. Right-click on **Breaklines** and hit **Add...** to invoke the **Add Breaklines** dialog box.

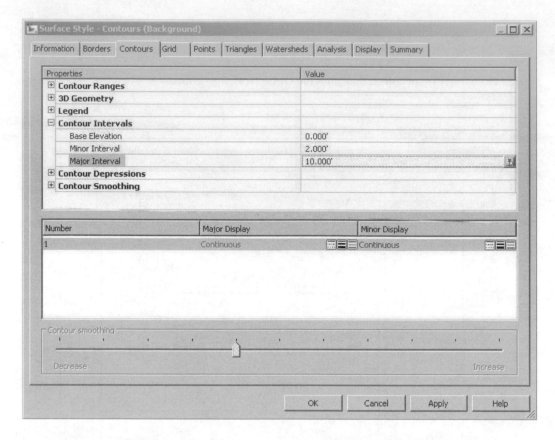

Figure 2-23   Surface Style

2. Type **Parking Lot Breaklines** into the **Description** field. **Type:** will be **Standard**, and the **Mid-ordinate distance:** will be **1′**, as shown in Figure 2-24. Hit **OK**.
3. When you are prompted to `Select objects:`, select the two building pads, the sidewalk breaklines, the two drainage vectors in the middle of the parking lot, and the last vector on Points 4 through 7. Hit **<Enter>** when finished picking the breaklines.
4. Turn off the **3D-Data** and **C-Topo-Existing Ground** layers, and you will see the Parking Lot contours.

Figure 2-25 shows that if you place your cursor inside the parking lot, a tooltip pops up and automatically provides elevational information for the Existing Ground as well as the Parking Lot surfaces. The next step is to develop contours for a corridor from the Corridor model.

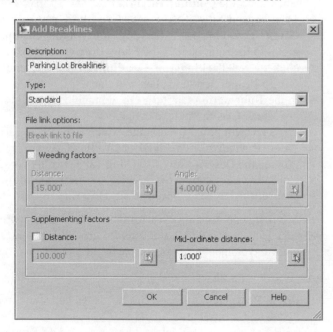

Figure 2-24   Add Breaklines

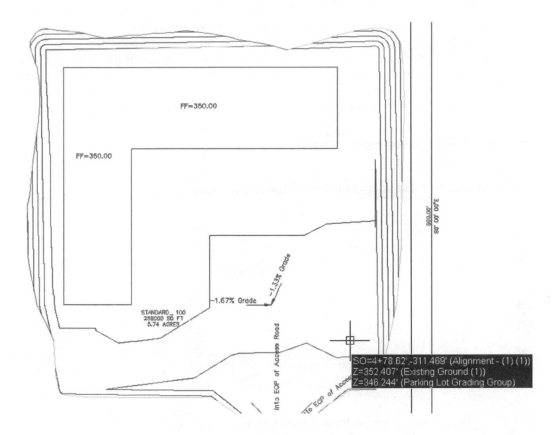

Figure 2-25 Site Contours

Exercise 2-22: Create Contours

1. Zoom into the corridor, or type **V** for **View** and select the **Access Road Plan View**, set it current, and hit **OK**.
2. Go to **Prospector**, expand **Corridors**, right-click **access road,** and choose **Properties....**
3. Choose the **Surfaces** tab, shown in Figure 2-26.
4. Click the first button on the top left that has a tooltip of **Create a corridor surface**. It uses the **Data type:** of **Links** and the **Specify code:** of **Top**.

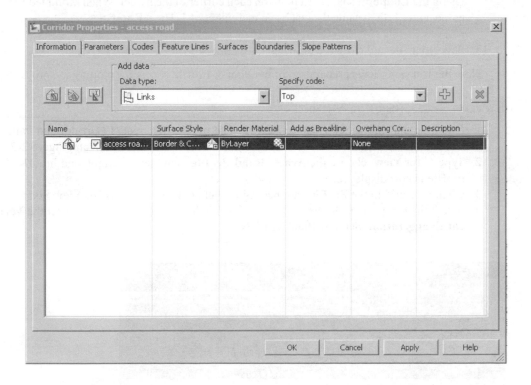

Figure 2-26 Corridor Properties-access road

5. The name **Access Road Surface** appears in the window below.
6. Click the button with the plus sign to the right of the **Specify code:** pop-down menu with a tooltip of **Add surface item**. It should be set to **Top**. The name **Access Road** can be expanded now, and you should see **Top**. This is the surface data from which the surface will be created.
7. Now select the **Boundaries** tab, as shown in Figure 2-27. This option trims the contours for the roadway right at the daylight cut and fill lines to ensure clean tie-out of the contours.

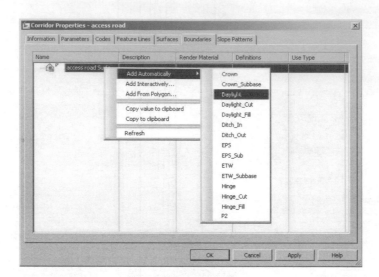

Figure 2-27 Corridor Properties Boundaries

8. Right-click on the **Access Road Surface** name.
9. Choose the **Add Automatically** option and then choose **Daylight** from the submenu. Hit **Apply**, then hit **OK**.
10. The contours for the Corridor should be displayed in AutoCAD now.

Congratulations! You have developed a corridor and a shopping center, all in 3D. Now place some property corner points on the parcel.

11. Zoom back to the **Plan View** of the parking lot.
12. From the **Points** pull-down menu, select **Create Points Miscellaneous**, then **Manual**. Using the **Endpoint** snap, set a point on each corner of the parcel. When prompted for the name, enter **1**, then name the rest by an increment of **1**. Hit **<Enter>** `Specify a point elevation <.>:` Hit **<Enter>**.
13. Save your file and close the drawing.

Now the last step shows preparation of the Plan & Profile sheets for plotting the project.

Exercise 2-23: Setting Up a P&P Sheet

To access student data files, go to www.pearsondesigncentral.com.

1. Open the drawing called Chapter-2k.dwg. The previously created Corridor and Parking Lot are shown with their respective contours, as shown in Figure 2-28 and Figure 2-29.
2. Type **V** for **View**, choose the **Access Road Profile** view, set it current, and hit **OK**. The profile is now displayed.
3. Click on a grid in the **Profile** and then right-click. Choose **Edit Profile View Style...**.
4. Select the **Graph** tab. On the right side of the dialog box is a parameter to set the **Vertical Exaggeration**. Set it to **10.00**. Hit **OK**.

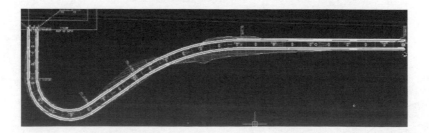

Figure 2-28 Corridor and Parking Lot are shown with Contours

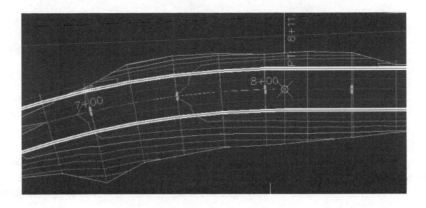

Figure 2-29   Close-up of Corridor and Parking Lot are shown with Contours

5. Right-click the button next to the **Model** button at the bottom of the screen to display the **Layout** tabs.
6. Right-click on the **Layout 1** tab and choose **Page Setup Manager...**. When the dialog box appears, select the **Modify** button to get to the **Page Setup** dialog box shown in Figure 2-30.

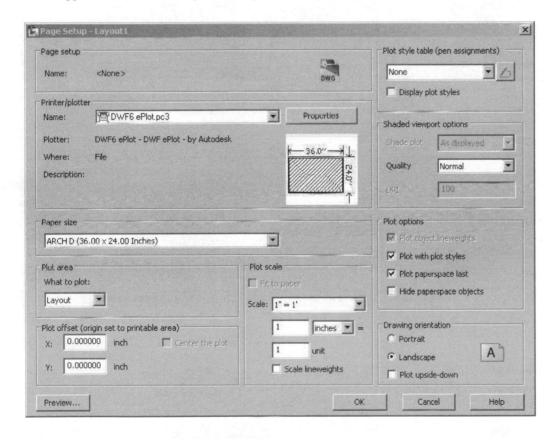

Figure 2-30   Page Setup

7. Set the **Plotter name:** to **DWF6 ePlot.pc3**.
8. Set the **Paper size** to **ARCH D, 36 × 24**. Hit **OK** and **Close**.

TIP   Selecting an exaggeration of **10.0** means that the vertical scale for the profile will be 1/10th that of the horizontal scale. This often-used factor can be switched to **5.0** for a flatter profile or even sometimes to **1.0** for a profile that is not exaggerated.

9. From the **View** pull-down menu, select **Viewports**. Select **New Viewports...**. A dialog box appears.
10. Choose **Two: Horizontal**. Hit **OK**. Pick a point in the upper left of the screen, then the lower right. Two viewports appear. Click on the viewport, then right-click, and choose **Properties**. Set the **Annotation scale** to **1″ = 50′**. Repeat for the second viewport.

11. At the bottom of the screen, toggle the **PAPER** button to **MODEL**. Pan the **Plan View** so you can see the corridor.
12. Pan the Profile into the Profile View so you can see it. Toggle back to **PAPER**.
13. Choose the **View** pull-down menu and select **Regen All**.
14. Right-click on **Layout 1**, and choose the **Rename** option. Rename it to **Plan & Profile**.
15. Now click on the **Layout 2** tab. After it is finished regenerating, right-click on **Layout 2**. Repeat the setup commands to create a 24″×36″ viewport. This time choose **Single** from the viewport options.
16. Stretch the viewport to take advantage of the whole sheet. Then click on the viewport; then right-click and choose the **Properties** command. Set the **Standard scale** for this viewport to **1:20**. If this will not fit on the paper, use a **1:30** scale.
17. Right-click on the **Layout 2** tab, and choose the **Rename** option. Rename it to **Plan Parking Lot**.
18. Choose the **View** pull-down menu and select **Regen All**.
19. These sheets or layouts are now ready for plotting. Refer to Figure 2-31.

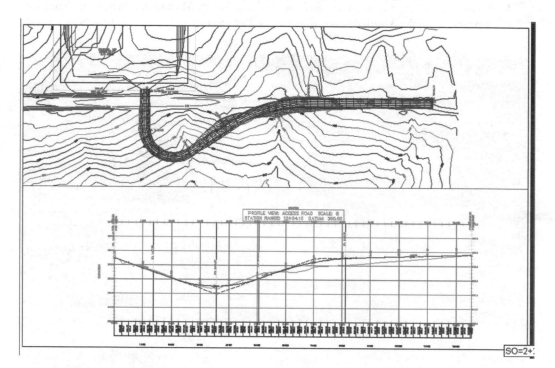

Figure 2-31   Plan & Profile

Note that you can make changes to the various styles involved so that finished ground contours appear differently than the Existing Ground contours. Refer to Figure 2-32. More detailed concepts like this will be covered in the later chapters.

Congratulations! You have completed the chapter's goal.

Job Skills will benefit from this chapter because it covered an entire project from start to finish using Civil 3D. Although it was fairly simple in scope, it touched on developing multiple surfaces, parcels, property corner points, centerlines, profiles, assemblies, and corridors. The project was completed by creating construction plans in paper space. These functions could be called *Minimum Proficiency Requirements*.

Minimum Proficiency Requirements are those tasks that everyone in design should be capable of performing. A manager in the company should be able to approach any designer or technician and ask that a surface be assembled, a centerline be created, a profile be computed, or a plot be output. Of course, the real value in being able to do these tasks is to understand the mathematics behind them. This chapter assumes that you understand at least the rudimentary math behind the automated computations; however, the remaining chapters in the book do not. The advanced chapters that follow begin by going over the math behind Civil 3D, provide instruction in many of the formulas, and teach the algorithms that you need to know to use the software properly.

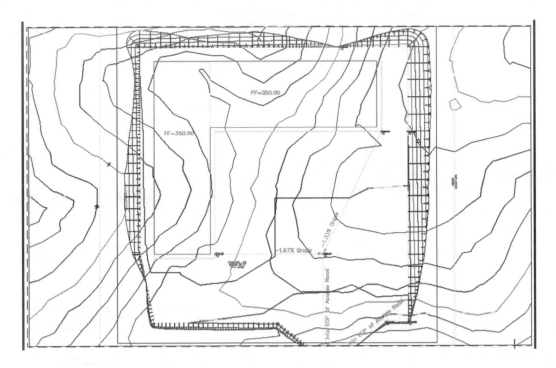

Figure 2-32 Completed site

CHAPTER SUMMARY

This chapter took you through a design project from start to finish. You prepared the ground surface from actual 3D project data, developed a property parcel for a shopping center, and prepared the labeling required for its drafting. Finally, you developed a finished ground profile and a corridor to put the road into 3D. Now we move on to points and point settings.

CHAPTER TEST QUESTIONS

Multiple Choice

1. One of the things that this chapter prepares you to do is
   a. Develop an alignment for an access road to the shopping center
   b. Design a hydraulic grade line for a storm sewer
   c. Design the shopping center buildings, walls, and roof trusses
   d. None of the above

2. Which of the following are Civil 3D objects?
   a. Corridors
   b. Surfaces
   c. Earthworks
   d. a and b

3. Mass points are
   a. Often from Photogrammetric sources
   b. In 3D with elevations
   c. Fairly evenly spaced across the site and are intended to densify the surface data
   d. All of the above

4. The following are types of surfaces:
   a. TIN and GRID
   b. Superelevation

   c. Building Restriction Lines
   d. Earthworks

5. Proximity breaklines
   a. Are 2D polylines
   b. Have elevations at each vertex in the polyline
   c. Are converted to 3D polylines for surface creation
   d. All of the above

6. A Wall breakline is
   a. Vertical
   b. Nearly vertical
   c. Flat
   d. None of the above

7. In a Profile View, which of the following are correct?
   a. The Horizontal Axis of the grid reflects the stationing
   b. Vertical Axis represents elevational data
   c. The grids represent specified spacing criteria
   d. All of the above

8. A vertical alignment may have the following components:
   a. A PI, PC, and PT
   b. A PRC and a PCC
   c. A broken back curve
   d. A PVI, PVC, and PVT

9. Vertical curves can be which of the following?

    a. Sag curves
    b. Crest curves
    c. Parabolic
    d. All of the above

10. A crest curve is

    a. Usually at the bottom of a valley
    b. At the top of a hill
    c. A flat segment of roadway
    d. None of the above

True or False

1. True or False: Working with Civil 3D is easier and more effective when a template is selected with no styles preset within it.

2. True or False: The precision for contour labeling should always be set for two decimal places.

3. True or False: The Contour Label Control Line should be set to fall on the **Zero** layer.

4. True or False: The user does not have to set Surface Names in Civil 3D.

5. True or False: A template for Surface Naming can be established, and it can be automatically incremented such that Surface 2 is created after Surface 1.

6. True or False: A Grid surface is for a surface of evenly spaced rectangular data whose elevations are interpolated from the data is desired.

7. True or False: Breaklines can be Proximity breaklines, Wall breaklines, and Breaklines from a file.

8. True or False: The Wall breakline option is used to represent perfectly vertical components of surfaces.

9. True or False: Parcels can have only four sides in Civil 3D.

10. True or False: The Profile View displays surface profiles but will not display a grid.

11. True or False: The Profile View displays new and/or existing profiles but not offset profiles for a single horizontal alignment.

12. True or False: Vertical tangents are segments that go only straight up in the air.

13. True or False: Vertical curves are often parabolic.

14. True or False: Vertical curves usually have a constant radius.

15. True or False: Subassemblies are made from assemblies.

16. True or False: Subassemblies allow for user definable parameters that can change the design of the corridor.

17. True or False: Assemblies govern the proposed corridor development.

18. True or False: A 3:1 side slope is a condition describing an elevation rise of 3' for every 1' horizontally.

19. True or False: Corridor feature lines have fixed properties and always look the same.

20. True or False: A Building Restriction Line (BRL) outlines the location of wetlands.

CHAPTER EXERCISES

1. How are the Existing Ground and finished ground interrelated?
2. How much horizontal distance is needed to tie out a sideslope of 3:1 when the elevation difference between the tie-out point and the ground is 10'?
3. How much horizontal distance is needed to tie out a sideslope of 4:1 when the elevation difference between the tie-out point and the ground is 10'?
4. What is a breakline as a concept when looking at a roadway of a ditch compared with the purpose of a breakline as used by the software in preparing a TIN model?
5. Can a contour have different elevations on its vertices?
6. What is the difference between subassemblies and assemblies?
7. How does the software differentiate between a slope and a grade?
8. Provide some examples of where styles come into play when designing and drafting a project in Civil 3D.
9. What types of data components can be added to a surface?
10. Are Parcels automatically annotated on creation, and if so, what controls this?
11. Why are vertical curves added to proposed roadway profiles?
12. Can a corridor be viewed in 3D?

The Simple, but Time-Honored Point

3

Chapter Objectives

- Create, edit, report, and label Civil 3D Point objects.
- Set Point settings involved in the aesthetics of point display.
- Use Geodetics with a combination of MAP 3D commands and POINT commands.
- Use and create Point Styles, Point Groups, and Description Key Sets.

INTRODUCTION

It is often proclaimed that the civil engineering business, with its adjunct partner of surveying, is a highly skilled and educated career and that individuals make a lot of money drawing invisible lines on the ground. Examples of these invisible lines are centerlines of roads and utilities and property, easement, and *right of way (ROW)* lines. They can be drawn in a CADD file, but engineers use points to identify them on the ground in the field, the idea being that these invisible lines begin and end at these points. The setting of these points has been referred to as *COGO*, or coordinate geometry.

Points are locations in space defined by *X*, *Y*, and *Z* values in the *Cartesian* coordinate system. These points have been used to identify objects for much of the history of civil engineering and surveying; hence, they are simple and time-honored.

Earlier in this text, you learned some of the background involving CADD related to civil engineering and the interface elements of the Civil 3D software. In Chapter 2, you explored the basic usage of the software, created a surface from Existing Ground data, and developed a shopping center on a piece of property with an access road and corridor providing ingress/egress to the shopping center. This provides an excellent background on which the remainder of the textbook will build. The detailed functionality of Civil 3D will be presented from this chapter forward.

right of way (ROW): The property typically owned by a government agency and usually dedicated for roadway usage. The roads must be built inside the state R.O.W. so that they are not running across private property.

COGO: Software geared toward solving coordinate geometry problems.

Cartesian: A word variation relating to the French mathematician René Descartes.

REVIEW OF FUNCTIONS AND FEATURES TO BE USED

This chapter uses engineering functions to create point data. There are 50 different ways to compute point data, almost all of which are crucial to developing project data in 2D as well as 3D. What sets this chapter apart from training manuals or software **Help** tools is that all of the exercises are paired with an AutoCAD file that has data set up to perform the commands instantly. No setup work is required to try out these functions. If you know some of these routines, you can easily try new routines by simply opening the file and running through that specific procedure.

Designers use several concepts in creating points that comprise a *bearing/bearing intersect*, a *distance/distance intersect*, and a variety of combinations of these operations. This chapter discusses the theory of what these mean before you commence performing computations. A review of some of the distance and angular concepts is necessary before performing computations based on them.

bearing/bearing intersect: Set points at the intersection of two bearings.

distance/distance intersect: Set points at the intersection of two distances.

Job skills will benefit from knowledge of point management because all phases of civil engineering use point data. Engineers use them when surveying the base information, whether collected via total station or GPS. Engineers also set points for proposed objects and finished grade spot shots. Contractors use them in construction by way of stakeout points, stringlines, and GPS data.

POINT BASICS

Points are very simple in concept. They occupy a specific location in 3D space and are defined by a numerical value for X, Y, and Z in the Cartesian coordinate system. These work well because AutoCAD's default system is also a Cartesian coordinate system. A simple method for keeping track of the X, Y, and Z axes is to use the *three-finger* rule. Make a fist with your left hand. Then extend your pointer finger straight out in front of you. Lift your thumb straight up. Extend your middle finger to the right so it is at a 90° angle to the pointer finger. Hold that position. The X-axis is equivalent to the pointer, the Y-axis is your thumb, and the Z-axis is represented by your middle finger. Now if you maintain that relationship, you can rotate your hand around, and the axes are all related to each other. There can be many X axes depending on what angle in which your pointer finger is pointing; however, the other fingers always maintain that orthogonal relationship, just like in a CAD system.

The two-dimensional Cartesian coordinate system is a subset of the three-dimensional coordinate system and is used by those performing 2D drafting functions. Civil 3D is a three-dimensional system, but it is flexible enough to operate in either two or three dimensions. Both options will be investigated in the following discussions.

The coordinate system is such that the location of a point, which we can call P, is established by three **real numbers** indicating the positions of the perpendicular projections from the point to three fixed, perpendicular, measured lines, called *axes*. The horizontal coordinate is denoted as X, the vertical coordinate is denoted as Y, and the height coordinate is called Z.

real numbers: Expressed by allowing decimals that have an infinite sequence of digits to the right of the decimal point.

Correspondingly, the axes are called the X-axis, the Y-axis, and the Z-axis, and the point that fills that space is defined as $P = (X, Y, Z)$. The Y-axis is located 90° from the X-axis. Together the X- and Y-axes produce a plane. The Z-axis projects orthogonally from the X-Y plane and is positive in one direction and negative in the other.

A point that has a coordinate of (0, 0, 0) is located at the origin of the coordinate system. Points can also occupy locations along the negative portions of the axes. Therefore, points defined as follows can all be legitimate:

$P = (10, 30, 55)$
$P = (12.3345, 111.3333, 0.0000)$
$P = (-45.33, -33.22, -10.00)$
$P = (10.55, 22.66, -66.67)$
$P = (2.02030405 \times 10^6, 3.01223344 \times 10^6, 1.43276566 \times 10^6)$
$P = (2.02030405 \times 10^{-6}, 3.01223344 \times 10^{-6}, 1.43276566 \times 10^{-6})$

Civil engineers usually express these values in terms of the Y-axis being a Northing, the X-axis being an Easting, and the Z-axis as an Elevation and refer to them in that order. Note that the X- and Y-axes are reversed from the standard Cartesian order in civil engineering. Therefore, a civil engineering/surveying point is denoted as $P = $ (N: 5000.0, E: 7500.00, Elev: 120.0), whereas in the Cartesian system, the same point would be represented as $P = (X: 7500.0, Y: 5000.0, Z: 120.0)$.

What can be accomplished with points and why are they used? Some uses for points in civil engineering and surveying arc as follows:

- Property corners for parcels of ownership
- Roadway alignment curves and tangent locations
- Building corners and Column locations
- Stakeout locations for the construction of features such as Edges of Pavement

In fact, virtually everything drawn in a CAD system such as AutoCAD uses point-based information somewhere because AutoCAD is a vector-based drawing system. This means that each graphic element must have a starting point and some formulaic method for constructing the location of where that element exists. For instance, objects are defined in several ways, and CAD systems do not always agree on the definitions, which can complicate translations between software applications. For instance, a horizontal arc can be located and defined using the radius point, a start angle, and an ending angle for the arc.

Example 3-1: In Figure 3-1, we have an arc defined by the center point of $X = 17.5219$ $Y = 7.3619$ $Z = 0.0000$, the radius length of 10.0000, a start angle of 22.5000, and an ending angle of 45.0000.

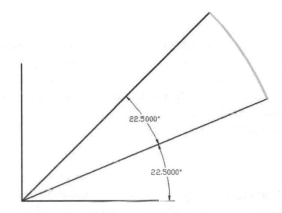

22.5000°

22.5000°

Figure 3-1   Angles

Another CAD program might use an entirely different algorithm to locate the same arc. For instance, the same arc could be described as having a center point of $X = 17.5219$ $Y = 7.3619$ $Z = 0.0000$, and a start angle dictated by a matrix containing the sine of the angle from the horizontal axis (sine $22.5° = 0.3826834$) and congruent with the sine of the angle from the vertical axis (sine $-67.5 = -0.9238/953$). The start angle is positive from the horizontal axis because it increases in the counterclockwise direction and negative from the vertical axis because it increases in a clockwise direction. This matrix places the arc in the correct quadrant. It then has a sweep angle of 22.5° from the angle computed from the matrix.

Before using Civil 3D to help solve point-based problems, it is important to know the algorithms and formulas behind these computations. Let us discuss some of the mathematical formulas involving point data by reviewing how to calculate a vector between two points.

A line (or vector) is defined as the connection between the beginning point and its corresponding ending point. Therefore, a line would exist if it connected from a point called $P1$ to a point called $P2$. A line would also exist if it began at a point $P1$, had a known angle from the X- or Y-axis, and had a distance component. The basic formula for a line is $AX + BY + C = 0$. In solving for Y,

$$Y = -AX/B - C/B$$

Substituting $m = -A/B$ and $b = -C/B$, the equation reduces to $Y = mX + b$, where the Y value is the location along the Y-axis, m is the slope of the line, X is the coordinate value along the X-axis, and b is the Y intercept (or the position the line crosses the Y-axis).

Example 3-2: If, for a line, the slope (m) = .5 and the Y-intercept (b) = 3, any value of Y along the line is a function of where X is. So if you know X, you can compute where the Y coordinate falls on the line. Therefore, for a line where $X = 10$, you get:

$$Y = (.5)(10) + 3 = 8$$

The length of the line is computed using the principals of a triangle that has sides A and B with a hypotenuse of C. Sides A and B are the horizontal and vertical components of the right triangle, and C is the hypotenuse.

The Pythagorean theorem of $A^2 + B^2 = C^2$ reduces to $C = \sqrt{A^2 + B^2}$

Following the same thought process, the length of a line bounded by two coordinates would be solved as shown here. These coordinates are in the *X, Y, Z* format.

$$P1 = (10, 20, 0)$$
$$P2 = (5, 15, 0)$$

Solve for ΔX or the change in *X* values = $(10 - 5) = 5$. This is the horizontal component.
Solve for ΔY or the change in *Y* values = $(20 - 15) = 5$. This is the vertical component.
Solve for ΔZ or the change in *Z* values = $(0 - 0) = 0$.

$$\therefore C = \sqrt{25 + 25} = \sqrt{50} = 7.0710678$$

If the line has a *Z* (or elevational) coordinate, then expand the formula as follows:

$$P_1 = (10, 20, 5)$$
$$P_2 = (5, 15, 10)$$

Solve for ΔX or the change in *X* values = $(10 - 5) = 5$. This is the horizontal component.
Solve for ΔY or the change in *Y* values = $(20 - 15) = 5$. This is the vertical component.
Solve for ΔZ or the change in *Z* values = $(5 - 10) = -5$. This is the elevational component. Note that the negative change in *Z* values is made into an absolute value by squaring it in the equation. Therefore, -5 squared = 25.

$$\therefore C = \sqrt{25 + 25 + 25} = \sqrt{75} = 8.66025$$

Point Aesthetics

Now that the chapter has covered various concepts of how to compute with points, discussion continues on issues regarding how points appear. A point conveys nothing else in its purest sense besides its position; however, civil engineers and surveyors do expect more from a point. For instance, in addition to the location of a point, points represent the locations of a variety of objects in the field, such as property corners, building corners, trees, manholes, or even locations of linear objects such as edges of pavement or sidewalks. Therefore, knowing what the point represents as well as its *X*, *Y*, and *Z* location are critical pieces of information.

In order to visualize what a point represents, you may want the ability to view the point differently depending on what the point's representation is. Sometimes there is text associated with the point that simply states what it is, such as "Ground Shot" or "Waterline." Another option is to vary the shape or symbol of the point. For example, the point shape might change depending on whether it is a property corner, perhaps displayed as a small circle ○, or if it represents a ground shot it might appear as an **X**-shaped tick mark.

Civil 3D has a myriad of ways to depict points and what they represent. The following short exercises begin an introduction to this. They create a New Point Style, which affects how the point appears; a New Label Style, which affects how the labeling for the point appears; a New Point File Format, which allows points to be imported or exported with your choice of formats; and a Description Key Set, which controls the point codes indicating what the point actually represents. In the procedures that follow, you also create a customized table for reporting point data.

To access student data files, go to www.pearsondesigncentral.com.

point styles: A definition of how the point should appear.

Exercise 3-1: Creating Point Styles

1. Create a new drawing in Civil 3D, use the template **_AutoCAD Civil 3D (Imperial) NCS .dwt**.
2. Choose the **Settings** tab on the **Toolspace** palette.
3. Expand **Point >> *Point Styles*.** The template drawing provides many pre-established styles. Notice a preset style called **Standard**, as shown in Figure 3-2. You could edit that or create a new one by right-clicking on **Standard**. This yields **Edit**, **Copy**, **Delete**, and **Refresh**, which are style management functions. Instead, create a new style.
4. Right-click on **Point Styles** and choose **New….**
5. Figure 3-3 shows the tabs for establishing a Point Style: **Information**, **Marker**, **3D Geometry**, **Display**, and **Summary**.
6. The **Information** tab is used to change the style name from **New Point Styles** to the name you prefer; in this case, call it **Prop-Corner**. Then select the **Marker** tab to identify the

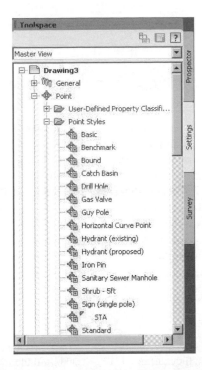

Figure 3-2   Point Styles

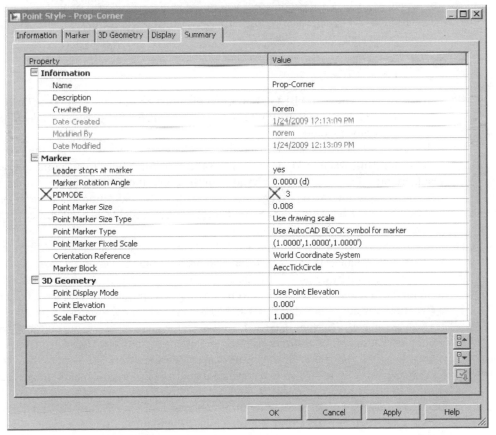

Figure 3-3   Point Style
dialog box

aesthetic appearance of a point symbol in AutoCAD. The marker can be an AutoCAD Point symbol or, more likely, a Civil 3D marker, which is selected from the panel of buttons. The buttons on the left indicate what the point should look like when placed. The two additional buttons on the right are superimposition buttons that can be laid over the style chosen on the left. Experiment with the options. Choose the "×" and note the **Preview** display on the right. Choose the cross "+" and observe the **Preview**. Now choose the superimposed circle and note the **Preview**. The **Custom marker style** options are shown in Figure 3-4.

Custom marker style:

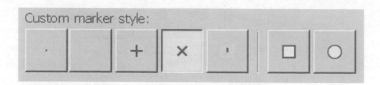

Figure 3-4   Custom
marker styles

7. Now select the second button from the left (that has no symbol on it) but leave the super-imposed circle turned on. This option might be used by a surveyor in denoting a property corner. The size and inches option in the top right of the box indicates that the symbology will plot a 0.1″ at the scale of the drawing. If you desire it to be larger or smaller, this value can be adjusted accordingly. You can also choose an option of **Use fixed scale**, **Use size in absolute units**, or **Use size relative to screen**, whereby the size of the marker is a percentage of the drawing screen size, in addition to **Use drawing scale**.

8. Continuing this exploration, note the lower left quadrant of the dialog box. You see an option called **Marker rotation angle**. This value can rotate the selected marker so that it always comes in, in a rotated position. One last option is choosing an AutoCAD block instead of a Civil 3D marker.

TIP   If blocks have been preset, they can simply be selected from the window. If your window is empty or if your organization wants you to use in-house-developed symbols, then right-click inside the window and choose **Browse....** Then locate the drive, folder, and block you would prefer to use.

9. In this case, use **AutoCAD BLOCK symbol for marker** and select the **AeccTickCircle**. Check the **Preview** and notice a circle symbol shows up. So any symbol you desire can be established for the marker.

10. Select the **3D Geometry** tab. Expand the **3D Geometry** item. Poke into the pop-down window for **Point Display Mode** under the **Value** column. Notice that a point can actually reside in three dimensions at the elevation of the point, it can be "flattened" to an elevation, or the elevation can be exaggerated by a scale factor. Selecting any of these options makes the **Point Elevation** or the **Scale Factor** option available as needed. Leave the option as it was at **Use Point Elevation**.

11. Now select the **Display** tab. This is where the layer, color, and so on are set for the Point Style in both 2D and 3D views. You can also preset if the marker and its associated label are to be turned on by default. To create a layer for the point, pick a point in the **Layer** column for the **Marker** row. A **Layer Selection** dialog box appears. Hit the **New...** button, and a **Create Layer** dialog box displays. Click under the **Values** column for **Layer Name**. Enter a layer name of **VF-Node-Ctrl-Ipf**. For the **Color** option, choose the button to select a color and choose **red**. Everything else will remain the default. Hit **OK.** You are back in the **Layer Selection** dialog box. Select the new layer **VF-Node-Ctrl-Ipf**. Hit **OK**. You are now back in the **Point Style—Prop Corner** dialog box, and the layer for the marker is set.

12. Now select the **Layer** cell for the **Label** row. Hit the **New...** button, and a **Create Layer** dialog box displays. Click under the **Values** column for **Layer Name**. Enter a layer name of **VF-Ctrl-Text**. For the **Color** option, choose the button to select a color and choose **green**. Everything else will remain the default. Hit **OK**. You are back in the **Layer Selection** dialog box. Select the new layer **VF-Ctrl-Text**. Hit **OK**. You are now back in the **Point Style—Prop Corner** dialog box, and the layer for the label is set. Under the **Color** column change the Layer colors to **ByLayer**. Hit **OK**.

13. On the **Toolspace** palette, right-click on **Point Styles** and choose **New...** again.

14. The **Information** tab is used to change the style name from **New Point Style** to the name you prefer; in this case call it **Planimetrics**. From the **Marker** tab, choose the "." and note the **Preview** display on the right. Leave the other settings in this tab as the default.

15. Now select the **Display** tab. This is where the layer, color, and so on are set for the Point Style in both 2D and 3D views. To create a layer for the point, pick a point in the **Layer** column for the **Marker** row. A **Layer Selection** dialog box appears. Hit the **New...** button, and a **Create Layer** dialog box displays. Click under the **Values** column for **Layer Name**. Enter a layer name of **VF-Node-Topo**. For the **Color** option, choose the button to select a color and choose **blue**. Everything else will remain the default. Hit **OK**. You are back in the **Layer Selection** dialog box. Select the new layer **VF-Node-Topo**. Hit **OK**. You are now back in the **Point Style—Planimetrics** dialog box, and the layer for the marker is set.

16. Now select the **Layer** cell for the **Label** row. Hit the **New...** button, and a **Create Layer** dialog box displays. Click under the **Values** column for **Layer Name**. Enter a layer name of **VF-Topo-Text**. For the **Color** option, choose the button to select a color and choose **green**. Everything else will remain the default. Hit **OK**. You are back in the **Layer Selection** dialog box. Select the new layer **VF-Topo-Text**. Hit **OK**. You are now back in the **Point Style—Planimetrics** dialog box, and the layer for the label is set.

17. Hit the **Summary** tab to inspect your settings. When ready, hit **Apply** and **OK**. Notice that there is a new Point Style name called **Planimetrics** in the **Settings** palette.

18. Save this drawing as **My Point Style-Initials.dwg**, substituting your initials where it says "initials" in the filename.

Exercise 3-2: Creating Label Styles

In this exercise, a new Label Style is created.

To access student data files, go to www.pearsondesigncentral.com.

1. Open MyPointStyle.dwg.
2. Choose the **Settings** tab on the **Toolspace** palette.
3. Expand **Point >> Label Styles** and notice a preset style called **Standard**. You can edit that or create a new one by right-clicking on **Standard**. This yields **Edit, New, Copy, Delete**, and **Refresh**, which are style management functions. Instead, create a new style.
4. Right-click on **Label Styles** and choose **New....**
5. In the **Label Style Composer** dialog box, the tabs for establishing the Label Style are **Information, General, Layout, Dragged State**, and **Summary**. In the **Information** tab, change the name to **My Point Label Style**.
6. Select the **General** tab shown in Figure 3-5, and change the **Text Style** to **Romans** (which has been preset in the drawing). Notice that the text style changes in the **Preview** to the right.

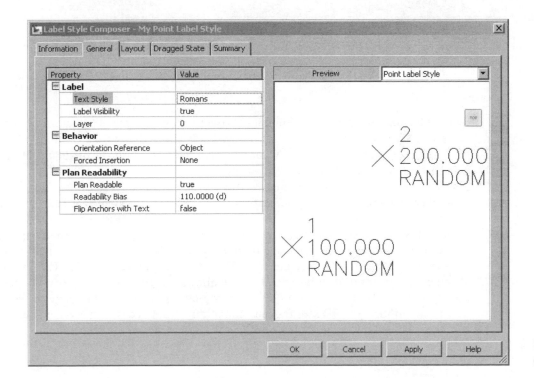

Figure 3-5 Label Style Composer dialog box

7. Leave the remaining defaults as they are. Hit **Apply** and **OK**.
8. From the **Points** pull-down menu, choose **Create Points...** to invoke the toolbar for point creation. Click on the first button and choose **Manual**.
9. Set a point at a coordinate of **1000,1000**. Give it a point description of **FG** and an elevation of **101.330**, and terminate the command.
10. In the **Toolspace**, go to the **Prospector** tab.
11. In the **Master View**, expand the item for your open drawing and expand the **Point Groups** item.
12. Right-click on **All Points**, and select **Properties....** The **Point Group Properties** dialog box opens as shown in Figure 3-6.

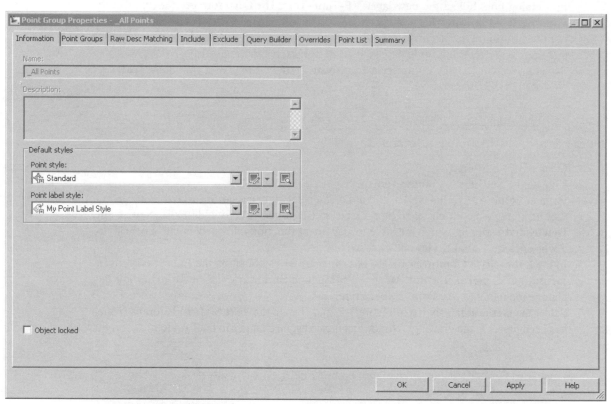

Figure 3-6   Point Group Properties dialog box

13. In the **Information** tab, go to the **Point label style:** option, pick in the pop-down window, and select **My Point Label Style** which you just created. Hit **Apply** and **OK**.
14. In AutoCAD, type **Z** for **Zoom** and **C** for **Center**. Type in a coordinate of **1000,1000** and a magnification or height of **25**.
15. You see a point placed with the Romans text style you requested (Figure 3-7). To see how your other changes to the settings affect the display, twist the drawing. Type in **Dview** and select the point you just placed when asked by the prompt. Hit **<Enter>**.
16. Choose **TW** for **Twist** and provide an angle of **215** (which would turn the point upside down). Hit **<Enter>** to complete the routine. Notice that the UCS icon and the point marker have rotated 215°, but the text orientation remained readable. The setting changed for **Orientation Reference to View** allows the point always to remain readable even when you Twist the view, usually for plotting purposes. This exercise shows how powerful the Civil 3D settings can be, and this is not necessarily a recommended setting for all points. Type **U** to **Undo** the creation of the point. Depending on how many commands you ran since you set the point, keep typing in **U** for Undo until the point is gone.

Figure 3-7   A Point

17. You can right-click on the **All Points** item and select **Properties**. When the **Properties** dialog box opens, in the **Information** tab, go to the **Point Label Style** option, pick in the pop-down window, and select **Standard**. Hit **Apply** and **OK**, and your points no longer use the style you created.

POINT GROUPS

Points are not actually Civil 3D objects in the same sense that surfaces and alignments are objects, although they share many characteristics with Civil 3D objects. For instance, points can be displayed in a drawing and modified graphically, and their manifestation is controlled using Styles and Label Styles. Yet they are technically not Civil 3D objects.

An excellent feature in Civil 3D is that points can be defined such that they fall into Point Groups; this helps immensely with organization. A Point Group is an object, and the point is a subset of the Point Group object. Whether a point is or is not an object does not make any real difference to you in practice, although knowing this may help you to understand better how points work.

There are two examples of how points will react differently than if they were objects. First, when a point is right-clicked and the **Properties** option is selected, this invokes the AutoCAD **Properties** dialog box, which describes the Point Group to which the point belongs but not the point itself. Second, when a point is selected, the **Layer** toolbar lists the **Point Group** layer information but not the actual **Point** layer information.

Point Groups are named collections of points that are used to organize and control points and their appearances in drawings. Point Groups have the following characteristics:

• They have enduring properties that can be easily reviewed or modified, either beforehand or retroactively.

• Displaying a points list shows the points included in a Point Group, and it can be updated automatically. This can occur when new points are input or modified that match the Point Group's properties or when the properties of a Point Group are modified.

• A Point Group can be locked to avoid unintentional modifications. Some aspects of Point Groups can be observed, accessed, and managed at the project level through the **Toolspace**.

A strong feature of Point Groups is that they allow you to manage many points at one time by using their group name. Point Groups give the computer the ability to sort through only the points needed for accessing or review. They also allow you to exclude unwanted points from a task such as exporting a point dump. Point Groups organize points that have similar descriptions such as "EP" for edge of pavement shots or points that are related by function such as DTM spot shots. There are many methods for developing Point Groups including defining them from a selection set or providing a range of point numbers. Further, these methods can be compounded on one another. In other words, the points in a Point Group called Road Points can also be included in a Point Group called Proposed DTM Points. Once they are established, they can be saved into the template for automatic use on future projects, thereby becoming part of the organization's CADD standards.

Job skills would benefit from the imaginative use of point groups beyond the obvious of grouping points according to their description or function. In other words, a point group called Monday's Points can be established for a surveyor importing point data for a job shot and collected on, say, Monday. This can be repeated for those obtained on Tuesday with a point group called Tuesday's Points. Then the surveyor can refer back to those groups to identify which points were collected on Monday versus those collected on Tuesday. Another possible use of point groups is to separate 3D points that are satisfactory for inclusion into a surface's development versus those that are two dimensional and not appropriate for use.

DESCRIPTION KEY SETS

The key to success in defining point groups is to have a strong description library for the point codes and their intended functions. If this is accomplished, you can assign point styles based on point descriptions, assign point symbology based on descriptions, and automatically populate point groups based on the descriptions. Obviously, this would benefit anyone setting points because a standardized mechanism would be used every time someone sets a storm manhole point. If all users used the preset description of, say, DMH for storm drain manholes, they would achieve a consistent look to their storm manhole symbologies and annotations in AutoCAD. In other words, the same symbol would always appear for the storm manhole along with a standardized description next to the point.

Description Key Sets: A library of codes that control how points are created, where they are created, and what they represent.

The CADD file layers would always be correct, and the point would always reside in the correct point group. The tool to accomplish this is called *Description Key Sets*. Table 3-1 shows an example of many of the point description codes that you may find on a survey project. The first column shows the description key code, the second column the description of the code, the third column the suggested layer for the point, the fourth column the symbol for the point, and the last column the related point symbol layer.

In the following two exercises, a Description Key Set (formerly called a Description Key Library for Land Desktop users) and then a Point Group are created.

Exercise 3-3: Creating Description Key Sets

The Description Keys built here can be used in developing Point Groups in Exercise 3-4.

To access student data files, go to www.pearsondesigncentral.com.

1. Launch Civil 3D and open MyPointStyle.dwg. Make sure that the **Toolspace** is displayed.
2. Click the **Settings** tab of the **Toolspace** to view the **Settings** panel. Pick **Master View** in the pop-down window at the top. Expand the **MyPointStyle.dwg** drawing name. Expand the **Point** item.
3. Right-click on the **Description Key Sets** and select **New….**
4. In the **Description Key Set Name** field, change the name from **New DescKey Set** to **MY-DESCRIPTIONS**. Hit **OK** to create the new Description Key Set and observe that it now exists under the **Description Key Sets** item.
5. Now that the Description Key Set called **MY-DESCRIPTIONS** is created, the keys can be defined for point and label styles. Click on **MY-DESCRIPTIONS** and right-click. Select **Edit Keys…** This displays a **Panorama** dialog box listing all currently defined keys, shown in Figure 3-8.

Figure 3-8   Description Key settings

Table 3-1 A Sample Listing of Description Keys

Code	Desc	Layer	Symbol	Symbol Layer
AC	AC UNIT	VF-NODE-TOPO	CG78	VF-TOPO-MISC
BB	BB/TOE	VF-NODE-BRKL-TOE	CG32	VF-BRKL
BD	BUILDING	VF-NODE-BLDG	CG32	VF-BLDG
BM	BENCH MK	VF-NODE-CTRL-BMRK	CG85	VF-CTRL
BP	BOLLARD	VF-NODE-TOPO-BOLL	CG33	VF-TOPO-MISC
BR	SOIL BORING	VF-NODE-TOPO-BORE	CG85	VF-TOPO-MISC
BSL	BRUSH LINE	VF-NODE-BLIN	CG32	VF-SITE-VEGE-BRSH
CD	CL DITCH	VF-NODE-DTCH-CNTR	CG32	VF-DTCH-CNTR
CF	CG FACE	VF-NODE-CURB-ROAD	CG32	VF-ROAD-CURB-FACE
CM	CONC MON	VF-NODE-CTRL-CMON	CG74	VF-CTRL
CO	CLEANOUT	VF-NODE-MHOL-SSWR	CG01	VF-SSWR-MHOL
CP	CLR	VF-NODE-ROAD-CNTR	CG32	VF-ROAD-CNTR
CV	ELECT UGND VLT	VF-NODE-POWR-EVLT	GV	VF-POWR-UNDR
DF	DRAINFIELD	VF-NODE-SSWR	CG32	VF-SSWR-DF
DK	BLDG DECK	VF-NODE-BLDG-DECK	CG32	VF-BLDG
EC	DRWY CONC	VF-NODE-DRIV-CONC	CG32	VF-DRIV-CONC
EG	EDG SHLDER	VF-NODE-PVMT-GRVL	CG32	VF-PVMT-GRVL-SLDR
ELM	ELEC MTR	VF-NODE-INST-EMTR	CG88	VF-POWR-INST-EMTR
EM	EVERGRN MED	VF-NODE-TREE-EVMD	EM	VF-SITE-VEGE-TREE
EP	EOP	VF-NODE-PVMT	CG32	VF-PVMT-EDGE
ES	EVERGRN SMLL	VF-NODE-TREE-EVSM	ES	VF-SITE-VEGE-TREE
EW	EDGE WATER	VF-NODE-TOPO-EWAT	CG32	VF-TOPO-EWAT
FC	FILLER CAP	VF-NODE-POWR-FCAP	CG33	VF-POWR-UNDR
FF	FIN FLR	VF-NODE-BLDG-FFLR	CG04	VF-BLDG
FH	FIRE HYD	VF-NODE-WATR-STRC	FH	VF-WATR-FIRE-HYDT
FLM	FENCE METAL	VF-NODE-SITE-FENC METL	CG32	VF-SITE-FENC
FLV	FENCE VINYL	VF-NODE-SITE-FENC-VINL	CG32	VF-SITE-FENC
FLW	FENCE WOOD	VF-NODE-SITE-FENC-WOOD	CG32	VF-SITE-FENC
FLY	FLY	VF-NODE-CTRL-FLY	FLY	VF-CTRL
FO	FIBER OPT	VF-NODE-COMM-FOPT	CG32	VF-COMM-FOPT
GD	GROUND SHOT	VF-NODE-TOPO-SPOT	CG36	VF-TOPO-SPOT
GR	GRD RAIL	VF-NODE-SITE-GDRS	CG32	VF-SITE-GRDS
GW	GUY WIRE	VF-NODE-POLE-GUYW	GW	VF-POWR-POLE
HC	HANDICAP MARKINGS	VF-NODE-MRKG-PRKG	HANDI	VF-PRKG-STRP
HR	HEDGEROW	VF-NODE-HEDG	CG32	VF-SITE-VEGE-HEDG
HS	HEAD STONE	VF-NODE-TOPO	CG78	VF-TOPO-MISC
IN	INLET	VF-NODE-STRM-INLT	CG04	VF-STRM-STRC
IPF	I PIPE FOUND	VF-NODE-CTRL-IPF	CG41	VF-CTRL
IPS	I PIPE SET	VF-NODE-CTRL-IPS	CG41	VF-CTRL
IRF	I ROD FOUND	VF-NODE-CTRL-IRF	CG41	VF-CTRL
IRS	I ROD SET	VF-NODE-CTRL-IRS	CG41	VF-CTRL
IV	IRRI VALV	VF-NODE-WATR-IRVA	CG94	VF-WATR-VALV
JW	WALL	VF-NODE-SITE-JWLL	CG32	VF-SITE-WALL
LA	LANDSCAPE	VF-NODE-VEGE-MISC		VF-SITE-VEGE-MISC
LE	EVERGRN LG	VF-NODE-TREE-EVLG	EL	VF-SITE-VEGE-TREE
LP	LIGHT POL	VF-NODE-POLE-LITE	CG92	VF-POWR-POLE

Table 3-1 (*Continued*)

MB	MAIL BOX	VF-NODE-TOPO	MAILBOX	VF-TOPO-MISC
MS	SDMH	VF-NODE-MHOL-STRM	CG01	VF-STRM-MHOL
MW	WATER MH	VF-NODE-MHOL-WATR	CG49	VF-WATR-MHOL
NV	INVERT	VF-NODE-STRM-STRC	CG04	VF-STRM-STRC
OH	OH WIRES	VF-NODE-POLE-OHWR	CG32	VF-POWR-POLE
OV	OVERHANG	VF-NODE-BLDG-OHAN		VF-BLDG
PD	TELE PED	VF-NODE-COMM-PED	CG34	VF-COMM
PH	PHOTO CTRL	VF-NODE-CTRL-PHOT	PH	VF-CTRL
PM	LANE STRIPES	VF-NODE-MRKG-ROAD	CG32	VF-ROAD-MRKG
POR	PORCH	VF-NODE-BLDG-PORC	CG32	VF-BLDG
PP	POWER POLE	VF-NODE-POLE-POWR	UPOLE	VF-POWR-POLE
RI	RIP RAP	VF-NODE-RRAP	CG32	VF-RRAP
RW	RET WALL	VF-NODE-SITE-RTWL	CG32	VF-SITE-WALL
SATV	SAT TV	VF-NODE-COMM-SATV	CG03	VF-COMM-SATV
SB	SHRUB	VF-NODE-SHRUB	CG134	VF-SITE-VEGE-BRSH
SM	SMH	VF-NODE-MHOL-SSWR	CG01	VF-SSWR-MHOL
SN	SIGN	VF-NODE-SIGN	SN	VF-SITE-SIGN
SP	TREE	VF-NODE-TREE-SPEC	CG133	VF-SITE-VEGE-TREE
STL	SEPTIC LID	VF-NODE-SSWR		VF-SSWR-MHOL
STON	PLANTED STONE	VF-NODE-CTRL-STON	CG43	VF-CTRL
STP	STEPS	VF-NODE-SITE-STPS	CG32	VF-SITE-STPS
STW	STONE WALL	VF-NODE-SITE-STWL	CG32	VF-SITE-WALL
TB	TOP OF BANK	VF-NODE-BRKL	CG32	VF-BRKL
TC	CG TOP	VF-NODE-CURB-ROAD	CG32	VF-ROAD-CURB-TOP
TF	TRANSF	VF-NODE-POWR-TRAN	TF	VF-POWR-TOWR
TL	TREE LARGE	VF-NODE-TREE-LARG	TL	VF-SITE-VEGE-TREE
TLN	TREE LINE	VF-NODE-TRLN	CG32	VF-SITE-VEGE-TROW
TM	TREE MED	VF-NODE-TREE-MED	TM	VF-SITE-VEGE-TREE
TR	TRAVERSE	VF-NODE-CTRL-TRAV	CG48	VF-CTRL
TS	TREE SMALL	VF-NODE-TREE-SM	TS	VF-SITE-VEGE-TREE
TX	TRAF SIG BOX	VF-NODE-POWR-STRC	TRAFCNTL	VF-POWR-STRC
UE	ELEC UGND	VF-NODE-POWR-UNDR	CG32	VF-POWR-UNDR
UG	GAS UGND	VF-NODE-POWR-UGAS	CG32	VF-POWR-UNDR
UM	UNKNOWN MH	VF-NODE-TOPO	MH_UTIL	VF-TOPO-MISC
UT	TELEPHONE	VF-NODE-COMM-UTEL	CG32	VF-COMM
UTV	UG CABLE TV	VF-NODE-CATV-UNDR	CG32	VF-CATV-UNDR
UW	IWATER UNGD	VF-NODE-WATR-UNGD	CG32	VF-WATR-VALV
VDH	VDOT MON	VF-NODE-CTRL-VDOT	CG73	VF-CTRL
WA	WALL ALIGN	VF-NODE-SITE-WAAL	CG32	VF-SITE-WALL
WE	WELL	VF-NODE-WATR-STRC	CG01	VF-WATR-WELL
WK	WALK	VF-NODE-TOPO-WALK	CG32	VF-TOPO-WALK
WM	WATER METER	VF-NODE-WATR-METR	WM	VF-WATR-MAIN
WT	WETLANDS	VF-NODE-WLND	CG01	VF-SITE-VEGE-WLND
WV	WATER VALV	VF-NODE-WATR-VALV	WV	VF-WATR-VALV
YH	YARD HYDRANT	VF-NODE-WATR-YAHY		VF-WATR-VALV

6. In the first cell of the **Code** column, enter **AC***.
7. In the next column, click the **Style** toggle **On**.
8. Click on the word **<default>** in the **Style** column, and the **Point Style** dialog box displays.
9. Use the list arrow to observe the list of available styles; select **Planimetrics** from the list, and hit **OK**.
10. In the next column, click the **Point Label Style** toggle **On**.
11. Click on the **<default>** in the **Point Label Style** column, and the **Point Label Style** dialog box displays. Choose **Standard**.
12. In the **Format** column, type **AC UNIT**. When these points are placed in Civil 3D, they will always be annotated as AC Units.
13. Then in the next column for **Layer**, click the **Layer** toggle **On**.
14. Click in the cell to the right of that toggle, and from the **Layer** list, select the **VF-Node-Topo** layer and hit **OK**.
15. Now create another Description Key. Right-click on the **AC** key and choose **Copy** from the shortcut menu. A **Copy of AC*** is created.
16. Click on the **Copy of AC*** and change the name to **IPF***.
17. Click in the **Style** column, and the **Point Style** dialog box displays.
18. Use the list arrow to observe the list of available styles; select **Prop-Corner** from the list, and hit **OK**.
19. In the next column, click the **Point Label Style** toggle **On**.
20. Click in the **Point Label Style** column, and the **Point Label Style** dialog box displays. Choose **Standard**.
21. In the **Format** column, type **I Pipe Found**. When these points are placed in Civil 3D, they will always be annotated as I Pipe Found.
22. Then in the next column for **Layer**, click the **Layer** toggle **On**.
23. Click in the cell to the right of that toggle, and from the **Layer** list, select the **VF-Node-Ctrl-Ipf** layer and hit **OK**.
24. Next create yet another Description Key. Right-click on the **AC** key and choose **Copy** from the shortcut menu. A **Copy of AC*** is created.
25. Click on the **Copy of AC*** and change the name to **MB***.
26. Click in the **Style** column, and the **Point Style** dialog box displays.
27. Use the list arrow to observe the list of available styles; select **Planimetrics** from the list, and hit **OK**.
28. In the next column, click the **Point Label Style** toggle **On**.
29. Click on the **<default>** in the **Point Label Style** column, and the **Point Label Style** dialog box displays. Choose **Standard**.
30. In the **Format** column, type **Mailbox**. When these points are placed in Civil 3D, they will always be annotated as Mailbox.
31. Then in the next column for **Layer**, click the **Layer** toggle **On**.
32. Click in the cell to the right of that toggle, and from the **Layer** list, select the **VF-Node-Topo** layer and hit **OK**.
33. The **Settings** should appear as shown in Figure 3-9. Now there are Description Keys for three items to use in preparing Point Groups in the following exercise.
34. Click the check mark in the upper right of the **Panorama** dialog box to save and close the Desckey Editor.

Code	Style	Point Label Style	Format	Layer	Scale Parameter	Fixed Scale Factor	Use dra
AC*	✓ Planimetrics	✓ Standard	AC UNIT	✓ VF-NODE-TOPO	✓ Parameter 1	☐ 1.000	☐ no
IPF*	✓ Prop-Corner	✓ Standard	I Pipe found	✓ VF-NODE-CTRL-IPF	✓ Parameter 1	☐ 1.000	☐ no
MB*	✓ Planimetrics	✓ Standard	Mailbox	✓ VF-NODE-TOPO	✓ Parameter 1	☐ 1.000	☐ no

Figure 3-9 Desckey Editor

Exercise 3-4: Creating Point Groups

This task defines a Point Group to help organize your points. It helps in accessing points, reporting on them, or exporting them. The Point Group is made up of our Property corner control points. By default, Civil 3D creates a point group called ALL.

1. While remaining in the same drawing, click the **Prospector** tab in the **Toolspace**.
2. Expand the drawing name item to view the Civil 3D object list.
3. Expand **Point Groups** to show the Point Group list.
4. Click on the **Point Group** item, right-click, and select **New...** from the shortcut menu.
5. In the **Information** tab, its name is Point Group-(1). Change the **Point Group** name to **Planimetrics**. Give it a description of **2D Planimetrics**. Refer to Figure 3-10.
6. Click the **Raw Desc Matching** tab and toggle on **AC*** and **MB***.

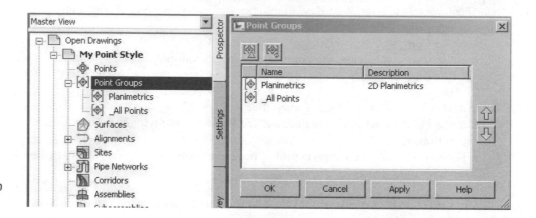

Figure 3-10   Point Group Editor

TIP   This instructs Civil 3D to include only those points that match the raw descriptions of AC* and MB*. As other Planimetric keys are defined, they can be added here as well by revisiting this procedure.

7. Click the **Include** tab and notice that the same two Description Keys are selected here. Hit **OK**.
8. The **Point Group**, **Planimetrics**, is now evident on the **Point Group** list. See Figure 3-10.
9. Now create a Point Group for the Control points. Click on the **Point Group** item, right-click, and select **New...** from the shortcut menu.
10. In the **Information** tab, its name is Point Group-(2). Change the **Point Group** name to **Control**. Give it a description of **Control Points**.
11. Click the **Raw Desc Matching** tab and toggle on **IPF***.
12. This instructs Civil 3D to include only those points that match the raw descriptions of IPF*. As other Control keys are defined, they can be added here as well by revisiting this procedure. Hit **OK**.
13. Under **Point Groups**, you will now see **All Points**, **Planimetrics**, and **Control**.

Now that the data organization is created within Civil 3D, the next step is to create some points to sample how this should work.

Exercise 3-5: Create Points

1. Type **Z** for **Zoom** and **<Enter>**. Then type **C** for **Center** and **<Enter>**. When asked for the center point, type **1000,1000**. When asked for the magnification or height, type **500**.
2. From the pull-down menus, choose **Points >> Create Points....**
3. The **Create Points** toolbar displays. Select the first button, with the tooltip called **Miscellaneous: Manual**.

4. When you are prompted with `Please specify a location for the new point:` Type **1000,1000**. The software then responds as follows.

5. `Enter a point description <.>:` **AC**

6. `Specify a point elevation <.>:` **112.33**

7. `Please specify a location for the new point:` **1100,1000**

8. `Enter a point description <AC>:` **IPF**

9. `Specify a point elevation <112.330'>:` **114.32**

10. `Please specify a location for the new point:` **1100,1100**

11. `Enter a point description <IPF>:` **MB**

12. `Specify a point elevation <114.320'>:` **<Enter>**

13. `Please specify a location for the new point:` **<Enter>** to terminate the command.

14. If, after the points are in place, there is an icon indicating that the object data are Out of Date, then right-click on the item **(Point Groups, Planimetrics)** and select **Update**. That should eliminate the icon indicating Out of Date and place the points into the Point Group object. Repeat for any other Point Groups that are Out of Date.

The data shown in the **Master View** of the **Prospector** are updated automatically to show the current status of data in the drawing. The **Prospector** dynamically updates its contents as you add and remove data and civil objects. Icons adjacent to the data entry tell you the status of the data, for example, if a surface is out of date or if a point group has changed. The **Prospector** should appear similar to Figure 3-11 after the Point Groups are created and the points are entered.

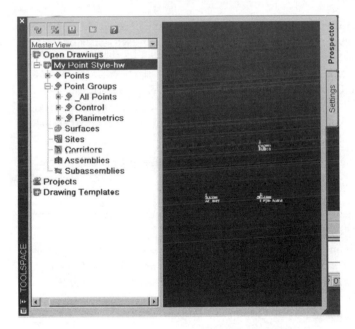

Figure 3-11   Prospector and Preview

Exercise 3-6: Creating Point File Formats

In this task, a ***Point File Format*** is defined to help when importing or exporting point data to external locations. Formats indicate the relative positions of the point data in the string being read. For instance, what is the first item in the string: a point number or a Northing? What is the second item in the string: an elevation or an Easting? By default, Civil 3D has a lot of predeveloped formats, but if you require one not already developed, it helps to know how to create a format.

point file format: Preformatted definitions for importing or exporting points.

1. While remaining in the same drawing, click the **Settings** tab in the **Toolspace**.
2. Expand the drawing name item to view the Civil 3D object list.
3. Click on the expand tree icon next to **Point File Formats** to show the list.
4. Click on the **Point File Formats** item, right-click, and select **New...** from the shortcut menu.
5. When the **Select Format Type** dialog box opens, choose **User Point file** and hit **OK**.
6. The **Point File Format** dialog box opens. Type in a format name of **LatLong**, as shown in Figure 3-12.

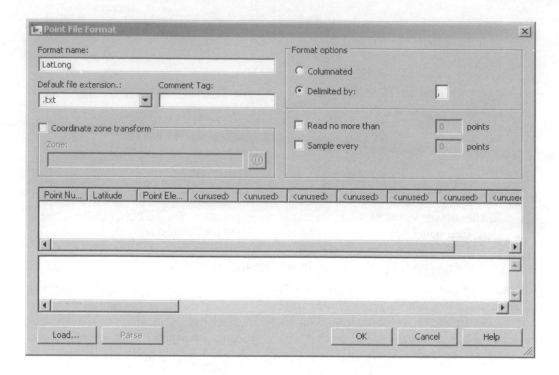

Figure 3-12   Point File Format

7. Choose the option for **Delimited by**: and type a comma (**,**) in the open field.
8. Near the bottom is a wide window with column headers labeled **unused**. Click on the first header on the left. A **Selection** dialog box opens. Click in the pop-down window and choose **Point Number**. Hit **OK**.
9. Click on the second header. Click in the pop-down window and choose **Latitude**. Hit **OK**.
10. Click on the third header. Click in the pop-down window and choose **Longitude**. Hit **OK**.
11. Click on the fourth header. Click in the pop-down window and choose **Point Elevation**. Hit **OK**. Hit **OK** to close out.

You have created a format that allows for importing or exporting data using **LatLong** data.

EXTERNAL DATA REFERENCES

External Data References:
Additional data files that can augment how point data are stored.

Civil 3D can create and maintain point database files that contain all of the point information in the project. ***External Data References*** are adjunct databases that can amend the information in this database. The data stored include the point number, optional point name, Northing, Easting, elevation, and point description. External Data References can allow you to either substitute point elevations when points are accessed through a point group or substitute point raw description data.

TIP   External Data References can be useful if your project is in Imperial units, but periodically you must report your elevations in Metric units.

External Data References allow you to link your custom point databases to Civil 3D. They are also called XDRefs. The XDRef is a pointer to a column of data in a custom Microsoft Access database. The key field is typically the point number. Then, when an XDRef is used to access a value for a point, the point number is looked up in the custom database, and the value from the specified column is used instead of the point's original value. These files are nondestructive in that they do not overwrite or alter the points in the drawing. Although this is not a highly used function, it can be very handy when the occasion arises.

Now that you have gained some experience in establishing Point Groups and related Description Key Sets, you will learn how to set points using some of the many **Point Creation** tools provided within the software. These are obtained using the **Points** pull-down menu, and these commands are described next.

The **Points** pull-down menu (Figure 3-13), is very clear and succinct, characteristic of all the pull-down menus. Some software manufacturers load up the menus with many commands, and users are often lost in finding the right command at the right time. Civil 3D menus are compact and easy to understand. The **POINTS** commands are as follows:

- **Create Points...** invokes the **Create Points** toolbar for setting points. There are 50 commands in this toolbar for sophisticated point geometry creation.

- **Create Point Group...** allows for the creation of Point Groups.

- **Edit Points** allows for modification of points.

- **Add Tables...** allows for importing point information in tabular format.

- **Utilities** allows for exporting points, identifying where points are located, transfer facilities, a Geodetic calculator, and the ability to create blocks from points.

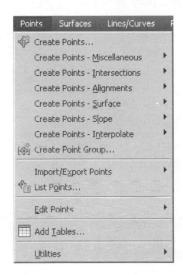

Figure 3-13   Points pull-down menu

Point Computations

The text mentioned earlier that there are 50 different methods for computing point data. The **Create Points** toolbar (Figure 3-14) contains these commands.

Figure 3-14   Create Points toolbar

Each button has an accompanying pop-down arrow for making selection choices. The buttons in the toolbar include the following functions:

- **Miscellaneous** sets 2D points using basic techniques.

- **Intersection** sets 2D points using intersectional criteria.

- **Alignment** sets 2D points using alignment-based information.

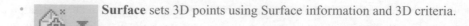 **Surface** sets 3D points using Surface information and 3D criteria.

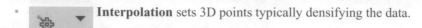 **Interpolation** sets 3D points typically densifying the data.

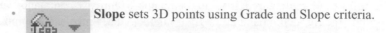 **Slope** sets 3D points using Grade and Slope criteria.

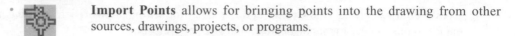 **Import Points** allows for bringing points into the drawing from other sources, drawings, projects, or programs.

Each of these commands will be discussed independently, so you can use them on projects easily.

Exercise 3-7: CREATE POINTS Commands

To access student data files, go to www.pearsondesigncentral.com.

1. Open the drawing called Chapter-3-Points.dwg.
2. Type **Z** for **Zoom** and **<Enter>**. Then type **C** for **Center** and **<Enter>**. When asked for the center point, type **1000,1000**. When asked for the magnification or height, type **200**. You can also type in **V** for **View** and choose a saved view called **Points-A**. Hit **Set Current** and hit **OK**.
3. Select the **Points** pull-down menu and choose the **CREATE POINTS...** command. The toolbar displays. Investigate the first tools in the leftmost icon first.

Miscellaneous Point Creation Commands

Exercise 3-8: Miscellaneous—MANUAL Command

 Figure 3-15 shows the **MANUAL** command, which allows you to pick the origin of the point using a mouse or key-in value.

Figure 3-15   Create Points—Manual

 The **MANUAL** command can be used to set points manually wherever they are needed.

 Job skills benefit because engineers always set points on objects representing property lines, easements, road centerlines, pipelines, and so on.

1. Select the first pop-down arrow and ensure that **Manual** is checked by clicking on it. This will also invoke the command.
2. Civil 3D responds in the command prompt with the following. Enter the responses as indicated.
3. `Please specify a location for the new point:` type **1000,1000 <Enter>**.
4. `Enter a point description <.>:` **IPF**
5. `Specify a point elevation <.>:` **122.45**
6. `The software responds with: N: 1000.0000' E: 1000.0000'`
7. `Please specify a location for the new point:`
8. This time use your mouse and pick a point about 3″ (on the screen) to the right and 3″ (on the screen) downward from the first point. At the prompt: `Enter a point description <.>:` Type **IPF**, `Specify a point elevation <.>:` **112.44**.
9. The software responds with: `N: 941.60139 E: 1077.4403'` (of course, your coordinates may differ because you are picking the point with your mouse). Hit **OK** to terminate.
10. Draw a line on the screen from the **Node** snap of Point 1 to the **Node** snap of Point 2.
11. Now select **Manual** again. This time when prompted to: `Please specify a location for the new point:` Select the Midpoint snap and snap to the midpoint of the line you just drew.
12. When prompted to `Enter a point description <.>:`, type **IPF**. When prompted to `Specify a point elevation <.>:`, type **116.77**. Hit **OK** to terminate.

The result should appear similar to Figure 3-16.

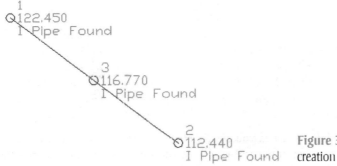

Figure 3-16   Result of Manual creation

Exercise 3-9: Miscellaneous—GEODETIC DIRECTION AND DISTANCE Command

 The next command, *GEODETIC DIRECTION AND DISTANCE*, allows for computing points based on the geodetic datum set in the drawing.

geodetic direction and distance: Computing a point using a geodetic datum, a geodetic azimuth, and a distance along the mathematical face of the Earth for that part of the country. For instance, 1000' along the face of the Earth is less than 1000' horizontally, since the Earth is curved.

The **GEODETIC DIRECTION AND DISTANCE** command is typically used when setting points over long distances where the face of the Earth becomes a consideration.

Job skills benefit here because some software manufacturers charge extra to obtain software that can perform this function.

1. Type **Z** for **Zoom** and **<Enter>**. Then type **C** for **Center** and **<Enter>**. When asked for the center point, type **11626006, 6865528**. When asked for the magnification or height, type **300**. You can also type in **V** for View and choose a saved view called **Points-B**. Hit **Set Current** and hit **OK**.

2. From the **Create Points** toolbar, choose the pop-down arrow on the first button and select **Geodetic Direction and Distance**. Respond to the prompts as follows.

3. `Please specify a location for the start point:`, type **11626006,6865528** **<Enter>**. The system responds with `Northing: 6865528.0000' Easting: 11626006.0000', Grid Northing: 6865528.0000' Grid Easting: 11626006.0000', Convergence: 0° 18' 43.40" Scale Factor: 1.000, Latitude: N38° 30' 00.00" Longitude: W78° 00' 00.01"`

4. `Geodetic azimuth <0° 00' 00.00">:` Hit **<Enter>**

5. `Geodesic distance <1.000>:` Type **100<Enter>**.

6. `Northing: 6865627.9936' Easting: 11626005.4554', Grid Northing: 6865627.9936', Grid Easting: 11626005.4554', Convergence: 0° 18' 43.40" Scale Factor: 1.000, Latitude: N38° 30' 00.99", Longitude: W78° 00' 00.01"`

7. `Enter a point description <.>:` **IPF**

8. `Specify a point elevation <.>:` **112.45**

9. `Please specify a location for the start point:` **<Enter>** to terminate.

azimuth: The North azimuth measures angles from the North axis, in a clockwise direction to 360°.

A Point 4 is created at a geodetic distance of 100′ along the curvature of the Earth in NAD 83 in northern Virginia at a geodetic *azimuth* of zero degrees. In order to test how this handled the computation, draw a line from the initial coordinate to the point placed and list the line for its length and direction.

10. Type **L** for line, and specify the first point at **11626006,6865528**.
11. Specify the next point using a **Node** snap to the point created from the last command.
12. Then type **LI** for **List** and select the line.
13. Civil 3D responds as follows:

```
LINE Layer: "0"
Space: Model space
Handle = 629
from point, X = 11626006.0000 Y = 6865528.0000 Z = 0.0000
to point, X = 11626005.4554 Y = 6865627.9936 Z = 112.4500
In Current UCS, Length = 99.9951, Angle in XY Plane = 90.3121
3D Length = 150.4793, Angle from XY Plane = 48.3552
Delta X = -0.5446, Delta Y = 99.9936, Delta Z = 112.4500
```

Notice the length of 99.9951, when you clearly entered 100′. The 100′ was the length along the face of the Earth; hence, the horizontal length of the line is something shorter. Save your drawing and remain in the drawing with your initials for the next exercise.

Exercise 3-10: Miscellaneous—RESECTION Command

 The next command is **RESECTION**. A resection creates a point at a location calculated from the measured angles between three known points.

This function is often used to locate a coordinate when you can see three other known positions and can measure their angles.

 Job skills benefit in that sailors use this same technique to locate their positions on the sea. If you plan to sail during your vacations or retirement, this routine will be helpful.

In this exercise, you are located to the upper right of Points 1, 2, and 3. Measure their angles as shown, where the angle from Point 2 to 3 is **28.7538°** and the angle from Point 2 to 1 is **56.7010°**.

1. Type **V** for **View** and choose a saved view called **Points-A**. Hit **Set Current** and hit **OK**.

2. From the **Create Points** toolbar, choose the pop-down arrow on the first button and select **Resection**. Respond to the prompts as follows.

3. `Specify first (backsight or reference) point:` Snap to Point 2 using a **Node** snap.

4. `Specify second point:` Snap to Point 3 using a **Node** snap.

5. `Specify third point:` Snap to Point 1 using a **Node** snap.

6. `Specify the angle between the first and second point <0.0000(d)>:` Type **28.7538**

7. `Specify the angle between the first and third point <0.0000(d)>:` Type **56.7010**

8. `Enter a point description <.>:` **IPF**

9. `Specify a point elevation <.>:` **0**

Notice in Figure 3-17 that Point 5 shows up at the convergence of the linework indicating the angles shot by the surveyor. Now you have a coordinate for your location. Save your drawing and remain in the drawing with your initials for the next exercise.

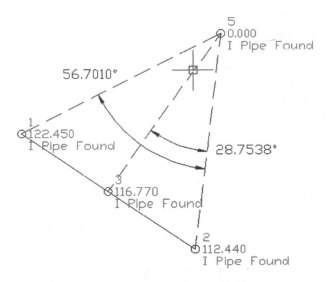

Figure 3-17   Result of Resection

Exercise 3-11: Miscellaneous—STATION/OFFSET OBJECT Command

 The next command, **STATION/OFFSET OBJECT,** creates a point based on the station and offset of a line or other object chosen for the computations. The offset is to the right if a positive value is indicated and to the left for a negative value.

TIP   The **STATION/OFFSET OBJECT** command can be used to set a point such as a manhole at a specific location relative to a known linear or curved object nearby.

1. From the **Create Points** toolbar, choose the pop-down arrow on the first button and select **Station/Offset Object**. Respond to the prompts as follows.

2. `Select an arc, line, polyline, lot line, or feature line:` Pick the line connecting Points 2 to 1 near Point 2 but not on Point 2.

3. `Starting station <0.000>:` Hit **<Enter>**.

4. `Specify a desired station <0.000>:` Type **55<Enter>**

5. `Specify an offset <0.000>:` Type **–45<Enter>**

6. `Enter a point description <.>:` **IPF**

7. `Specify a point elevation <.>:` **0**

8. `Specify desired station:` Hit **<Esc>** or **<*Cancel*>** several times to terminate the routine.

9. Notice Point 6 shows up 55′ from Point 2 in a direction toward Point 1 and 45′ to the left of the line. This works on several types of objects, however, only on independent objects.

If you wish to set points using stations/offsets based on alignments, then use a command upcoming in the third button from the left called **Alignment: Station/Offset**.

Save your drawing and remain in the drawing with your initials for the next exercise.

Exercise 3-12: Miscellaneous—AUTOMATIC Command

 The next command, **AUTOMATIC**, creates points based on the curvilinear objects selected by the operator.

 TIP This method allows very rapid point placement on many objects at once and can be used to establish property corner points for a parcel.

To access student data files, go to www.pearsondesigncentral.com.

1. In the same drawing, Chapter-3-Points.dwg or Chapter-3-Points (with your initials).dwg, turn on the layer called **V-Misc-Objs**. Some lines and arcs will display. Type **Regen** if the arcs are not obvious.
2. From the **Create Points** toolbar, choose the pop-down arrow on the first button and select **Automatic**. Respond to the prompts as follows.
3. `Select arcs, lines, lot lines, or feature lines:` Select all of the linework that was on the layer that you just turned on.
4. `Enter a point description <.>:` **IPF**
5. `Specify a point elevation <.>:` **<Enter>**
6. `Enter a point description <IPF>:` **<Enter>**
7. `Specify a point elevation <.>:` **<Enter>**
8. Repeat this for all other requests for point description and Elevation.
9. Hit **<Enter>** to terminate when complete.
10. Notice that points are automatically placed on all of the key geometric locations of the arcs and lines, including radius points of the arcs.

Save your drawing and remain in the drawing with your initials for the next exercise.

Exercise 3-13: Miscellaneous—ALONG LINE/CURVE Command

 The next command, **ALONG LINE/CURVE**, creates points based on *curvilinear objects* at a distance along the object.

curvilinear objects: These include arcs and spirals. Arcs or circular curves have a constant radius from beginning to end. Spirals have constantly changing radii from start to end.

1. In the same drawing, and from the **Create Points** toolbar, choose the pop-down arrow on the first button and select **Along Line/Curve**. Respond to the prompts as follows.
2. Select an arc, line, polyline, lot line, or feature line: Pick the yellow arc on the Layer **V-Misc-Objs**.
3. `Specify a distance:` Type **25**
4. `Enter a point description <.>:` **IPF**
5. `Specify a point elevation <.>:` **<Enter>**
6. `Specify a distance:` **50**
7. `Enter a point description <IPF>:` **<Enter>**
8. `Specify a point elevation <.>:` **<Enter>**
9. `Specify a distance:` **<Enter>** to terminate.
10. You now have points (18 and 19) along the yellow arc at distances of 25′ and 50′ from the beginning of the arc. Refer to Figure 3-18.

Exercise 3-14: Miscellaneous—ON LINE/CURVE Command

 The next command, **ON LINE/CURVE**, creates points based on curvilinear objects at their key points. This command is similar to **AUTOMATIC** in its results.

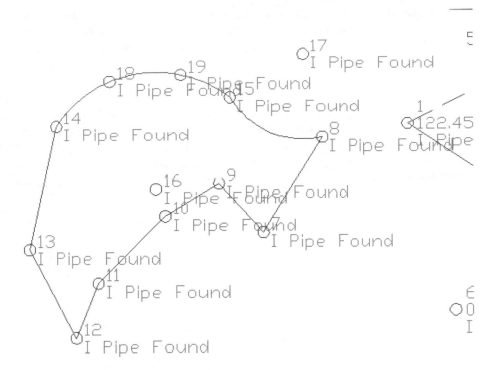

Figure 3-18   Result of Miscellaneous Along Line/Curve

Exercise 3-15: Miscellaneous — DIVIDE OBJECT Command

The next command, **DIVIDE OBJECT**, creates points by the number of segments you request on an object. This command could be used to set stakeout points for landscape planting off to the side of a property line.

TIP

In this case, the landscape architect may have outlined that four equally spaced trees are to be planted in order to meet **greenspace** requirements for the subdivision. You usually do not want to set stakeout points at the actual location of the prospective trees because as soon as the contractor begins digging, the stakes will be knocked out of the ground. So it usually is a good idea to set them safely off to the side of the construction area.

greenspace: An area dedicated to the preservation or replacement of vegetation that may be reduced as a result of construction. Planning professionals often ensure that requirements for greenspace are met for a project.

1. To begin this routine, **Draw** a line from **850,1050** to **930,1075**.
2. Then from the **Create Points** toolbar, choose the pop-down arrow on the first button and select **Divide Object**. Respond to the prompts as follows.
3. `Select an arc, line, polyline, lot line, or feature line:` Select the line you just drew at the right end.
4. `Enter the number of segments <1>:` **3**
5. `Specify an offset <0.000>:` **25**
6. `Enter a point description <.>:` **IPF**
7. `Specify a point elevation <.>:` **<Enter>**
8. `Enter a point description <IPF>:` **<Enter>**
9. `Specify a point elevation <.>:` **<Enter>**
10. `Enter a point description <IPF>:` **<Enter>**
11. `Specify a point elevation <.>:` **<Enter>**
12. `Enter a point description <IPF>:` **<Enter>**
13. `Specify a point elevation <.>:` **<Enter>**
14. Hit **<Enter>** to terminate.
15. Save the drawing. You can close and open it as needed as you progress through these exercises.

The system places Points 20 through 23, in this case, where the line would have three segments including the endpoints, and at an offset of 25′. Of course you could set an offset of 0 and achieve the points right on the object. Save your drawing and remain in the drawing with your initials for the next exercise.

Exercise 3-16: Miscellaneous—MEASURE OBJECT Command

 This exercise sets points using the **CREATE POINTS—MEASURE OBJECT** command. Notice that the **DIVIDE OBJECT** and **MEASURE OBJECT** commands seem like companion commands to the **DIVIDE** and **MEASURE** AutoCAD commands. They work essentially as they do in AutoCAD, except that they set point objects as shown in Figure 3-19.

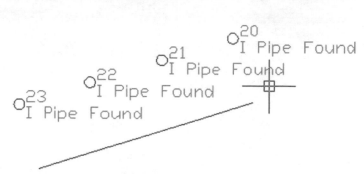

Figure 3-19   Result of Measure Object

 The **MEASURE OBJECT** command could be used to set stakeout points to the side of a culvert. You usually do not want to set stakeout points right on the centerline of a culvert because as soon as the contractor begins digging, the stakes will be knocked out of the ground, rendering them useless. So it usually is a good idea to set them safely off to the side of the construction area.

Miscellaneous—POLYLINE VERTICES—MANUAL Command

 The next computations set points on polylines. The first example, using the **POLYLINE VERTICES—MANUAL** command, sets points on a polyline using a manual approach. You might use this when you want to create points on a building pad that has a specific, flat elevation. Type in the desired elevation before setting the points, and the software will use it when creating the points.

Exercise 3-17: Miscellaneous—POLYLINE VERTICES—AUTOMATIC Command

 The next computation, using the **POLYLINE VERTICES—AUTOMATIC** command, sets points on polylines automatically. The previous command was pretty automatic, so how is this different? This one sets the elevations for the building pad automatically, assuming that the pad is set at the correct elevation to start with. You might use this when you want to create points on a building pad that has a preset, flat elevation.

1. Continuing on in the same drawing, erase the points from the previous command using the **ERASE** command in AutoCAD.
2. Now use the **MOVE** command in AutoCAD to move the building object up to an elevation of **100**. Use the AutoCAD **REC** command to create a rectangle for the building object. Type **M<Enter>**, select the pad and hit **<Enter>**. When prompted to Specify base point or displacement: Type **0,0,100<Enter><Enter>**.
3. This has caused the building to move up to an elevation of 100′.
4. From the **Create Points** toolbar and using the pop-down arrow next to the first icon, choose **Polyline Vertices—Automatic**. Respond to the prompts as follows.
5. Select a polyline object: Select the polyline you just moved to elevation 100.
6. Enter a point description <.>: **IPF**

7. `Enter a point description <IPF>:` **\<Enter\>**
8. `Enter a point description <IPF>:` **\<Enter\>**
9. `Enter a point description <IPF>:` **\<Enter\>**
10. You will be prompted to `Select a polyline object` when it has set points on your object. Hit **\<Enter\>** to terminate. Notice all of the points are automatically set with an elevation of 100 because the software read it directly from the polyline.

Save your drawing and remain in the drawing with your initials for the next exercise.

Miscellaneous—CONVERT AUTOCAD POINTS Command

 The next tool uses the **CONVERT AUTOCAD POINTS** command to create Civil 3D points from AutoCAD points. You might use this when you have a drawing that already has points; however, they are simple AutoCAD points, without any point numbers, elevation, or descriptions.

 You may use **CONVERT AUTOCAD POINTS** when points have been created from a GIS system and you wish to use them in Civil 3D with intelligence.

Miscellaneous—CONVERT SOFTDESK POINT BLOCKS Command

 The last command in this area, **CONVERT SOFTDESK POINT BLOCKS**, creates Civil 3D points from Softdesk points. This is a legacy item for users of Softdesk software. Refer back to the discussion in the introduction to this text for information on the role Softdesk played in the development of Civil 3D software.

 You might use the **CONVERT SOFTDESK POINT BLOCKS** command when you have a drawing that already has points in it that were generated by Softdesk software and you want them to be used in Civil 3D.

Intersection-Related Point Creation Commands

The commands that are investigated next are those related to intersections of a variety of objects. These types of commands have been used in surveying for a long time, but they were possibly referred to by other terms. For instance, the first command shown in Figure 3-20, called **DIREC-**

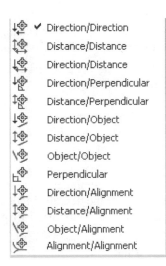

Figure 3-20   Direction/Direction

bearings: Measure a heading and are broken into four 90° quadrants: North, South, East, and West.

DIRECTION/DIRECTION, begins by asking for a point from a known position and angle toward a specific direction pointing toward infinity. It then asks for a second point and an angle also pointing toward infinity. Unless these angles are equal, producing a parallel set of vectors, they must intersect at some location. This is where a point will be created. Very often in surveying tasks, the angle would be established by using a *bearing*. This routine function then would typically be called a Bearing, Bearing intersect. Although the software does allow for the angle entry to be in bearings, it also allows for azimuths and other methods for establishing the angle; hence the name of the command is **DIRECTION/DIRECTION**, because it is not limited only to bearing entry. This next section of the text explores how these commands operate and identifies the reasons for using them.

Exercise 3-18: Intersection—DIRECTION/DIRECTION Command

 The **DIRECTION/DIRECTION** command is used to create a point that is the result of the intersection of two vectors.

 This is also called a Bearing/Bearing intersect by many surveyors.

 There are many reasons to use this routine, but one might be that a tangent is established for the centerline of a roadway, let us call it Main Street. Another vector was established for First Avenue. While the surveyor was collecting the data, he or she determined that shooting a point at the intersection of First and Main was too dangerous due to traffic volume. However, the surveyor made a note that the vectors would continue as established, with no curves or additional bends until they met at the intersection. This would be a good example of using the **DIRECTION/DIRECTION** command to set the point at the intersection of First and Main.

To access student data files, go to www.pearsondesigncentral.com.

1. Open the drawing called My Point Style-Intersections.dwg.
2. Using the **V** for **View** command, highlight the view called **Points-A**, hit **Set Current**, and then hit **OK**.
3. Select the **Points** pull-down menu and choose the **Create Points...** command. The toolbar displays. First investigate the tools in the second button from the left. Notice the drop-down arrow to the right of the second icon from the left. It shows the information in Figure 3-20 starting with **Direction/Direction**. Select **Direction/Direction**.
4. When you are prompted to Specify start point: Type in an *X, Y* coordinate of **850, 950**.

A tick mark displays with a rubber-banding red vector emanating from the tick, indicating an angular data entry is required. The prompt allows for **B** for bearings entry, **Z** for Azimuth entry.

5. Respond to the prompts as follows. Specify direction at start point or [Bearing/aZimuth] : Type **B** (for Bearing).
6. Quadrants - NE = 1, SE = 2, SW = 3, NW = 4, as shown in Figure 3-21.
7. Specify quadrant (1-4) or [aZimuth/Angle] : Type **1**
8. Specify bearing or [aZimuth/Angle] : Enter **64.5631**
9. Specify an offset <0.000>: **<Enter>**

The software not only allows for a Bearing/Bearing intersect to be computed but also allows for a Bearing, offset at a specified distance to be computed to the intersection of another Bearing, offset at a specified distance. Hit **<Enter>** for the defaulted 0.000 for these offsets. This information sets the first vector and a tick mark with a vector arrow displays. It now needs the second vector information to continue.

10. Specify start point: Enter **1000,950**

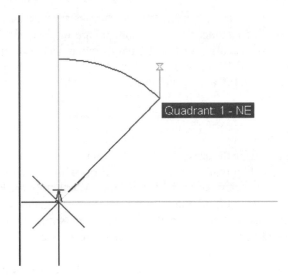

Figure 3-21   Quadrant angles

11. `Specify direction at start point or [ Bearing/aZimuth] :` Type **B** (for Bearing).
12. `Quadrants - NE = 1, SE = 2, SW = 3, NW = 4`
13. `Specify quadrant (1-4) or [ aZimuth/Angle] :` **4**
14. `Specify bearing or [ aZimuth/Angle] :` **48.1752** (Figure 3-22).

Figure 3-22   Entering Bearings

15. `Specify an offset : <0.000>:` **<Enter>**
16. `Enter a point description <.>:` **IPF**
17. `Specify a point elevation <.>:` **<Enter>**
18. A point is now placed at the desired location (Figure 3-23).
19. Hit **<Esc>** to terminate.

Figure 3-23   Two angles established for Direction/Direction

Exercise 3-19: Intersection—DISTANCE/DISTANCE Command

The next routine creates a point from the intersection of two circles. You establish a center point and a radius for the first circle; a center point and a radius for the second circle; and the system computes whether one or more solutions is found, tells you about it, and then asks you to select the one point that solves your problem or allows you to accept multiple points if they are found. This is called the **DISTANCE/DISTANCE** command.

The **DISTANCE/DISTANCE** command may be used to compute an arc on a piece of property for which the radius and the starting and ending points of the arc are known, say from a curve table on a plat. Or perhaps little else is known and it needs to be drawn.

In this on-the-job example, a parcel exists on a cul-de-sac. The side lot lines are known by distance and bearings on the plat, but the only information available to draw it is the arc radius. So the trick here is to locate the center of the arc because then AutoCAD can be used to draw the arc using the **Start, Center and End** option. This is a great use for the **DISTANCE/DISTANCE** command because the arc begins and ends at the ends of the property lines.

To access student data files, go to www.pearsondesigncentral.com.

1. Continue in the same drawing, or open the drawing called My Point Style-Intersections.dwg.
2. Using the **V** for **View** command, highlight the view called **Points-B**, hit **Set Current**, and then hit **OK**. You see the property lines. An arc with a 50′ radius will close the property.
3. Select the **Points** pull-down menu and choose the **Create Points...** command. The toolbar displays. First investigate the tools in the second button from the left. Notice the drop-down arrow to the right of the second icon from the left. Select **Distance/Distance**. Respond to the prompts as follows.
4. `Please specify a location for the radial point:` Pick an **Endpoint** snap at the end of the open side of the left property line. `Enter radius <0.000>:` Type **50**
5. `Please specify a location for the radial point:` Pick an **Endpoint** snap at the end of the open side of the right property line. `Enter radius <0.000>:` Type **50**
6. The software computes two possible solutions and asks, `Point or [All] <All>:` Use the mouse to pick a point near the bottom green tick mark in Figure 3-24, because that is where the arc radius is intended to be.

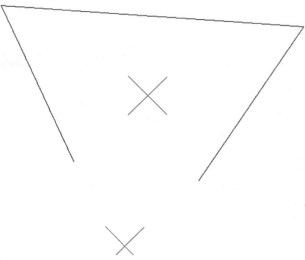

Figure 3-24   Distance/Distance command

7. `Enter a point description <.>:` **IPF**
8. `Specify a point elevation <.>:` **<Enter>**
9. Hit **<Esc>** to terminate the command when asked, `Please specify a location for the radial point:`, because the software thinks you will continue with more problems.
10. Now type **A** for **Arc** in AutoCAD; using the **Endpoint** osnap, select the open end of the right parcel line. Then type **C** for **Center** of arc and use the **Node** osnap to select the point you just located. Finish by using the **Endpoint** osnap and select the open end of the left parcel line. An arc now exists representing the cul-de-sac.
11. Save the file.

Exercise 3-20: Intersection—DIRECTION/DISTANCE Command

Civil 3D performs many more related functions but varies the parameters in each solution. Continue with these functions so that you try each one at least once.

To access student data files, go to www.pearsondesigncentral.com.

> Perhaps you are trying to identify a conflict with a 200-year-old elm tree. The proposed roadway may be the direction vector and the tree needs to have a 55′ clearance in order to remain healthy. Does the proposed roadway conflict with this clear zone?

TIP

1. Continue in the same drawing, or open the drawing called My Point Style-Intersections.dwg.
2. Using the **Layer** command, turn on the layer called **V-Misc-Objs**.
3. Using the **V** for **View** command, highlight the view called **Points-A**, hit **Set Current**, and then hit **OK**. You see a vector arrow and a circle for which you need to compute points. Compute one or more points for where the vector crosses the circle. It has a radius of 55′.
4. Select the **Points** pull-down menu if the **Create Points** toolbar is not displayed, and choose the **Create Points…** command. The **Create Points** toolbar displays.

You are still investigating the tools in the second button from the left. Using the drop-down arrow to the right of the second icon from the left, choose **Direction/Distance**. Respond to the prompts as follows.

5. `Please specify a location for the radial point:` Pick a point at the center of the circle in the view using the **Center** osnap.
6. `Enter radius <0.000>:` Type **55** for the radius.
7. `Specify start point:` Pick the left end of the vector arrow using the **Endpoint** osnap.
8. `Specify direction at start point or [ Bearing/aZimuth] :` Pick the end of the vector arrow at the arrowhead using the **Endpoint** osnap.
9. `Specify an offset <0.000>:` **<Enter>** Accept 0.000 because you will not be off-setting the vector as it intersects with the circle.
10. The software solves the problem and offers two potential solutions, as shown in Figure 3-25. You can pick a point near the green tick mark to indicate your choice of solution or hit **<Enter>** for **All**. `Point or [ All] <All>:` **<Enter>**
11. `Enter a point description <.>:` **IPF**
12. `Specify a point elevation <.>:` **<Enter>**
13. `Enter a point description <,>:` **IPF**
14. `Specify a point elevation <.>:` **<Enter>**
15. When asked to continue the routine with the prompt: `Please specify a location for the radial point:` Hit **<Esc>** to cancel out and terminate.

Two points exist on the perimeter of the circle where the vector would cross it, if it did. So in this example, there is a conflict between the proposed road and the tree's clear zone. The road must be moved a little farther away from the tree. Refer to Figure 3-26.

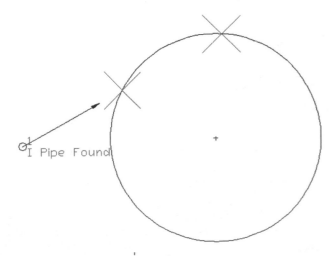

Figure 3-25   Two possible solutions

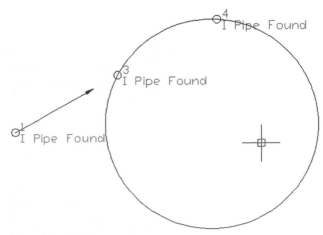

Figure 3-26   Two points are set

Exercise 3-21: Intersection—DIRECTION/PERPENDICULAR Command

 The next command, **DIRECTION/PERPENDICULAR**, can be used to compute the location of a point on a property line from the corner of a building.

 TIP We often must locate points on a property line from the corner of a building to ensure that we have met minimum clearances to the building restriction lines or property lines as dictated by the local ordinances.

To access student data files, go to www.pearsondesigncentral.com.

1. Continue in the same drawing, or open the drawing called My Point Style-Intersections.dwg.
2. Using the **Layer** command, turn on the layer called **V-Misc-Objs**.
3. Using the **V** for **View** command, highlight the view called **Points-C**, hit **Set Current**, and then hit **OK**. You see a property parcel surrounding a house. Compute a point where the house corner is perpendicular to the right property line.
4. Select the **Points** pull-down menu and choose the **Create Points**... command. The **Create Points** toolbar displays.
5. Using the drop-down arrow to the right of the second icon from the left, choose **Direction/Perpendicular**. Respond to the prompts as follows.
6. `Specify start point:` Pick a point using the **Endpoint** osnap on the property corner at the top of the parcel.
7. `Specify direction at start point or [Bearing/aZimuth]:` Pick a point using the **Endpoint** osnap on the property corner at the bottom right of the parcel. A yellow vector appears on the right parcel line. Refer to Figure 3-27.

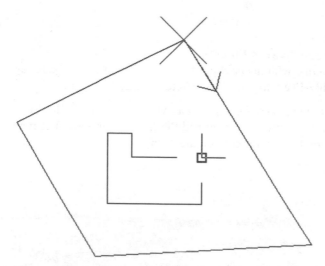

Figure 3-27   Direction/Perpendicular command

8. `Specify an offset <0.000>:` Type **10** indicating a 10′ building restriction line.
9. `Please specify a location for the perpendicular point:` Using the **Endpoint** osnap, pick a point on the right corner of the structure as shown in Figure 3-27.
10. `Enter a point description <.>:` Hit **<Enter>**
11. `Specify a point elevation <.>:` Hit **<Enter>**
12. When asked to continue the routine with the prompt: `Specify start point:` Hit **<Esc>** to cancel out and terminate.
13. A point is placed at the desired location.

Exercise 3-22: Intersection—DISTANCE/PERPENDICULAR Command

 The next command, **DISTANCE/PERPENDICULAR**, can be used to compute the location of a point on a property line from the corner of a building to a circular set of parameters.

 TIP   The **DISTANCE/PERPENDICULAR** command can be used to set a point on the arc of a cul-de-sac radially from the corner of a building.

To access student data files, go to www.pearsondesigncentral.com.

1. Continue in the same drawing, or open the drawing called My Point Style-Intersections.dwg.
2. Using the **Layer** command, turn on the layer called **V-Misc-Objs**.
3. Using the **V** for **View** command, highlight the view called **Points-B**, hit **Set Current**, and then hit **OK**. You see a property parcel surrounding a house. Compute a point where the house corner is perpendicular (or radial) to the property line.
4. Select the **Points** pull-down menu and choose the **Create Points**... command. The **Create Points** toolbar displays.
5. Using the drop-down arrow to the right of the second icon from the left, choose **Distance/Perpendicular**. Respond to the prompts as follows.
6. `Please specify a location for the radial point:` Using the **Center** osnap, pick a point on the arc to locate the radius point of the arc.
7. `Enter radius <0.000>:` Using the **Endpoint** osnap, pick a point at the end of the arc so it can compute the radius from the two points.
8. `Please specify a location for the perpendicular point:` Using the **Endpoint** osnap, pick a point at the corner of the building nearest the arc.
9. `Enter a point description <.>:` **<Enter>**
10. `Specify a point elevation <.>:` **<Enter>**
11. When asked to continue the routine with the prompt: `Please specify a location for the radial point:` Hit **<Esc>** to cancel out and terminate.

You see a point placed on the arc, radially from the corner of the house in Figure 3-28.

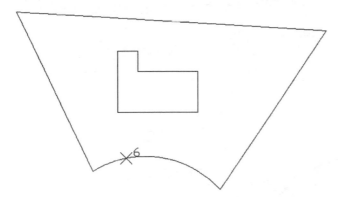

Figure 3-28   Distance/Perpendicular command

Exercise 3-23: Intersection—DIRECTION/OBJECT Command

 The next command, **DIRECTION/OBJECT**, can be used to compute a point along a direction toward an object.

 TIP   An example of use for the **DIRECTION/OBJECT** command is to set the location of a point on a property line from the corner of a building to a circular set of parameters. You want to compute a point where the culvert crosses the back property line.

Job skills benefit from being able to perform geometry commands such as these because they are required skills for every designer and surveyor.

To access student data
files, go to
www.pearsondesigncentral.com.

1. Continue in the same drawing, or open the drawing called My Point Style-Intersections.dwg.
2. Using the **V** for **View** command, highlight the view called **Points-D**, hit **Set Current**, and then hit **OK**. You see a property parcel surrounding a house. Compute a point where the culvert crosses the back property line.
3. Select the **Points** pull-down menu and choose the **Create Points**... command. The **Create Points** toolbar displays.
4. Using the drop-down arrow to the right of the second icon from the left, choose **Direction/Object**. Respond to the prompts as follows.
5. `Select an arc, line, polyline, lot line, or feature line:` Pick the back property line.
6. `Specify an offset <0.000>:` **<Enter>**
7. `Specify start point:` Using the **Endpoint** osnap, pick a point at the top end of the culvert line.
8. `Specify direction at start point or [Bearing/aZimuth]:` Using the **Endpoint** osnap, pick a point at the bottom end of the culvert line.
9. `Specify an offset <0.000>:` **<Enter>**
10. `Enter a point description <.>:` **<Enter>**
11. `Specify a point elevation <.>:` **<Enter>**
12. `Select an arc, line, polyline, lot line, or feature line:` Hit **<Esc>** to cancel out and terminate.

A point is placed on the property line where the culvert crosses it. Refer to Figure 3-29.

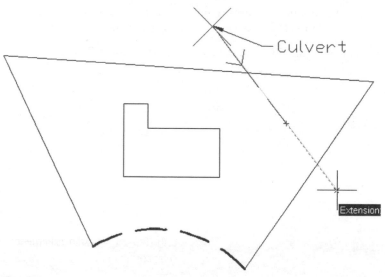

Figure 3-29   Direction/Object command

Exercise 3-24: Intersection—DISTANCE/OBJECT Command

 The next command, **DISTANCE/OBJECT**, can be used to compute the location of a point(s) at a distance from an object to another object.

 The **DISTANCE/OBJECT** command would allow placement of a point(s) on a property line from, say, the corner of a building to a minimum distance from the building corner.

A job skill evident in a command such as this might include being able to compute a point(s) for trees to be placed on the property line so that they are not closer to the house than 35′.

To access student data files, go to www.pearsondesigncentral.com.

1. Continue in the same drawing, or open the drawing called **My Point Style-Intersections.dwg**.
2. Using the **V** for **View** command, highlight the view called **Points-D**, hit **Set Current**, and then hit **OK**. You see a property parcel surrounding a house. Compute point(s) on the right property line to plant trees no closer than 35′ from the house.
3. Select the **Points** pull-down menu and choose the **Create Points**... command. The **Create Points** toolbar displays.
4. Using the drop-down arrow to the right of the second icon from the left, choose **Distance/Object**. Respond to the prompts as follows.
5. `Select an arc, line, polyline, lot line, or feature line:` Select the right property line.
6. `Specify an offset <0.000>:` **<Enter>**
7. `Please specify a location for the radial point:` Using the **Endpoint** osnap, pick a point at the bottom right corner of the house.
8. `Enter radius <0.000>:` **35**
9. `Point or [All] <All>:` **<Enter>**
10. `Enter a point description <.>:` **<Enter>**
11. `Specify a point elevation <.>:` **<Enter>**
12. `Enter a point description <.>:` **<Enter>**
13. `Specify a point elevation <.>:` **<Enter>**
14. `Select an arc, line, polyline, lot line, or feature line:` Hit **<Esc>** to cancel out and terminate.

Two points (Figure 3-30) are placed on the property line, each at a minimum distance of 35′ from the house corner.

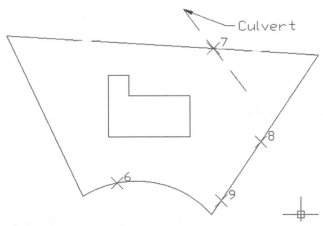

Figure 3-30   Distance/Object command

Exercise 3-25: Intersection—OBJECT/OBJECT Command

  The next command, **OBJECT/OBJECT**, can be used to compute the location of a point that results from the intersection of two objects.

  You may want to compute a point where the culvert would intersect the right (or east) property line if it were to be extended.

To access student data
files, go to
www.pearsondesigncentral.com.

1. Continue in the same drawing, or open the drawing called My Point Style-Intersections.dwg.
2. Using the **V** for **View** command, highlight the view called **Points-D**, hit **Set Current**, and then hit **OK**. You see a property parcel surrounding a house. Compute a point where the culvert crosses the right property line if it were to be extended.
3. Select the **Points** pull-down menu and choose the **Create Points**... command. The **Create Points** toolbar displays.
4. Using the drop-down arrow to the right of the second icon from the left, choose **Object/Object**. Respond to the prompts as follows.
5. `Select an arc, line, polyline, lot line, or feature line:` Select the right property line.
6. `Specify an offset <0.000>:` **<Enter>**
7. `Select an arc, line, polyline,lot line, or feature line:` Select the culvert line.
8. `Specify an offset <0.000>:` **<Enter>**
9. `Enter a point description <.>:` **<Enter>**
10. `Specify a point elevation <.>:` **<Enter>**
11. `Select an arc, line, polyline, lot line, or feature line:` Hit **<Esc>** to cancel out and terminate.

Notice a new point was placed on the right property line where the culvert would cross it if it did (Figure 3-31).

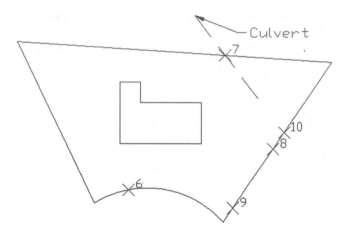

Figure 3-31   Object/Object command

Exercise 3-26: Intersection—PERPENDICULAR Command

 The next command, **PERPENDICULAR**, can be used to compute the location of a point that results from the intersection of two objects. This command allows you to compute the perpendicular easily.

 Many objects in civil engineering are perpendicular to items, and this routine simplifies these computations. For instance, side lot lines are usually perpendicular to front or back property lines, or side roads are typically perpendicular to main roads. Because computing a perpendicular is relatively easy, doing so can cut down on construction and surveying stakeout errors.

To access student data
files, go to
www.pearsondesigncentral.com.

1. Continue in the same drawing, or open the drawing called My Point Style-Intersections.dwg.
2. Using the **V** for **View** command, highlight the view called **Points-D**, hit **Set Current**, and then hit **OK**. You see a property parcel surrounding a house. Compute a point perpendicular to the back property line from a point outside the parcel.
3. Select the **Points** pull-down menu and choose the **Create Points**... command. The **Create Points** toolbar displays.
4. Using the drop-down arrow to the right of the second icon from the left, choose **Perpendicular**. Respond to the prompts as follows.

5. `Select an arc, line, polyline, lot line, or feature line:` Select the back property line.
6. `Please specify a location for the perpendicular point:` **890,1570**
7. `Enter a point description <.>:` **<Enter>**
8. `Specify a point elevation <.>:` **<Enter>**
9. `Select an arc, line, polyline, lot line, or feature line:` Hit **<Esc>** to cancel out and terminate.

A new point has been placed along the back property line as shown in Figure 3-32, indicating the perpendicular intersection to the property line from the point beginning at 890,1570.

The next several commands all have to do with computing points from criteria that intersect with alignments.

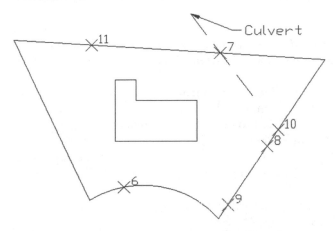

Figure 3-32   Perpendicular command

Exercise 3-27: Intersection—DIRECTION/ALIGNMENT Command

 The next command, **DIRECTION/ALIGNMENT**, can be used to compute the location of a point that results from the intersection of an angle with an alignment.

 You might use the **DIRECTION/ALIGNMENT** command to compute a point using the incoming bearing of a side road and where it intersects the main roadway, which has been defined as an alignment. The example might be similar to that used in the -**DIRECTION/DIRECTION** command; however, this uses a predefined alignment.

1. Continue in the same drawing, or open the drawing called My Point Style-Intersections.dwg.
2. Using the **V** for **View** command, highlight the view called **Points-E**, hit **Set Current**, and then hit **OK**. You see an alignment. Compute a point where a bearing crosses the alignment.
3. Select the **Points** pull-down menu and choose the **Create Points**... command. The **Create Points** toolbar displays.
4. Using the drop-down arrow to the right of the second icon from the left, choose -**Direction/Alignment**. Respond to the prompts as follows.
5. `Select an alignment object:` Select someplace on the alignment.
6. `Specify an offset <0.000>:` **<Enter>**
7. `Specify start point:` **50,1500**
8. `Specify direction at start point or [ Bearing/aZimuth] :` **B**
9. The system reminds us of the quadrant numbers. `Quadrants - NE = 1, SE = 2, SW = 3, NW = 4`
10. `Specify quadrant (1-4) or [ aZimuth/Angle] :` **3**
11. `Specify bearing or [ aZimuth/Angle] :` **60.4931**
12. `Specify an offset <0.000>:` **<Enter>**
13. `Enter a point description <.>:` **<Enter>**
14. `Specify a point elevation <.>:` **<Enter>**
15. `Select an alignment object:` Hit **<Esc>** to cancel out and terminate.

Notice that a new point has been placed on the alignment between stations 3+50 and 4+00.

To access student data files, go to www.pearsondesigncentral.com.

Exercise 3-28: Intersection—DISTANCE/ALIGNMENT Command

 The next command, **DISTANCE/ALIGNMENT**, can be used to compute the location of a point that results from the intersection of a circular distance from a point with an alignment.

The **DISTANCE/ALIGNMENT** command could be used to compute a point 100′ from the end of an alignment.

To access student data files, go to www.pearsondesigncentral.com.

1. Continue in the same drawing, or open the drawing called My Point Style-Intersections.dwg.
2. Using the **V** for **View** command, highlight the view called **Points-E**, hit **Set Current**, and then hit **OK**. You see an alignment. Compute a point 100′ from the end of the alignment.
3. Select the **Points** pull-down menu and choose the **Create Points**... command. The **Create Points** toolbar displays.
4. Using the drop-down arrow to the right of the second icon from the left, choose **Distance/Alignment**. Respond to the prompts as follows.
5. `Select an alignment object:` Select someplace on the alignment.
6. `Specify an offset <0.000>:` **<Enter>**
7. `Please specify a location for the radial point:` Using the **Endpoint** osnap, pick a point at the northern end of the alignment.
8. `Enter radius <0.000>:` **100**
9. `Enter a point description <.>:` **<Enter>**
10. `Specify a point elevation <.>:` **<Enter>**
11. `Select an alignment object:` Hit **<Esc>** to cancel out and terminate.

Notice that a point was placed at around station 6+00 on the alignment.

Exercise 3-29: Intersection—OBJECT/ALIGNMENT Command

 The next command, **OBJECT/ALIGNMENT**, can be used to compute the location of a point that results from the intersection of a circular distance from a point with an alignment.

You might use the **OBJECT/ALIGNMENT** command to compute a point on the alignment where a culvert crosses the alignment.

The job skill apparent in this routine is that designers and surveyors need these types of computations on a daily basis because utilities intersect with alignments routinely.

To access student data files, go to www.pearsondesigncentral.com.

1. Continue in the same drawing, or open the drawing called My Point Style-Intersections.dwg.
2. Using the **V** for **View** command, highlight the view called **Points-E**, hit **Set Current**, and then hit **OK**. You see an alignment. Compute a point on the alignment where a culvert crosses the alignment.
3. Select the **Points** pull-down menu and choose the **Create Points**... command. The **Create Points** toolbar displays.
4. Using the drop-down arrow to the right of the second icon from the left, choose **Object/Alignment**. Respond to the prompts as follows.
5. `Select an alignment object:` Select someplace on the alignment.
6. `Specify an offset <0.000>:` **<Enter>**
7. `Select an arc, line, polyline, lot line, or feature line:` Select someplace on the culvert that is around station 1+25.

8. `Specify an offset <0.000>:` **\<Enter>**
9. `Enter a point description <.>:` **\<Enter>**
10. `Specify a point elevation <.>:` **\<Enter>**
11. `Select an alignment object:` Hit **\<Esc>** to cancel out and terminate.

Notice that a point was placed at around station 1+25 on the alignment exactly where the culvert crossed the alignment.

Exercise 3-30: Intersection—ALIGNMENT/ALIGNMENT Command

The next command, **ALIGNMENT/ALIGNMENT**, can be used to compute the location of a point that results from the intersection of one alignment to another alignment.

TIP   You might use the **ALIGNMENT/ALIGNMENT** command to compute a point where a 12′ edge of pavement on the main road meets the 12′ edge of pavement for the side street.

1. Continue in the same drawing, or open the drawing called My Point Style-Intersections.dwg.
2. Using the **V** for **View** command, highlight the view called **Points-F**, hit **Set Current**, and then hit **OK**. You see an alignment. Compute a point where a 12′ edge of pavement on the main road meets the 12′ edge of pavement for the side street.
3. Select the **Points** pull-down menu and choose the **Create Points**... command. The **Create Points** toolbar displays.
4. Using the drop-down arrow to the right of the second icon from the left, choose **Alignment/Alignment**. Respond to the prompts as follows.
5. `Select an alignment object:` Select someplace on the longer alignment (it has a curve in it)
6. `Specify an offset <0.000>:` **12**
7. `Select an alignment object:` Select someplace on the shorter alignment (it has no curve in it).
8. `Specify an offset <12.000>:` **\<Enter>**
9. `Enter a point description <.>:` **\<Enter>**
10. `Specify a point elevation <.>:` **\<Enter>**
11. `Select an alignment object:` Hit **\<Esc>** to cancel out and terminate.

To access student data files, go to www.pearsondesigncentral.com.

Notice that a point was placed at around station 3+00 on the main road alignment at a 12′ offset. If an offset of **-12** were provided, the point would be on the left side of the roadway.

These commands and exercises conclude the Intersection-based commands in Civil 3D.

Alignment-Related Point Commands

The next set of **POINT CREATION** commands have to do with Alignments. An alignment must exist for these to do their job.

Exercise 3-31: Alignment—STATION/OFFSET Command

The next command, **STATION/OFFSET**, can be used to compute the location of a point(s) that have station and offset values relative to an alignment.

TIP   The **STATION/OFFSET** command might be used to locate Planimetric features such as fire hydrants or mailboxes at a variety of stations when they are a standard distance off the face of a curb.

To access student data
files, go to
www.pearsondesigncentral.com.

Surveyors usually develop stakeout points at the end of every project to identify for the construction contractor where structures need to be built. This routine accomplishes that.

1. Continue in the same drawing, or open the drawing called My Point Style-Intersections.dwg.
2. Using the **V** for **View** command, highlight the view called **Points-G**, hit **Set Current**, and then hit **OK**. You see an alignment. Compute points representing mailboxes at the stations provided at offsets that are 16′ to the right and left of the roadway centerline.
3. Select the **Points** pull-down menu and choose the **Create Points**... command. The **Create Points** toolbar displays.
4. Using the drop-down arrow to the right of the third icon from the left, choose **Station/Offset**. Respond to the prompts as follows.
5. Select alignment: Select someplace on the alignment.
6. Specify station along alignment: **75**
7. Specify an offset <0.000>: **16** (which indicates 16′ to the right of the alignment).
8. Enter a point description <.>: **MB**
9. Specify a point elevation <.>: **<Enter>**
10. Specify station along alignment: **75**
11. Specify an offset <16.000>: **-16**
12. Enter a point description <.>: **MB**
13. Specify a point elevation <.>: **<Enter>**
14. Specify station along alignment: **150**
15. Specify an offset <-16.000>: **<Enter>**
16. Enter a point description <.>: **MB**
17. Specify a point elevation <.>: **<Enter>**
18. Specify station along alignment: **150**
19. Specify an offset <-16.000>: **16**
20. Enter a point description <.>: **MB**
21. Specify a point elevation <.>: **<Enter>**
22. Specify station along alignment: **225**
23. Specify an offset <16.000>: **<Enter>**
24. Enter a point description <.>: **MB**
25. Specify a point elevation <.>: **<Enter>**
26. Specify station along alignment: **225**
27. Specify an offset <16.000>: **-16**
28. Enter a point description <.>: **MB**
29. Specify a point elevation <.>: **<Enter>**
30. Specify station along alignment: **300**
31. Specify an offset <-16.000>: **<Enter>**
32. Enter a point description <.>: **MB**
33. Specify a point elevation <.>: **<Enter>**
34. Specify station along alignment: **300**
35. Specify an offset <-16.000>: **16**
36. Enter a point description <.>: **MB**
37. Specify a point elevation <.>: **<Enter>**
38. Specify station along alignment: **<Enter>** to terminate.

Figure 3-33 shows eight points representing mailboxes that will be placed along the alignment at the specified stations and 16′ to the right and left of the roadway up to station 3+00.

Exercise 3-32: Alignment—DIVIDE ALIGNMENT Command

 The next command, **DIVIDE ALIGNMENT**, can be used to compute the location of a point(s) that have station and offset values relative to an alignment.

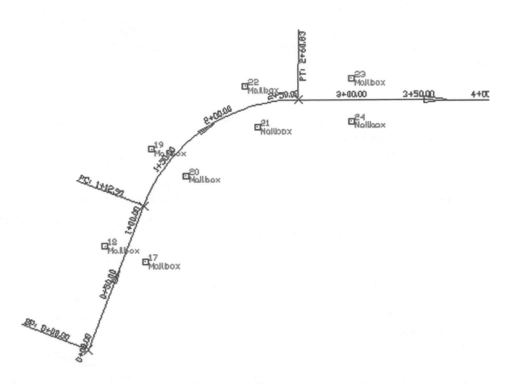

Figure 3-33   Station/
Offset command

TIP

> The **DIVIDE ALIGNMENT** command might be used to compute points for the excavation
> for tree bulbs such that there are 22 trees planted at an offset of 50' to the right side of the
> roadway following construction.

To access student data
files, go to
www.pearsondesigncentral.com.

1. Continue in the same drawing, or open the drawing called My Point Style-Intersections.dwg.
2. Using the **V** for **View** command, highlight the view called **Points-G**, hit **Set Current**, and
   then hit **OK**. You see an alignment. Compute points for the excavation for tree bulbs such
   that there are 22 trees planted on the right side of the roadway following construction.
3. Select the **Points** pull-down menu and choose the **Create Points**... command. The **Create
   Points** toolbar displays.
4. Using the drop-down arrow to the right of the third icon from the left, choose **Divide
   Alignment**. Respond to the prompts as follows.
5. `Select alignment:` Select someplace on the alignment.
6. `Enter the number of segments <1>:` **21**
7. `Specify an offset <0.000>:` **50**, which indicates that they will be placed to the
   right side.
8. `Enter a point description <.>:` **<Enter>**
9. `Specify a point elevation <.>:` **<Enter>**

Continue hitting **<Enter>** as the software prompts for point descriptions and point elevations until it is finished putting 22 points on the right side of the road. When prompted to `Select
alignment:` hit **<Enter>** to terminate. You see the points on the right side of the road.

Exercise 3-33: Alignment—MEASURE ALIGNMENT Command

 The next command, **MEASURE ALIGNMENT**, can be used to compute the location of
a point(s) that has station and offset values relative to an alignment.

TIP

> The **MEASURE ALIGNMENT** command might be used to compute points for the stake-
> out of the road. You may want points placed at 25' intervals at an offset of 50' to the left
> side of the roadway.

To access student data
files, go to
www.pearsondesigncentral.com.

A large part of a surveyor's job is to produce construction stakeout points for roadways, and this is exactly how they would be developed.

1. Continue in the same drawing, or open the drawing called My Point Style-Intersections.dwg.
2. Using the **V** for **View** command, highlight the view called **Points-G**, hit **Set Current**, and then hit **OK**. You see an alignment. Place points at 25′ intervals at an offset of 50′ to the left side of the roadway.
3. Select the **Points** pull-down menu and choose the **Create Points**... command. The **Create Points** toolbar displays.
4. Using the drop-down arrow to the right of the third icon from the left, choose **Measure Alignment**. Respond to the prompts as follows.
5. `Select alignment:` Select someplace on the alignment.
6. `Starting station <0+00.00>:` **<Enter>**
7. `Ending station <6+58.53>:` **<Enter>**
8. `Specify an offset <0.000>:` **-50**, which indicates that the points will be on the left side of the road.
9. `Enter an interval <10.000>:` **25**
10. `Enter a point description <.>:` **<Enter>**
11. `Specify a point elevation <.>:` **<Enter>**

Continue hitting **<Enter>** as the software prompts for point descriptions and point elevations until it is finished putting points on the left side of the road. When prompted to `Select alignment:` hit **<Enter>** again to terminate. You see the points on the left side of the road in Figure 3-34.

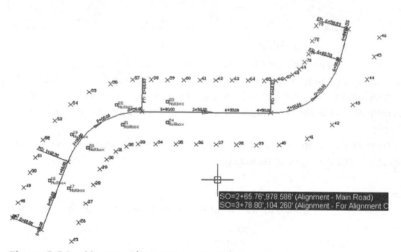

Figure 3-34   Measure Alignment command

Exercise 3-34: Alignment—AT GEOMETRY POINTS Command

 The next command, **AT GEOMETRY POINTS**, can be used to compute the location of a point(s) that has station and offset values relative to an alignment.

You want points placed at the geometrically important locations of the alignment; namely, the Points of Curvature (PCs), Points of Tangency (PTs), Spiral to Curve, Radius Points, and Points of Intersections (or PIs). If spirals are included, their corresponding points will be placed as well. These are defined and detailed in Chapter 6 on alignments. With these points identified, a surveyor has the criteria needed to lay out the centerline of the road on the construction site.

To access student data files, go to www.pearsondesigncentral.com.

1. Continue in the same drawing, or open the drawing called My Point Style-Intersections.dwg.
2. Using the **V** for **View** command, highlight the view called **Points-G**, hit **Set Current**, and then hit **OK**. You see an alignment. Place points at the geometrically important locations of the alignment.
3. Select the **Points** pull-down menu and choose the **Create Points**... command. The **Create Points** toolbar displays.
4. Using the drop-down arrow to the right of the third icon from the left, choose **At Geometry Points**. Respond to the prompts as follows.
5. `Select alignment:` Select someplace on the alignment.
6. `Starting station <0+00.00>:` **<Enter>**
7. `Ending station <6+58.53>:` **<Enter>**
8. `Enter a point description <.>:` **<Enter>**
9. `Specify a point elevation <.>:` **<Enter>**

Continue hitting **<Enter>** as the software prompts for point elevations until it is finished putting points on the alignment. When prompted to `Select alignment:` hit **<Enter>** again to terminate. You see the points located at all of the critical geometric points of the road. The point descriptions are automatic because they relate to the point being located such as the BOA (Beginning of Alignment), EOA (End of Alignment), PC, PT, PI, or RP.

Exercise 3-35: Alignment—RADIAL OR PERPENDICULAR Command

 The next command, **RADIAL OR PERPENDICULAR**, can be used to compute the location of a point(s) that has station and offset values relative to an alignment.

 You often need to compute points at radial or perpendicular locations from an alignment.

This command can be used to locate where a side street may intersect the roadway.

To access student data files, go to www.pearsondesigncentral.com.

1. Continue in the same drawing, or open the drawing called My Point Style-Intersections.dwg.
2. Using the **V** for **View** command, highlight the view called **Points-G**, hit **Set Current**, and then hit **OK**. You see an alignment. Place points at radial or perpendicular locations on the alignment.
3. Select the **Points** pull-down menu and choose the **Create Points**... command. The **Create Points** toolbar displays.
4. Using the drop-down arrow to the right of the third icon from the left, choose **Radial or Perpendicular**. Respond to the prompts as follows.
5. `Select alignment:` Select someplace on the alignment.
6. `Specify a point that is radial or perpendicular to the current alignment:` Pick a point using the **Endpoint** osnap at the end of the arc at station 5+77.23. The software will confirm this as Station: 5+77.23 with Offset: 74.096′ (Figure 3-35).
7. `Enter a point description <.>:` **<Enter>**
8. `Specify a point elevation <.>:` **<Enter>**
9. `Select alignment:` **<Enter>** to terminate.

Exercise 3-36: Alignment—IMPORT FROM FILE Command

 The next command, **IMPORT FROM FILE**, can be used to import points that were generated based on an alignment and use station, offset values relative to that alignment. The software uses the next available point numbers and prompts for the information needed as it goes.

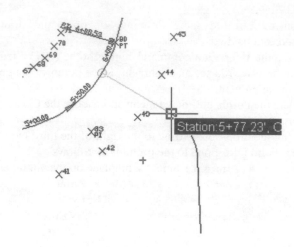

Figure 3-35   Radial or Perpendicular command

To access student data
files, go to
www.pearsondesigncentral.com.

1. Continue in the same drawing, or open the drawing called My Point Style-Intersections.dwg.
2. Using the **V** for **View** command, highlight the view called **Points-G**, hit **Set Current**, and then hit **OK**. You see an alignment. Import alignment based points.
3. Select the **Points** pull-down menu and choose the **Create Points**... command. The **Create Points** toolbar displays.
4. Using the drop-down arrow to the right of the third icon from the left, choose **Import from File**.

To access student data
files, go to
www.pearsondesigncentral.com.

5. A dialog box opens called **Import Alignment Station and Offset File**. Select the file called **Points-import file-sta-off.txt** in the Support files folder for this textbook and hit the **Open** button.
6. The software then prompts you to choose the format for this file. The options are as follows: 1. Station, Offset, 2. Station, Offset, Elevation, 3. Station, Offset, Rod Reading, HI, 4. Station, Offset, Description, 5. Station, Offset, Elevation, Description, 6. Station, Offset, Rod Reading, HI Description.
7. Enter file format (1/2/3/4/5/6):<0>: **1** (This file uses format 1, station, offset.)
8. It then needs to know what the delimiter is between data items. Our file uses commas.
9. 1. Space, 2. Comma
10. Enter a delimiter (1/2): <0>: **2**
11. Enter an invalid indicator for Station Offset <-99999>: **<Enter>**
12. Select alignment: **pick alignment.**

Notice that several points enter the file to the left and right of the alignment as shown in Figure 3-36.

This concludes the segment on placing Alignment-based points into your project. The file My Point Style-Intersections-Complete.dwg shows the results of these examples.

Surface-Related Point Commands

This next segment delves into procedures for placing Surface-related points into a project drawing.

The next command in this toolbar item is for creating new points based on an alignment's profile information. This can be used for creating 3D stakeout data of the roadway's crown, for example. The command is called **PROFILE GEOMETRY POINTS**. You are requested to select the alignment and the profile in question. The software then sets the points on the alignment with 3D elevations.

The ability to adjust point elevations based on a surface also exists. This is a very beneficial routine if points have been set to a surface using the **RANDOM POINTS** command. If the surface is modified and updated, the points that were dependent on that surface can be updated automatically. Change the elevation for a point or a group of points by selecting a location on a surface. This command can be found under the **Points** pulldown >> **Edit Points**>> **Elevations from Surface...**

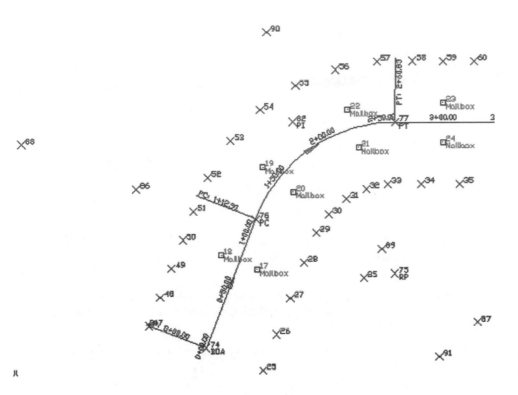

Figure 3-36   Import from File command

Exercise 3-37: Surface—RANDOM POINTS Command

 The next command, **RANDOM POINTS** (Figure 3-37), can be used to set points based on surface data.

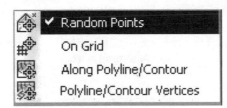

Figure 3-37   Random Points command

> **TIP**
>
> The elevation values for these points are extracted directly from the surface information. This avoids having to hand-calculate the elevations and place them in manually. Hand calculations are prone to typographical errors and miscalculation.

The software uses the next available point numbers and prompts for other information as it goes.

1. Open the drawing called Chapter 3-a.dwg.
2. Using the **V** for **View** command, highlight the view called **Points-H**, hit **Set Current**, and then hit **OK**. You see a surface. Set some points based on this surface.
3. Select the **Points** pull-down menu and choose the **Create Points**... command. The **Create Points** toolbar displays.
4. In the **Create Points** toolbar, and using the drop-down arrow to the right of the fourth icon from the left, choose **Random Points**.

To access student data files, go to www.pearsondesigncentral.com.

Figure 3-38   Closed contours

You see some closed contours in the view (Figure 3-38), and you will be placing a couple of points within the closed contours to give others an idea of the elevations in this area. Respond to the prompts as follows.

5. `Select a surface object:` Pick any contour for the surface.
6. `Please specify a location for the new point:` Select a point within one of the closed contours, as shown in Figure 3-38, for Point 1.
7. `Enter a point description <.>:` **FG**
8. `Please specify a location for the new point:` Select a point within one of the closed contours, as shown in Figure 3-38, for Point 2.
9. `Enter a point description <FG>:` **<Enter>**
10. `Please specify a location for the new point:` Select a point within one of the closed contours, as shown in Figure 3-38, for Point 3.
11. `Enter a point description <FG>:` **<Enter>**
12. `Please specify a location for the new point:` **<Enter>**
13. `Select a surface object:` **<Enter>** to terminate.

Exercise 3-38: Surface—ON GRID Command

 The next command, **ON GRID**, can be used to set points in a grid based on surface data. The elevation values are extracted directly from the surface information. This avoids having to hand-calculate the elevations and place them in manually. The software uses the next available point numbers and prompts for other information as it goes.

 You often need to place points on the corners of a grid overlaid onto a surface. It provides a representative sampling of the elevations occurring on that surface.

 If the **ON GRID** command is used on a Grid Volume type of surface, you can achieve cut and fill values of the proposed work as compared with those of the existing surface.

To access student data
files, go to
www.pearsondesigncentral.com.

1. Continue in the same drawing, or open the drawing called Chapter 3-a.dwg.
2. Using the **V** for **View** command, highlight the view called **Points-II**, hit **Set Current**, and then hit **OK**. You see a surface. Set some points based on this surface.
3. Select the **Points** pull-down menu and choose the **Create Points**... command. The **Create Points** toolbar displays.
4. Using the drop-down arrow to the right of the fourth icon from the left, choose **On Grid**. Respond to the prompts as follows.
5. Select a surface object: Pick any contour for the surface.
6. Specify a grid basepoint: **14900,18275**
7. Grid rotation <0.0000 (d)>: **<Enter>**
8. Grid X spacing <5.0000>: **50**
9. Grid Y spacing <50.0000>: **<Enter>**
10. Specify the upper right location for the grid: **15150,18475**
11. Change the size or rotation of the grid/grid squares [Yes/No] <No>: **N**
12. Enter a point description <.>: **FG**
13. Continue hitting **<Enter>** as the software prompts for point descriptions until it is finished putting points on the grid. When prompted to Select a surface: again, hit **<Enter>** to terminate. See Figure 3-39.

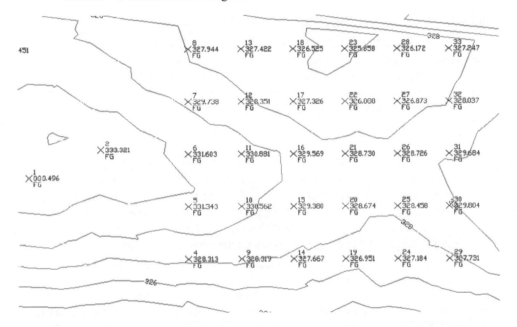

Figure 3-39   Points set on a Grid

Exercise 3-39: Surface—ALONG POLYLINE/CONTOUR Command

The next command, **ALONG POLYLINE/CONTOUR**, can be used to set points on a polyline or contour at a user-defined interval. The elevation values are extracted directly from the surface information. This can be used to set points on an alignment directly from the surface in 3D. The software uses the next available point numbers and prompts for other information as it goes.

TIP

The **ALONG POLYLINE/CONTOUR** command can be used to set the rim elevations of manholes with a distance of 300' between manholes on the proposed road surface.

1. Continue in the same drawing, or open the drawing called Chapter 3-a.dwg.
2. Using the **V** for **View** command, highlight the view called **Points-H**, hit **Set Current**, and then hit **OK**. You see a surface and a polyline along the road running east to west. Set some points based on this surface right on the polyline.
3. Select the **Points** pull-down menu and choose the **Create Points**... command. The **Create Points** toolbar displays.

To access student data
files, go to
www.pearsondesigncentral.com.

4. Using the drop-down arrow to the right of the fourth icon from the left, choose **Along Polyline/Contour**. Respond to the prompts as follows.
5. `Select a surface object:` Pick any contour for the surface.
6. `Distance between points <10.0000>:` **50**
7. `Select a polyline or contour:` Select the Polyline with the heavy lineweight.
8. `Enter a point description <.>:` **FG**
9. Continue hitting **<Enter>** as the software continues to place a point every 50′ along the alignment. Hit **<Enter>** to terminate.

Notice in Figure 3-40 that the polyline now has points every 50′ along it.

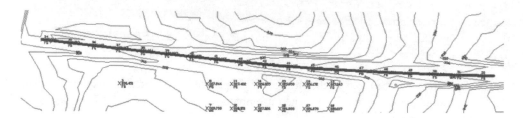

Figure 3-40   Along Polyline/Contour command

Exercise 3-40: Surface—POLYLINE/CONTOUR VERTICES Command

 The next command, **POLYLINE/CONTOUR VERTICES**, can be used to set points on a polyline or contour at the vertices of the polyline, and elevation values are extracted directly from the surface information. This can be used to set points on a building pad when the surface already has the pad elevations built into it. The software uses the next available point numbers and prompts for other information as it goes.

 TIP   This routine can be used for many tasks such as establishing a daylight buffer for grading a site out. A polyline can be drawn at an offset from the property boundary, and points can be established on this polyline from the existing ground surface. When those points are included in the Proposed ground surface, they ensure a tie-out to the existing ground. This example sets points on the centerline based on the existing ground surface.

To access student data files, go to www.pearsondesigncentral.com.

1. Continue in the same drawing, or open the drawing called Chapter 3-a.dwg.
2. Using the **V** for **View** command, highlight the view called **Points-H**, hit **Set Current**, and then hit **OK**. You see a surface and a polyline along the road running east to west.
3. Select the **Points** pull-down menu and choose the **Create Points**... command. The **Create Points** toolbar displays.
4. Using the drop-down arrow to the right of the fourth icon from the left, choose **Polyline/Contour Vertices**. Respond to the prompts as follows.
5. `Select a surface object:` Pick any contour for the surface.
6. `Select a polyline or contour:` Select the rectangular polyline.
7. `Enter a point description <.>:` **FG**, continue hitting **<Enter>** until points are placed at all the corners, hit **<Enter>** to terminate.

Notice that points now exist on the building corners.
This concludes our segment on placing Surface-based points into your project.

Exercise 3-41: IMPORT POINTS Command

 Our next command is **IMPORT POINTS** and can be used to import point data from an external file. A good option within this routine is the ability to create a point group as it executes.

To access student data files, go to www.pearsondesigncentral.com.

1. Continue in the same drawing, or open the drawing called Chapter 3-a.dwg.
2. Using the **V** for View command, highlight the view called **Points-L**, hit **Set Current** and then hit **OK**. You will see existing ground contours. We will import point data from a file provided with your data set for this text.

To access student data files, go to www.pearsondesigncentral.com.

3. Select the **Points** pull-down menu and choose the **Create Points...** command. The **Create Points** toolbar displays.
4. Use the seventh icon from the left to choose **Import Points**. A dialog will display. Use the **PNEZD (comma delimited)** format option. A display of other formats is shown in Figure 3-41. PNEZD stands for Point, Northing, Easting, Elevation, Description.

```
Autodesk Uploadable File
ENZ (comma delimited)
ENZ (space delimited)
External Project Point Database
NEZ (comma delimited)
NEZ (space delimited)
PENZ (comma delimited)
PENZ (space delimited)
PENZD (comma delimited)
PENZD (space delimited)
PNE (comma delimited)
PNE (space delimited)
PNEZ (comma delimited)
PNEZ (space delimited)
PNEZD (comma delimited)
PNEZD (space delimited)
```

Figure 3-41   Formats

5. Select the source file in the student data files called **Points-Import file-PNEZD.txt**.
6. Toggle **On** the **Add Points** to **Point Group** option as shown in Figure 3-42.
7. Hit the button to the right of the pop-down window and provide a name for the new Point Group called **Import-EG Points**.

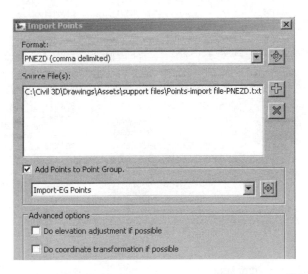

Figure 3-42   Import Points, Add Points to Point Group

8. Turn **Off** the toggles for the **Advanced Options** and hit **OK**.
9. The points in this file are imported into the project shown in Figure 3-43 and are in the preset view called **Points-L**.
10. Save this drawing as we will use it again later.

You will also notice that the **Prospector** tab in the **Toolspace** (Figure 3-44) shows the new Point Group called **Import-EG Points**. When selected, it displays all of the points within the group.

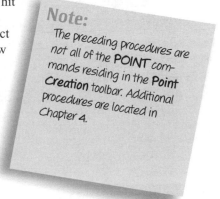

Note:
The preceding procedures are not all of the **POINT** commands residing in the **Point Creation** toolbar. Additional procedures are located in Chapter 4.

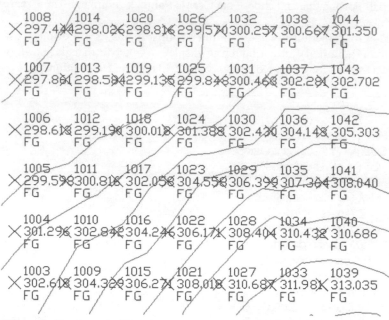

Figure 3-43   Imported Points

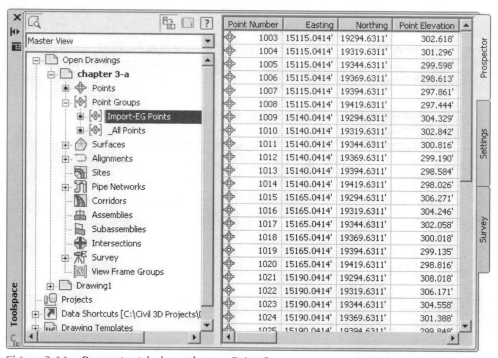

Figure 3-44   Prospector tab shows the new Point Group

TIP

There is one additional icon on the far right of the toolbar. This allows for the toolbar to be expanded or contracted. If it is expanded, some fields show up that allow for the creation of Point Styles, Point Label Styles, and Point Layers in the event you would like to create or switch these on the fly. Also, notice that a pushpin is included in the banner of the toolbar. This pins the toolbar, placing it in a fixed location, and also shrinks the toolbar down to a small placeholder when the cursor moves outside the toolbar. To display the expanded toolbar, move the cursor over the placeholder.

Continue with the Points Pull-Down Menu

Next is a discussion of some other capabilities within the **Points** pull-down menu in Civil 3D (Figure 3-45).

The **CREATE POINT GROUP...** command allows the creation of point groups such as the one created in Exercise 3-41 on **Import Points**.

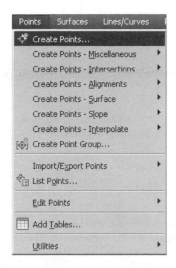

Figure 3-45 The Points pull-down menu

The **EDIT POINTS** commands modify points. The choices follow.

- **Points...** allowing for the tabular editing of point data where the **Panorama** displays with cells of all pertinent point data as shown in Figure 3-46. By clicking in a cell, you can edit the information on the fly. By checking the green check mark on the upper right of the box, you can effect the change immediately.

Point Number	Easting	Northing	Point Elevation	Name	Raw Description	Full Description	Description ▲
3	14561.9281'	18563.3096'	325.528'		FG	FG	
4	14611.6411'	18557.9596'	324.513'		FG	FG	
5	14661.3540'	18552.6095'	325.148'		FG	FG	
6	14711.0670'	18547.2595'	325.913'		FG	FG	
7	14760.7799'	18541.9094'	326.654'		FG	FG	
8	14810.4929'	18536.5594'	327.387'		FG	FG	
9	14860.2058'	18531.2094'	328.070'		FG	FG	
10	14909.9188'	18525.8598'	328.965'		FG	FG	
11	14959.6603'	18520.7844'	329.820'		FG	FG	
12	15009.4510'	18516.2160'	330.445'		FG	FG	

Figure 3-46 Point Editor Panorama box

- **Point Groups...** (Figure 3-47) allows you to change the display order for point groups in a drawing and allows for updating out-of-date point groups. This dialog box can also be used to select a point group when you need it for an application such as adding a point group to a surface data set. The **Show Point Group Differences** button in the top left of the dialog box allows for reviewing and updating out-of-date point groups. The **Update Point Group** button, the second button in the top left of the dialog box, allows updating all out-of-date point groups. A point group is out of date when an exclamation mark within a yellow shield is displayed next to a point group name.

- **Datum...** updates points that were set, perhaps to an assumed elevation, to a corrected benchmark elevation. Points with no elevation values are not adjusted. Points that need to be changed individually can be altered via the **Edit Points** or **List Points** commands. This command does not really warrant further procedure because it asks only one question, `Change in elevation or [ Reference] :` to which you type in the amount of elevation change you want to accomplish.

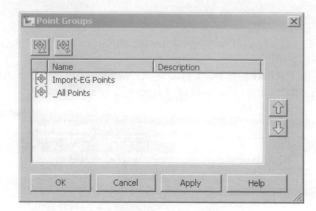

Figure 3-47   Point Groups

General: In the Points drawings, the drawings are set up for the points creation to be set to Prompt for Point Names; unless this is changed the points routines won't work. Any new drawings work fine.

- **Elevations from Surface...** assigns surface elevations to a feature line, survey figure, parcel line, or 3D polyline.

- **Renumber...** allows points to be renumbered by using an additive factor. In other words, say that you have points already set from Point 1 through Point 115. Now a field crew is bringing in a new set of points that happen to overlap your point numbers. You cannot have multiple points with the same point number, so something has to give and someone must renumber his or her points. In Civil 3D, use the **Renumber** command to add a factor of, say, 1000 to the points already set and you then have points ranging from 1001 to 1115, thereby clearing the way for new points in the 1 to 115 range. This command does not really warrant further procedure because it asks only one question, `Enter an additive factor for point numbers:` to which you type in the amount of change you want to add to the existing numbering.

Exercise 3-42: Creating Automated Tables—ADD TABLES Command

The next command in the **Points** pull-down menu is the **ADD TABLES...** command. Refer to Figure 3-48. This builds point tables based on the points or point groups in the drawing.

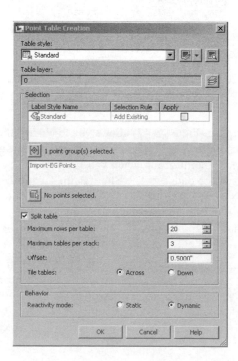

Figure 3-48   Creating Automated Tables

1. Continue in the same drawing, or open the drawing called Chapter 3-a.dwg. Type **Z** **<Enter>** for Zoom and **E** **<Enter>** for Extents..

2. Under the **Points** pull-down menu, choose the **Add Tables...** command. A **Point Table Creation** dialog box displays.

3. If you want a customized table for the points, select a predeveloped one under the **Table style** pop-down or use the arrow in the drop-down arrow next to the icon just to the right of the **Table style** window. Select **Create New** or **Edit Current Selection** to customize a table. In this example, click the **Edit Current Selection** and the **Table Style—Standard** dialog box opens, shown in Figure 3-49. Under the **Information** tab, you can change the name, which would make sense if you selected **New**. Otherwise, choose the **Data Properties** tab, where you can elect to wrap text or to have the table maintain view orientation (in the event that your view is twisted to accommodate a plotting orientation). Also you can affect how your titling and column headers display when the table splits, if it is set up to split. **Title style**, **Header style**, and **Data style** are selected here as well. In the **Structure** window, the table can be customized to show any related columns that you wish.

To access student data files, go to www.pearsondesigncentral.com.

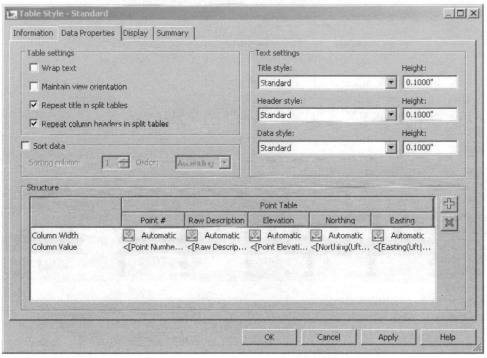

Figure 3-49   Table Style dialog box

4. You can customize this table to show latitude and longitudinal values along with the co-ordinates, point numbers, and elevations for the points in your drawing. The buttons to the right of the window allow you to **add** columns or **delete** them. Hit the **Plus** button to add a column. A new column becomes available next to the **Easting** column, albeit with no header yet.

5. Double-click on the blank header and a **Text Component Editor—Column Contents** dialog box appears. In the blank window, type **Latitude** and hit **OK**.

6. Now double-click in the cell in the **Latitude** column and in the **Column Value** row. A **Text Component Editor—Column Contents** dialog box opens. Make sure you are in the **Properties** tab. In the **Properties** pop-down, select **Latitude** from the alternatives.

7. Then click the **arrow** button just to the right of the window, to send the option into the blank window on the right.

8. Notice that you can choose the **Format** tab and change text properties if you wish. Hit **OK**. You are in the **Table Style—Standard** dialog box again.

9. Repeat this sequence to add in the longitudinal information.
10. Hit the **Plus** button to add a column. A new column becomes available next to the **Latitude** column, again with no header yet.
11. Double-click on the blank header and a **Text Component Editor—Column Contents** dialog box appears. As shown in Figure 3-50, in the black window, type **Longitude** and hit **OK**.

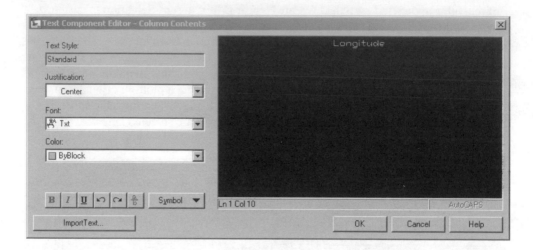

Figure 3-50   Text Component Editor

12. Now double-click in the cell in the **Longitude** column and in the **Column Value** row. A **Text Component Editor—Column Contents** dialog box opens, shown in Figure 3-51. Make sure you are in the **Properties** tab. In the **Properties** pop-down, select **Longitude** from the alternatives.

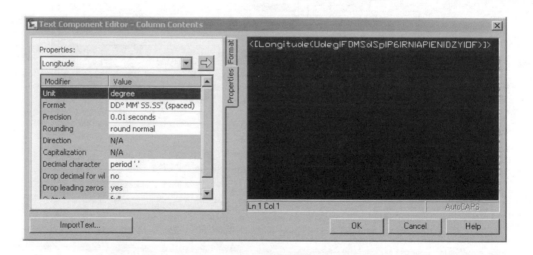

Figure 3-51   Text Component Editor—Column Contents

13. Then click the **arrow** button just to the right of the window, to send the option into the black window on the right.
14. Notice that you can choose the **Format** tab and change text properties if you wish. Hit **OK**. You are in the **Table Style—Standard** dialog box again.
15. Click on the **Display** tab (Figure 3-52). Here you can set colors, component layers, and such for appearance's sake. Hit **OK**.
16. You arc in the **Point Table Creation** dialog box.
17. In the center of the dialog box, hit the button where it says **No Point Groups** selected.
18. Choose the Point Group created in the **Import Points** exercise called **Import EG-Points**, and hit **OK**. The dialog box should now appear as in Figure 3-48.
19. Leave the **Split table** option checked **On** and retain the default values.
20. Hit **OK**. When prompted for `Select upper left corner:` pick a point well outside the site and off to the right.

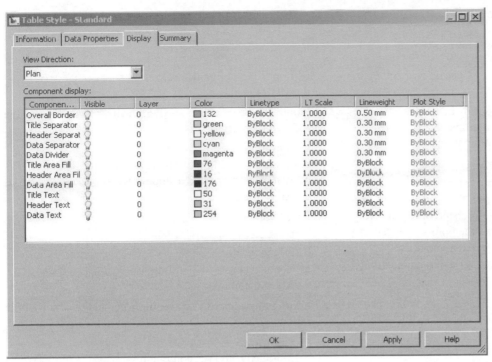

Figure 3-52   Table Style Display

21. The table appears with the data it had initially as well as with the latitude and longitude because the file has a geodetic datum established for northern Virginia, NAD 83, U.S. foot.

The next command in the **Points** pull-down menu are the **UTILITIES** commands, which include the following:

- **Quick View Project** displays a tick mark where points exist in the external project point information, assuming one exists.

- **Draw Project Extents** draws a rectangle around the extents of the project's points from external project point information, assuming one exists.

- **Zoom to Project Extents** places your view as if it did a **ZOOM EXTENTS** of the project's points from external project point information, assuming one exists.

- **Replace Softdesk Point Blocks** converts Softdesk point blocks to AutoCAD Civil 3D points.

- **Convert Land Desktop Points...** converts AutoCAD Land Desktop points to AutoCAD Civil 3D points.

- **Convert from AutoCAD Points** converts AutoCAD point objects to AutoCAD Civil 3D points.

- **Create Blocks from COGO Points...** creates blocks at the location of specified COGO point locations.

- **Geodetic Calculator** allows for computing a coordinate from a lat/long, or a lat/long from a coordinate, once a geodetic zone is set in the file.

CHAPTER SUMMARY

Understanding and using points is essential to civil engineering. Points are locations in space defined by X, Y, and Z values; they are used to identify objects such as property corners. This chapter discussed computation methods and concepts necessary for performing computations; coordinate systems; Point Groups; and Description Key Sets. It then moved into point computations using commands found on the **Create Points** toolbar.

CHAPTER TEST QUESTIONS

Multiple Choice

1. Some uses for points in civil engineering and surveying are:

   a. Property corners for parcels of ownership
   b. Roadway earthworks computations
   c. Developing renderings and animations
   d. None of the above

2. Point groups have the following characteristics:

   a. They have enduring properties that can be easily reviewed or modified, either beforehand or retroactively.
   b. Displaying a points list shows the points included in a point group and it can be updated automatically.
   c. A point group can be locked to avoid unintentional modifications.
   d. All of the above

3. Which of the following codes can be used in the Description Key Set?

   a. AC
   b. YARDINLET
   c. 1033
   d. All of the above

4. The **Point Creation** toolbar allows for the following operation:

   a. Automatically checking that all points on a project are correct
   b. Setting points by snapping to objects
   c. Setting all points to the correct elevational value required by the project
   d. None of the above

5. Points can be created for which of the following circumstances?

   a. Locating points related to alignments
   b. Locating points related to surfaces
   c. Importing points from external files
   d. All of the above

6. Points can be established when the user has which of the following criteria?

   a. Elevations
   b. A starting point, a distance, and a grade
   c. A starting point and a slope
   d. All of the above

7. Points can be:

   a. Defined or set
   b. Edited or modified
   c. Reported on
   d. All of the above

8. Editing of points can be accomplished using which of the following?

   a. **Panorama**
   b. AutoCAD **MOVE** command
   c. **Prospector**
   d. All of the above

9. A point can be located if the user has which of the following criteria?

   a. An Easting, an X coordinate, and a Z coordinate
   b. Two Northings and a Time value
   c. A line depicted by a beginning and an ending location
   d. None of the above

10. Some typical needs for a designer to set points would be for:

    a. Stakeout purposes
    b. Identifying the locations of existing condition planimetrics
    c. Spot shots
    d. All of the above

True or False

1. True or False: COGO is an acronym for Consolidated, Orthogonal Geometry Organization.

2. True or False: Points are defined using the Cartesian coordinate system and consist of X, Y, and Z values.

3. True or False: The Y-axis is located 180° from the X-axis.

4. True or False: A line (or vector) is defined as the connection between the beginning point and its corresponding ending point.

5. True or False: A line exists if it begins at a Point P1, has a known slope distance, and has a distance component.

6. True or False: The Civil 3D user must first perform several setup options in order to use the **Points** commands.

7. True or False: Contractors will never use the points that engineers set.

8. True or False: Civil 3D has a myriad of ways to depict points and what they represent, and Point Styles is the vehicle used to accomplish this.

9. True or False: Point Styles is limited to Civil 3D symbols, and user-defined blocks may not be used.

10. True or False: Point Groups are named collections of points and are used to associate points that have relationships, such DTM points, Property Corner points, and so on.

11. True or False: Points in Point Groups cannot be overlapped with other Point Groups.

12. True or False: Description Key Sets are used to authorize the use of the Civil 3D software.

13. True or False: Point File Formats can be customized to include formats not delivered with the Civil 3D software.

14. True or False: External Data References (XDRefs) are AutoCAD files that can be cross-referenced into the AutoCAD drawing.

15. True or False: The **Points** pull-down menu is a very sophisticated menu with over 50 **Point Creation** commands.

CHAPTER EXERCISES

1. What is the difference between coordinate values of X, Y and N, E?

2. What is the value of Y for a line represented by a formula of $Y = (.25)(10) + 5$?

3. Find the length of the vector between Points $P1 = 10,10,0$ and $P2 = 15, 12,0$.

4. Plot that same point in AutoCAD. What angle exists between this vector and the X-axis?

5. What is the slope of this vector?

6. If a line starts at $P3 = 5,5,0$ and has a slope of .333 and a length of 10′, what is the ending coordinate?

7. Create a **Point Group**.

8. Using the **Points >> Create Points** toolbar, select **Miscellaneous Convert AutoCAD Points** to convert AutoCAD points to Civil 3D points.

    Type **Point** at the command prompt to create an AutoCAD point (which is not a Civil 3D point). The software responds with Specify a point: Type a coordinate of **1850,1975,230.54**. Notice a dot shows up inside the parcel polyline you were working with in the last couple of exercises. It actually resides at an elevation of 230.54. Use **Miscellaneous Convert AutoCAD Points** to create a Civil 3D point at this precise location in 3D.

9. The next example is to set points using the **Create Points— Measure Object** command.

    To begin this exercise, **Draw** a line from **850,1025** to **930,1050**.

    Then from the **Create Points** toolbar, choose the pop-down arrow on the first button and select **Measure Object**.

    Use a Starting station of **0.0000** and an Ending station of **83.815**, set points using a 20′ offset right, from the line, with an interval of **10.00**, a point description of IPF, and just hit **<Enter>** for the point elevation. Set 7 points each at a 20′ offset to the right of the line every 10′.

10. This question has you set points on polylines using the **Polyline Vertices—Manual** command.

    Using the **Zoom Center** command, choose a zoom center point of **2000,2000** with a magnification or height of **500**.

    Draw a polyline starting at an X, Y coordinate of **1750,1900** to **1850,2100** to **2100,2000** to **2100,1875**, and close it by typing **C**.

    From the **Create Points** toolbar and using the pop-down arrow next to the first icon, choose **Polyline vertices— Manual** and set a point on each vertex using a default elevation of **100.0** for the proposed building pad, and use the IPF description for each point as it is set.

A Tip of the Hat to Surveyors– More Points!

4

Chapter Objectives

The objectives of this chapter are similar to those of Chapter 3 in that many point setting routines are described. These additional examples are probably more geared toward surveyors because of their heavy reliance on point information during their daily workflow. However, designers could also use some of these functions to save time in performing a variety of computations.

INTRODUCTION

This material was in the appendix in previous versions of the text. Due to the increasing interest of surveyors in the product, however, we moved it to this chapter to make it follow Chapter 3. This information is included to provide surveyors, instructors, and the reader with additional routines and procedures for using the extensive set of Point-related commands in the **Create Points** toolbar. The commands in this chapter are no less powerful nor less useful than those in Chapter 3 and should be given equal respect in learning and use in production.

REVIEW OF FUNCTIONS AND FEATURES TO BE USED

The features in this chapter are the same as those for Chapter 3, but with more examples to help surveyors make greater use of Civil 3D during their daily workflow.

When using the files for this chapter, please note that the files are still referenced to Chapter 3 because they are all point-related examples.

CREATING "THINKING POINTS"

The next segment delves into procedures for placing Interpolation-related points into a project drawing. Refer to Figure 4-1. These commands allow the ability to generate "thinking points."

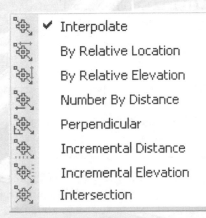

- ✔ Interpolate
- By Relative Location
- By Relative Elevation
- Number By Distance
- Perpendicular
- Incremental Distance
- Incremental Elevation
- Intersection

Figure 4-1   "Thinking points"

Thinking points are points that may or may not be used in design, but they will assuredly be used to develop other data.

Consider that you know the elevation of a flow line of a curb and are wondering what the elevation would be if you went in a specified direction for a specified distance at a specific grade or slope. And then, depending on where it landed, you would make a decision on what would happen next. Decide whether the point is too high or too low or erase it and provide different criteria. These are thinking points because they allow you to see the results of design criteria rapidly and then either proceed forward or step back and try again with little or no cost.

Exercise 4-1: Interpolation—INTERPOLATE Command

 The next command, **INTERPOLATE**, can be used to set intermediate points in 3D. The software uses the next available point numbers and prompts for other information as it goes.

The **INTERPOLATE** command might be used to densify a data set for DTM triangulation.

To access student data
files, go to
www.pearsondesigncentral.com.

1. Continue in the same drawing, or open the drawing called Chapter 3-a.dwg.
2. Using the **V** for **View** command, highlight the view called **Points-I**, hit **Set Current**, and then hit **OK**. You see two points already set, Points 1001 and 1002. You will densify these by adding three points in between them at prorated elevations based on the two points' elevations.
3. Select the **Points** pull-down menu and choose the **Create Points** command. The **Create Points** toolbar displays.
4. Using the drop-down arrow to the right of the fifth icon from the left, choose **Interpolate**.
5. `Pick a first point object:` Select Point 1001 with your mouse; no Osnap is needed.
6. `Pick a second point object:` Select Point 1002 with your mouse; no Osnap is needed.
7. `Enter number of points <0>:` **3**
8. `Specify an offset <0.000>:` **0**, this will create the new points on line with the 1001 and 1002.
9. `Enter a point description <.>:` **Spot**
10. `Enter a point description <Spot>:` **<Enter>**
11. `Enter a point description <Spot>:` **<Enter>**
12. Hit **<Esc>** to terminate.

Notice that three new points were created in between Points 1001 and 1002.

Exercise 4-2: Interpolation—BY RELATIVE LOCATION Command

 The next command, **BY RELATIVE LOCATION**, can be used to set points in 3D by using Grade, Slope, Elevational, or Difference based criteria.

The **BY RELATIVE LOCATION** command can be used to create proposed ground points based on the engineer's desired slope, grade, or elevation. These thinking points can be used to test what elevations, slopes, and grades might result based on the data you are providing in your design.

To access student data
files, go to
www.pearsondesigncentral.com.

1. Continue in the same drawing, or open the drawing called Chapter 3-a.dwg.
2. Using the **V** for **View** command, highlight the view called **Points-I**, hit **Set Current**, then hit **OK**. You see two points already set, Points 1001 and 1002. You will set a point from one of the contour endpoints toward Point 1001 at a grade of 2%.

3. Using the drop-down arrow to the right of the fifth icon from the left, choose **By Relative Location**.

4. `Specify first point or [Entity]` : Pick a point at an endpoint of a contour with the **Endpoint** Osnap.

5. `Specify an elevation for the first control point <356.000'>`: **<Enter>**

6. `Specify second point`: Pick a point on Point 1001 using the **Node** Osnap.

7. `Specify an elevation for the second control point or [Difference/ Slope/Grade] <356.911'>`: **g**

TIP

Note that a comment is warranted here to explain the other options available. **Difference** allows you to enter a change in height from the first elevation and can be either plus or minus. So if the first elevation is 360.00, a difference can be applied of, say, 5' so that the second elevation becomes 365.00. **Slope** is similar to **Grade** except that it refers to a ratio instead of a percentage. Slopes are in values such as 2:1, 3:1, and so forth, where the 2:1 means 2' horizontally for every 1' vertically. Of course, you are using the **Grade** option in the example where 2% is 2' vertically for every 100' horizontally.

8. `Grade (percent) or [Slope] <0.00>`: **2**
9. `First Elev: 356.000', Second Elev: 358.617', Elevation Difference: 2.617 Horiz Dist: 130.850, Grade: (percent): 2.00, Slope: (run:rise): 50.00:1`
10. `Distance:` **100**
11. `Specify an offset <0.000>`: **<Enter>**
12. `Enter a point description <.>`: **Spot**
13. Hit **<Esc>** to terminate.

Notice that a new point showed up 100' from the contour endpoint you selected. The elevation is established at a 2% grade from the contour elevation in a direction toward the Point 1001.

Exercise 4-3: Interpolation—BY RELATIVE ELEVATION Command

The next command, **BY RELATIVE ELEVATION**, can be used to set points in 3D by using Grade, Slope, Difference, or Elevational criteria. This is different from the previous command in that it establishes the grade to be met but then requests the final elevation to be set. It then sets a point at the desired elevation using the grade computed at whatever horizontal distance it takes to meet the elevation prescribed.

TIP

Again, these can establish thinking points that allow you to consider the results of moving ahead with your actions. They can be used to find out where a point falls running at, say, –2% until it hits a critical hydraulic grade elevation of, say, 101.33. If the point falls into the next county, then it likely is not feasible. If it falls near the ditch flowline, then maybe it makes sense.

1. Continue in the same drawing, or open the drawing called Chapter 3-a.dwg.
2. Using the **V** for **View** command, highlight the view called **Points-I**, hit **Set Current**, and then hit **OK**. You see two points already set, Points 1001 and 1002. You will set a point starting at 1002, heading toward 1001, and hold the grade between them such that it keeps traveling until it meets the elevation specified.
3. Using the drop-down arrow to the right of the fifth icon from the left, choose **By Relative Elevation**.
4. `Specify first point or [Entity]` : Pick a point on Point 1002 with the **Node** Osnap.

To access student data files, go to www.pearsondesigncentral.com.

5. `Specify an elevation for the first control point <360.000'>:` **<Enter>**
6. `Specify second point:` Pick a point on Point 1001 using the **Node** Osnap.
7. `Specify an elevation for the second control point or [Difference/Slope/Grade] <356.911'>:` **<Enter>**
8. `First Elev: 360.000', Second Elev: 356.911', Elevation Difference: −3.089, Horiz Dist: 187.628, Grade: (percent): −1.65, Slope: (run: rise): −60.74:1, Elevation <0.000'>:` Type in **356** to see where a point of elevation 356 would land if it held the slope between Point 1002 and Point 1001.
9. `Specify an offset <0.000>:` **<Enter>**
10. `Enter a point description <.>:` **<Enter>**
11. It then allows you to continue setting new points at new specified elevations, so hit **<Esc>** to terminate. Notice that a point was set to the right of Point 1001 at exactly the elevation of 356.00.

Exercise 4-4: Interpolation—NUMBER BY DISTANCE Command

 The next command, **NUMBER BY DISTANCE**, can be used to set interpolated points in 3D by using the Grade between two other 3D objects.

 The **NUMBER BY DISTANCE** command can be used to densify your data set. This can be important when you have too little data where the TIN activity can cause ambiguous results.

To access student data files, go to www.pearsondesigncentral.com.

1. Continue in the same drawing, or open the drawing called Chapter 3-a.dwg.
2. Using the **V** for **View** command, highlight the view called **Points-I**, hit **Set Current**, and then hit **OK**. You see two points already set, Points 1001 and 1002.
3. Using the drop-down arrow to the right of the fifth icon from the left, choose **Number By Distance**.
4. `Specify first point or [Entity] :` Pick a point on a contour vertex using the **Endpoint** Osnap.
5. `Specify an elevation for the first control point <356.000'>:` **<Enter>**
6. `Specify second point:` Pick a point on Point 1002 with the **Node** Osnap.
7. `Specify an elevation for the second control point or [Difference/Slope/Grade] <360.000'>:` **<Enter>**
8. `First Elev: 356.0009, Second Elev: 360.000', Elevation Difference: 4.000, Horiz Dist: 97.374, Grade: (percent): 4.11 Slope: (run:rise): 24.34:1`
9. `Enter number of points <0>:` **3** so you set three intermediate points between these two objects.
10. `Specify an offset <0.000>:` **<Enter>**
11. `Enter a point description <.>:` **<Enter>**
12. `Enter a point description <.>:` **<Enter>**
13. `Enter a point description <.>:` **<Enter>**
14. `Enter number of points <0>:` **<Esc>** to terminate.

Exercise 4-5: Interpolation—PERPENDICULAR Command

 The next command, **PERPENDICULAR**, can be used to set points in 3D at a perpendicular location from a point to a vector.

 On a project, you often need to identify the elevation of a centerline for a driveway as it hits the flowline of a curb. The **PERPENDICULAR** command can be used to accomplish that or similar 3D perpendicular tasks.

To access student data files, go to www.pearsondesigncentral.com.

1. Continue in the same drawing, or open the drawing called Chapter 3-a.dwg.
2. Using the **V** for **View** command, highlight the view called **Points-1**, hit **Set Current**, and then hit **OK**. You see two points already set, Points 1001 and 1002.
3. Using the drop-down arrow to the right of the fifth icon from the left, choose **Perpendicular**.
4. `Specify first point or [Entity]`: Pick a point on Point 1002 with the **Node** Osnap.
5. `Specify an elevation for the first control point <360.000'>`: **<Enter>**
6. `Specify second point`: Pick a point on Point 1001 with the **Node** Osnap.
7. `Specify an elevation for the second control point or [Difference/Slope/Grade] <356.911'>`: **<Enter>**
8. `First Elev: 360.000', Second Elev: 356.911', Elevation Difference: -3.089, Horiz Dist: 187.628, Grade: (percent): -1.65, Slope: (run: rise): -60.74:1`
9. `Please specify a location that is perpendicular to the interpolated line`: Pick a point on the circle in the view with the **Center** Osnap.
10. `Specify an offset <0.000>`: **<Enter>**
11. `Enter a point description <.>`: **<Enter>**
12. Hit **<Esc>** to terminate.

Exercise 4-6: Interpolation—INCREMENTAL DISTANCE Command

The next command, **INCREMENTAL DISTANCE**, can be used to set points in 3D by using Grade, Slope, Elevational, or Difference based criteria. The variation of this command is that it sets points at specified intervals, say, every 25'.

 This routine might be used to create a centerline of driveway elevations at the flowline of a curb section every 75' based on the grade of the curb section.

To access student data files, go to www.pearsondesigncentral.com.

1. Continue in the same drawing, or open the drawing called Chapter 3-a.dwg.
2. Using the **V** for **View** command, highlight the view called **Points-I**, hit **Set Current**, and then hit **OK**. You see two points already set, Points 1001 and 1002.
3. Using the drop-down arrow to the right of the fifth icon from the left, choose **Incremental Distance**.
4. `Specify first point or [Entity]`: Pick a point on a contour vertex using the **Endpoint** Osnap.
5. `Specify an elevation for the first control point <356.000'>`: **<Enter>**
6. `Specify second point`: Pick a point on Point 1001 with the **Node** Osnap.
7. `Specify an elevation for the second control point or [Difference/Slope/Grade] <356.911'>`: **<Enter>**
8. `First Elev: 356.000', Second Elev: 356.911', Elevation Difference: 0.911, Horiz Dist: 44.815, Grade: (percent): 2.03, Slope: (run:rise): 49.19:1`
9. `Distance between points <10.0000>`: **<Enter>**
10. `Specify an offset <0.000>`: **<Enter>**
11. `Enter a point description <.>`: **<Enter>**
12. `Enter a point description <.>`: **<Enter>**
13. `Enter a point description <.>`: **<Enter>**
14. `Enter a point description <.>`: **<Enter>**
15. `Distance between points <10.0000>`: Hit **<Esc>** to terminate.

Exercise 4-7: Interpolation—INCREMENTAL ELEVATION Command

The next command, **INCREMENTAL ELEVATION**, can be used to set points in 3D by using Grade, Slope, Elevational, or Difference based criteria. The variation of this command is that it will set points at specified Elevational intervals, say, every 1'.

To access student data
files, go to
www.pearsondesigncentral.com.

TIP This routine might be used to create points that have only even elevations, such as 360.0, 361.0, 362.0, 363.0. This could be helpful in a planning exercise in which the planner is trying to obtain a rough feel for the design possibilities.

1. Continue in the same drawing, or open the drawing called Chapter 3-a.dwg.
2. Using the **V** for **View** command, highlight the view called **Points-J**, hit **Set Current**, then hit **OK**. You see two contours that you will work with that have white circles identifying them.
3. Using the drop-down arrow to the right of the fifth icon from the left, choose **Incremental Elevation**.
4. `Specify first point or [Entity] :` Pick a point on a contour vertex inside the circle on the green contour using the **Endpoint** Osnap.
5. `Specify an elevation for the first control point <360.000'>:` **<Enter>**
6. `Specify second point:` Pick a point on a contour vertex inside the circle on the brown contour using the **Endpoint** Osnap.
7. `Specify an elevation for the second control point or [Difference/Slope/Grade] <366.000'>:` **<Enter>**
8. `First Elev: 360.000', Second Elev: 366.000', Elevation Difference: 6.000, Horiz Dist: 250.535, Grade: (percent): 2.39, Slope: (run:rise): 41.76:1`
9. `Elevation Difference <0.000'>:` **1**
10. `Specify an offset <0.000>:` **<Enter>**
11. `Enter a point description <.>:` **<Enter>**
12. `Enter a point description <.>:` **<Enter>**
13. `Enter a point description <.>:` **<Enter>**
14. `Enter a point description <.>:` **<Enter>**
15. `Enter a point description <.>:` **<Enter>**
16. `Elevation Difference <1.000'>:` Hit **<Esc>** to terminate.

Exercise 4-8: Interpolation—INTERSECTION Command

 The next command, **INTERSECTION**, can be used to set points in 3D by using the slope of a vector defined via two points or a 3D object with another object that crosses the first object's path.

TIP The **INTERSECTION** command could be helpful in determining the elevation at the edge of pavement where an underground utility crosses the edge of pavement, or where a roadway crown might intersect another roadway centerline. This occurs in 3D.

To access student data
files, go to
www.pearsondesigncentral.com.

1. Continue in the same drawing, or open the drawing called Chapter 3-a.dwg.
2. Using the **V** for **View** command, highlight the view called **Points-J**, hit **Set Current**, then hit **OK**. You see two contours that you will work with that have white circles identifying them. You also see a white line that crosses the path if the two circles were connected.
3. Using the drop-down arrow to the right of the fifth icon from the left, choose **Intersection**.
4. `Specify first point or [Entity] :` Pick a point on a contour vertex inside the circle on the green contour using the **Endpoint** Osnap.
5. `Specify an elevation for the first control point <360.000'>:` **<Enter>**
6. `Specify second point:` Pick a point on a contour vertex inside the circle on the brown contour using the **Endpoint** Osnap.

7. `Specify an elevation for the second control point or [Difference/ Slope/Grade] <366.000'>:` **\<Enter\>**
8. `First Elev: 360.000', Second Elev: 366.000', Elevation Difference: 6.000, Horiz Dist: 250.535, Grade: (percent): 2.39, Slope: (run:rise): 41.76:1`
9. `Specify an offset <0.000>:` **\<Enter\>**
10. `Specify first point or [Entity]:` **e**
11. `Select an arc, line, lot line, feature line, or polyline or [Points]:` Select the line crossing the path between the two circles.
12. `Specify offset from entity <0.000>:` **\<Enter\>**
13. `Enter a point description:` **\<Enter\>**
14. Hit **\<Esc\>** to terminate.

This concludes this segment on placing Interpolation-based points into your project.

Performing Slope-Based Computations

This next segment delves into procedures for placing Slope-based points in the file. See Figure 4-2. These additional 3D commands can be used as thinking points or directly within the design as 3D data points. These commands are interesting because they solve real-life problems that engineers encounter. For instance, the **SLOPE—HIGH/LOW POINT** command can take a known slope in one direction, intersect it with a known slope in another direction, and set the intersection point in 3D.

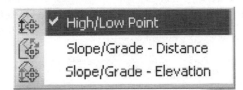

Figure 4-2   Placing Slope-based points

Exercise 4-9: SLOPE—HIGH/LOW POINT Command

 The next command, **HIGH/LOW POINT**, can be used to set points in 3D by using the slope of one vector and intersecting it with the slope of another vector. This could be helpful in the following situation.

> **TIP** This can be solved for many design conditions, but one example in particular might be in a subdivision, while grading between two houses. There is a drainage envelope around each house, assuring that drainage occurs away from the house. If one house is higher than the other and has a differing drainage slope, you may want to locate a center of swale point where the two envelopes intersect so you can guide the drainage toward either the front or the back of the houses.

1. Continue in the same drawing, or open the drawing called Chapter 3-a.dwg.
2. Using the **V** for **View** command, highlight the view called **Points-K**, hit **Set Current**, then hit **OK**. You see two house templates with drainage envelopes around them. You will set a high/low point between the two houses, which are at different finish floor elevations and have 10′ drainage envelopes.
3. Using the drop-down arrow to the right of the sixth icon from the left, choose **High/Low Point**.
4. `Specify start point:` Select a point on the lower right drainage envelope corner of the left house using the **Endpoint** Osnap.

To access student data files, go to www.pearsondesigncentral.com.

5. `Specify second point:` Select a point on the lower left drainage envelope corner of the right house using the **Endpoint** Osnap.
6. `First Slope (run:rise) or [Grade] <Horizontal>:` **g** to indicate that you will give it a grade (in %).
7. `Grade (percent) or [Slope] <0.00>:` **–5,** this is a 5% downward grade. (Remember that grades are in % whereas slopes are in ratios.)
8. `Grade: (percent): −5.00, Slope: (run:rise): −20.00:1`
9. `Second Grade (percent) or [Slope] <−5.00>:` **–.05,** to indicate that the second grade will be 1/2 % downward. Therefore, the first grade is coming down faster because the house is at a 2′ higher elevation while the second grade is coming down slower because that house is lower. This allows an intersection point to be computed between the two drainage envelopes that can be used as a center of swale point. The swale can guide drainage between the houses to either the front or the back of the property.
10. `Grade: (percent): −0.05, Slope: (run:rise): −2000.00:1, New point:` `X: 15876.168, Y: 19170.945, Z: 348.997.` Note that a tick mark displays where the new computed point will be placed if you proceed with the command. If the point will fall in an unsatisfactory location, type **n** for **No** at the next prompt and redo the command with different, more satisfactory data.
11. `Add point [Yes/No] <Yes>:` **y**
12. `Enter a point description <.>:` **<Enter>**
13. `Specify start point:` Hit **<Esc>** to terminate.
14. Save this drawing as you will use your results to perform the next two exercises.

Exercise 4-10: Slope—SLOPE/GRADE—DISTANCE Command

 The next command, **SLOPE/GRADE—DISTANCE**, can be used to set points in 3D by using the elevation of an object and providing it with Slope, Grade, and Distance criteria to set another point in 3D.

 The **SLOPE/GRADE—DISTANCE** command could be helpful in designing a swale between two houses after a low point has been constructed as was accomplished in the previous exercise. A designer can extend the swale between the houses for, say, 50′ at a grade of −2%, thereby ensuring drainage away from the houses toward the front or back of the property.

To access student data files, go to www.pearsondesigncentral.com.

1. Continue in the same drawing.
2. Using the **V** for **View** command, highlight the view called **Points-K**, hit **Set Current**, and then hit **OK**. You see two house templates with drainage envelopes around them. You will use the high/low point set in the last exercise to design a swale to convey drainage between the two houses.
3. Using the drop-down arrow to the right of the sixth icon from the left, choose **Slope/Grade—Distance**.
4. `Specify start point:` Select the point placed using the **High/Low Point** command in the last example using the **Node** Osnap.
5. `Elevation <348.997′>`
6. `Specify a point to define the direction of the intermediate points:` Pick a point in the front yard of the houses (in other words, to the north and between the two houses).
7. `Slope (run:rise) or [Grade] <Horizontal>:` **g**
8. `Grade (percent) or [Slope] <0.00>:` **–1**
9. `Grade: (percent): −1.00, Slope: (run:rise): −100.00: 1`
10. `Distance:` **100,** you will set points 100′ from the first point you picked.
11. `Enter the number of intermediate points <0>:` **4,** you will set four intermediate points along the way with one last point at 100′.
12. `Specify an offset <0.000>:` **<Enter>,** this allows for offset points if desired; you will say none.

13. `Add ending point [Yes/No]  <Yes>:` **\<Enter\>**
14. `Enter a point description <.>:` **\<Enter\>**
15. `Enter a point description <.>:` **\<Enter\>**
16. `Enter a point description <.>:` **\<Enter\>**
17. `Enter a point description <.>:` **\<Enter\>**
18. `Enter a point description <.>:` **\<Enter\>**
19. `Elevation <348.997'>:` **\<Enter\>**
20. `Specify a point to define the direction of the intermediate points:` Hit **\<Esc\>** to terminate.

You should see several points developed between the two houses in Figure 4-3.

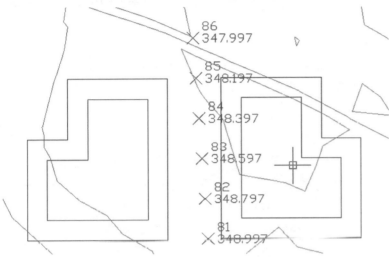

Figure 4-3   Points set between two houses

Exercise 4-11: Slope—SLOPE/GRADE—ELEVATION Command

The next command, **SLOPE/GRADE—ELEVATION**, can be used to set points in 3D by using the elevation of an object and providing it with Slope, Grade, and Elevation criteria to set another point in 3D.

> **TIP**   This **SLOPE/GRADE—ELEVATION** command differs from the previous command in that it asks for the ending elevation instead of a distance. You can use it to lay some points out for the front yard of the left house in the example.

1. Continue in the same drawing.
2. Using the **V** for **View** command, highlight the view called **Points-K**, hit **Set Current**, and then hit **OK**. You see two house templates with drainage envelopes around them. The points you placed between the two houses should be there from the previous exercise. Use the last point placed in the front yard to set some new points. Select the last point in the front yard, provide a direction to the west (or left), and travel at a grade of positive 4% until you hit an elevation of 351.5.
3. Using the drop-down arrow to the right of the sixth icon from the left, choose **Slope/Grade—Elevation**.
4. `Specify start point:` Select the last point placed in the front yard from the last exercise using the **Node** Osnap.
5. `Elevation <347.997'>:`
6. `Specify a point to define the direction of the intermediate points:` Pick a point in the front yard of the left house (in other words, to the left, but somewhere in the front yard of the left house).

7. Slope (run:rise) or [Grade] <Horizontal>: **g**
8. Grade (percent) or [Slope] <0.00>: **4**
9. Grade: (percent): 4.00, Slope: (run:rise): 25.00:1 Ending Elevation: **351.5**
10. Enter the number of intermediate points <0>: **3**
11. Specify an offset <0.000>: **<Enter>**
12. Add ending point [Yes/No] <Yes>: **<Enter>**
13. Enter a point description <.>: **<Enter>**
14. Enter a point description <.>: **<Enter>**
15. Enter a point description <.>: **<Enter>**
16. Enter a point description <.>: **<Enter>**
17. Elevation <347.997'> **<Enter>**
18. Specify a point to define the direction of the intermediate points: Hit **<Esc>** to terminate.

Notice that the last point placed has an elevation of 351.500, as shown in Figure 4-4, which is what was requested. The points are placed such that their grade is 4% from the first point chosen.

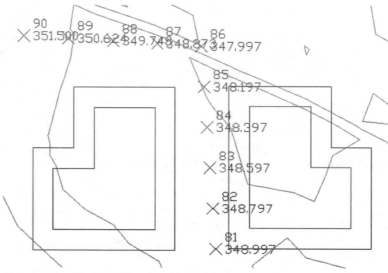

Figure 4-4   The last point placed is at elevation 351.500

CHAPTER SUMMARY

Because this chapter simply expands on the previous chapter, the summary is the same as it was for Chapter 3. In essence, understanding point-based features is important for anyone working on a civil project. Some team members place different emphasis on points depending on their contribution to the project. Make no mistake about it, however, someone is establishing points for everything on the site at some time during the project cycle.

CHAPTER TEST QUESTIONS

Multiple Choice

1. What are "thinking points"?
   a. Points used to help construct additional data
   b. Points that might create temporary locational information that can be used to carry on with a thought process
   c. Points that allow the user to see the results of design criteria so that moving forward on that track can be analyzed
   d. All of the above

2. Which type of design information can be developed with "thinking points"?
   a. Deciding how much flow exists in a channel
   b. Deciding whether a point is satisfactory with regard to elevations, slopes, and grades based on the data the user is providing
   c. Deciding if a surveyor should stake out the point or allow GPS machine guidance to do it
   d. All of the above

3. How is the term *slope* different from *grade*?

   a. Slope refers to anything with a percentage, such as 2%.
   b. Slope refers to a rise:run relationship.
   c. Grade refers to something underground.
   d. Grade refers to run:rise relationships.

4. A data set of points can be used to:

   a. Densify a data set based on information from raw data
   b. Densify a data set with additional points constructed from criteria from other points
   c. Densify a data set to reduce the number of points within it
   d. None of the above

5. Points can be set in 3D at specified intervals of, say, 50′ by using:

   a. **Grade** or **Slope**
   b. Elevational criteria
   c. Difference based criteria
   d. All of the above

6. If the user wanted to create points that have only even elevations such as 100.0, 101.0, 102.0 they would use which routine?

   a. **INCREMENTAL DISTANCE**
   b. **INCREMENTAL ELEVATION**
   c. **BY RELATIVE LOCATION**
   d. **INTERPOLATE**

7. A point can be set in 3D by intersecting the slope of one vector and intersecting it with the slope of another vector using which command?

   a. **INTERSECT POINT**
   b. **SLOPE/GRADE—DISTANCE**
   c. **HIGH/LOW POINT**
   d. None of the above

8. Which of the following commands might be used to densify a DTM?

   a. **DENSIFY DTM VERTICES**
   b. **THINKING POINTS**
   c. **INTERPOLATE**
   d. All of the above

9. Which of the following routines would best solve a traverse balancing issue for a non-closed traverse?

   a. **BY RELATIVE LOCATION**
   b. **INTERPOLATE**
   c. **BY RELATIVE ELEVATION**
   d. None of the above

10. Which of the following routines can be used to set points based on a percent and distance from another object?

   a. **SLOPE DISTANCE STORY STAKE**
   b. **FIXED SLOPE FROM OBJECT**
   c. **SLOPE/GRADE—DISTANCE**
   d. All of the above

True or False

1. True or False: A line exists if it begins at a point P1, has a known slope distance, and has a distance component.

2. True or False: Point file formats can be customized to include formats not delivered with the Civil 3D software.

3. True or False: The **Points** pull-down menu is a very sophisticated menu with over 50 point creation commands.

4. True or False: The **NUMBER BY DISTANCE** command can be used to densify your data set.

5. True or False: The **INTERSECTION** command cannot determine the elevation at the edge of a pavement where an underground utility crosses the edge of the pavement.

6. True or False: "Thinking points" are never used in design.

7. True or False: "Thinking points" should never be plotted.

8. True or False: The **INCREMENTAL ELEVATION** command is used to set points at specified distance intervals.

9. True or False: The **HIGH/LOW POINT** command allows you to set a point in a swale.

10. True or False: The **INCREMENTAL ELEVATION** command cannot be used to set points by slope.

CHAPTER EXERCISES

1. Using the **SLOPE/GRADE—DISTANCE** routine, how many points can be set between two other points if a distance of 100 is used with the number of points being set to 10 with an ending point?

2. Using the **HIGH/LOW POINT** command, what is the value of a new point being created from two objects of equal elevation, 10 feet apart, if they both extend at a 2% grade?

3. Using the **HIGH/LOW POINT** command, what is the value of a new point being created from two objects of equal elevation, 10 feet apart, if they both extend at a 2:1 slope?

4. Using the **SLOPE/GRADE—ELEVATION** command, what is the elevation of a new point if you started at a

location of elevation 100′ at 5% with an ending elevation of 120′, with 10 intermediate points and an ending point?

5. In the example above, how many points are created?

6. Using the **SLOPE/GRADE—ELEVATION** command, what is the elevation of a new point if you started at a location of elevation 100′ at 5% with an ending elevation of 120′, with 10 intermediate points and no ending point?

7. In the example above, how many points are created?

8. Using the **INCREMENTAL DISTANCE** routine, how many points are generated using an entity of 20′ in length, equal elevations of 0.0, and a distance between points of 10′?

9. Using the **BY RELATIVE LOCATION** routine, how many points are generated using an entity of 20′ in length, equal elevations of 0.0, and a distance of 5′?

10. Using the **NUMBER BY DISTANCE** command, how many points are generated if you are asked to Enter number of points and respond with 5?

Surveying

5

Chapter Objectives

- Understand how the Surveying interface operates within Civil 3D.
- Understand the application of Surveying Objects.
- Perform traverse balancing tasks.
- Understand how to reduce field data collection files.

INTRODUCTION

This chapter introduces you to surveying with Civil 3D. This technology was added to the 2007 release and largely completes the offering for use throughout the enterprise. With this technology, the surveying department can now develop the entire base data required for a project; the planning department can perform initial, preliminary designs; and the engineering department will take the project to final design. On completion, the project's data are likely to return to the surveying department for quality assurance/control and stakeout, or Machine Control data preparation.

The Civil 3D surveying functionality includes the following functions and abilities:

- The Prospector's Survey interface. Surveyors can view the numeric data along with previews; locate data visually, such as traverse or figures, in AutoCAD; and even change properties and values of the data using simple, succinct pull-down menus.

- Import, manage, and edit data collector field data.

- Enter, edit, balance, and report on open or closed traverses.

- Manage and edit survey equipment libraries.

- Manage and edit figure prefix libraries for automatic linework generation. This concept is similar to what has been offered in Autodesk's Land Desktop software, in which linework is collected in the field and given a prefix. For example, tops of curbs can be given prefixes such as TC1, TC2, and so on. The figure prefix library contains an entry called TC, so the software treats anything beginning with TC as a TC item, thereby correctly establishing the layering for the linework. This allows multiple edges of pavement to be open in the data collector simultaneously. The user should build this carefully so that other linework items do not mistakenly fall into the prefix. Consider something like a Tree and a Traverse station. If a Tree is prefixed with TR*, TRV descriptions would also be captured.

- The **Prospector's** inclusion of an interface collection for traverse networks, figures, and survey points, and the ability to manage and oversee these collections visually.

- Create survey figures directly from AutoCAD linework. This is even new to Land Desktop users.

- Develop terrain model breaklines from figures that have a specific prefix. In other words, perhaps linework coded with a BRKL prefix is intended to be breaklines for the Digital Terrain Model (DTM), and so many include tops and toes of channels, ridge lines, and so on. Users can now send those figures that have a BRKL prefix, for example, directly into the surface.

- The use of the Vault to protect the data for which surveyors are ultimately responsible.
- Output design data and surfaces in formats compatible with Topcon (via Carlson Connect), Trimble (via Trimble Link), and Leica (via Leica X-change) GPS Machine Control equipment.

The purpose of this chapter is to introduce you to some fundamental surveying concepts and provide basic procedures for developing survey data on projects.

REVIEW OF FUNCTIONS AND FEATURES TO BE USED

The text provides instruction in the functions for traverse entry, balancing traverse angles, how to compute the errors that are inherent in traverse computations, and the mathematics behind balancing the error of a traverse. Once the theories and algorithms are covered in the chapter, the discussion moves into automating these calculations in Civil 3D.

SURVEYING FUNCTIONS

Surveyors perform many functions in the process of developing engineering projects. They are responsible for collecting the base information consisting of existing conditions prior to design. This often includes identifying the property's boundary; the environmental conditions affecting the site such as wetlands and water bodies; the planimetric features, which are the buildings and other infrastructure on the site; and the topography, which consists of the three-dimensional conditions.

The method for collecting these data begins at the courthouse to identify the legal bounds of the property. These bounds are drawn up by the surveyor in a Civil 3D file using the Parcels and Rights of Way discussed in Chapter 6. These might be augmented by existing centerlines, easements, and so on.

Surveying of Parcels

There are two main methods for specifying parcel geometries: metes and bounds, and the U.S. Public Lands Survey System.

Metes and bounds are used primarily in the original colonial states in the United States. They were found to be too ambiguous, and the country converted to the U.S. Public Lands Survey System to improve confidence in the system. Metes and bounds describe property as beginning at a certain point, often a physical feature such as a tree or fence post. The property is then described by distances and bearings to another physical feature. Because a property's physical features deteriorate over time, they become ambiguous. Consider a parcel defined by a river's edge. During flooding the edge may move significantly, so the owner might actually lose land as the river erodes the banks or when a tree falls down.

The U.S. Public Lands Survey System (PLSS) was created to eliminate these ambiguities because rectangular-shaped boundaries use a methodical formula. The system is regulated by the U.S. Department of the Interior, Bureau of Land Management (BLM). The PLSS generally divides land into 6-mile-square townships. Townships are divided into 36 one-mile-square sections. Sections can be further divided into quarter sections, quarter-quarter sections, or irregular government lots as shown in the figure on page 129. The government sets a permanent survey monument at each section corner and at quarter-section corners.

The north-south line in the figure that runs through the initial point is called the Principal Meridian. The east-west line that runs through the initial point is called a Base line and is perpendicular to the Principal Meridian. Once the parcel is less than 10 acres, metes and bounds are used to further quantify the boundary.

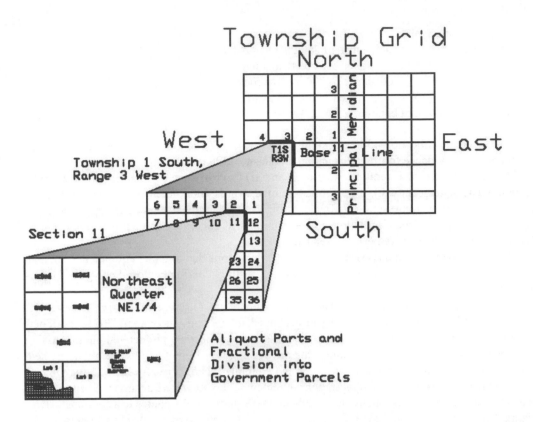

Township Grid

Section 11

Township 1 South,
Range 3 West

Northeast
Quarter
NE1/4

Aliquot Parts and
Fractional
Division into
Government Parcels

Example 5-1: A PLSS Description

Each section may be subdivided into smaller parcels (aliquot parts). For example, a ten-acre parcel could be described as:

- NE 1/4 SE 1/4 SE 1/4 sec. 15, T2N, R2W Minsk, Ne.

- Translation: the Northeast quarter of the southeast quarter of the southeast quarter of section 15, Township 2 North, Range 2 West of the Minsk Meridian.

Descriptions are read from left to right, but locating the property is easier if one reads from right to left or from a larger division to a smaller one.

Example 5-2: Metes and Bounds

The metes and bounds description below defines the property shown in the following figure.

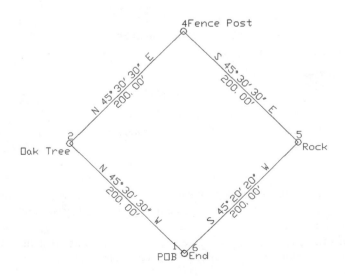

Beginning at a POB;
Thence n 45°30'30" w a distance of 200.00' to an oak tree;
Thence n 45°30'30" e a distance of 200.00' to a fence post;
Thence s 45°30'30" e a distance of 200.00' to a rock;
Thence s 45°20'20" w a distance of 200.00' to end;
Which is the point of beginning.

Following the collection of data or simultaneously, field collection techniques are employed to find physical evidence for the information on the site. GPS or total station equipment may be used to locate these data accurately. Precise 2D and 3D Control must be established for the project before any significant work is performed. In other words, monuments are established on the properties that are tied into state-certified control. These monuments can be occupied time and time again, and allow specific relations to be performed, as surveying and construction occur so that all aspects of the site are perfectly related.

The developed control has errors in its initial calculations due to either equipment or human error. The error is then eliminated from the control, creating a perfectly closed polygon, the vertices of which become the control monuments.

Other surveying techniques include aerial photogrammetry, GIS research, and GPS surveying. An example of an aerial photogrammetry project in Chapter 7 consists of about 200 acres of natural ground. Photogrammetry is the surveying task of flying above a project and photographing it using a zigzag pattern in which similar images at slightly different angles are photographed. Photographs are placed in the stereodigitizer and calibrated using Visually Identifiable Objects (VIOs) that are set using GPS or total station equipment. These now have accurate 3D coordinates that are set to the VIOs in the photos, thus calibrating everything in the photos to a coordinate. Digitizing then captures features and breaklines. This excellent method for collecting large amounts of data quickly has accuracies of about 0.01' for every thousand feet the aircraft is flying above the site. These data are typically verified by localized equipment such as total stations to ensure that the accuracies are met. The data produced from the stereodigitizing consist of CAD data usable by software such as Civil 3D.

A rapidly increasing methodology for collecting data is through the use of GPS equipment. Base stations are set on the project, again tied into state monumentation. The surveyor uses a rover with a GPS antenna that communicates with the base station to compute relative coordinates of the distance the rover is from the base station. Because the base station is tied down, the rover can be tied down relative to it, thus producing very accurate results. A new technology under development all over the world is the use of Imaginary Reference Stations. Using this technology, organizations collect a variety of certified base stations, tie them into a central server, amass errors, and correct for those errors. When a rover ties into the network, its location is computed, and an imaginary base station is created virtually at the location of the rover. Interpolated error corrections occur on the server and send postcorrected data (that is, coordinates) directly to the rover for immediate, and direct use in surveying or construction. See Figures 5-1 and 5-2 for graphics on how this works.

These systems are operational in many parts of the world. In the United States, they tend to be accessible in certain regions where this technology is in development. Many state DOTs are behind this development, as are private interests.

Developing Traverse Data

When a surveyor creates the traverse, he or she occupies a known location and typically backsights another known location. The angle between the two locations is now established. Then foresights are shot to new locations that may be accessible to the project. The idea is to locate positions that will be needed as the site is surveyed and built. These positions should be in as open an area as possible so they can be seen from as many points of view as possible in order to establish control for that portion of the project. A position would be useless if the surveyor could not see it. This then determines how many traverse points are required.

Once the setup station is identified and a backsight is created, turned angles and distances are captured to establish the next location (turned angles are discussed in Chapter 6).

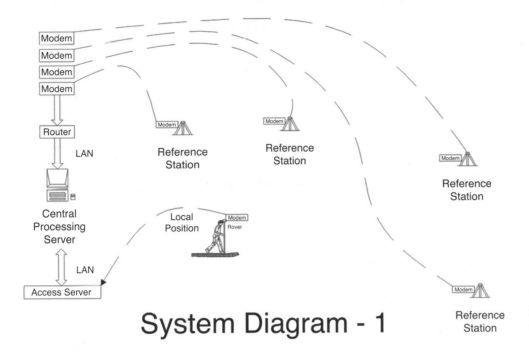

Figure 5-1   The process for Imaginary Reference Stations—initializing the rover

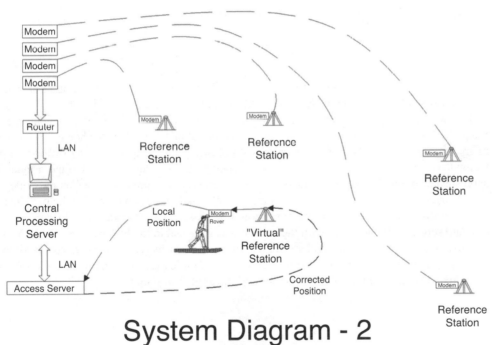

Figure 5-2   The process for Imaginary Reference Stations—error corrections obtained

Example 5-3: Creating a Traverse

The figure shown here has an occupied station at A, a backsight at B and foresight traverse shots at C, D, E, and returns to A.

You now create a traverse using the following data. The procedure here is simple in order to convey the ideas involved, but the same techniques can be used on larger, more sophisticated traverses.

The traverse setup is on Point *A* located at 1000,1000. Backsight *B* is located 500′ at a bearing of South 45-00-00 West of Point *A*. A turned angle of 90-00-00 degrees and a distance of 500′ produces Point *C*. Then *C* is occupied with Point *A* being the backsight. A turned angle of 269-50-00 and a distance of 499.90′ produces Point *D*. Point *D* is then occupied with *C* being the backsight to locate Point *E*. A turned angle of 270-00-00 and a distance of 500′ are used to locate Point *E*. Then *E* is occupied with a backsight to *D* to locate Point *A* again at a turned angle of 270-00-00 and a distance of 500′. Refer to Figure 5-3. There is not a closed traverse because error has been placed into the com-

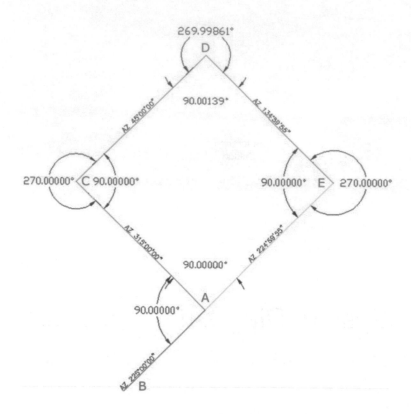

Figure 5-3   Traverse data

putations. Clearly, surveyors do not intentionally add error, yet the equipment might, or perhaps a prism is not held perfectly plumb to the shot. Maybe ambient conditions such as heat or fog have affected the line of sight. To replicate this error, the bust of 0.1′ and 1 degree has been entered, and a method known as the Compass rule will be used to correct this error. This method has been used for many years and still holds some favor because it is easily hand-calculated for verification purposes. Computer automation has improved traverse balancing by allowing surveyors to use a much more sophisticated method called least squares, but this exercise concentrates on the Compass rule.

Using the Compass rule, first correct for the bad angles and then for the bad distances. To correct for the angles, this figure should be closed. The intention was to start at Point *A* and return to Point *A*, but with the error it was impossible to close back precisely. You need to determine how much angular error and distance error there is. It is necessary to know how many degrees should be in the figure, and certain simple methods can obtain that information. Closed figures with *n* sides are *n*-gons and the angles sum up to

$$(n-2) \times 180$$

TIP

So a figure with

3 sides is a triangle and has 180°.

4 sides is a rectangle and has 360°.

5 sides is a pentagon and has 540°.

6 sides is a hexagon and has 720°.

7 sides is a heptagon and has 900°.

8 sides is an octagon and has 1080°.

9 sides is a nonagon and has 1260°.

10 sides is a decagon and has 1440°.

12 sides is a dodecagon and has 1800°.

15 sides is a 15-gon and has 2340°.

So, based on this information there should be 360° in Figure 5-3. Let us find out what we have and correct it in the following manner (see Table 5-1).

Table 5-1	Adjustment of Angles		
Point	Measured Interior Angle	Average Correction (Degrees)	Adjusted Angle (Degrees)
A	90.0	−0.0003475	89.9996525
C	90.0	−0.0003475	89.9996525
D	90.00139	−0.0003475	90.0010425
E	90.0	−0.0003475	89.9996525
Result:	360.00139	0.00139	360.00

Note that the sum of the interior angles is 360.5139 (it should be 360-00-00); therefore, the average correction is .5139/4 vertices = 0.1285. This is applied to the angles, and because it is an average, it is subtracted. By the time the error is applied to Point E, the entire error of .5139 degrees has been distributed.

Computation of Azimuths for the Traverse

We will now compute the relative azimuths of each traverse segment. The azimuth of AB is 225.0 degrees and with the turned angle of $BAC = 90.0$ degrees, the azimuth of AC is 315.0 degrees. We will now occupy each setup, then backsight the previous setup and turn an interior angle to obtain the next setup. We will apply the corrected turned angle to each vertex.

315.0 = AC
−180, to flip the line of sight from C to A
135.0 = CA
−89.9996525 = C, subtract adjusted interior angle of C from azimuth
45.0003475 = CD
+180, to flip the line of sight from D to C
225.0003475 = DC
−90.0010425 = D
134.999305 = DE
+180
314.999305 = ED
−89.9996525 = E
224.9996525 = EA
+180
404.9996525 = AE
−89.9996525 = A
315.0 = AC

This check proves it is now balanced because we ended up at the angle where we began. Point A eventually comes back to 1000,1000 (within 0.001, anyway).

Example 5-4: Computing a Traverse Misclosure and Relative Precisions

In this exercise, we will compute the non-closure or linear misclosure based on the incorrect distance(s). We do this by computing how far off the error is in the "x" direction and how far it is off in the "y" direction. These values are Departure and Latitudes. Refer to Figure 5-4.

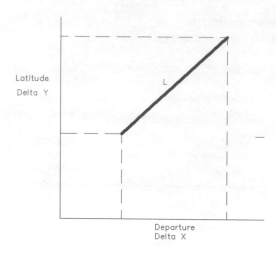

Figure 5-4   Departure and Latitude Diagram

Departure and Latitudes

Departures are eastings/westings, whereas latitudes are northings/southings.

Departures = L sin (alpha)
Latitudes = L cos (alpha)

where the angle alpha is from north (straight up) to line L.

Linear misclosure is the square root of the departure of misclosure squared plus the latitude of misclosure squared or

$$\sqrt{(\text{dep. misclosure})^2 + (\text{lat. misclosure})^2}. \text{ See Table 5-2.}$$

Table 5-2   Table Computation of Departures and Latitudes

Station	Preliminary Azimuths	Length	Departures	Latitudes
A	315.0	500	−353.553	353.553
C	45.0003475	499.9	353.485	353.480
D	134.999305	500	353.5578	-353.549
E	224.9996525	500.0	−353.551	-353.555
A				
	Sum =	1999.9	−.0612	0.071

Linear misclosure $= \sqrt{(-0.612)^2 + (.071)^2}$

$\qquad\qquad\quad = \sqrt{(0.003745 + .00504)} = 0.09373$ ft.

Relative precision = Linear misclosure/Traverse length

$\qquad\qquad\quad = 0.09373/1999.9 = 0.0016 \quad .00046867 = 1'/21336.8'$

Compass Rule

Adjusts the departures and latitudes of traverse courses in proportion to their lengths. See Table 5-3.

Correction in departure for $AC =$

$$-\frac{(\text{total departure misclosure})}{\text{Traverse perimeter}} \times \text{Len } AC$$

Correction in latitude for $AC =$

$$-\frac{\text{(total latitude misclosure)}}{\text{Traverse perimeter}} \times \text{Len } AC$$

.0612/1999.9 × 500.0 = .0153 ft.

0.071/1999.9 × 500.0 = .01775 ft.

For C to D:

.0612/1999.9 × 499 9 = 0.01529 ft.

0.071/1999.9 × 499.9 = .01774 ft.

Station	Preliminary Azimuths	Unadjusted			Balanced		Coordinates	
		Length	Dep.	Lat.	Dep.	Lat.	X East	Y North
A			(.0153)	(.01775)			1000	1000
	315.0	500	−353.553	353.553	−353.5377	353.57075		
C			(.0153)	(.01775)			646.4623	1353.57075
	45.0003475	499.9	353.485	353.480	353.5003	355.49775		
D			(.01529)	(.01774)			1000.0354	1707.0685
	134.999305	500	353.5578	−353.549	353.5731	−353.5313		
E			(.0153)	(.01775)			1353.6085	1353.5372
	224.9996525	500	−353.551	−353.555	−353.5357	−353.5373		
A							1000.0	999.9999
Summary =		1999.9	−.0612	0.071	0.0	−.0001		

Table 5-3   Table of Compass Rule

ELECTRONIC FIELD RECORDERS OR DATA COLLECTORS

Using field records, surveyors also collect data. When the rod person places the prism on the shot to be located, a shot code and a possible linecode will be determined if the shot also represents linework such as a crown or edge of pavement. Point codes were discussed in Chapter 3 (see Table 3-1). These codes describe the points, and the libraries place the shot on the correct layers, with the correct symbology and annotation. In the case of linework, there are also linecode libraries.

SURVEY LANGUAGE

This is also known as the field book format.

Point Creation Commands

AD = ANGLE DISTANCE, locates points/linework by a turned angle, distance

AD (point) [angle] [distance] (descript)

AD [VA] (point) [angle] [distance] [vert angle] (descript)

AD [VD] (point) [angle] [distance] [vert distance] (descript)

AUTO PT NUMBERING, for automatic point numbering

AP ON (point)

AP OFF

BEARING DISTANCE, locates points/linework by bearing, distance

BD (point) [bearing] [quadrant] [distance] (descript)

BD [VA] (point) [bearing] [quadrant] [distance] [vert angle] (descript)

BD [VA] (point) [bearing] [quadrant] [distance] [vert distance] (descript)

DEFLECTION DISTANCE, locates points/linework by deflection angle, distance

DD (point) [angle] [distance] (descript)

DD [VA] (point) [angle] [distance] [vert angle] (descript)

DD [VD] (point) [angle] [distance] [vert distance] (descript)

FACE 1, locates point from a traverse station. Using horizontal angle measured on face 1, distance

FACE 2, locates point from a traverse station. Using horizontal angle measured on face 2, distance

F1 (DIRECT), F2 (INVERTED)

F1/F2 (point) [angle] [distance] (descript)

F1/F2 [VA] (point) [angle] [distance] [vert angle] (descript)

F1/F2 [VD] (point) [angle] [distance] [vert distance] (descript)

LAT LONG (point) [latitude] [longitude] (descript)

NE, sets a 2D point.

Is a Control Point and is not moved in traverse balancing

NEZ, sets a 3D point.

Is a Control Point and is not moved in traverse balancing

NE SS, 3D pt side shot (not fixed in observation database, can be overwritten)

NE (point) [North] [East] (descript)

NEZ (point) [North] [East] (elev) (descript)

NE SS (point) [North] [East] (elev) (descript)

PRISM [height]

PT OFFSET (point) [offset] (ahead)

SKIP

STADIA, reduces a distance measured using stadia rod intercept

STADIA (point) [angle] [distance] [rod] (vert angle) (descript)

AZ = AZIMUTH DISTANCE, locates points/linework by azimuth, distance

ZD (point) [azimuth] [distance] (descript)

ZD [VA] (point) [azimuth] [distance] [vert angle] (descript)

ZD [VD] (point) [azimuth] [distance] [vert distance] (descript)

Point Location Commands

AZ [point 1] [point 2] [azimuth]

B [point1] [point 2] [bearing] [quadrant]

BS [point] (orientation), **backsight a known point**

STN [point] (inst. height) (descript), **occupy a station**

Point Information Commands

A [point 1] [point 2] [point 3]

AZ [point 1] [point 2]

B [point 1] [point 2]

D [point 1] [point 2]

DISP PTS (point 1) (point 2)

GRADE [point 1] [point 2]

INV PTS [point 1] [point 2]

INVERSE RADIAL [backsight] [station]

SLOPE [point 1] [point 2]

SD [point 1] [point 2]

VD [point 1] [point 2]

Point Editing Commands

DEL PTS [point 1] (point 2)

MOD DESC [point 1] [descript]   MOD EL [point 1] [elev] MOD ELS [point 1] [point 2] [elev]

MOD ELS BY [point 1] [point 2] [amount]

Figure Commands

AREA [figure]

BEG [figure], **begins a figure called {FIGURE}**

C3, next three shots are on a curve. The first shot should be on the beginning of the curve, the next shot about midway around the arc, and the last shot should be on the end of the curve.

CLOSE

CLOSE BLD, closes to connect the last point to the first point by creating two right-angled segments to close a building

CLOSE RECT [offset], closes objects such as sheds, storm structures

CONT [figure], continues a figure called {FIGURE}. This command assumes that the last point in the existing figure is the point to continue from. It continues a figure from the back end.

CRV = TANGENT CURVE

CRV [DELTA, LENGTH, DEFL, MID, TAN, CHORD] [radius] [value]

END, ends the current figure

These Figure commands draw figures using a data collector or manual input; they do not set points.

FIG AD [angle] [distance] FIG DD [deflection] [distance] FIG ZD [azimuth] [distance]

FIG BD [bearing] [quadrant] [distance]   FIG NE [Northing] [Easting]

ID FIG

INVERSE FIG [figure]

MAPCHECK [figure]

OFFSET [figure] [distance]

PC, next shot is on PC. The shot after that must be a PT.

POINT [point]

RT [distance], is a great command for drawing a building that has 90-degree corners and measured wall lengths

SET (point)

START [figure], restarts a figure called {FIGURE} from the beginning of the figure

These XC commands are for drawing nontangential curves.

XC = EXTEND CURVE

XC ZD (BULB) [radius] [chord-az] [chord-dis]

XC BD (BULB) [radius] [chord-brg] [quad] [chord-dis]

XC AD (BULB) [radius] [chord-angle] [chord-dis]

XC DD (BULB) [radius] [chord-defl] [chord-dis]

XC C3 [pt on curve] [endpt]

XC PTS [radius] [radpt] [endpt]

Intersection Commands

AZAZ [pnt 1] [az 1] [off 1] [pt 2] [az 2] [off 2]

BB [pnt 1] [brg 1] [quad 1] [off 1] [pnt 2] [brg 2] [quad 2] [off 2]

LNLN [pnt 1] [pnt 2] [off 1] [pnt 3] [pnt 4] [off 2]

RKAZ [point] [radius] [pnt 1] [azimuth] [offset]

RKBRG [point] [radius] [pnt 1] [brg] [quad] [offset]

RKLN [point] [radius] [pnt 1] [pnt 2] [offset]

RKRK [pnt 1] [radius 1] [pnt 2] [radius 2]

SAVE [NORTH, SOUTH, EAST, WEST, 1, 2, ALL] (point) (descript)

SAVE [NEAR, FAR] (point) [ref pt#] (descript)

SAVE PICK (point) (descript)

SQ [ref 1] [ref 2] [ref]

Figure Correction and Manipulation Commands

DEL FIG [fig]   DISP FIGS

Equipment Correction Commands

ANGLES [RIGHT, LEFT] [ZENITH, NADIR, HORIZ]

ATMOS [ON, OFF] COLL [ON, OFF] CR [ON, OFF]

EDM OFFSET [offset]

HORIZ ANGLE [RIGHT, LEFT]

PRESS [pressure] [INCH, MBAR, MM]

SF [factor]

PRISM CONSTANT [constant]   PRISM OFFSET [offset]

TEMP [temperature] [F, C, K]

UNITS [METER, FOOT] [DMS, DECDEG, GRAD, MILS, RADIANS]

VERT ANGLE [ZENITH, NADIR, HORIZ]

Baseline Commands

BL IS [point 1] [point 2] [station]   BL PT (point 1) [station] (offset)(descript)

BL INV [point 1] (point 2)

Centerline Commands

CL IS [figure] (station) (point)

CL INV [point 1] (point 2)

CL PT (point) [station] (offset) (skew angle) (descript)

CL PT BY [point] [station 1] [offset] [distance] (station 2) (descript)

CL ELEV (point) [station] [offset] [elev] (descript)

CL ROD (point) [station] [offset] [rod] (descript)

CL VD (point) [station] [offset] [vert distance] (descript)

HI [elev]

XS [station]

XS ELEV (point) [offset] [elev] (descript)

XS ROD (point) [offset] [rod] (descript)

XS VD (point) [offset] [vert distance] (descript)

AutoCAD Related Commands

PAN   SHELL   REDRAW   ZOOM PT [point]

ZOOM [WINDOW, EXTENTS, PREVIOUS, W, P, E, A]

Miscellaneous Commands

CALC [formula]   DITTO   [ON, OFF]   HELP (command)   HISTORY

OUTPUT [ON, OFF] TRAV [ON, OFF]

Unit Conversions for Distance

Unit	Symbol	Equation
Inches	"	
Feet	'	1 ft – 12 inches
Yards	Y	1 yd = 3 ft
Rods	R	1 rod = 16.5 ft
Chains	C	1 chain = 66 ft
Links	L	1 link = 1/100 chain – 0.66 ft
Meters	M	1 ft – 0.3048 m
Millimeters	MM	1 mm = 1/1000 m
Centimeters	CM	1 cm = 1/100 m
Kilometers	KM	1 km = 1000 m

Mathematical Operations

Sometimes a surveyor needs to compute distances, angles, bearings, or azimuths, and these commands also perform mathematical calculations. Occasionally, an angle, bearing, or distance is needed, but the surveyor may be unsure of what the value is. However, it might be possible to define this information from existing points.

The following commands—**ANGLE, AZIMUTH, BEARING, SLOPE, GRADE, VERTICAL DISTANCE, SLOPE DISTANCE, and DISTANCE** commands—display angle, azimuth, or distance values. However, when they are placed inside parentheses, they can be used to compute these values and send them into other commands. For instance:

ZD 5000 (AZ 500 501) (D 503 504) uses the azimuth from point 500 to point 501, and the distance from point 503 to point 504 to set point 5000.

The built-in functions can also be used in conjunction with the [Calc] command. For example:

CALC (A 10 20 30)/2 returns half the angle from point 10 to point 20 to point 30.

The **ANGLE** and **AZIMUTH** commands always return an angle. This value can be used in any command that requires an angle or an azimuth. For example:

ZD 5000 (SLOPE 10 20) 1000 uses the slope angle between point 10 and point 20 to set point 1000.

AD VA 5000 250.3000 600.00 (SLOPE 10 20).

Files Produced When Balancing

When an analysis is run and the network is adjusted, the following files are created and stored:

- **an<traversename>.trv:** Displays the horizontal closure and angular error
- **fv<traversename>.trv:** Displays a report of raw and adjusted elevations from the vertical adjustment methods
- **ba<traversename>.trv:** Displays the adjusted station coordinates derived from balancing the angular error and horizontal closure with no angular error
- **<traversename>.lso:** Displays the adjusted station coordinates based on Horizontal Adjustment Type setting (Compass rule)

Secrets of Survey Functions

A file exists in the folder C:\Documents and Settings\All Users\Application Data\Autodesk\C3D 2010\enu\Survey\ called **translat.ref** File. This file can be customized to control the order in which the user would prefer to enter the data parameters.

```
#   Translator File for SURVEY
#   Line
#   —
#   1    Description
#   2    Command Number, # of Command Phrases, # of data elements,
#            Auto Point Data #, Check for last literal,
#            Variable command element, Variable data element,
#            Batchable command
#   3    Command Phrase1 #, Command Phrase2 #, ...
#   4    Data Mnemonic1, Data Mnemonic2, ...
#   5    Data Order1, Data Order2, ...
#   6    NULL
#   7    Blank Line
```

Example
```
BD
32,1,4,1,1,0,0,1
12
P,B,Q,D
1,2,3,4
NULL
```

Another file that exists in the same folder is called **language.ref file**. It contains the potential synonyms for each of the commands in the field book language. For instance, if the user would prefer to call the AD command "LOC" for *locate,* then LOC can be added to command #1.

A listing of the default synonyms is shown here; however, this file can be customized for use in Civil 3D.

```
# SYNONYM FILE FOR SURVEY
# Phrase Number, SYNONYM1, SYNONYM2, SYNONYM3, ....
1,AD,ANG-DIST
2,ADJ,ADJUST
3,A,ANG,ANGLE,ANGLES,ANGS
```

4,AUTO,AP

5,ATMOSPHERE,ATMOS

6,AZ,AZM,AZIMUTH

7,AZAZ

8,AZ-DIST,ZD

9,AZSP,AZSPI,AZ-SPI,AZ-SPIRAL

10,B,BEARING,BRG,BRGS,BEARINGS

11,BB,BRG-BRG

This allows for your preference in using these commands. If your common terminology is not shown, it can be added to this file. For instance, instead of storing a point using NE, we like to say STO and add this to number 74.

12,BD,BRG-DIST

13,BEG,BEGIN,BEGINS

14,BL,BASELINE

15,BOWDITCH,COMPASS

16,BRK,BRG-ARC,BARC,BRG-RK

17,BS,BACKSIGHT,BACKSITE

18,BSP,BRG-SPI,BSPI

19,BY,INC,INCRE,INCREMENT

20,CHORD,CHRD

21,CL,CENTERLINE,CLINE

22,COLL,COLLIMATION

23,CONSTANT

24,CONT,CONTINUE

25,CR,CURVATURE

26,CRANDALL,CRAND

27,CV3,C3

28,CURVE,CRV,CV

29,DD,DEFL-DIST

30,DESC,DESCR,DESCRIPT,DESCRIPTION

31,DEL,DELETE

32,DEPTH

33,DISPLAY,DISP,DSP,LIST

34,D,DIST,DISTANCE,DIS,HD,HDIST,LENGTH

35,DELTA

36,EDM

37,EL,ELEV,ELEVATION

38,ELEVATIONS,ELS,ELEVS

39,END,ENDS,E

40,ENTITY,ENT

41,EXIT,QUIT,STOP

42,FC1,F1,FACE1

43,FC2,F2,FACE2

44,FACTOR,FACT

45,DEFL,DEFLECTION

47,FILE

49,FOR

50,FROM

51,FS,FORESIGHT,FORESITE

53,HI

56,INDEX

57,INV,INVERSE

58,IS

59,JOB

61,LEVEL,LV

62,LINE,LN

63,LINE-LINE,LNLN

64,LINE-SPI,LNSP

65,LOC,LOCATE,LOCATION

66,LOW,LO

72,MOD,MODIFY

74,NE,NORTH-EAST

75,NEW

76,NEZ

77,NULL

78,OBJ,OBJECT

79,OFF

80,OFFSETS,OFFSET

81,ON

82,PT,POINT,PNT

83,PNTS,PTS,POINTS

84,PAN

85,PC

86,PD,PAR-DIST,PAR-DIS

87,PRC

88,PRESS,PRESSURE

89,PRISM

90,RAD,RADIAL,RADIUS

91,RECALL

92,REDRAW,R

94,RK,ARC

95,RKB,ARCB,ARC-BRG,RKBRG

96,RKAZ,ARCAZ,ARC-AZ,RKZ

97,RKLN,ARCLN,ARC-LINE

98,RKRK,ARCARC,ARC-ARC

99,RKSP,ARCSP,ARCSPI,ARC-SPIRAL,ARC-SPI

100,ROD

101,ROTATE,ROT

102,SAVE,KEEP

103,SCALE
104,SCS
105,SIDESHOTS,SIDESHOT,SS
106,SF,SCALEFACTOR
107,SL,SEA-LEVEL
108,SYMBOLS,SYM,SYMBOL
109,SPIRAL,SPI,SP
110,SPSP,SPISPI,SPI-SPI,SPIRAL-SPIRAL
111,SQ,SQ-OFF,SQOFF,SQUARE-OFF,SQUARE
112,STADIA
113,START
114,STN,STATION,STA
115,TAN-OFF,TANOFF
116,TAN,TANGENT
117,TEMP,TEMPERATURE
118,TIME,DATE
119,TO
120,TRANSIT
121,TRANSLATE,TRANS
122,TRAVERSE,TRAV,TRV
123,UNIT,UNITS
125,VA
126,VD,VDIST
127,VERTICAL,VERT
128,VIEW
129,W,WINDOW
130,XSECT,XS,XSECTION
131,SD,SDIST
132,ZOOM,Z
137,COMMAND,CMD
138,INFO,INFORMATION
139,EXTENTS,E
140,PREV,P,PREVIOUS
141,DITTO
142,SQRT
144,WAIT
145,WHILE
146,SIGNATURE
147,OUTPUT,OUT
148,MID,MIDORD,MID-ORDINATE
149,PICK
150,NEAR
151,FAR
152,ALL
153,XC,NC
154,BULB

155,RUN
156,BATCH
157,FBK
200,RIGHT,RT,RT-TURN
201,ZENITH
202,HORIZ,HORIZONTAL,HOR
203,NADIR
204,LEFT,LT
205,USFOOT,USFEET
206,METER,METERS,METRIC
207,FOOT,FEET
208,DMS
209,GRAD,GRADS
210,DECDEG
211,MIL,MILS
212,FAHREN,F,FAHRENHEIT
213,K,KELVIN
214,CELSIUS,CENTIGRADE,C
215,MM
216,INCH,INCHES
217,MBAR
218,GRADE,G
219,SLOPE
220,NORTH
221,SOUTH
222,EAST
223,WEST
224,MAPCHECK,MAPCHK,CHECK,CHK
225,AREA
226,RECT,RECTANGLE,RECTANG
227,CIRC,CIRCLE
228,CLOSE
229,RENAME
230,NAME
231,SSS
232,SAS
233,SAA
234,SSA
235,ASS
236,ASA
237,AAS
238,TRIANGLE,TRI,TRIANG
239,SOLVE
241,BLDG,BUILDING,BLD,BUILD
242,FIGURE,FIG
243,FIGURES,FIGS

244,SKEW

245,SET

246,LAT,LATITUDE

247,LONG,LON,LONGITUDE

248,ID,IDENT,IDENTIFY

249,SKIP

250,BACKUP

251,HISTORY,HIST,H

252,CALCULATE,CALC,CA

253,HELP,?

254,EDIT

255,MCS

256,MCE

257,RADIANS,RADS

Example 5-5: Computing a Traverse Adjustment in Civil 3D

The following procedure takes the reader through an entire survey project, beginning with a closed traverse taken from field notes to entering the field shot locations and then checking the traverse with a cross loop. This is usually done for quality assurance/control and accuracy purposes.

Field Notes

BS	STA @	FS	Angle RT.	DISTANCE
4	1	2	278-05-06	513.43
		(6)Mon 101	61-14-49	214.84
		(7)IPF A	311-23-25	23.85
1	2	3	291-45-07	440.52
		(8)Mon 102	163-14-58	221.69
2	3	4	260-24-37	308.20
		(9)IPF B	49-04-04	54.45
3	4	1	249-45-10	347.68
		(10)IPF C	54-31-01	49.62

Cross Loop Field Notes

BS	STA @	FS	Angle RT.	DISTANCE
2	1	1A	53-28-13	204.12
1	1A	1B	150-14-00	198.54
1A	1B	3	230-27-34	171.85
1B	3	4	297-59-58	308.20

Coordinates for Mon 101: $N = 10177.65460149$ $E = 10446.77951350$

Mon 102: $N = 10094.69083254$ $E = 9532.42708331$

The survey task is as follows:

1. Enter and adjust traverse loop 1–4.
2. Rotate to control monuments.
3. Enter and rotate boundary to pipe found and complete ties.
4. Enter and adjust cross loop.

The following procedure should allow the user to complete this task.

5. Set up drawing, set up points settings, description keys.
6. Set point for Traverse #1 by N/E (occupied station).
7. Set point for Traverse #4 by N/E (BS).
8. Traverse settings are no vertical, angles right.
9. Traverse entry (occupy #1, BS 4, Locate 2,3,4,1).
10. Traverse loops, define loops, should be OK.
11. Traverse loops, check adjust loop.
12. Traverse loops, adjust loop.
13. Command line, traverse/sideshots, sideshot settings
14. Command line, traverse/sideshots, sideshot entry

Now enter the monuments.

15. Set point for Mon 101, 102 by N/E (using real coordinates).
16. Set layer for boundary.
17. Draw boundary using COGO, Lines, By direction.
18. Set label preferences.
19. Label property lines.
20. Check closure of property lines.
21. Fillet, R = 0, to close.
22. Align to fit into place.
23. Checkpoints, modify project.
24. Update labels if needed.
25. Enter cross loop.
26. Edit Points, Erase 101-102.
27. Edit field book file (ensure that N/E exists for points 1–4).
28. Define traverse loop.
29. Traverse analysis.

Civil 3D File for Adjusting a Closed Traverse

The following FBK file can be built to automate the traverse development in Example 5-5. This can be conducted in Windows Notepad and run by using the **Import Field Book** option, which is available when right-clicking on the traverse created in the **Survey Toolspace**.

```
NE 1 2000 2000 "TRV 1"
NE 4 2347.68 2000 "TRV 4"
STN 1
BS 4
AD 2 278.050600 513.43 "TRV 2"
STN 2
BS 1
AD 3 291.450700 440.52 "TRV 3"
STN 3
BS 2
AD 4 260.243700 308.20 "TRV 4"
STN 4
BS 3
AD 1 249.451000 347.68 "TRV 1"
```

Civil 3D File for Adjusting a Traverse Cross Loop

This FBK file for Example 5-5 can be edited in Notepad as well and run by right-clicking on a new traverse created in the **Survey Toolspace**.

NE 1 10070.5376 10260.5491 "TRV 1"

NE 2 10132.4980 9750.8695 "TRV 2"

NE 3 10518.9622 9962.3056 "TRV 3"

NE 4 10418.1471 10253.5486 "TRV 4"

STN 1

AUTO OFF

BS 2

AD 101 53.281300 204.12 "TRV 1A"

STN 101

BS 1

AD 102 150.140000 198.54 "TRV 1B"

STN 102

BS 101

AD 3 230.273400 171.85 "TRV 3"

STN 3

BS 102

AD 4 297.595800 0.00 "TRV 4"

Refer to Figure 5-5 for an image of the completed traverse following import.

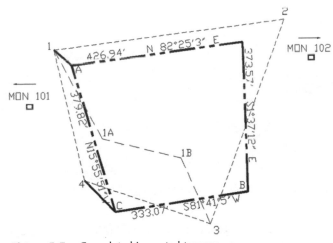

Figure 5-5   Completed imported traverse

Exercise 5-1: Computing a Traverse Reduction in Civil 3D—1

1. Open the drawing Chapter 5-a.dwg.
2. In the **Toolspace**, click on the **Survey** tab.
3. Right-click on the **Survey Databases** item; select **New local survey database….**
4. Name it **Chapter 5** when the dialog box appears to name the database.
5. In the **Toolspace**, right-click on **Networks** and choose **New…**; when the dialog box for naming appears, type in **Chapter 5**.
6. Expand **Networks**, right-click on **Chapter 5**, and select **Edit field book…**; select **Survey-TRAV.fbk** from where your files are stored for the textbook. It contains the following data, all in the field book language:

UNIT FOOT DMS

HORIZ ANGLE RIGHT

To access student data
files, go to
www.pearsondesigncentral.com.

```
          PRISM CONSTANT 0
          PRISM OFFSET 0
          EDM OFFSET 0
          CR OFF
          ATMOS OFF
          COLLIMATION OFF
          JOB CHAP-5
          !NOTE TRAVERSE DEMO
          TRAVERSE DEMO
          SCALE FACTOR 1.000000
          VERT ANGLE ZENITH
          END
          NE 1 1000 1000 "STA1"
          NE 2 646.44660941 646.44660941 "STA2"
          END
          STN 1
          !AZ 1 2 225.000000
          !PRISM 0.000000
          BS 2
          AD 3 90.0 500.000 "STA3"
          STN 3
          BS 1
          AD 4 269.5 499.9 "STA4"
          STA 4
          BS3
          AD 5 270 500 "STA5"
          STA 5
          BS 4
          AD 1 269.5 500
          STA 1
          BS 5
```

7. This data set stores Points 1 and 2 using a **Control Point** command (NE). It then occupies Point 1, backsights 2, and locates 3. It then occupies 3, backsights 1, and locates 4. Then it occupies 4, backsights 3, and locates 5. Then it occupies 5, backsights 4, and locates 1 again.

8. Close the file.

9. Expand **Networks**, right-click on **Chapter 5**, and select **Import> Import field book...**; the **Field book filename (.FBK)** dialog box appears. Select **Survey-TRAV.fbk** from where your files are stored for the textbook. The **Import Field Book** dialog box displays, as shown in Figure 5-6. Accept the data as shown and hit **OK**.

10. When the import is complete, the traverse shown in Figure 5-7 is computed.

11. Note in the **Survey** item under **Chapter 5** that two control points, 1 and 2, have been created. These will not be moved during traverse balancing. Expand **Setups** under **Networks, Chapter 5** and notice that Stations 1, 3, 4, 5, and 1 are described.

12. Right-click on **Traverses**, select **New...**, and type in **Chapter 5** in the naming dialog box.

13. Then click on **Traverses**, and in the preview window, fill in the Initial Station (1), Initial Backsight (2), Stations (3-5,1), and Final Foresight (1) fields, as shown in Figure 5-8.

14. Then a dialog box, shown in Figure 5-9, may appear that indicates you have made changes and not applied them. Hit **Yes** to apply the changes now.

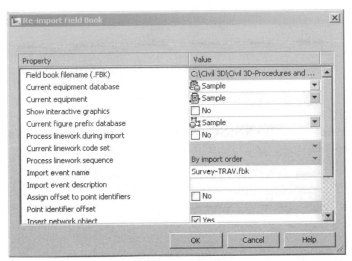

Figure 5-6   Import Field Book dialog box

Figure 5-7   Imported traverse

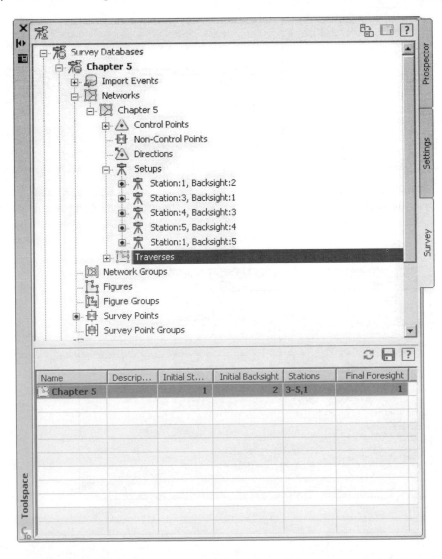

Figure 5-8   Defining the traverse stations

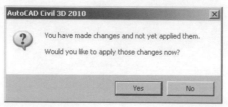

Figure 5-9

15. Click **Chapter 5** under Traverses and right-click. From the choices, select **Traverse analysis...** .
16. The dialog box shown in Figure 5-10 is displayed.
17. Accept the settings and hit **OK**.
18. You may get a dialog box that reads, **WARNING: User-specified traverse limits not met**. Hit **OK**. A notepad opens with traverse information.

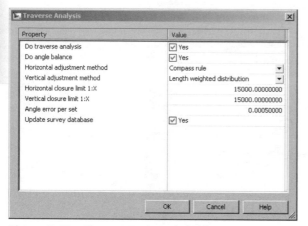

Figure 5-10 Traverse Analysis dialog box

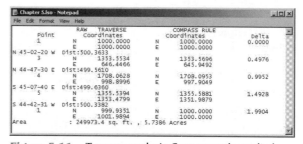

Figure 5-11 Traverse analysis-Compass rule applied report

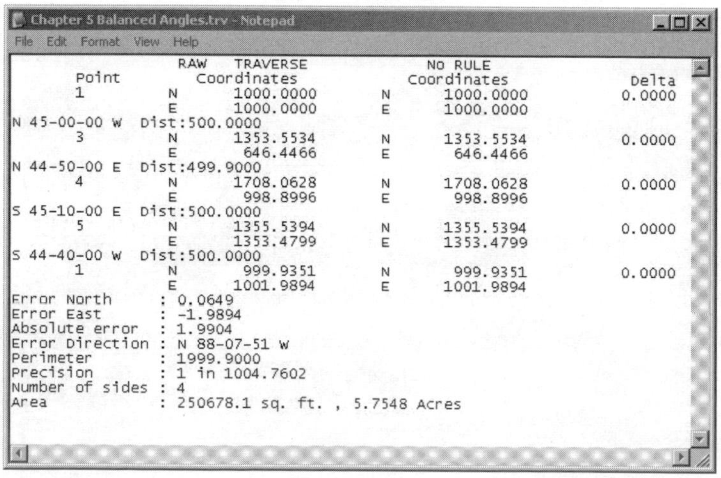

Figure 5-12 Traverse analysis, balanced angles report

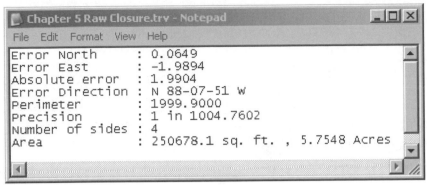

Figure 5-13   Traverse analysis report

Exercise 5-2: Computing a Traverse Reduction in Civil 3D—2

In this exercise, you execute the field books described earlier in the traverse loop and cross check example. Use the field books constructed based on the field notes and run them through the Civil 3D software.

1. Open the drawing Chapter 5-b.dwg.
2. In the **Toolspace**, click on the **Survey** tab.
3. Right-click on the **Survey Databases** item; select **New local survey database....**
4. Name it **Chapter 5-b** when the dialog box appears to name the database.
5. Right-click on **Networks** and choose **New...**; when the dialog box for naming appears, type in **Chapter 5-b**.
6. Expand **Networks**, right-click on **Chapter 5-b**, and select **Import> Import field book...**; select **Chapter 5-b.fbk** from where your files are stored for the textbook. Accept any defaults that appear on executing.
7. The loop traverse will import.
8. Right-click on **Networks** and choose **New....**
9. Name the new network **Chapter 5-b cross check.** Hit **OK.**
10. Expand **Networks**, right-click on **Chapter 5-b cross check**, and select **Import> Import field book...**; select **Chapter 5-b-crosscheck.fbk** from where your files are stored for the textbook.
11. When the **Import Field Book** dialog box appears, hit **OK.**
12. A dialog box may appear that warns that Point 1 exists. Select **Ignore all.**
13. The cross check traverse computes. Note that it is an open traverse.
14. Expand the **Network** called **Chapter 5-b.** Right-click on the **Traverses** item and hit **New...**; name it **Chapter 5-b** and hit **OK.**
15. Click on **Traverses** and in the preview window fill in the following data: the Initial Station (1), Initial Backsight (4), Stations (2,3,4,1), and Final Foresight (1).
16. Click on Chapter 5-b under Traverses, then a dialog box may appear that indicates you have made changes and not applied them. Hit **Yes** to apply the changes now.
17. Right-click on the traverse **Chapter 5-b** and select **Traverse Analysis....**
18. When the **Traverse Analysis** dialog box appears, accept the defaults and hit **OK.**
19. The Notepad files for the Compass rule, a balanced angle analysis, and the traverse analysis display, as shown in Figures 5-14, 5-15, and 5-16. Again note in the Compass rule how Point 1 returns to 2000,2000 after balancing.

To access student data files, go to www.pearsondesigncentral.com.

```
File Edit Format View Help
                  RAW   TRAVERSE              COMPASS RULE
      Point        Coordinates              Coordinates           Delta
        1      N       2000.0000        N       2000.0000       0.0000
               E       2000.0000        E       2000.0000
N 81-54-54 W  Dist:513.4309
        2      N       2072.2098        N       2072.2107       0.0011
               E       1491.6732        E       1491.6725
N 29-50-13 E  Dist:440.5203
        3      N       2454.3366        N       2454.3382       0.0021
               E       1710.8466        E       1710.8452
S 69-45-10 E  Dist:308.1994
        4      N       2347.6774        N       2347.6794       0.0028
               E       2000.0024        E       2000.0005
S 00-00-00 W  Dist:347.6794
        1      N       1999.9974        N       2000.0000       0.0035
               E       2000.0024        E       2000.0000
Area        : 155303.0 sq. ft. , 3.5653 Acres
```

Figure 5-14   Traverse analysis report—Compass rule applied report

```
File Edit Format View Help
                  RAW   TRAVERSE                NO RULE
      Point        Coordinates                Coordinates          Delta
        1      N       2000.0000        N        2000.0000       0.0000
               E       2000.0000        E        2000.0000
N 81-54-54 W  Dist:513.4300
        2      N       2072.2098        N        2072.2098       0.0000
               E       1491.6732        E        1491.6732
N 29-50-13 E  Dist:440.5200
        3      N       2454.3366        N        2454.3366       0.0000
               E       1710.8466        E        1710.8466
S 69-45-10 E  Dist:308.2000
        4      N       2347.6774        N        2347.6774       0.0000
               E       2000.0024        E        2000.0024
S 00-00-00 W  Dist:347.6800
        1      N       1999.9974        N        1999.9974       0.0000
               E       2000.0024        E        2000.0024
Error North    : 0.0026
Error East     : -0.0024
Absolute error : 0.0035
Error Direction: N 42-16-02 W
Perimeter      : 1609.8300
Precision      : 1 in 454175.0004
Number of sides: 4
Area           : 155302.9 sq. ft. , 3.5653 Acres
```

Figure 5-15   Traverse analysis, balanced angles report

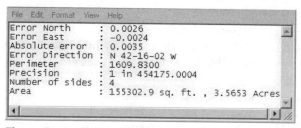

```
File Edit Format View Help
Error North    : 0.0026
Error East     : -0.0024
Absolute error : 0.0035
Error Direction : N 42-16-02 W
Perimeter      : 1609.8300
Precision      : 1 in 454175.0004
Number of sides : 4
Area           : 155302.9 sq. ft. , 3.5653 Acres
```

Figure 5-16   Traverse analysis report

Reduce the cross check traverse.

21. Expand the network called **Chapter 5-b-crosscheck**. Right-click on the **Traverses** item and hit **New...**; name it **Chapter 5-b-crosscheck** and hit **OK**.
22. Click on **Traverses** and in the preview window, fill in the following data: the Initial Station (1), Initial Backsight (2), Stations (101,102), and Final Foresight (3).
23. Right-click on **Chapter 5-b-crosscheck** and choose **Traverse Analysis...**.
24. Click on Chapter 5-b-crosscheck under Traverses.
25. Then a dialog box may appear that indicates you have made changes and not applied them. Hit **Yes** to apply the changes now.
26. Then click **Chapter 5-b-crosscheck** and right-click. From the choices, select **Traverse analysis...**. When the **Traverse Analysis** dialog box appears, accept the defaults and hit **OK**.

27. The Notepad files for the traverse analysis, a balanced angle analysis, and the Compass rule display, as shown in Figures 5-17, 5-18, and 5-19. Your results may differ slightly.

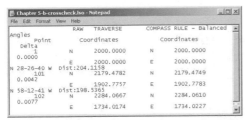

Figure 5-17   Traverse analysis report-Compass rule applied report

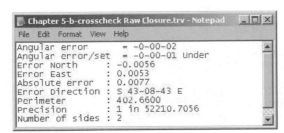

Figure 5-18   Traverse analysis report

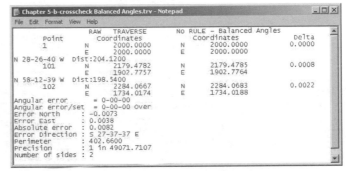

Figure 5-19   Traverse analysis, balanced angles report

TIP   When importing field books containing field collected data, the approach is exactly the same except, of course, that you may not reduce the traverse. You will simply see the data import into the Civil 3D drawing.

Exercise 5-3: Performing a Field Book Reduction in Civil 3D

You now execute a field book that will import an example of field-collected planimetric features. It will draw linework for an edge of pavement that was collected using a total station.

1. Open the drawing Chapter 5-c.dwg.
2. In the **Toolspace**, click on the **Survey** tab.
3. Right-click on the **Survey Databases** item; select **New local survey database....**
4. Name it **Chapter 5-c** when the dialog box appears to name the database.
5. Right-click on the **Chapter 5-c database** and select **Open survey database**. If the right-click menu has only **Close survey database**, then it is already open.
6. Right-click on **Networks** and choose **New...**; when the dialog box for naming appears, type in **Chapter 5-c**.
7. Expand **Networks**, right-click on **Chapter 5-c**, and select **Import> Import field book...**; select **Chapter 5-c.fbk** from where your files are stored for the textbook. Accept any defaults that appear on executing.
8. You may get a dialog box asking whether you wish to abort; say **No**.
9. The processing begins, and a roadway edge of pavement and two associated buildings will be drawn.

To access student data files, go to www.pearsondesigncentral.com.

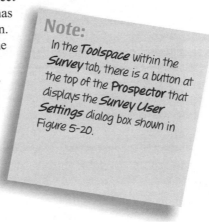

Note:
In the **Toolspace** within the **Survey** tab, there is a button at the top of the **Prospector** that displays the **Survey User Settings** dialog box shown in Figure 5-20.

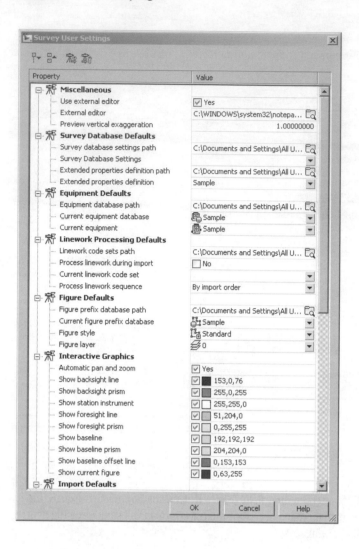

Figure 5-20   Survey User Settings dialog box

You have just imported the field book and automatically drawn the points and linework collected in the field. The previous exercises illustrate how powerful this aspect of the Civil 3D software is. The entire survey department can now use Civil 3D to develop existing ground base information that the engineering design team can use directly. The surveyor will, of course, receive the data from the engineers at the back end of the project for checking and stakeout preparation or 3D/GPS data preparation for the contractor. The formatting of this data is covered in Appendix A on data sharing.

CHAPTER SUMMARY

This chapter introduced you to surveying in Civil 3D. The technology allows you to develop the entire base required for a project, from the initial designs to quality control and data preparation.

CHAPTER TEST QUESTIONS

Multiple Choice

1. The survey features added to the 2007 release include which of the following?

   a. Traverse entry, editing, and management
   b. Traverse balancing
   c. Importing filed data collector files
   d. All of the above

2. The interface for the surveying capabilities includes which of the following?

a. Importing of SRTM satellite data
b. Automatically pounding hubs and stakes into the ground
c. Enabling the software to set up total stations so field crews are no longer needed
d. None of the above

3. The survey functionality allows users to create the formats required for 3D/GPS Machine Control equipment. Which manufacturers are supported?

a. Topcon, Trimble, Leica
b. Caterpillar, Komatsu, VanNatta
c. Mercedes, Range Rover, Ford
d. All of the above

4. Survey functions include which of the following?

a. Collecting planimetric and 3D data of existing conditions
b. Quality control of engineering data and preparation of stakeout data for construction
c. Computing property boundaries
d. All of the above

5. The types of data surveyors prepare includes which of the following?

a. Proposed finished ground engineering, drainage improvements, stormwater retention facilities
b. Surface data, geometric data, and control data
c. Site improvements for dams, airport, or highways
d. Design of subdivisions, harbors, and treatment plants

6. Which of the following pertains to traverse data established by surveyors?

a. They are often tied into control monuments.
b. They are repeatedly occupied and used in surveying and perhaps construction and provide a constant location from which to compute additional point data.
c. They are usually corrected for errors caused by human, ambient, or instrument lapses.
d. All of the above

7. When a traverse is corrected and balanced, what components are corrected?

a. The area within the closed traverse is corrected and rounded.
b. The control points governing the traverse are moved to new and more accurate locations.
c. The points or vertices of the traverse figure with its incorrect distances and angular errors are corrected.
d. All of the above

8. Surveyors also work in which of the following areas?

a. Aerial photogrammetry, GIS research, and GPS surveying
b. Hydraulic drainage computations for custom drainage structures
c. Designing beams and columns for standard building structures
d. None of the above

9. Why are VIOs (Visually Identifiable Objects) used in aerial photogrammetry?

a. They can be seen in the photographs.
b. They have horizontal and vertical control associated with them.
c. They assist in calibrating everything in the photo to a known coordinate.
d. All of the above

10. What makes Imaginary Reference Stations an interesting technology for surveyors?

a. They eliminate the need for base stations for many surveyors.
b. They create virtual stations that interpolate errors and corrections.
c. They are being developed by both public and private concerns.
d. All of the above

True or False

1. True or False: Civil 3D can create, edit, and balance traverses; import field shot data; and draw linework and points.

2. True or False: 2D and 3D control points are often established randomly and are never tied to anything official.

3. True or False: In photogrammetry, a VIO is a Vertical Interference Obstacle that interferes with the airplane's flight path.

4. True or False: We use the Compass rule to find North when we are in the field.

5. True or False: A polygon with six sides should have the sum of the interior angles equal to 750 degrees.

6. True or False: There are several files produced when balancing a traverse. They include analysis files, which display horizontal closure and angular error, a file showing raw and adjusted elevations; a file showing the balancing of the angular error; and the final adjusted coordinates.

7. True or False: The survey language can be customized so that the order of the data entry can be changed to the user's preferences.

8. True or False: The survey language can be customized so that the actual names of the commands (such as AD or BS) can be changed to what the user prefers.

9. True or False: An interface specifically developed for the surveyor exists in Civil 3D.

10. True or False: Civil 3D will perform the Compass rule only when balancing traverses.

CHAPTER EXERCISES

1. What functions do surveyors perform on engineering projects? Do surveyors work in two dimensions or three?
2. Why is establishing project control important?
3. How many degrees does a 16-sided closed traverse have inside it?
4. How might the following table be adjusted to correct the angular error in this traverse?

Adjustment of Angles			
Point	Measured Interior Angle	Average Correction (Degrees)	Adjusted Angle (Degrees)
A	120.5		
B	110.0		
C	110.5		
D	99.5		
E	100.0		
	———	———	———
Result:			

5. When speaking of traverse misclosure, what is the latitude and departure?
6. What is the relative precision for a 1000′ traverse that has a linear misclosure of 0.1?
7. If a traverse has a departure of 0.2 and a latitude of 0.3, what is the linear misclosure?
8. When using the survey language in Civil 3D, what do the following commands indicate: STA 10, BS 5?
9. When using the survey language in Civil 3D, what do the following commands indicate: NE 10 1000 1000, NE 5 1500 1000?
10. When shooting a traverse, why does it not close perfectly?

Civil 3D—The Modern Curvilinead

6

Chapter Objectives

- Understand the mathematics behind the Civil 3D geometry tools.
- Understand distances; bearings; information on traverses used for establishing control on projects; and formulas for circles, arcs, triangles, and lines.
- Use Civil 3D for creating and editing these geometry items.
- Use the many **Transparent** commands that are in Civil 3D.
- Understand how to develop, label, and edit alignments and parcels.

INTRODUCTION

Civil 3D is a modern curvilinead. What is a curvilinead? It is an instrument that draws curvilinear and rectilinear objects. The "3D" in Civil 3D could stand for Design, Delineation, Depiction because of its strengths in developing curvilinear and rectilinear geometry objects. This chapter begins with some of the formulas needed to design geometry and discusses curvilinear linework generation; roadway alignment; and parcel creation, editing, and drafting. The ability to modify these data and the development of curvilinear 2D geometry (Lines, Arcs, Spirals), parcels, alignments, and labels are discussed in detail.

REVIEW OF FUNCTIONS AND FEATURES TO BE USED

This chapter uses engineering functions to compute angles, slopes, and distances. Civil 3D has many tools for creating lines and curves, and this chapter examines how these are then used to create disciplinary objects such as alignments and parcels.

COMPUTATIONS OF LINES AND THEIR ANGLES

In a vector-based program, points create lines. Points occupy a position consisting of only an X coordinate, a Y coordinate, and a Z coordinate. A linear connection of the dots occurs with a clear start, a distance, and direction. Refer to Figure 6-1 for a line starting at 0, 0 and continuing through a point of 7.5, 2.5.

The points can be Civil 3D points or simply just AutoCAD points or picks on the screen, but they are points nevertheless. When drawing lines in AutoCAD, you can easily find out information about them by using the **LIST** command. But where does the **LIST** command compute its results from? Can these results be accomplished by hand, using manual techniques? You certainly should be able to reproduce these results using manual techniques just in case you want to check the computer. One of the worst things that someone using a computer can do when asked, "How do you know that the value is correct?" is to say, "Because the computer said so." A better response would be, "I know this is a correct estimate of the value based on my knowledge of the

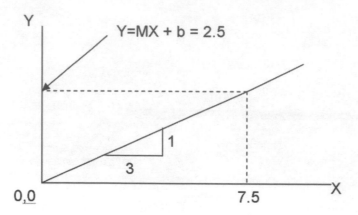

Figure 6-1   A vector

software's algorithms and the data I developed." It is necessary to know the engineering and mathematical formulas behind these algorithms, and each chapter in this text explores them. This chapter discusses linear and curvilinear computations.

Example 6-1: Find the Angle of a Two-Dimensional Line from the X Axis

To find the angle from the X axis of the two-dimensional line with the same coordinate values as shown in Figure 6-1, follow this process:

Slope $= \Delta Y/\Delta X = (20 - 15)/(10 - 5) = 5/5 = 1$

The angle then is computed as: $(ATAN((ABS)slope)) = ATAN(1) = 45°$

Example 6-2: Find the Angle of a Three-Dimensional Line from the X Axis

To find the angle from the X axis of the three-dimensional line with the same coordinate values as shown in Figure 6-1, follow this process:

Slope $= \Delta Z/\sqrt{A^2 + B^2} = (5 - 10)/(7.0710678) = 0.70710678$

The angle then is computed as: $(ATAN((ABS)slope) = ATAN(0.70710678) = 35.254°$
The formula for a line, $Y = mX + b$, was discussed in Chapter 3 under Point Basics.
The Y coordinate equals the slope of the line times the X coordinate plus the y intercept.
Therefore, in Figure 6-1, $m = .333$, $X = 7.5$, and $b = 0$; $Y = 2.5$.

DISTANCES AND BEARINGS

Distances and bearings are used to show course and lengths for many items such as parcel lines, boundaries, alignments, pipelines, and so forth. The bearing has four quadrants, each no larger than 90 degrees. It always starts at either north or south and is followed by the angle and then the direction to which it turns, which is either east or west. See Figure 6-2.

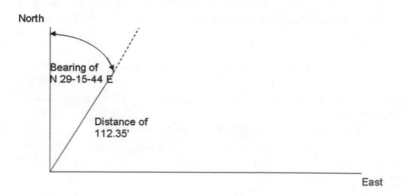

Figure 6-2   Bearing quadrants

3D Linework Uses Slope Distances for Distance Measurement

Distances measured can include horizontal lengths, vertical lengths, *slope distances*, or vertical angles. Figure 6-3 shows what these are in establishing data connecting Point *A* to Point *B*.

slope distances: The distance measured from Point *A* to Point *B* along an incline. It will always be longer than the horizontal distance when the slope is not horizontal or vertical.

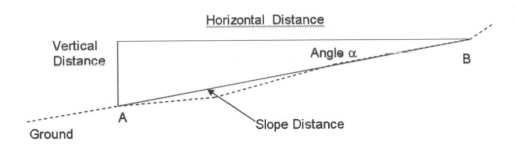

Figure 6-3   Slope distances

Example 6-3: Computing the Difference in Height Between Rods

As shown in Figure 6-4,

Rod reading = 7.21′
Rod reading = 2.63′
Difference in Elevation = 7.21−2.63 = **4.58′**

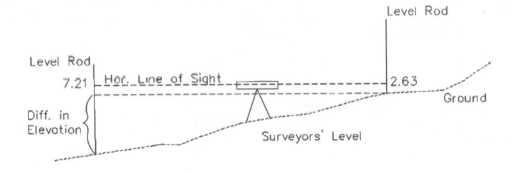

Figure 6-4   Computing the difference in height between rods

Control Surveys

Control surveys establish reference points and reference lines for preliminary and construction surveys. Vertical reference points called benchmarks are also established. These are then tied into state coordinate systems, property lines, road centerlines, or arbitrary grid systems. The various types of tie-in methods are shown in Figure 6-5.

control survey: Sets the "monumentation" for the project. All survey shots and references typically come from or tie back to this monumentation.

- Type A, rectangular tie-in, is also known as a right angle offset. Remember in Chapter 3 how many commands assisted us in developing these Perpendiculars?

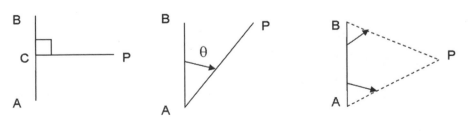

Figure 6-5   Tie-in methods

- Type B, polar tie-in, is also known as the angle/distance technique.
- Type C, intersection tie-in, uses two angles from a baseline to locate a position.

Example 6-4: Stationing

Distances along baselines are called stations, as in Figure 6-6. Right angles can be achieved from the baseline. The distance along this right angle is called an offset.

Station 2 + 36.517 is 236.517′ from the intersection of Elm and Pine. The left corner of the building is 236.517′ from Elm and 40.01′ at a 90 degree angle from Pine.

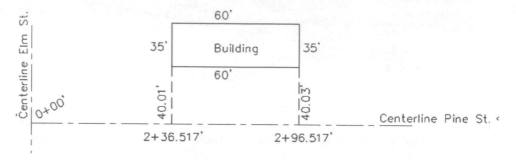

Figure 6-6   Stationing

Example 6-5: Doubling the Angle

A surveying technique to enhance precision when shooting data in the field is called Doubling the Angle. The angles are effectively shot and computed twice for each interior angle. Due to human error, ambient condition error, or equipment error, these measures are often slightly different. So the surveyor often creates a mean of the two angles, anticipating that the mean angular error is less than any one of the angles independently.

Station	Direct Angle	Double Angle	Mean
A	101-24-00	202-48-00	101-24-00
B	149-13-00	289-26-00	149-13-00
C	80-58-00	161-57-00	80-58-30
D	116-20-00	232-38-00	116-19-00
E	92-04-00	184-09-00	92-04-30
		Total Degrees	538-119-00 = 539-59-00
			(Is this correct?)

The total number of degrees within a closed polygon depends on the number of sides and is computed using the following formula. ANGULAR CLOSURE = $(N - 2) \times 180$; therefore, our polygon = $3 \times 180 = 540\text{-}00\text{-}00$. So subtracting these yields 540-00-00 minus 539-59-00 = 01′-00″ ERROR. See Figure 6-7.

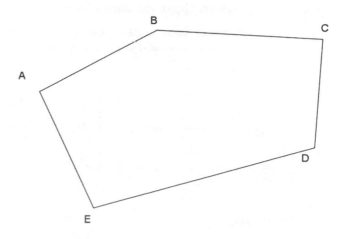

Figure 6-7   Polygons

Vector Data and Formulas

As a refresher, to fully understand the computations that the Civil 3D software performs, the following information is provided along with examples. Formulas for computing the data manually are also included.

Circles

- Radius, Perimeter, Area

Right Triangles

- Lengths of sides, Interior angles

Curvilinear Objects Including Arcs, Circular Curves, and Spirals

- Arc definition, Chord definition
- Define the components of an arc
- Formulas for computing Arc Length (L), Radius (R), Chord length (C), Mid-ordinate chord distance (M), External *secant* (E), and Tangent length (T)
- Define the components of a spiral
- Types of horizontal curves

secant: A line that intersects a circle twice. An external secant is the part of the secant that is outside the circle or arc.

Circle Formulas

Radius = 1/2 × Diameter
Pi radians = 180°
1 radian − 180/π
2 Pi radians = 360
Perimeter = 2 × π × r or, π × Diameter
Area = π × r^2

Right Triangle Definitions and Formulas

$a^2 + b^2 = c^2$
$a^2 = (c^2 - b^2)$
$b^2 = (c^2 - a^2)$
$c^2 = (a^2 + b^2)$

Sides

Tan = Opposite/Adjacent
Sin = Opposite/Hypotenuse
Cos = Adjacent/Hypotenuse
$A + B + C = 180°$

Note

$A° = 180° - 90° - B°$ or, $90° - B° \rightarrow B° = 90° - A°$
$A° = \text{Tan}^{-1}(b/a)$ or $\text{Sin}^{-1}(b/c)$ or $\text{Cos}^{-1}(a/c)$
$B° = \text{Tan}^{-1}(a/b)$ or $\text{Sin}^{-1}(a/c)$ or $\text{Cos}^{-1}(b/c)$

Example 6-6: Triangles

If the right triangle in Figure 6-8 has a 27.5′ base and a height of 38.7′, how would you find:

1. The angle B.

$B = \text{Tan}^{-1}(\text{opp/adj}) = \text{Tan}^{-1}(38.7/27.5) = 54.60261522$
$0.60261522 \times 60 = 36.1569$
$0.1569 \times 60 = 9.414 = 54 - 36 - 9$

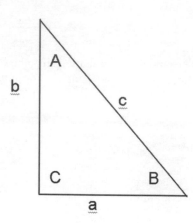

Figure 6-8   Triangles

2. The remaining angle of the triangle:

   $90 - 54.6026 = 35.40$

3. The length of the hypotenuse:

   $c = \sqrt{((27.5)^2 + (38.7)^2)} = 47.48'$

4. The area of the triangle:

   $(27.5 \times 38.7)/2 = 532.13 \text{ ft}^2$

5. What is the closest distance from C to any point along the hypotenuse?

   We know angle $B = 54.6026°$

   We know that Sin $(54.6026) = $ opp/hyp

   If $X = Y/Z$, then $Y = X \times Z$ and $Z = Y/X$, then 27.5 $\times$ Sin $(54.6026) = 22.42'$

6. Where does the shortest distance line intersect the hypotenuse in relation to point A?

   We know two sides of the new triangle so,

   $a^2 + b^2 = c^2$ and that $c = 22.42$ and $b = 27.5$

   $a = \sqrt{(c^2 - b^2)} = \sqrt{((27.5)^2 - (22.42)^2)} = 15.92'$

Because a right triangle is being divided into smaller right triangles, the interior always remains the same as with the original triangle.

Example 6-7: A Practical Problem

See Figure 6-9. A homeowner wants to remove the existing tree and put a well there. County regulations say the well must be 50′ from the drain field and 25′ from the house. Does it work?

   The measured distance from the tree to the house = 26′; OK. The distance from the drain field to the house is 32.5′. Distance from the tree to the drain field = $\sqrt{(32.5^2 + 26^2)} = 41.60$; not OK. See Figure 6-10.

   Suggested new location for well could be:

   An alternative #1 might be: $a = \sqrt{(c^2 - b^2)} = \sqrt{(50^2 - 32.50^2)} = 38'$

   An alternative #2 might be: $b = \sqrt{(50^2 - 26^2)} = 42.71$, say, 43′

From the corner of the drain field looking at the corner of the house, what is the angle to locate the proposed well?

   For alternative #2,

   $A = \text{Tan}^{-1} (40/32.5) = 50.9°$

   $= \text{Sin}^{-1} (40/50) = 53.13°$

   $= \text{Cos}^{-1} (32.5/50) = 49.45°$

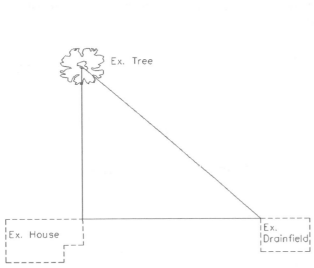

Figure 6-9   Locating a proposed well—1

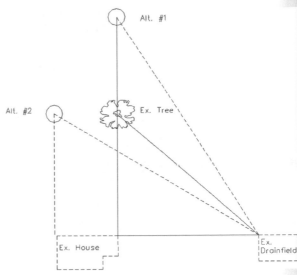

Figure 6-10   Locating a proposed well—2

CURVILINEAR OBJECTS—ARCS, CIRCULAR CURVES, AND SPIRALS—DEFINITIONS AND FORMULAS

Another aspect of drawing is the ability to compute curves and arcs. Arcs are defined as those curvilinear objects that have a fixed radius, and curves are those objects that may have a fixed radius but may also be dynamic. Spirals and parabolas fall into the curve category.

Some specific formulas for computing arc data and spiral data need to be discussed in detail before moving toward automated solutions.

Arcs have two definitions: the Arc definition (Figure 6-11) and the Chord definition (Figure 6-12). The Arc definition is the most widely used and typically used by highway designers and other land development staff. It is also called the *Roadway definition*. The Chord method is called the *Railway definition*.

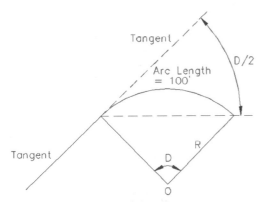

Figure 6-11   The Arc definition

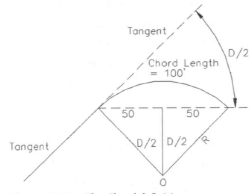

Figure 6-12   The Chord definition

The *Arc method* of curve calculation occurs where the degree of curve is measured over an arc length of 100′. The formulas are:

$D_a/100 = 360°/(2 \times PI \times R)$,
$D_a = 36000/(2 \times \pi \times R)$, or
$D_a = 5729.578/R$.
$R = 5729.578/D_a$. If $D_a = 1°$, then $R = 5729.578$ units and $\pi = 3.14159\ldots$
And $R = 5729.578/D_a$. If $D_a = 1°$, then $R = 5729.578′$ and $\pi = 3.14159\ldots$
And $R = 5729.578/D_a$. If $D_a = 1°$, then $R = 5729.578$ m and $\pi = 3.14159\ldots$

The *Chord method* of curve calculation occurs where the degree of curve is measured over a chord length of $100'$. The formulas are:

$\text{Sin } (D_c/2) = 50/R$

$R = 50/\text{Sin } (1/2)D_c$, where D_c is in degrees.

If $D_c = 1°$, then $R = 5729.648$ units.

Circular Curves.   According to Figure 6-13,

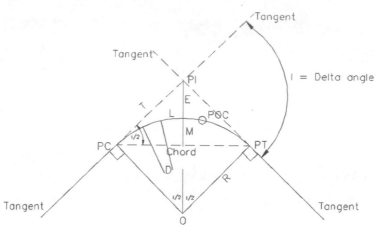

Figure 6-13   Circular Curves

PI = Point of Intersection

PT = Point of Tangency

T = Tangent length

L = Length of curve

E = External distance

$D = D_a$ degree of curve, arc definition

$D = D_c$ degree of curve, chord definition

POC = Point on Curve

PC = Point of Curvature

I = Deflection angle (Delta)

R = Radius

C = Chord length

M = Middle ordinate distance

PRC = Point of Reverse Curvature (not shown)

PCC = Point of Compound Curvature (not shown)

Arc Formulas.   Note in the formulas, the difference between the *letter I* and the *number 1*.

$L = 100 \times I°/D_a°$ $\qquad L = RI$ (where I is in radians), *or* $RI\pi/180$

$R = 5729.578/D_a°$ $\qquad\qquad T = R \times \text{Tan } (I/2)$

$C = 2R \times \text{Sin } (I/2)$ $\qquad\quad R/(R + E) = \text{Cos } (I/2)$

$E = R((1/\text{Cos } (I/2)) - 1)$ $\quad (R - M)/R = \text{Cos } (I/2)$

$M = R(1 - \text{Cos } (I/2))$ $\qquad E = T \times \text{Tan } (I/4)$

$M = E \times \text{Cos } (I/2)$ $\qquad\quad R = 50/(\text{Sin } (D/2))$

Example 6-8: Basic Curve Formulas

If $I = 45$, $L = 75$, then $R = 95.49$, $T = 39.55$, $C = 73.09$, $E = 7.87$,
   $M = 7.27$, $D_a = 60.0000$
$75 = (100 \times 45)/D_a$, therefore $D_a = (100 \times 45)/75 = 60.0000$
$R = 5729.578/60 = 95.49$; $E = 95.49((1/\text{Cos}(I/2)) - 1) = 95.49$
   $\times 0.08239 = 7.867$
$M = 95.49 \times (1 - (\text{Cos}(I/2))) = 95.49 \times (1 - .92387) = 7.268$
$C = 2(95.49) \times \text{Sin}(45/2) = 73.08$

Example 6-9: Curve Application

Two highway tangents intersect with a right intersection angle $I = 12\text{-}30\text{-}00$ at station $0 + 152.204$ m. If a radius of 300 m is to be used for the circular curve, prepare the field book notes to the nearest minute in order to lay out the curve with 20 m staking.

Note:
The deflection angle for a chord length of 20 m from the PC is $(20/L)(1/2)$. The field notes are set up in the following table.

Solution:

$T = R \times \text{Tan}(I/2) = 300 \times \text{Tan}(6°15')$
   $= 32.855$ m
$L = RI\pi/180 = (300)(12.50)(\pi)/180$
   $= 65.450$ m
Station of PI $= 0 + 152.204$
$-T = -(0 + 32.855)$
Station of PC $= 0 + 119.349$
$+L = +(0 + 65.450)$
Station of PT $= 0 + 184.799$ m

Station	Chord Dist from PC	Point	Deflection Angle
0 + 184.799	65.450	PT	6-15-00
0 + 180	60.651		5-47-30
0 + 160	40.651		3-52-55
0 + 140	20.651		1-58-19
0 + 120	0.651		00-03-44
0 + 119.349	0	PC	00-00-00
Procedure:	$180 - 119.349 = 60.651$		
	$(60.651/65.45) \times 6.25 = 5.7917° = 5\text{-}47\text{-}30°$		

Example 6-10: Centerline Curve

Find the arc distance for the roadway centerline shown in Figure 6-14. If this were a complete circle, the perimeter would be:

$2\pi r = 2\pi200 = 1256.64'$
Therefore, $27°/360° \times 1256.64 = 94.25'$.
Shortcut $= (\text{angle} \times R)/57.30 = 94.25'$
Partial area $= \text{angle}/360 \times \pi r^2$
Shortcut $= (\text{angle} \times R^2)/114.59 = 9424.91$ ft^2

Example 6-11: Miscellaneous Applications for Curve Solutions

These concepts can be used in widely varying problems. Here is an example of a pipe problem in which you need to compute flow through a pipe. A 48″ diameter RCP is flowing 14″ deep (Figure 6-15). What are the area of flow and wetted perimeter?

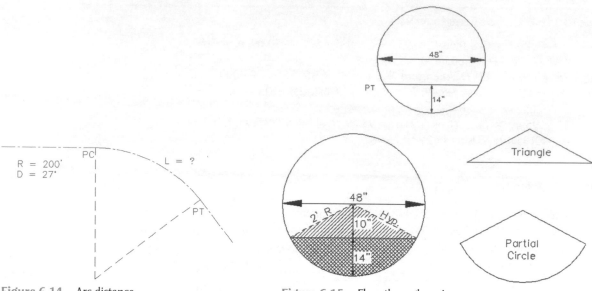

Figure 6-14   Arc distance   **Figure 6-15**   Flow through a pipe

Figure the angles of the triangle and base width (across water surface).

Cos angle = Adjacent/Hypotneuse
Angle = Cos − 1 (0.83′/2.0′) = 65.4807°

Then, the total angle across the water surface = 2 × 65.4807 = 130.9614°
The base width = $\sqrt{(c^2 - a^2)}$ = $\sqrt{(22 - 0.832)}$ = 1.82′
Then, the total width of the water surface = 2 × 1.82 = 3.64′
Figure the flow area. Area (triangle) = ((base × height)/2) × 2; the 2s cancel out.

3.64 × 0.83 = 3.02 ft²
Area of water = angle × R^2/114.59 = 130.9614 × 22/114.59 = 4.57 ft²

Flow area = 4.57 − 3.02 = 1.55
The wetted perimeter = angle × R/57.30 = 130.95614 × 2/57.30 = 4.57′

This information could be used in Mannings formula as follows:
The RCP is sloped at a grade of 5%. We know that the n = 0.013 for Mannings

friction coefficient. Then, $Q = A \times \left(\dfrac{A}{Wp}\right)^{2/3} \times \sqrt{S} \times \left(\dfrac{1.486}{n}\right)$

$$Q = 1.55 \times \left(\frac{1.55}{4.57}\right)^{2/3} \times \sqrt{0.05} \times \frac{1.486}{0.013} = 19.26 \text{ cfs.}$$

Spiral Definitions and Formulas.   Spirals are used to create a smooth transition as one travels from a tangent to a curve and then back out to a tangent again. Figure 6-16 shows the parameters for coming into a spiral. The parameters are the same for leaving a spiral.

TS = Tangent to spiral point
SC = Spiral to Curve
CS = Curve to spiral
PI = Point of Intersection
D = Total deflection angle
D_s = Spiral delta angle
D_c = Circular curve delta
T = Total tangent length
R = Radius of circular curve
L = Length of spiral
LT = Long tangent
ST = Short tangent
X = Total "Horizontal" Spiral length

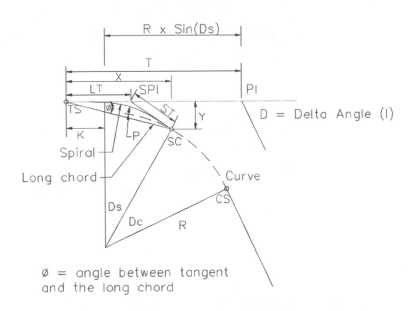

$\emptyset$ = angle between tangent
and the long chord

Figure 6-16   Spirals

Y = Total "Vertical" Spiral Length
P = Offset of the tangent line to the PC of the shifted curve
K = Abscissa of the PC of the shifted circular curve referred to the straight
   end of the spiral
SPI = Spiral PI

Formulas for Approximate Solutions to Spiral Problems

$$Y/L = \sin(\phi) \qquad\qquad Y = L \times \sin(\phi)$$
$$X_2 = L_2 - Y_2 \qquad\qquad X = \sqrt{(L_2 - Y_2)}$$
$$K = X/2 \qquad\qquad\qquad P = Y/4$$
$$LT = (\sin(2/3 \times \phi)) \times L/\sin(\phi) \qquad ST = (\sin(1/3 \times \phi)) \times L/\sin(\phi)$$

Types of Horizontal Curves.   The curves shown in Figure 6-17 illustrate the various types of curves that are in the civil engineering business. The ***broken back curve*** is usually not allowed by review agencies because the tangent is not tangent to the curve.

broken back curve: An alignment that has a linear segment either coming into or leaving an arc that is not tangent to the arc. This is usually not allowed in most jurisdictions.

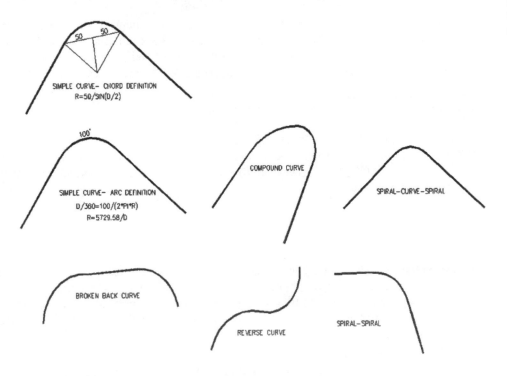

SIMPLE CURVE- CHORD DEFINITION
R=50/SIN(D/2)

SIMPLE CURVE- ARC DEFINITION
D/360=100/(2*PI*R)
R=5729.58/D

COMPOUND CURVE

SPIRAL-CURVE-SPIRAL

BROKEN BACK CURVE

REVERSE CURVE

SPIRAL-SPIRAL

Figure 6-17   Types of horizontal curves

CIVIL 3D'S DEFAULT ANGULAR SYSTEM

In Civil 3D, the default angle definitions occur using the Cartesian system, in which the positive X direction is to the right on the screen or monitor and negative X is to the left. Positive Y is up the screen, and negative Y is down. Positive Z is basically in the user's face with negative Z going into the monitor. Angles increase counterclockwise from 0° along the X axis to 360°, back to the X axis. Figure 6-18 shows a 90° angle from the X axis.

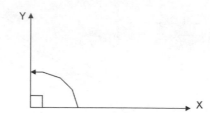

Figure 6-18   Angles in AutoCAD

Another default in AutoCAD and Civil 3D is that the units for the angles tend to be set to decimal degrees and 0 places of precision. These should also be set up prior to usage so that the desired angles and criteria are to the company's liking. Some people prefer to use degrees, minutes, and seconds as the angle units type, and the precision is usually set to, at least, the nearest second. If you prefer to use decimal degrees, then the precision should be to at least four places. The software converts any output listings to the units the user sets. So if the units are set to decimal degrees and a **LIST** command is issued, the CAD system responds with decimal degrees as part of the listing. If the units are set to degrees, minutes, and seconds, then the system responds accordingly. These can be flipped at any point in the working session to achieve the desired units reporting.

CONVERTING DECIMAL DEGREES TO D-M-S

If the user must perform these computations manually, here are some examples of converting angular units from decimal degrees to degrees, minutes, and seconds.

Example 6-12: Angular Conversions Decimal Degrees to D-M-S

49.5566° breaks down to 49° and 0.5566 of a degree. Then, multiply 0.5566 degree × 60 (minutes per degree) to get the number of minutes, which = 33.396 minutes. Now you have 33 minutes and 0.396 of a minute. Then multiply 0.396 minute × 60 seconds per minute to get the number of seconds, which is = 23.76 seconds. Therefore, 49.5566° = 49°−33′−23.76″.

Example 6-13: Angular Conversions D-M-S to Decimal Degrees

To convert DMS 49°−33′−23.76″ to decimal degrees, perform the following: 23.76″/60 (seconds per minute) = 0.396 minute. Then add the 33′ to the 0.396′ to get 33.396′. Then divide 33.396′ by 60 (minutes per degree) and get 0.5566 degree. Then add the 49° to the 0.5566 to get 49.5566°.

ANGLES IN CIVIL ENGINEERING

Now that you can compute the angles of linework manually and based on the Cartesian coordinate system, it is time to discuss in more depth how to talk about angles in terms that civil engineers and surveyors use. This industry uses angles to describe many things, such as property line directions, road centerline directions, and construction instructions for stakeout. Some of the types of important angles to understand are interior angles, azimuths, bearings, cardinal directions, deflection angles, and turned angles.

Interior angles (Figure 6-19) measure the angle between two linear objects. The angle can be acute or obtuse.

Figure 6-19   Interior angles

An azimuth can be measured from either the North or South. The North azimuth measures angles from the North axis, in a clockwise direction to 360°. The South azimuth measures angles from the South axis, clockwise to 360°.

Bearings (Figure 6-20) measure a heading and are broken into four quadrants: North, South, East, and West. Each quadrant has 90°. The quadrant usually referred to as quadrant 1 is the North-East quadrant and measures from North and turns toward the East. Therefore, a bearing of N 45°−30′−30″ E is located by facing North and turning toward the East an angle of 45°−30′−30″. Quadrant 2 is South-East and begins by facing South and turning the angle toward the East. Quadrant 3 is South-West and also begins by facing South but turns toward the West. Quadrant 4 is North-West, begins by facing North and turning the angle toward the West.

There are also angles known as cardinal directions, which are North, South, East, and West, routinely seen in describing the heading of a hurricane. "Hurricane Ivan is heading North-North-West," which is halfway between North and North-West. In degrees that would be N 22°−30′−00″ W.

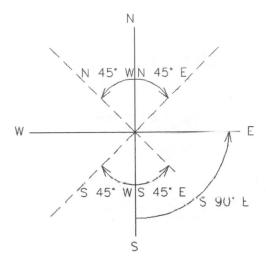

Figure 6-20   Bearings

Figure 6-21 illustrates a person standing at Point B, looking forward at the angle defined from Point A to Point B and then turning 28°−16′−51″ to the right to get to Point C. This shows deflection angles.

Figure 6-22 illustrates a person standing at Point B, looking back at Point A, and then turning 208°−16′−51″ to the right to get to Point C. This shows turned angles.

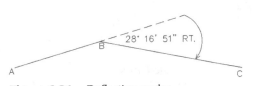

Figure 6-21   Deflection angles

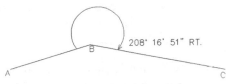

Figure 6-22   Turned angles

On the subject of angles, there are two other types of angle measurement—one called Grads, and another called Radians. A Grad is 1/400th of a circle, where North is what would be zero, East is 100 g, South is 200 g, West is 300 g, and back to North is 400 g. This angular system is used in some international countries and by the United States Department of State. A Radian is 180°/π and is often used in computer programming and in the calculation of some arc formulas.

Exercise 6-1: Units

1. Begin the Civil 3D software. Be sure that the Dynamic UCS at the bottom of the screen is turned off.
2. Draw a line from **11,7** to **38,18** and terminate the command.
3. Then type **LIST** at the command prompt. The software responds as follows.

```
Select objects:
```

Select the object, hit **<Enter>**, and this listing will display:

```
LINE Layer: "0"
Space: Model space
Handle = 3F2
from point, X = 11.0000 Y = 7.0000 Z = 0.0000
to point, X = 38.0000 Y = 18.0000 Z = 0.0000
Length = 29.1548, Angle in XY Plane = 22
Delta X = 27.0000, Delta Y = 11.0000, Delta Z = 0.0000
```

Note the angle of 22 degrees. Is it an even 22°?

4. Next, at the command prompt, type **UN** for **Units** to bring up the **Units** dialog box. See Figure 6-23.

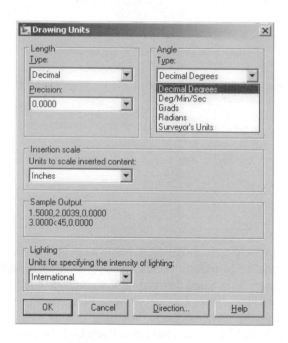

Figure 6-23   Units dialog box

5. Note under the **Angle Type** pop-down window are the supported angle types. **Decimal Degrees** is the default. The default **Precision** is set to 0; hence there is no precision for display beyond the nearest degree. Set the **Precision** to **4** decimal places (0.0000)and hit **OK**.
6. Type **LIST** again, select the line, and hit **<Enter>**. Notice that the angle shown now is 22.1663 degrees.
7. Next, at the command prompt, type **UN** again to bring up the **Units** dialog box.
8. Under the **Angle Type** pop-down window, choose **Deg/Min/Sec** and hit **OK**. Type **LIST** again, select the line, and hit **<Enter>**. Notice that the Angle in *XY* Plane = 22d9′59″.
9. Next at the command prompt, type **UN** again to bring up the **Units** dialog box.
10. Under **Angle Type** pop-down window, choose **Surveyor's Units** and hit **OK**. Type **LIST** again, select the line, and hit **<Enter>**. Notice that the Angle in *XY* Plane is a bearing of N 67d50′1″ E.

Many Geometry commands can be performed using the **Parcels** and **Alignments** menus. Discussion of other tools as well will follow but here is a brief explanation of the menu pulldowns for Parcels and Alignments.

The **Parcels** pull-down menu (Figure 6-24) commands include:

Create Parcel by Layout... invokes the **Parcel Layout Tools** toolbar.

Create Parcel from Objects allows for creating new parcels from entities.

Create ROW allows for creating automatic offsets for Right of Way creation.

Edit Parcel includes Edit Parcel Segments, Edit Parcel Properties, and Renumber/Rename Parcels.

Edit Parcel Elevations offers many options for editing parcel elevations.

Add Parcel Labels adds specific labels to parcels.

Add Tables allows for creating property tables of lines, arcs, and so on.

The **Alignments** pull-down menu (Figure 6-25) commands are as follows:

Create Alignment by Layout... invokes the **Create Alignment - Layout** toolbar.

Create Alignment from Polyline allows for creating new alignments from polylines.

Edit Alignment Geometry... invokes the **Layout** toolbar for editing alignments that already exist.

Reverse Alignment Direction allows the same.

Design Criteria Editor... invokes the **Design Criteria Editor** dialog box.

Add Alignment Labels adds specific labels to alignments.

Add Tables allows for creating alignment tables of lines, arcs, and so on.

Figure 6-24   The Parcels pull-down menu

Figure 6-25   The Alignments pull-down menu

GEOMETRY COMPUTATIONS

Now that the chapter has covered the basic and fundamental mathematics behind curvilinear and rectilinear geometry, discussion proceeds with the capabilities of Civil 3D in these areas. Again, enormous functionality exists within AutoCAD alone, and because it is a prerequisite to know AutoCAD, coverage of those routines within Civil 3D follows.

In addition to investigating some of the primitive geometry tools, the tools for creating parcels and alignments are also explored.

THE TRANSPARENT COMMANDS TOOLBAR

You can use **Transparent Commands** within other commands that need data entry consisting of multiple points such as the AutoCAD **LINE** command. Figure 6-26 shows the **Transparent Commands** toolbar. These can be used just like the AutoCAD **Transparent Commands** by preceding them with an apostrophe. You can also pick them as needed from the toolbar. A user can

Figure 6-26   The Transparent Commands toolbar

set a series of points using that data entry format because it remains in that data entry mode until you change it or exit.

The Civil **Transparent Commands** are used to enter values based on information that can be supplied when you are prompted for a radius, a point, or a distance. Most of these commands are used to specify point locations within another operation, such as the creation of property lines for parcel data. These commands provide great flexibility of obtaining information from data already existing within the drawing without forcing you to accumulate the information ahead of time. This allows you to calculate the location for a point from a variety of angles and distances.

Job skills will benefit because these routines save hours of manual computation for designers.

They are fun to use and provide excellent visuals as you work with them. The command definitions from left to right across the toolbar are described as follows with the accompanying abbreviation that can be typed in as the command is being used.

 'AD—Angle Distance

 'BD—Bearing Distance

 'ZD—Azimuth Distance

 'DD—Deflection Distance

 'NE—Northing Easting

 'GN—Grid Northing Grid Easting

 'LL—Latitude Longitude

 'PN—Point Number

 'PA—Point Name

 'PO—Point Object

 'SS—Side Shot

 'SO—Station Offset

 Transparent command filters exist at this location in the toolbar. These allow for selecting point information by Point Number, by selecting the Point anywhere the point data are visible, or via a Northing/Easting entry.

 Three additional commands include: **Profile Station from Plan, Profile Station and Elevation from Plan**, and **Profile Station and Elevation** from COGO Point. These commands prompt for and allow for you to select information for the profile by referring to the plan view of the alignment. These can be beneficial in that an important location can be identified using plan view objects that cannot be seen when viewing the profile. This could be the location of a horizontal utility manhole, for instance.

'PSE—Profile Station Elevation

 'PGS—Profile Grade Station

 'PGL—Profile Grade Length

 'MR—Match Radius

 'ML—Match Length

Exercise 6-2: The **'AD** Command

You now explore how these commands work. Let us begin with the **'AD** command. This command allows you to build linework using a turned angle and distance (Figure 6-27).

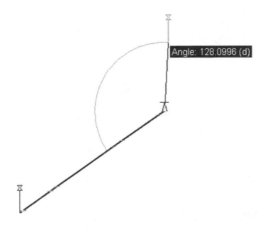

Figure 6-27   Turned angle and distance

TIP

The **'AD** command can be used to describe a traverse based on an occupied point, a backsight, turned angles, and distances.

1. Open the drawing called Chapter-6-Geometry.dwg.
2. Using the **V** for **View** command, highlight the view called **Geom-A**, hit **Set Current**, and then hit **OK**. You draw linework using turned angles and distances from the line visible on the screen.
3. Type **L** for **Line**. Follow the prompts:
4. `LINE Specify first point`: Using an **Endpoint** Osnap pick the northern end of the line in the view.
5. `Specify next point or [Undo]`: Type **'AD** or select the first icon on the **Transparent Commands** toolbar.
6. `>>Specify ending point or [.P/.N/.G]`: Using an **Endpoint** Osnap pick the southern end of the line in the view.
7. `Current angle unit: degree, Input: DD.DDDDDD (decimal)`

To access student data files, go to www.pearsondesigncentral.com.

TIP

If the prompt shows DD.MMSS then you can type 128d5'58.56" or change the drawing settings so it asks for DD.DDDDDD. This is done by going to the **Toolspace**, clicking on the **Settings** tab, right-clicking on the drawing name, and choosing **Edit Drawing Settings**. Choose the **Ambient Settings** tab and expand the **Angle**. Change the **Value for the Format** to the desired setting.

8. >>Specify angle or [Counter-clockwise] : Type **128.0996**
9. >>Specify distance: **75**
10. Resuming LINE command.
11. Specify next point or [Undo] : (922.68 1060.78 0.0)
12. Specify next point or [Undo] :
13. Current angle unit: degree, Input: DD.DDDDDD (decimal)
14. >>Specify angle or [Counter-clockwise] : **279.8302** (Figure 6-28).

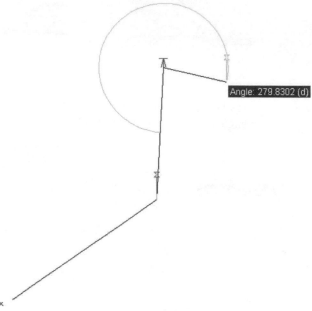

Figure 6-28   Turned angle of 279.8302

15. >>Specify distance: **100**

    Resuming LINE command.

16. Specify next point or [Undo] : (1020.15 1038.41 0.0)
17. Specify next point or [Close/Undo] :

    Current angle unit: degree, Input: DD.DDDDDD (decimal)

18. >>Specify angle or [Counter-clockwise] : **233.3313** (Figure 6-29).

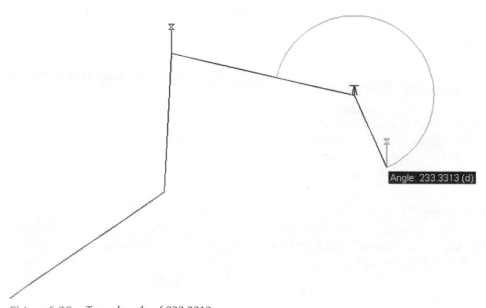

Figure 6-29   Turned angle of 233.3313

19. `>>Specify distance:` **75**
20. `Resuming LINE command.`
21. `Specify next point or [Close/Undo]:` `(1050.34 969.758 0.0)`
22. `Specify next point or [Close/Undo]:`
23. `Current angle unit: degree, Input: DD.DDDDDD (decimal)`
24. `>>Specify angle or [Counter-clockwise]:` **\<Esc\>**

   `Resuming LINE command.`

25. `Specify next point or [Close/Undo]:` **\<Esc\>** to terminate.
26. Save your file with the same name and a suffix of your initials.

Notice the almost video game–style graphics that appear to help you through the computations. The yellow marker simulates a station setup while the green "rodman" is placed at the backsight and the red "rodman" is placed at the foresight location. The red arc indicates that the computations are using a turned angle from the backsight to the foresight.

Exercise 6-3: The '**BD** Command

This command allows you to build linework using a bearing and distance.

Job skills will benefit from the use of the '**BD** command because surveyors routinely draw property and easement linework using distances and bearings.

1. Continue in the same drawing or open the drawing you just saved.
2. Using the **V** for **View** command, highlight the view called **Geom-A**, hit **Set Current**, and then hit **OK**. You draw linework using a bearing and distance from where you left off in the previous command. You can also use the line visible on the screen if you did not perform the last exercise. Of course, your results may vary from the figure somewhat.
3. `Command:` **L**
4. `LINE Specify first point:` Using an **Endpoint** Osnap, pick the end of the last line you drew in the previous exercise. It is near 1050, 969.
5. `Specify next point or [Undo]:` Type '**BD** or select the second icon on the **Transparent Commands** toolbar. A reminder displays: `Quadrants - NE = 1, SE = 2, SW = 3, NW = 4`
6. `>>Specify quadrant (1-4):` **1**, for Northeast quadrant (Figure 6-30).

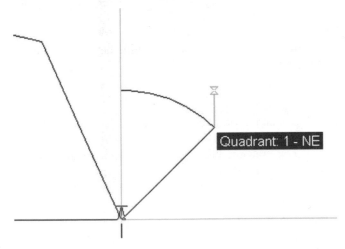

Figure 6-30   The Northeast quadrant

7. A reminder displays: `Current direction unit: degree, Input: DD.MMSSSS (decimal dms)`
8. `>>Specify bearing:` **41.3329**, indicates a bearing angle of 41 degrees, 33 minutes, and 29 seconds.
9. `>>Specify distance:` **75**
10. `Resuming LINE command. Specify next point or [Undo]:` `(1100.1 1025.88 0.0)`

11. `Specify next point or [Undo]: Quadrants - NE = 1, SE = 2, SW = 3, NW = 4`

12. `>>Specify quadrant (1-4): ` **3** `Current direction unit: degree, Input: DD.MMSSSS (decimal dms)`

13. `>>Specify bearing:` **16.1907**

14. `>>Specify distance:` **80**

15. `Resuming LINE command. Specify next point or [Undo]: (1077.62 949.102 0.0)`

16. `Specify next point or [Close/Undo]: Quadrants - NE = 1, SE = 2, SW = 3, NW = 4`

17. `>>Specify quadrant (1-4):` **<Esc>** twice to terminate.

18. Save your file with the same name and a suffix of your initials.

Exercise 6-4: The 'ZD Command

This command allows you to build linework using an azimuth (from North) and distance (Figure 6-31).

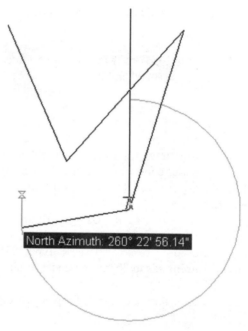

North Azimuth: 260° 22' 56.14"

Figure 6-31   Linework using a North Azimuth

TIP   If your jurisdiction requires the use of Azimuth (or South Azimuth), the **'ZD** command assists in laying out deed information.

1. Continue in the same drawing or open the drawing you just saved.

2. Using the **V** for **View** command, highlight the view called **Geom-A**, hit **Set Current**, and then hit **OK**. You draw linework using a bearing and distance from where you left off in the previous command. You can also use the line visible on the screen if you did not perform the last exercise. Of course, your results may vary from the figure somewhat.

3. `Command:` **L**

4. `LINE Specify first point:` Using an **Endpoint** Osnap, pick the end of the last line you drew in the previous exercise. It is near 1077,949.

5. `Specify next point or [Undo]:` Type **'ZD** or select the third icon on the **Transparent Commands** toolbar.

   `Current direction unit: degree, Input: DD.MMSSSS (decimal dms)`

6. `>>Specify azimuth:` **260.2256**

7. `>>Specify distance:` **100**

8. `Resuming LINE command. Specify next point or [Undo]: (979.023 932.395 0.0)`

9. `Specify next point or [Undo]:` `Current direction unit: degree, In-put: DD.MMSSSS (decimal dms)`
10. `>>Specify azimuth:` **<Esc>** twice to terminate.
11. Save your file with the same name and a suffix of your initials.

Exercise 6-5: The 'DD Command

This command allows you to build linework using a deflection angle and a distance (Figure 6-32).

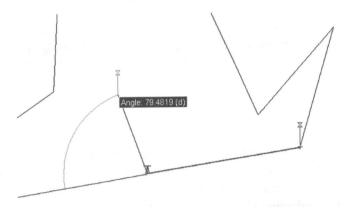

Angle: 79.4819 (d)

Figure 6-32   Deflection angle and a distance

1. Continue in the same drawing or open the drawing you just saved.
2. Using the **V** for **View** command, highlight the view called **Geom-A**, hit **Set Current**, and then hit **OK**. You draw linework using a bearing and distance from where you left off in the previous command. You can also use the line visible on the screen if you did not perform the last exercise. Of course, your results may vary from the figure somewhat.
3. `Command:` **L**
4. `LINE Specify first point:` Type in '**DD** or select the fourth icon on the **Transparent Commands** toolbar. Using an **Endpoint** Osnap, pick the end of the last line you drew in the previous exercise. It is near 979,932.
5. `>>Select line or [Points]:`
6. `Current angle unit: degree, Input: DD.MMSSSS (decimal dms)`
7. `>>Specify angle or [Counter-clockwise]:` **79.4819**
8. `>>Specify distance:` **75**
9. `>>Specify ending point or [.P/.N/.G]:` **<Esc>** twice to terminate.
10. Save your file with the same name and a suffix of your initials.

Notice that each of these commands keeps you in the data entry mode until you switch to another to terminate.

Exercise 6-6: The 'NE Command

This command allows you to build linework using a key-in of the Northing and Easting.

TIP

The nice part of the '**NE** command allows for data entry using the numeric keypad, which expedites the typing.

1. Continue in the same drawing or open the drawing you just saved.
2. Using the **V** for **View** command, highlight the view called **Geom-A**, hit **Set Current**, and then hit **OK**. You draw linework using a bearing and distance from where you left off in the previous command. You can also use the line visible on the screen if you did not perform the last exercise. Of course, your results may vary from the figure somewhat.
3. `Command:` **L**
4. `LINE Specify first point:` Using an **Endpoint** Osnap, pick the end of the last line you drew in the previous exercise. It is near 953,1003.

5. `Specify next point or [Undo]`: Type **'NE** or select the fifth icon on the **Transparent Commands** toolbar.
6. `>>>>Enter northing <0.0000>`: **960**
7. `>>>>Enter easting <0.0000>`: **950**
8. `>>>>Enter northing <0.0000>`: **<Esc>** twice to terminate.
9. Save your file with the same name and a suffix of your initials.

The 'GN Command

This command allows you to build linework using a key-in of the grid Northing and grid Easting. Again, a nice feature allows for data entry using the numeric keypad, which expedites the typing. This is similar to the geodetic calculator used earlier because it reads the geodetic zone when placing points.

The 'LL Command

This command allows you to build linework using a key-in of the latitude and longitude. This is similar to the geodetic calculator because it reads the geodetic zone when placing points.

Exercise 6-7: The 'PN Command

This command allows you to build linework using a key-in of the point number.

> **TIP** This command is not limited to simply typing a point number; it can also connect multiple points using commas and apostrophes. For instance, you can draw a polyline by starting at a point number of, say, 100 and for the remaining vertices of the polyline you can refer to points in the file by 101-110, 100, which will draw linework through the consecutive points 101 through 110 and connect back to the starting point of 100.

1. Continue in the same drawing or open the drawing you just saved.
2. Using the **V** for **View** command, highlight the view called **Geom-A**, hit **Set Current**, and then hit **OK**. You draw linework using a bearing and distance from where you left off in the previous command. You can also use the line visible on the screen if you did not perform the last exercise. Of course, your results may vary from the figure somewhat.
3. `Command`: **L**
4. `LINE Specify first point`: Using an **Endpoint** Osnap, pick the end of the last line you drew in the previous exercise. It is near 950,960. Type **'PN** or select the eighth icon on the **Transparent Commands** toolbar.
5. `Specify next point or [Undo]`:
6. `>>Enter point number`: **2**
7. `Resuming LINE command. Specify next point or [Undo]`: (908.038 1000.71 0.0)
8. `Specify next point or [Undo]`:
9. `>>Enter point number`: **<Esc>** twice to terminate.
10. Save your file with the same name and a suffix of your initials.

Exercise 6-8: The 'PO Command

This command allows you to build linework using a pick of a point on the screen without snapping to it. You can pick any visible portion of the point or its text attributes.

1. Continue in the same drawing or open the drawing you just saved.
2. Using the **V** for **View** command, highlight the view called **Geom-A**, hit **Set Current**, and then hit **OK**. You draw linework using a bearing and distance from where you left off in the previous command. You can also use the line visible on the screen if you did not perform the last exercise. Of course, your results may vary from the figure somewhat.

3. `Command:` **L**
4. `LINE Specify first point:` Using an **Endpoint** Osnap, pick the end of the last line you drew in the previous exercise. It is near 908,1000. Type **'PO** or select the tenth icon on the **Transparent Commands** toolbar and ensure that dynamic input is disabled.
5. `Select point object:` Simply pick on the word **UNIT** for Point 2.
6. `Resuming LINE command. Specify first point:` `(908.038 1000.71 0.0)`
7. `Specify next point or [Undo]:`
8. `>>Select point object:` Hit **<Enter>**.
9. `>>Specify next point or [Undo]:` Type in **950,960**
10. `Resuming LINE command.`
11. `>>Specify next point or [Undo]:` **<Esc>** to terminate.
12. Save your file with the same name and a suffix of your initials.

Exercise 6-9: The 'SS Command

This command allows you to build linework using side shot data. You pick an occupied point on which to establish your station and then a second point representing your backsight. Following that you provide an angle and distance to locate your object.

1. Continue in the same drawing or open the drawing you just saved.
2. Using the **V** for **View** command, highlight the view called **Geom-B**, hit **Set Current**, and then hit **OK**. You see an alignment in the view. You draw linework using a station and off-set of this alignment.
3. Type **L** for **Line** or pick it from the **Draw** toolbar.
4. `Command: 1 LINE Specify first point:` Using a **Center** Osnap, pick the center of the circle near the alignment shown at the bottom of the drawing.
5. `Specify next point or [Undo]:` Type **'SS** or select the eleventh icon on the **Transparent Commands** toolbar.
6. `>>Specify ending point or [.P/.N/.G]:` **.P**
7. `Current angle unit: degree, Input: DD.MMSSSS (decimal dms)`
8. `>>Specify angle or [Counter-clockwise/Bearing/Deflection/aZimuth]:` **60.9261**, as in Figure 6-33.

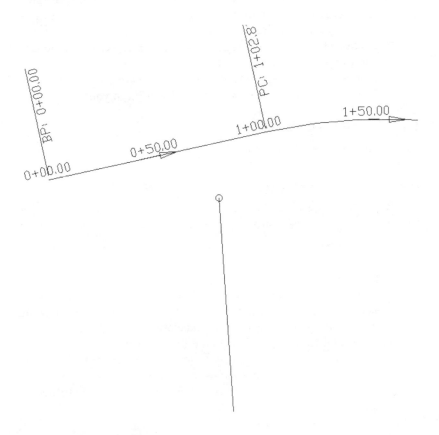

Figure 6-33 Building linework using side shot data

9. >>Specify distance: **100**
10. Resuming LINE command. Specify next point or [Undo]: (1010.87 699.428 0.0)
11. Specify next point or [Undo]: Current angle unit: degree, Input: decimal
12. >>Specify angle or [Counter-clockwise/Bearing/Deflection/aZimuth] : **<Esc>** to terminate. Erase the circle for the next exercise.
13. Save your file with the same name and a suffix of your initials.

Exercise 6-10: The '**SO** Command

This command allows you to build linework using a station and offset (positive for right and negative for left) from an alignment.

This routine is useful because it also works inside other AutoCAD commands and references the alignment in question. It can be used to draw manholes at a station offset from an alignment.

1. Continue in the same drawing or open the drawing you just saved.
2. Using the **V** for **View** command, highlight the view called **Geom-B**, hit **Set Current**, and then hit **OK**. You see a shot alignment in the view. Draw linework using a station and offset of this alignment.
3. Type **C** for **CIRCLE** or pick it from the **Draw** toolbar.
4. CIRCLE Specify center point for circle or [3P/2P/Ttr (tan tan radius)] : Type '**SO** or select the twelfth icon on the **Transparent Commands** toolbar.
5. >>Select alignment: Pick the alignment in the view.
6. >>Specify station along alignment: **75**
7. >>Specify station offset: **25**
8. Resuming CIRCLE command. Specify center point for circle or [3P/2P/Ttr (tan tan radius)]: (920.909 655.768 0.0)
9. Specify radius of circle or [Diameter] :
10. >>Specify station along alignment: **<Esc>** to terminate the station, offset part of the routine.
11. Resuming CIRCLE command. Specify radius of circle or [Diameter] : **1.5**
12. Save your file with the same name and a suffix of your initials.

Exercise 6-11: The '**PSE** Command

This command allows you to build linework using profile, station, and elevation criteria.

When using this routine, notice that graphics appear to show you where the station you type is on the profile. A graphic then appears to show you the elevation that you type.

To access student data files, go to www.pearsondesigncentral.com.

1. Open the drawing called Chapter-6-Profile.dwg.
2. Using the **V** for **View** command, highlight the view called **Access Road-Profile View**, hit **Set Current**, and then hit **OK**. You see a shot profile in the view. You draw a bridge crossing over the road using a station and elevation data from this profile.
3. Type **L** for **Line** or pick it from the **Draw** toolbar.
4. Command: 1 LINE Specify first point: Type '**PSE** or select the seventeenth icon on the **Transparent Commands** toolbar.
5. >>Select a Profile View: Pick a grid line in the profile.
6. >>Specify station: **300**

7. \>\>Specify elevation: **364**
8. Resuming LINE command. Specify first point: (18300.0 21640.0 0.0)
9. Specify next point or [Undo]:
10. \>\>Specify station: **300**
11. \>\>Specify elevation: **355**
12. Resuming LINE command. Specify next point or [Undo]: (18300.0 21550.0 0.0)
13. Specify next point or [Undo]:
14. \>\>Specify station: **350**
15. \>\>Specify elevation: **355**
16. Resuming LINE command. Specify next point or [Undo]: (18350.0 21550.0 0.0)
17. Specify next point or [Close/Undo]:
18. \>\>Specify station: **350**
19. \>\>Specify elevation: **364**
20. Resuming LINE command. Specify next point or [Close/Undo]: (18350.0 21640.0 0.0)
21. Specify next point or [Close/Undo]:
22. \>\>Specify station: **<Esc>** twice to terminate.
23. Save your file with the same name and a suffix of your initials.

You see the outline of an overhead bridge in a thick linestyle (Figure 6-34).

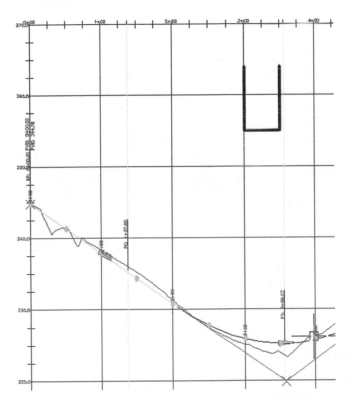

Figure 6-34   Using profile, station, and elevation criteria

Exercise 6-12: The **'PGS** Command

This command allows you to build linework using profile, grade, and station criteria (Figure 6-35).

TIP

Note that these commands can be used for almost any AutoCAD command. For instance, you can draw a pipe in profile while maintaining the grade of the pipe. You can draw the invert of the pipe, and the other invert can be established using a grade and station.

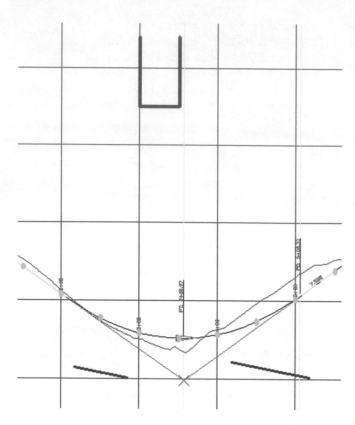

Figure 6-35   Using profile, grade, and station criteria

To access student data files, go to www.pearsondesigncentral.com.

1. Continue on the same drawing, or open the drawing called Chapter-6-Profile.dwg.
2. Using the **V** for **View** command, highlight the view called **Access Road-Profile View**, hit **Set Current**, and then hit **OK**. You see a shot profile in the view. You draw a culvert from a point at −2% using the profile data.
3. Type **L** for **Line** or pick it from the **Draw** toolbar.
4. `Command: l LINE Specify first point:` **18217,21215**
5. `Specify next point or [Undo]:` Type **'PGS** or select the eighteenth icon on the **Transparent Commands** toolbar.
6. `>>Select a Profile View:` Pick a grid line in the profile.
7. `>>Specify grade <0.00>:` **−2**
8. `>>Specify station:` **285**
9. `Resuming LINE command. Specify next point or [Undo]:` (18285.0 21201.4 0.0)
10. `Specify next point or [Undo]:`
11. `>>Specify grade <-2.00>:` **<Esc>** twice to terminate.
12. Save your file with the same name and a suffix of your initials.

Exercise 6-13: The **'PGL** Command

This command allows you to build linework using profile, grade, and length criteria.

To access student data files, go to www.pearsondesigncentral.com.

1. Continue on the same drawing, or open the drawing called Chapter-6-Profile.dwg.
2. Using the **V** for **View** command, highlight the view called **Access Road-Profile View**, hit **Set Current**, and then hit **OK**. You see a shot profile in the view. You draw a culvert from a point at −2% using the profile data.
3. Type **L** for **Line** or pick it from the **Draw** toolbar.
4. `Command: l LINE Specify first point:` **18418,21222**
5. `Specify next point or [Undo]:` Type **'PGL** or select the nineteenth icon on the **Transparent Commands** toolbar.
6. `>>Select a profile view:` Pick a grid line in the profile.
7. `Current grade input format:` percent
8. `>>Specify grade <0.00>:` **−2**
9. `>>Specify length:` **100**

10. `Resuming LINE command. Specify next point or [Undo]:` (18518.0 21202.0 0.0)
11. `Specify next point or [Undo]:`
12. `Current grade input format: percent`
13. `>>Specify grade <-2.00>:` **<Esc>** twice to terminate.
14. Save your file with the same name and a suffix of your initials.

You can continue drawing linework in the **'PGL** command if you have a series of pipe inverts to draw. This command can be used to draw anything in the profile that has a length and grade, such as the bottom of a ditch.

Exercise 6-14: The **'MR** and **'ML** Commands

These commands allow you to build linework by matching the radius or length of an object.

The **'MR** and **'ML** commands are excellent for obtaining data from other criteria either known or within the file somewhere. Remember to use these as you create parcel and alignment data in the future.

1. Continue on the same drawing, or open the drawing called Chapter-6-Profile.dwg.
2. Using the **V** for **View** command, highlight the view called **Geom-D**, hit **Set Current**, and then hit **OK**. You see an arc and a line.
3. Type **C** for **Circle** or pick it from the **Draw** toolbar.
4. `Command:` **CIRCLE** `Specify center point for circle or [3P/2P/Ttr (tan tan radius)]:` **19135, 20050**
5. `Specify radius of circle or [Diameter]:` Type **'MR** or select the next to last icon on the **Transparent Commands** toolbar.
6. `>>Select entity to match radius:` Pick the arc on the screen.
7. Notice a circle shows up with the same radius of the arc.
8. Type **L** for **Line** or pick it from the **Draw** toolbar.
9. `Command: l LINE Specify first point:` **18530,20100**
10. `Specify next point or [Undo]:` Type **'ML** or select the last icon on the **Transparent Commands** toolbar.
11. `>>Select entity to match length:` Pick the line on the screen.
12. Notice a line shows up with the same length as the other line.
13. `Resuming` **LINE** `command. Specify next point of [Undo]:`
14. `Specify next point or [Undo]:` **<Esc>** to terminate.
15. Save your file with the same name and a suffix of your initials.

To access student data files, go to www.pearsondesigncentral.com.

PARCELS

This next section explores parcel information. You begin with the Parcel Settings and move toward generating parcels and see how Civil 3D handles them in a state-of-the-art manner.

Parcel Development in Civil 3D

Due to the potential complexities of laying out parcels, the Autodesk Civil 3D includes a wide range of tools to assist in the construction of the primitive components of the parcels; namely, the horizontal geometry, the lines, and the arcs. We have already seen the concepts in the earlier examples of the dynamic link that exists between the display styles for an object and the appearance of the object. The act of updating an object's style results in automatic changes to the appearance

To access student data files, go to www.pearsondesigncentral.com.

Table Styles: A library of styles for constructing tables that report on point information.

of the object in AutoCAD. For example, if you update the label style for a parcel, the parcel linework annotation is updated. Open the file Chapter-6-Parcel.dwg from the student data files.

Open the **Settings** tab in the **Toolspace**. If you expand **Parcel**, notice Parcel Styles, Label Styles, *Table Styles*, and Commands. See Figure 6-36. Please note that although you are working with Chapter 6 drawings the styles in this chapter will refer to Chapter 4 styles that were created for a previous textbook.

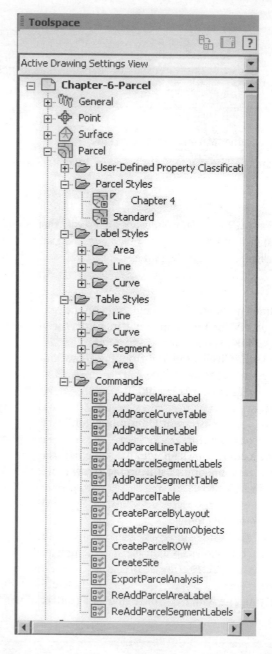

Figure 6-36   Parcel settings

These styles are discussed in detail, but generally the **Parcel Styles** handle how the parcel appears, what displays, and on which layers. The **Label Styles** control what annotation appears and how it looks for the components of the parcel; in other words, the area and the rectilinear and curvilinear linework. The **Table Styles** control how tables involving parcel data appear and which layers are involved. The **Commands** settings include preestablished settings for the details of building annotation and tables, such as units and precisions.

Exercise 6-15: Creating Parcel Styles

This exercise allows some serious practice in establishing styles for parcels. Civil 3D allows for some new features that are often used to add to the aesthetics of parcel drafting such as placing a

To access student data
files, go to
www.pearsondesigncentral.com.

hatch pattern around the edge of the parcels. You explore this and annotation styles as well in the next series of exercises.

1. Open the file Chapter-6-Parcel.dwg.
2. Type **V** for **View** highlight the view called **Parcel – A**, hit **Set Current**, and then hit **OK**.
3. Then go to the **Settings** tab in the **Toolspace**; expand the items for **Parcel**.
4. Open **Parcel Styles**, and you see **Standard** and **Chapter 4**. These can be edited by right-clicking on them and choosing **Edit…**. Right-click on the **Chapter 4 Style** item and select **Edit…**.
5. In the **Information** tab, ensure that **Chapter 4** is the name of the style. Choose the **Design** tab in the dialog box. This is where the **Fill** setting is set. It defaults to 5′. This sets a 5′ hatch around the perimeter of the parcel, which is often found on engineering and surveying drawings as a highlighting method for parcels.
6. Choose the **Display** tab and turn **On** the **Parcel Area Fill** layer, so you can see the fill when it occurs. The **Parcel Segment** layer can be set under the **Layer** column. The layer **V-Prcl-Sgmt** is set to **red**, and the layer **V-Prcl-Htch** is set to color **254**. Hit **OK** to exit.

You now have a Parcel Style called Chapter 4 with layers set for the parcels.

Exercise 6-16: Creating an Area Label Style

Now create an Area Label Style for the parcels.

1. In the same drawing, expand **Label Styles**, expand **Area**, right-click on the **Chapter 4 Area Style** and choose **Edit…**.
2. In the **Information** tab, ensure that **Chapter 4 Area Style** is the name. Select the **General** tab and observe the settings.
3. Click in the **Value** column for **Text Style**, and you see a button with three dots (ellipses) on it. Click this button to see the available styles.
4. Select **Romans**
5. Select the **Layout** tab next as in Figure 6-37. Note in the **Value** column for the **Property** of **Text** Contents. Click in the **Value** column for this item, and you see a button with three dots (ellipses) on it. Click this button and notice how the field and the related appearance of the area text can be altered. The **Preview** window on the right of Figure 6-38 can be edited by the user, and prefixes or suffixes can be typed in if needed. Hit **OK**.
6. Now select the **Dragged State** tab and observe the settings in here that control the properties for labels when they are dragged away from their initial insertion points. Hit **OK**.

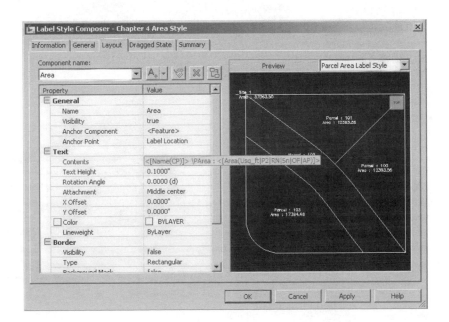

Figure 6-37   Parcel Label Style Composer

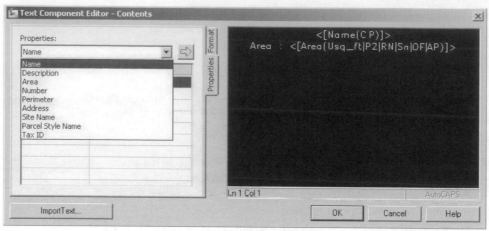

Figure 6-38   Text Component Editor

TIP   The **Summary** tab provides a single location to review and set all of the settings at once. This is a great destination for experts.

7. Go to the **Settings** tab in the **Toolspace**; under the **Label Styles**, you use the **Standard** Style for Lines and Curves, but you may want to take a moment to review these by selecting either **Lines** or **Curves**, right-clicking, and choosing **Edit...**. Hit **OK** to depart the editing.

Although most of the settings are fairly routine and easy to understand, let us pause for a moment to explore some settings that may not be so self-evident. Expand the item for **Commands**. Right-click on the **CreateParcelbyLayout** setting and choose **Edit Command Settings...**. An **Edit Command Settings** dialog box displays, shown in Figure 6-39. The interesting settings to

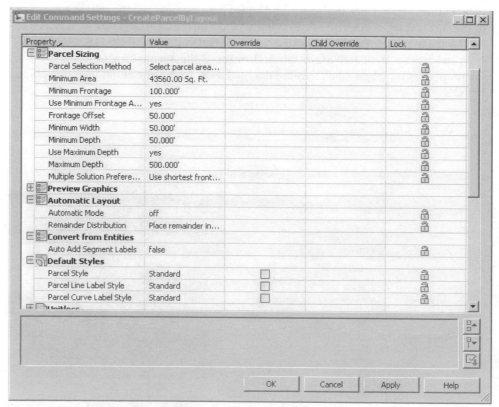

Figure 6-39   Edit Command settings

take note of are the blue icons. The blue icons, expanded in Figure 6-39, specify the default options for **Parcel** commands.

At the bottom of this same dialog box, select the **Transparent Commands** settings, shown in Figure 6-40. A myriad of settings here control whether you have Northings/Eastings or *X/Y* prompts; whether you are prompted for the third dimension; the order in which latitude/longitude will be prompted, and the units in which slopes and grades will be set.

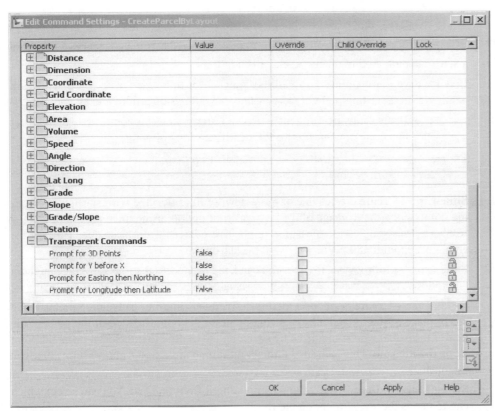

Figure 6-40   Transparent Commands settings

TIP   Observe these settings carefully because they are similar to the **Command Settings** in other items.

Now that you have explored many of the settings controlling parcel development and display, let us create some using the commands provided.

In this same drawing and in the view provided earlier, **Parcel-A**, you will create some linework for a parcel.

From the **Parcels** pull-down menu, choose **Create Parcel by Layout....** A toolbar displays as shown in Figure 6-41. Note that it can be expanded/retracted by using the arrow at the far right of the toolbar.

Figure 6-41   Parcel Layout Tools

The commands available are described from the left and are referred to as Buttons 1 through 10 in their descriptions that follow:

Button 1: **Create Parcel**

Button 2: **Add Fixed Line—Two Points** draws a lot line as a line segment. Choose a starting point and an endpoint to create it.

Button 3: **Add Fixed Curve:**

- **Fixed Curve (Three point)** draws a lot line as a curved component. You would define a starting point, a point on curve, and an endpoint.

- **Fixed Curve (Two points and radius)** draws a lot line as a curve component. You would define a starting point, a radius value, the curve's direction, and an endpoint.

Button 4: **Draw Tangent-Tangent with No Curves** draws a connected series of lot line components. You would identify a series of points.

Button 5: This button has several options to it including:

- **Slide Line—Create** creates one or more new lot lines defined with starting and ending points along the frontage of the lot or, at your option, using an angle relative to the frontage. These angles are measured in positive degrees, from 0 degrees (toward the endpoint) through 180 degrees (toward the start point).

- **Slide Line—Edit** moves a lot line. You can keep or modify the line's frontage angle in this routine.

- **Swing Line—Create** develops a lot line defined with starting and ending points along the frontage of the lot and a fixed swing point on the opposite side of the parcel. The size of the parcel can be modified by swinging the lot line to intersect a different point along the frontage. This is limited through minimum areas and frontage limits that you establish.

- **Swing Line—Edit** moves a lot line by pivoting it from one end. You can select which end to use as the swing point on the fly.

- **Free Form Create** develops a new lot line. You can define an attachment point to begin and then use bearings, azimuths, or a snap to a second attachment point to complete the command.

Button 6: **PI Commands** for:

- **Inserting** creates a vertex at the point clicked on a parcel segment.

- **Deleting** eliminates a vertex that is selected on a parcel segment. It then redraws the lot line between the vertices on either side to repair the parcel line. This command can delete or merge parcels depending on how the vertex was deleted.

- **Breaking Apart PIs** separates endpoints at a vertex selected with a separation distance you specify. This command does not delete or merge parcels; it does, however, make them incomplete, and the components that are affected become geometry elements. These elements become parcels again once any loose vertices are reconnected to a closed figure.

Button 7: **Delete Sub-entity** eliminates parcel components. If a sub-entity is eliminated when it is not shared by another parcel, the parcel is deleted. If a shared sub-entity is eliminated, the two parcels that shared it are merged together.

Button 8: **Parcel Union** merges two adjacent parcels together where the first parcel selected determines the identity and properties of the joined parcel, similar to the AutoCAD **PEDIT** command. **Dissolve Parcel Union** does the same.

Button 9: **Pick Sub-entity** selects a parcel component for display in the **Parcel Lay-out Parameters** dialog box. Use the **Sub-entity Editor** before choosing this command.

Button 10: **Sub-entity Editor** displays the **Parcel Layout Parameters** dialog box that allows for the review or editing of attributes of selected parcel components.

Undo and **Redo** buttons are used for creating and editing parcel data.

The graphics capabilities that accompany these commands are extraordinary. Following are some examples of how they work

Exercise 6-17: Create Parcel By Layout

1. Remain in the same drawing. Type **V** for **View**, highlight the view called **Parcel-A**, hit **Set Current**, and then hit **OK**. In the **Prospector**, expand **Open Drawings**, expand the **Chapter-6-Parcel.dwg** expand **Sites**, expand **Site 1**.
2. Then right-click on **Parcels**. Choose **Properties…**.
3. Under the **Composition** tab, set the **Site parcel style** to **Chapter 4**, which was created earlier. Set the **Site area label style** to **Chapter 4 Area Style**, also created earlier. Hit **Apply** and **OK**.
4. In the **Chapter-6-Parcel.dwg** drawing, select **Create Parcel By Layout…** from the **Parcels** pull-down menu.
5. When the **Parcel Layout Tools** toolbar displays, select the second from the left button **Add Fixed Line-Two Points** command. The dialog box for **Create Parcels-Layout** displays. Set the **Parcel Style** to **Chapter 4**. Set the **Area label style** to **Chapter 4 Area Style**. Turn **On** the toggle for **Automatically add segment labels**. Hit **OK**.
6. When it asks for a start point, use an **Endpoint** snap to select the point at **16000,19000**, which is a vertex of the parcel polyline already drawn in the file.
7. Then using Endpoint snaps, select the vertices of the polyline in a clockwise fashion. You must specify a start point for each line. Set the second and third vertex, and stop after selecting an endpoint at the third vertex at $X = 16268.9231$ $Y = 19285.9656$.

 TIP Note that after you draw one line, you must begin the next line again, unlike an AutoCAD line.

8. While staying in the command, select the third button in the toolbar, **Add Fixed Curve-Three Point**. Use an **Endpoint** snap to select the third vertex; use a **Nearest** snap to pick a point on the curve and an **Endpoint** snap to select the fourth vertex.
9. Then use the second button, **Add Fixed Line**, to select a first point at the endpoint at the fourth vertex and the second point at the beginning of the parcel where you started.
10. When the software asks for a new start point, hit **<Enter>** and then type **X** for **Exit**, as shown in the command prompt. You see a parcel, fully developed with annotation and hatching, as discussed in the setup of the settings earlier. Make sure that all layers are turned on.

If you look in the **Prospector** (Figure 6-42), you see this parcel listed there, with a **Preview** of the parcel.

Exercise 6-18: Editing Parcel Data

1. To edit the parcel, use the **Create Parcel by Layout…** from the **Parcels** pull-down menu again.
2. This time select button 6, **Insert PI**.

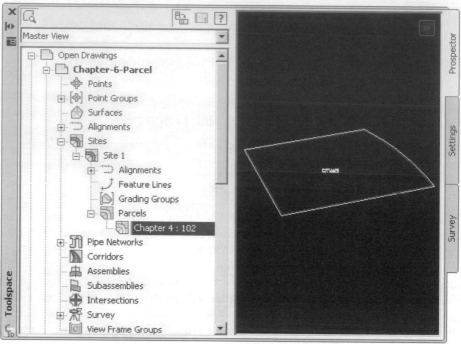

Figure 6-42   Preview of the Parcel

3. When prompted, pick the north parcel line. It requests that you pick a point for the new PI. Type **16100,19300** as the new PI location. Hit **<Enter>** twice to terminate and **X** to leave the routine.
4. You see the parcel updated with the new PI, new annotation, and a new area. The **Prospector** is updated if you select **Refresh** when right-clicking the parcel item. Refer to Figure 6-43.

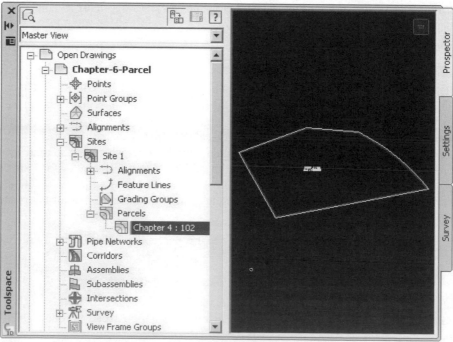

Figure 6-43   Updated Preview of the Parcel

Exercise 6-19: Creating Parcel Data from Objects

A second option for creating parcel data is to select it directly from predrawn entities. Let us perform an example of this.

1. Type **V** for **View** and select the view called **Parcel—B**, hit **Set Current,** and then hit **OK**.
2. A copy of the same parcel data displays. Select **Create Parcel from Objects** from the **Parcels** pull-down menu.
3. `Select lines, arcs or polylines to convert into parcels or [Xref]:` Select the polyline displayed. Hit **<Enter>**.
4. The dialog box for **Create Parcels-From objects** displays (Figure 6-44). Set the **Parcel style** to **Chapter 4**. Set the **Area label style** to **Chapter 4 Area Style**. Turn **On** the toggle for **Automatically add segment labels.** Hit **OK**.

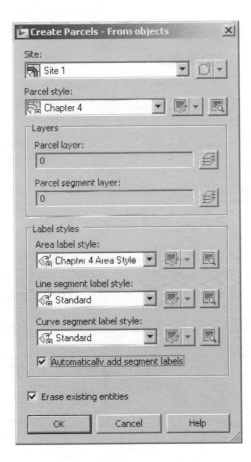

Figure 6-44   Create Parcels dialog box

5. Again the parcel is defined, hatched, labeled, and displayed in the **Prospector**. Note that you may need to choose **Refresh** from the right-click menu to see both parcels in the **Prospector** and make sure that all layers are turned on.

Exercise 6-20: Creating Rights of Way

Another command within the **Parcels** pull-down menu is the **Create ROW** command. This creates a right of way along an alignment. When a right of way is developed, adjacent parcel boundaries are offset by a user-specified distance from the right of way on each side of the alignment. Radii can be defined for end returns that exist along the right of way at intersections.

The **Right of Way** command works like a parcel, albeit a narrow variation of a parcel. When the **Create ROW** command is used, it prompts you to pick parcels. If an alignment is found on one of the edges of the selected parcels, a right of way is created in accordance with the preestablished parameters.

1. Type in **V** for **View** and select the view called **Parcel—C**, hit **Set Current**, and then hit **OK**. This shows an alignment and several parcels along the alignment.

2. Select **Create Parcel from Objects** from the **Parcels** pull-down menu.

3. `Select lines, arcs or polylines to convert into parcels or [Xref]:` Select the polylines of the three parcels in the view. Hit **<Enter>**.

4. The dialog box for **Create Parcel-From objects** displays. Set the **Parcel style** to **Chapter 4.** Set the **Area label style** to **Chapter 4 Area Style.** Turn **On** the toggle for **Automatically add segment labels.** Hit **OK**.

5. Again the parcels are defined, hatched, labeled, and displayed in the **Prospector.** Make sure that all layers are turned on.

6. Now choose the command **Create ROW** from the **Parcels** pull-down menu. When it asks you to select the parcels, choose the three parcels you just created, and hit **<Enter>**. Then the **Create Right of Way** dialog box, shown in Figure 6-45, displays to obtain the criteria for developing the ROW.

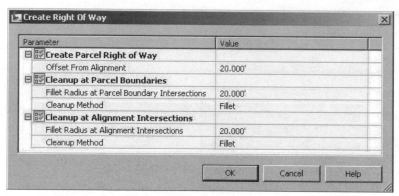

Figure 6-45   Create Right of Way dialog box

7. Set the value for **Offset from alignment** to **45.** Set the fillet radius for **Cleanup at parcel boundaries** to **35.** Set the fillet radius for **Cleanup at alignment intersections** to **35** as well. Hit **OK**.

8. The configuration should appear as shown in Figure 6-46.

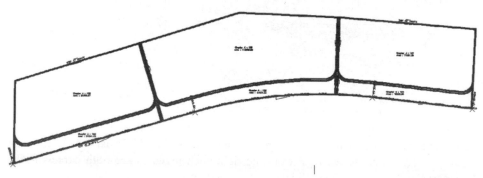

Figure 6-46   Results of parcel layout

For the next step in this exercise, you will add a line table.

9. Type in **V** for **View** and select the view called **Parcel—C.** This shows an alignment and several parcels along the alignment.

10. Select **Add Tables** from the **Parcels** pull-down menu. Select **Add Line....**

11. The **Table Creation** dialog box displays, as shown in Figure 6-47.

In the selection window in the center of the dialog box, turn on the **Apply** button and make sure it is checked as in Figure 6-47. Then hit **OK**. A table is on your cursor and asks you to pick a point for the table.

Pick a point away from the parcel graphics. It appears as shown in Figure 6-48. Other tables can be brought in as well for curves and areas.

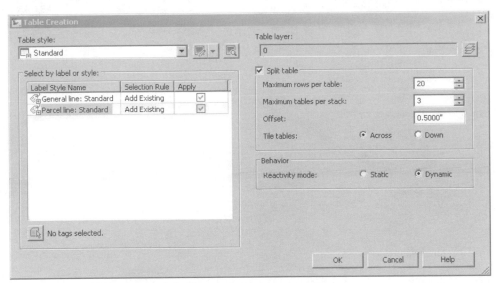

Figure 6-47   Table Creation dialog box

Line Table		
Line #	Length	Direction
L1	250.000	N0° 37' 57.21"E
L2	388.861	N72° 47' 09.54"E
L3	245.234	S16° 18' 58.54"E
L4	312.186	S72° 47' 09.54"W
L5	296.177	N87° 47' 36.99"W
L6	233.308	N1° 32' 20.88"E
L7	240.185	S2° 46' 36.64"W
L8	412.792	S85° 32' 05.26"E

Figure 6-48   Completed table

ALIGNMENTS

Alignments are developed to assist engineers, surveyors, and contractors in their computations and layout of projects. Alignments provide a common structure by which they can refer to the corridor, locate the positions easily, and be able to duplicate that location reliably. An alignment consists of *primitive elements,* such as lines, arcs, and spirals. Although each of these is an independent component, when strung together they create an alignment and can be thought of and referred to as a single object.

Alignments can be used in all corridor situations whether they are roadways, channels, aqueducts, or utilities such as waterlines.

The notion of *stationing* is what unifies thinking about alignments. Stationing (Figure 6-49) is a mathematical concept whereby the beginning of the alignment commences with a value, say 0, and this number increases by the lengths of the lines, arcs, and spirals until terminating at the end of the alignment. To make it a little easier to understand and work with, stationing also includes the concept of dividing the actual linear value by 100′. In other words, station 2 + 50 would be located 250′ from the beginning of the alignment. Station 18 + 32.56 would be 1,832.56′ from the beginning. The even stations are denoted on the left side of the plus sign and the leftover value is on the right side of the plus sign. Unless otherwise instructed, corridor alignments often begin with the station 10 + 00 or 1000′. This allows for changes to be made to the

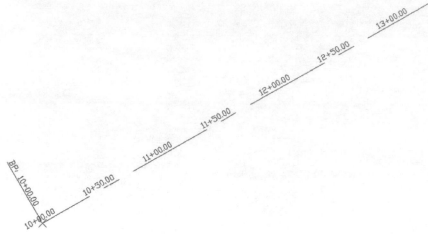

Figure 6-49   Stationing

alignment, and, within reason, you will at least remain in positive numbers when computing stationing. For example, if you began a roadway at station 0+00, it could happen that a superior would want to extend the roadway length 100′ from the beginning, thereby causing the beginning station to be −1+00. This causes potential confusion simply because of the addition of negative numbers. Anything designers can do to simplify the design and construction process pays off in the long run, and this is one of those things it is important to do.

In combination with stationing, a concept of offset values is also used in conjunction with alignments. Typically, a positive offset is to the right of the alignment, and a negative value is to the left, when looking forward toward increasing stationing. This additional concept allows users to locate objects, either existing or proposed, using the stationing for the alignment as the baseline for computations. For instance, it would not be difficult to locate a proposed fire hydrant with a station of 18+32.56 and an offset of 55′ (Right), or the corner of a drain inlet at station 9+55.32 and an offset of −14.5′ (Left).

One last item associated with alignments and their respective stationing is the concept of station equations or equalities. This is a situation in which the roadway begins, say, at station 10+00 and perhaps the alignment is 2000′ long. Thus, the ending station is 30+00. Now let us further say that a side road intersects the roadway halfway through it, at station 20+00. The hypothetical State Department of Transportation (DOT) has decided that the intersecting roadway is the predominant roadway and yours is not. Therefore, it decrees that your roadway will have your stationing from the beginning and will maintain your stationing until it intersects with the side road. At that point, the DOT wants the stationing of your road to pick up where the side street leaves off and continue on until your road ends.

This is where a station equation will exist. Our roadway stationing begins at 10+00 and progresses until station 20+00 where the side road enters the project, as in Figure 6-50.

If the side road has an ending station of, say, 11+96.32 when it intersects your road, then your road continues from that point onward accumulating its additional stationing values and adding them to the 11+96.32 from the side road. So your road would end at station 11+96.32

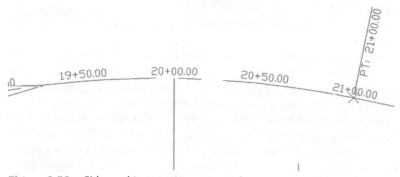

Figure 6-50   Side road intersecting main road

plus 10+00 remaining after the side road intersects your road for a total ending station of 21+96.32. To complicate things just a little further, note that the stationing could be decreasing instead of increasing. If it were, then your road could end at 11+96.32. It could also occur that there would be multiple stations on the alignment of the same value depending on how the station equations are applied to the alignment. See Figure 6-51.

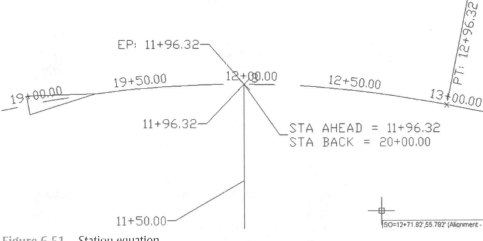

Figure 6-51   Station equation

In a subdivision corridor, items that reference horizontal alignments are gutters, sidewalks, and lot corners; water, sanitary, and storm sewers; catch basins; and manholes. This conversation is limited for the time being to roadway applications. However, they can be generalized to the other aforementioned project types.

The criteria used for the design of horizontal alignments for roadways are represented in terms of number of lanes, design speeds, and minimum curve radii. The minimum radius for curves increases with design speed such that large radius curves are required for high vehicle speeds. Correspondingly, there also tends to be a minimum radius once you go below a certain design speed, such as that found in residential subdivisions. A governmental agency, perhaps a DOT, usually specifies horizontal alignment design criteria for highways. For subdivision roads, it may be the county's highway department or the municipality that dictates the design criteria.

Horizontal Alignment Development in Civil 3D

Autodesk Civil 3D includes a robust toolset to assist in the construction of the primitive components of the horizontal alignment; namely, the horizontal geometry, the lines, arcs, and spirals. You have already seen the concepts in previous examples of the dynamic link that exists between the display styles for an object and the appearance of the object. The act of updating an object's style results in automatic changes to the appearance of the object in AutoCAD. For example, if you update a component within the alignment, a ripple-through effect updates profiles, sections, and annotations as well. There are similar tools for developing alignments as there are for creating parcel data. You can draw the alignment using polylines and convert them to alignment objects, or you can use the **Layout** toolbar to develop the design with alignment tools custom developed for use in design alignments.

Exercise 6-21: Alignment Settings

Alignment creation is explored in this section, beginning with the **Alignment Settings**. You see how Civil 3D handles them in a state-of-the-art manner.

1. Remain in the same drawing, Chapter-6-Parcel.dwg.
2. Open the **Settings** tab in the **Toolspace**. If you expand **Alignments**, notice **Alignment Styles**, **Design Checks**, **Label Styles**, **Table Styles**, and **Commands**. Each of these is discussed in detail, but generally the **Alignment Styles** handle how the alignment appears, what will display, and on what layers. The **Label Styles** control what annotation

To access student data files, go to www.pearsondesigncentral.com.

appears and how it will look for the components of the alignment; in other words, the stationing, equations, alignment components, station/offsets, and so on. The **Table Styles** setting (Figure 6-52) controls how tables involving alignment data appear and what layers are involved. The **Commands** settings, include preestablished settings for the details of building annotation and tables, such as units and precisions.

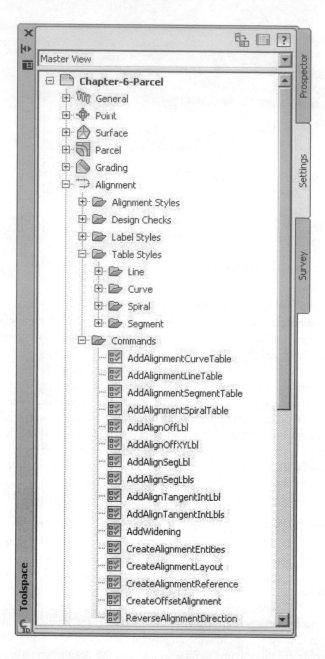

Figure 6-52   Table Styles setting

3. Right-click on the **Alignment Styles** item and select **New....** The **Information** tab allows for naming and optional descriptions. In the name field, type **Chapter 4—Alignments**.
4. The **Design** tab allows you to control the **Grip Edit Behavior**. This can be enabled or disabled as a toggle, and it controls whether the cursor snaps to a specified increment when grip editing the radius of a curve in the alignment. The **Radius snap value** specifies the curve's incrementing radius. Enable the **Grip edit behavior** and set the value to **25**.
5. In the **Display** tab, you can set the layers for individual components of the alignment if you want. For this example, set the color for **Lines** to **red** and the color for **Curves** to **green**.
6. Hit **Apply** and **OK**.
7. Now click on the **Label Styles** item, select **Station**, and then right-click on **Major Station**. Select **New....**

8. Click on the **Information** tab, type in the name of your style as **Chapter 4—Major Stations Label Style**.
9. Then in the **Layout** tab, Figure 6-53, under the **Text Property,** click in the **Value** column for **Contents**. Notice that a button appears on the right side of the field. Click on the button with the ellipsis (…).

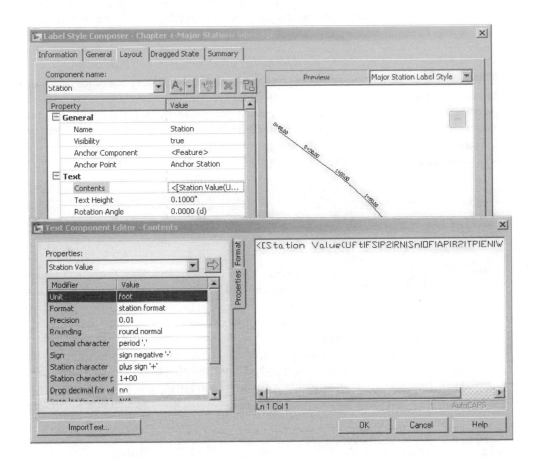

Figure 6-53   Text Component Editor—Label Text

10. A dialog box called **Text Component Editor—Contents** displays.
11. You see the formula in the window to the right. There is a parameter in the formula, **P2** for Precision to 2 decimal places. Click in there and delete the entire current formula.
12. In the **Modifier** column, notice the **Precision** item. Click in the **Value** column for this modifier. The default is 0.01. Change it to **1**.
13. *This next step is important.* Make sure you click the button with the **right arrow** on it to send the parameter change into the formula window to the right.
14. If you look in the formula, notice that the parameter **P** is now set to **0**.
15. Hit **OK**. The **Preview** in the **Label Style Composer** shows the stationing with no decimal places now.
16. Hit **Apply** and **OK** to exit.
17. Repeat this for the **Minor Stations** and call the label style **Chapter 4—Minor Stations Label Style**. Repeat Steps 8 through 15 for the **Minor Label Styles**.

This exercise should provide you with an idea of how the settings for alignments work. They are intended to be prebuilt into the Civil 3D product and then take effect on the creation of the alignment.

Now that you have gone through these basic examples, note that the dialog boxes for all the settings work essentially the same way and have the same types of parameters. This is true for the Label Styles for Label Sets; all the Stationing styles; the styles for lines, curves, spirals, and tangent intersections; and Table Styles.

The dialog boxes for the **Commands** section of the **Settings** were discussed under **Parcels, Command Settings**.

Fixed, Floating, and Free Lines and Curves

In getting started developing alignment objects, an important concept must be discussed first. That concept involves Constraint-based commands and the creation of fixed, floating, and free lines and curves. These objects can be edited dynamically, and the objects retain their tangencies.

A Fixed entity is fixed in its position and is defined by criteria such as a radius or located points. It is not dependent on other entities for geometry development or tangency. A Floating entity is always tangent to one entity and is defined by the parameters provided or is dependent on one other entity to define its geometry. A Free entity is always tangent to an entity before and after it and must have at least two other entities to which to attach that define its geometry.

Although a user can always develop polylines to create their alignments, there are also some state-of-the-art tools in the **Alignment Layout Tools** toolbar. They are called up by choosing the **Alignments** pull-down menu and selecting **Create Alignment by Layout**. The **Create Alignment—Layout** dialog box first displays asking you for some initial alignment style parameters, but then the **Alignment Layout Tools** toolbar displays (Figure 6-54). The commands available within it are described from the left and are referred to as Buttons 1 through 16 in their descriptions:

Figure 6-54 Alignment Layout Tools toolbar

Button 1:   This button has three choices. They are **Tangent-Tangent (No Curves)**, **Tangent-Tangent (With curves)**, and **Curve and Spiral Settings....** By using the **Tangent-Tangent** command, you can pick a series of points end-to-end in order to draw a fixed alignment in a fashion similar to drawing AutoCAD lines. The choices provide options to insert free curves automatically at each PI. These commands can be used effectively to create quick layouts of an alignment. The lines and curves can be modified by the user, and as the linework is edited, it always maintains tangency.

Button 2: **Insert PI**.

Button 3: **Delete PI**.

Button 4: **Break-Apart PI**.

Button 5: This button allows for creating **Fixed**, **Floating**, **and Free lines**. This concept is defined by the characteristics inherent within each type of line. These commands have several options tools, including:

- The **Fixed Line** commands allow you to enter a fixed line through two points, or you can enter a fixed line through two points where the line is tangent to the end of the selected fixed or floating entity.

- The **Floating Line** commands allow you to enter floating lines through points that are always tangent to fixed or floating curves, or you can enter a floating line tangent through a point. The lines drawn are always tangent to the end of fixed or floating curves.

- The **Free Line (Between two curves)** command allows you to enter a free line that is always tangent to a Fixed or Floating curve, either before or after the line.

Button 6: This button has several options to it including:

- **Fixed Curve** and **More Fixed Curves** commands allow you to enter a fixed curve using 3 points, or you can enter a fixed curve using the following criteria to define the curves as shown in Figure 6-55.

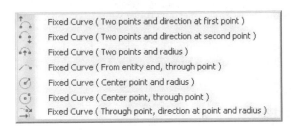

Figure 6-55   Fixed Curve and More Fixed Curves commands

- The first three commands are performed by specifying two points and some additional criteria. They all achieve a fixed curve through three points.
- The next command develops a fixed curve tangent to the end of an entity and through a chosen point. This achieves a fixed curve through three points that is also tangent to the end of the entity you selected.
- Following that is the fixed curve developed by selecting a center point, providing a radius, and a curve direction, which achieves a fixed circle.
- The next command allows entering a fixed curve by specifying a center point, a pass-through point, and the curve's direction, which achieves a fixed curve that passes through the specified point.
- The last command enters a fixed curve by specifying a point, the curve's direction at the point, and a radius, which achieves a fixed circle with a center point and a radius.

Floating Curve and **More Floating Curves** commands allow you to enter floating curves using a variety of criteria that will be maintained on modification of those curves (Figure 6-56). The **Floating Curve** allows you to enter a floating curve that is attached to a fixed or floating line or curve entity, by specifying a radius, a pass-through point, and an angle range. This achieves a floating curve, which is always tangent to the entity to which it is attached. The submenu **More Floating Curves** is shown in Figure 6-56 and differs from the **Fixed** commands in that these entities are not pinned to any specific location in the drawing. These commands are described as follows:

- **Floating Curve (From entity end, through point)** which achieves a floating curve that is always tangent to the entity to which it is attached.
- **Floating Curve (From entity end, radius, length)** which achieves a floating curve entity that always starts at the end of the entity to which it is attached.
- **Floating Curve (From entity end, through point, direction at point)** which achieves a floating curve that remains tangent to the entity to which it was attached.

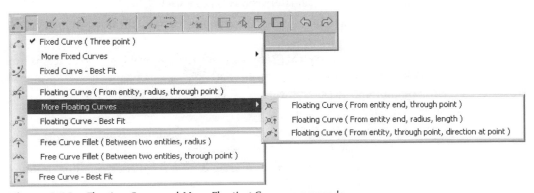

Figure 6-56   Floating Curve and More Floating Curves commands

The **Free Curve** commands allow you to enter free curves using a variety of criteria. **Free Curve Fillet (Between two entities, radius)** adds a curve between two entities with a specified angle range and radius.
Free Curve Fillet (Between two entities, through point) adds a curve between two entities with a specified pass-through point.

Free Curve (Best Fit) adds the most probable curve between two entities that remains tangent to the two entities.

Some new constraint-based tools have been added and, based on the information presented here, it should be obvious how to use them.

These next three button tools are for spiral design.

Button 7:   **Floating Spirals**

- **Floating Line with Spiral (From curve, through point)** adds a floating spiral from an entity with a line at its end.

- **Floating Line with Spiral (From curve end, length)** adds a floating spiral from an entity with a line at its end.

Button 8:   (More) **Floating Spirals**

- **Floating Curve with Spiral (From entity end, radius, length)** adds a floating spiral from an entity based on the radius and length provided.

- **Floating Curve with Spiral (From entity, radius, through point)** adds a floating spiral from an entity based on the radius and a point provided.

- **Floating Reverse Curve with Spirals (From curve, radius, through point)**

- **Floating Reverse Curve with Spirals (From curve, two points)**

- **Free Spiral-Curve-Spiral (Between two entities)** will prompt you to select the incoming and outgoing tangents and then prompt for spiral lengths and a radius for the curve.

- **Free Compound Spiral-Curve-Spiral-Curve-Spiral (Between two tangents)**

- **Free Reverse Spiral-Curve-Spiral-Spiral-Curve-spiral (Between two tangents)**

Button 9: Allows for a large number of sophisticated spiral geometry commands. These routines are summarized in the commands which follow:

- **Fixed Spiral** develops a spiral with a spiral in length and a curve radius.

- **Free Spiral (Between two entities)** requests length and radius information and then shows extraordinary graphics in the placement of the object.

- **Free Compound Spiral-Spiral (Between two curves)** develops two spirals back to back.

- **Free Reverse Spiral-Spiral (Between two curves)** develops two spirals back to back but in a reverse curve scenario.

- **Free Compound Spiral-Spiral (Between two tangents)**

- **Free Compound Spiral-Line-Spiral (Between two curves, spiral lengths)** develops two spirals back to back.

- **Free Reverse Spiral-Line-Spiral (Between two curves, spiral lengths)** develops two spirals back to back but in a reverse curve scenario.

- **Free Compound Spiral-Line-Spiral (Between two curves, line length)** develops two spirals back to back.

- **Free Reverse Spiral-Line-Spiral (Between two curves, line length)** develops two spirals back to back but in a reverse curve scenario.

Button 10: **Convert AutoCAD line and arc** creates a fixed two-point line or three-point curve alignment entity from an AutoCAD object.

Button 11: **Reverse Sub-entity Direction** does the same.

Button 12: **Delete Sub-entity** eliminates alignment components.

Button 13: **Edit best fit data for all entities** displays a table of data for all alignment sub-entities that were created by best fit.

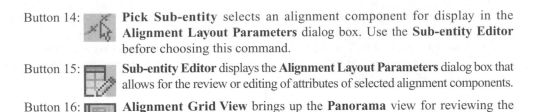

Button 14: **Pick Sub-entity** selects an alignment component for display in the **Alignment Layout Parameters** dialog box. Use the **Sub-entity Editor** before choosing this command.

Button 15: **Sub-entity Editor** displays the **Alignment Layout Parameters** dialog box that allows for the review or editing of attributes of selected alignment components.

Button 16: **Alignment Grid View** brings up the **Panorama** view for reviewing the alignment.

Undo and **Redo** buttons are used for creating and editing data.

How to Design an Alignment

Now let us use some of the alignment development routines to check out the advantages that Civil 3D provides to its users. Begin with the first **Layout** tool in the toolbar.

Exercise 6-22: Tangent-Tangent (With Curves)

1. Open the file called Chapter 6 Alignments-2.dwg.
2. Type **V** for **View** and select **Align-A**, hit **Set Current** and then hit **OK**.
3. Set your current layer to **C-Road-Cntr**.
4. Turn **Off** the surface's contour layers on **C-Topo-Existing Ground**.
5. From the **Alignments** pull-down menu, select **Create Alignment by Layout...**.
6. Accept the defaults except choose the **Alignment Style** of **Chapter 4—Alignments** and set the site to **Site 1**. Figure 6-57 shows this dialog box. Hit **OK** when finished.
7. The **Alignment Layout Tools** toolbar now displays.
8. Using the **down arrow** next to the first button, select **Curve and Spiral Settings...** (Figure 6-58).

To access student data files, go to www.pearsondesigncentral.com.

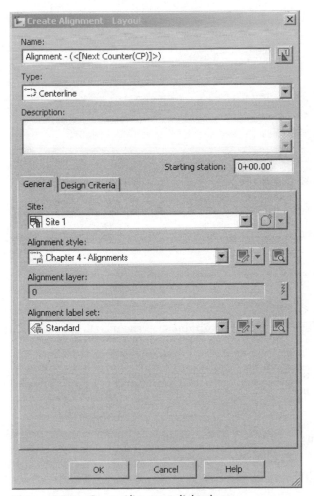

Figure 6-57   Create Alignment dialog box

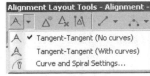

Figure 6-58   Curve and Spiral Settings...

9. In the **Curve and Spiral Settings** dialog box that displays, use the Clothoid type, which is the most commonly used, and hold the **200′** radius.

10. Now from the first button choose the command **Tangent-Tangent (With curves)**. At the command prompt when asked to provide the first point, type in the following coordinates: **14685,18545**. Then follow these instructions.

11. `Specify next point:` **15175,18510**
    `Specify next point:` **15250,18275**
    `Specify next point:` **15475,18175**
    `Specify next point:` **<Enter>** twice to terminate.

12. **Zoom** in on the **Alignment** and notice it has the component coloring as described earlier. Curves are already developed. Annotation is evident as well.

13. Now pick the **Alignment** and grips appear. Select a grip on the PI for the first curve. Drag it slightly to a new location while watching the curve. Do not move the PI so far that the curve cannot be computed and causes it to disappear. Cancel when finished moving the PI.

14. Now go to the **Alignments** pull-down menu and choose **Edit Alignment Geometry....** Select the alignment, and the **Alignment Layout Tools** toolbar appears. Choose the command on the right of the toolbar called **Alignment Grid View**, and the **Panorama** displays. Scroll through the **Panorama** and notice that the alignment held the radii of 200′.

Exercise 6-23: Insert PI

Now use the second tool called **Insert PI**.

1. Again, go to the **Alignments** pull-down menu and choose **Edit Alignment Geometry....** Select the **Alignment** in Figure 6-59, and the **Alignment Layout Tools** toolbar appears.

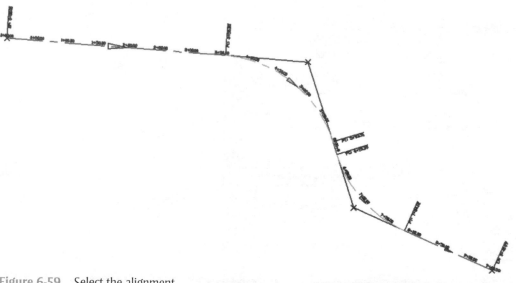

Figure 6-59   Select the alignment

2. Choose the second command, **Insert PI**.

3. `Pick point near PI to insert:` use the **Midpoint** snap and pick the first tangent **<Enter>**.

4. It places a new PI at 1+77.90, and a label appears.

5. Now pick the **Alignment** and notice that grips appear at keypoints on the alignment.

6. There are different types of grips denoted by their shape and include square, triangular, and circular grips. The Square grips are on alignment endpoints and allow the entire tangent component to be moved. The curves are the connecting segments and hold their radius as the tangent is relocated. The circular grips identify the curve geometry in the alignment. These can be slid along the tangents to lengthen or shorten the curve. The triangular grips are located at the PIs and can be moved to any other location as needed. When they are moved, they drag the curve along all the while holding the radius of the curves. Refer to Figure 6-60.

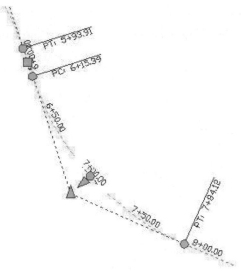

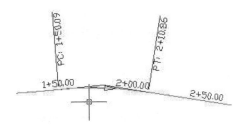

Figure 6-60   Edit with grips   **Figure 6-61**   Specifying a radius

7. Experiment with moving and relocating these grips. Move the PI grip for the PI you just added and observe how the alignment recomputes and redisplays.

8. Move that PI to a coordinate at or near an X,Y of **14865,18560**.

9. Then pick the **Alignment**, right-click, and select **Edit Alignment...** to redisplay the **Layout** toolbar.

10. Choose the **down arrow** on the sixth button from the left in the toolbar. When the menu drops down, select the command **Free Curve Fillet (Between two entities, radius)**.

11. `Select first entity:` Pick the tangent before the PI you just created.

12. `Select next entity:` Pick the tangent after the PI you just created.

13. `Is curve solution angle [Greaterthan180/Lessthan180] <Lessthan180>:` It is, so hit **<Enter>**.

14. `Specify radius in or [curveLen/Tanlen/Chordlen/midOrd/External]` : Type **250**.

15. `Select first entity:` **<Enter>** to terminate. Refer to Figure 6-61.

Notice that you now have a new curve in the alignment with a radius of 250′.

Exercise 6-24: Grips

Because you have seen several types of grips, let us take a moment to experiment further with these grips.

1. Pick the **Alignment** and notice that grips appear at keypoints on the alignment.

2. Move the circular grip for a curve and slide it along the tangent. Observe how the curve gets shorter or longer.

3. Grab a rectangular grip for an internal tangent segment and move it to a new location. Watch how the tangents and curves attached to it become relocated as well, while maintaining the curve radius.

Exercise 6-25: Using Spirals in Alignments

The software also supports spirals within the alignments. State DOTs use spirals in different ways. In some states, entrance and exit ramps for highways may be designed using spiral mathematics. Remember from the earlier description in this chapter that a spiral is a constantly changing radius. This differentiates spirals from simple arcs, which have a constant radius. You often need more physical space to build spiral ramps than those with arcs; hence you might find that the Texas DOT uses spirals more often than does the DOT in the Washington, DC, region, which has less available space. You may find that the DOT uses arcs for urban design but requires spirals for rural design for the same reasons.

For the alignment here, you will add a spiral to the end of the alignment.

1. Pick the **Alignment**, right-click, select **Edit Alignment Geometry...**, and the **Alignment Layout Tools** toolbar appears.
2. Choose the eighth icon from the left and from the pop-down menu options choose **Floating curve with Spiral (From entity end, radius, length)**.
3. `Select entity to attach to:` Use the **Endpoint** snap and snap to the right end of the alignment.
4. `Selected entity must be part of main entity. Select entity to attach to:` Select alignment.
5. `Specify radius <200.000'>:` **100**.
6. `Specify spiral in length or [A] <200.000'>:` **200**.
7. `Specify curve direction [Clockwise/cOunterclockwise] <Clockwise>:` Hit **<Enter>**.
8. `Specify length:` **200 <Esc>**.

Observe that a spiral curve has been added to the end of the alignment as expected; refer to Figure 6-62. Notice that the stationing is automatically continued from the previous length of the alignment.

When an alignment is being constructed, you may want to know detailed information about any of the components.

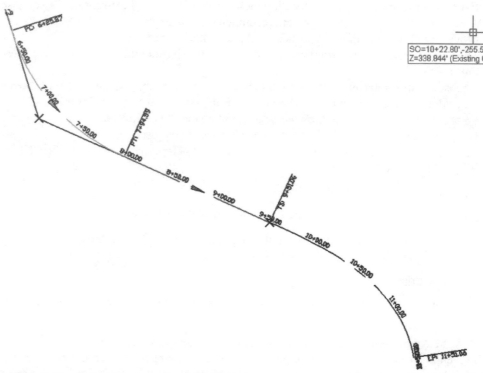

Figure 6-62   A spiral curve has been added to the end of the alignment

Exercise 6-26: Spiral Information

Run through the following routine to obtain information about the spiral, which as you know can become quite complex in its mathematics.

1. Pick the **Alignment**, right-click, select **Edit Alignment Geometry...**, and the **Alignment Layout Tools** toolbar appears.
2. Pick the **Edit best fit data for all entities** the fourth icon in the toolbar from the right. Then select the command **Pick Sub-entity**, the third icon from the right.
3. Select the **Spiral Component**.
4. A **Criteria** window is populated with all of the spiral criteria for your inspection. See Figure 6-63.

Notice that you can pick any sub-entity to obtain its respective data as well.

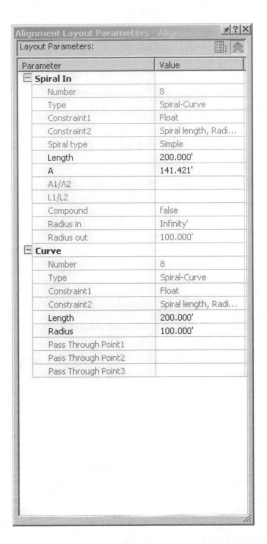

Figure 6-63 Spiral criteria

Exercise 6-27: Fixed Lines and Curves

The next routine explores creating fixed lines and curves and shows what these features offer.

1. In the same file called Chapter 6 Alignments-2.dwg type **V** for **View** and select **Align-A**, hit **Set Current**, and then hit **OK**.
2. Set your current layer to **C-Road-Cntr**.
3. Turn off the surface's contour layers on **C-Topo-Existing Ground**.
4. From the **Alignments** pull-down menu, select **Create Alignment by Layout**. The **Create Alignment – Layout** dialog box appears. Select **Site 1** for the site, hit **OK**. This brings up the **Alignment Layout Tools** toolbar.
5. Select the black **down arrow** for the fifth icon from the left, and select the command called **Fixed Line (Two points)**. Enter the following data to construct that line and stay in the **Layout** toolbar when you are finished creating the line.
6. `Specify start point:` **15200,18700**.
7. `Specify next point:` **@200<30**. **Zoom** out to see it.
8. Now select the black **down arrow** for the sixth icon from the left, and select the command called **More Fixed Curves**. In the submenu, choose the **Fixed Curve (From entity end, through point)**.
9. `Select entity for start point and direction:`
10. Pick near the end of the line you just drew.
11. `Specify end point:` **15900,18800**. Notice the curve emerges from the end of the line and is also tangent. The alignment expands with the associated stationing.
12. Once again, stay in the **Layout** toolbar.
13. Now use a command to add another tangent from the end of the curve.

14. Select the black **down arrow** for the fifth icon from the left, and in the submenu, choose the **Floating Line (From curve end, length)**. Enter the following data to construct that line.

15. `Select start point.` Use the **Endpoint** snap and snap to the end of the curve you just drew.

16. `Specify length:` **400.**

17. Notice that a line emerges from the end of the curve that is also tangent to the end of the curve. See Figure 6-64.

18. Hit **<Enter>** to terminate the routine and leave the **Layout** toolbar.

Figure 6-64   Line emerges that is tangent to curve

If at some point you accidentally left the **Layout** toolbar, no problem. Just select the **Alignment,** right click, and choose **Edit Alignment...** to reenter the toolbar.

TIP   Do not pick **Create From Layout** when attempting to edit an alignment because this creates a **New alignment.**

There is a pull-down menu in Civil 3D 2010 shown in Figure 6-65, and it is called **Lines/Curves,** which will be familiar to Land Desktop users.

Several routines for establishing horizontal linework exist here and can assist in geometry computations.

Create Lines

These commands allow for drawing linework as follows (see Figure 6-66):

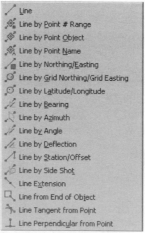

Figure 6-65   The Lines/ Curves pull-down menu

Figure 6-66   The Create Lines commands

Line between 2 points, Lines between a list of points, Lines between Point Objects, Lines by Point Name, Northing/Easting or Grid Northing/Grid Easting, by Lat/Long, by directions such as Bearing and Distance or Azimuth, by Angle, by Deflection angle, by Station and Offset (great for right-of-way plats), by Sideshot, by Extension or trims a line by a specified distance from an object, off of the end of a curve, spiral, or another line, tangent to an object, or creates perpendiculars to a specified object.

Create Curves

These commands allow for drawing curvature as follows (see Figure 6-67):

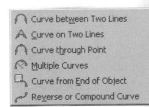

Figure 6-67 The Create Curves commands

Curve between Two Lines draws curves between two tangents using other curve data.

Curve on Two Lines draws curve on two tangents, while leaving the tangent lines intact.

Curve through Point draws curve on two tangents, but passing through a P.O.C.

Multiple Curves draws curve on two tangents, using compound curves as you might see in an off-ramp of an interstate highway.

Curve from End of Object draws curve tangent from the end of an existing line or arc.

Reverse or Compound draws a reverse or compound curve from the end of existing curve.

Create Best Fit

These commands create best fit Lines, Curves and Parabolas using a least squares algorithm. (This works well with existing road centerlines.)

Attach Multiple

This is a great command for attaching arcs, lines, and spirals!

CHAPTER SUMMARY

In this chapter, you were introduced to drawing curvilinear and rectilinear objects. You learned the formulas needed to design the geometry, and you learned about curvilinear linework generation; roadway alignment; and parcel creation, editing, and drafting. The chapter also covered how to modify the data.

CHAPTER TEST QUESTIONS

Multiple Choice

1. Tie-in methods include which of the following?
   a. Rectangular tie-in
   b. Polar tie-in
   c. Intersection tie-in
   d. All of the above

2. The total number of degrees within a closed polygon depends on the number of sides and is computed using the following formula:
   a. ANGULAR CLOSURE = $(N) \times 180$
   b. ANGULAR CLOSURE = $(N - 2) \times 180$
   c. ANGULAR CLOSURE = $180/\pi$
   d. ANGULAR CLOSURE = $(N - 2)/180$

3. The Arc method of curve calculation occurs where:
   a. The degree of curve is measured over a chord length of 100′
   b. The degree of curve is measured at a radius of 100′
   c. The degree of curve is measured over an arc length of 100′
   d. None of the above

4. The following terms are associated with horizontal arcs:
   a. PVI, PVT, PVC
   b. ST, TS, SC, CS
   c. PI, POC, PRC, PC, PT
   d. All of the above

5. Some of the types of important angles to understand for civil design are:

   a. Interior angles, azimuths, bearings
   b. Cardinal directions
   c. Deflection angles, turned angles
   d. All of the above

6. For constraint-based design, there are:

   a. Fixed objects
   b. Free objects
   c. Floating objects
   d. All of the above

7. Constraint-based design includes the following objects:

   a. Splines and spirals
   b. Polylines
   c. Terrain models
   d. Civil 3D lines and curves

8. Civil 3D will:

   a. Automatically label alignments on creation
   b. Draft alignments based on styles
   c. Annotate stationing equations or equalities
   d. All of the above

9. Civil 3D **Parcel** commands will:

   a. Locate buildings on lots
   b. Fit structures into tight BRL line limits
   c. Warn when BRL lines are violated
   d. None of the above

10. In a subdivision corridor, items that reference horizontal alignments comprise:

    a. Gutters, sidewalks, and lot corners
    b. Utilities such as water, sanitary
    c. Storm drainage structures such as catch basins and manholes
    d. All of the above

True or False

1. True or False: **Transparent** commands occur without the user knowing about them.

2. True or False: A bearing has two quadrants: North and South.

3. True or False: Intersection tie-in uses two angles from a baseline to locate a position.

4. True or False: Distances along baselines are called stations.

5. True or False: The distance along the station and at a right angle to it is called an offset.

6. True or False: Arcs have a constantly changing radius.

7. True or False: Spirals and parabolas fall into the rectilinear category.

8. True or False: There are two type of arcs, and they are defined using the Roadway and Railway methods.

9. True or False: A PI for an arc is an abbreviation for Point of Interest.

10. True or False: A POC for an arc is an abbreviation for Point of Curvature.

11. True or False: Interior angles are measured only in buildings.

12. True or False: An azimuth angle can be measured from North, South, East, or West and cannot exceed 90 degrees.

13. True or False: Constraint-based design allows designers to embed certain parameters into objects that will be retained during modifications.

14. True or False: Free objects must have both incoming and outgoing objects to define them.

15. True or False: Floating objects must have an incoming object to define them correctly.

CHAPTER EXERCISES

1. What is the slope of a line with coordinates of 5000,5000 and 5100,5050?
2. What is the bearing of that same line in Problem 1?
3. What is a slope distance?
4. Describe the term *stationing* as used in alignment design.
5. How are station/offset values used?
6. Use the **Layout** toolbar to create fixed, free, and floating lines and fixed, free, and floating curves. Draw two unconnected fixed lines. Then add a floating curve to the two lines and note how it reacts after you leave the **Layout** toolbar and edit the grips.
7. Use the **Layout** toolbar to create fixed, free, and floating lines and fixed, free, and floating curves. Draw two unconnected fixed curves. Then add a floating line to the two curves and note how it reacts after you leave the **Layout** toolbar and edit the grips.

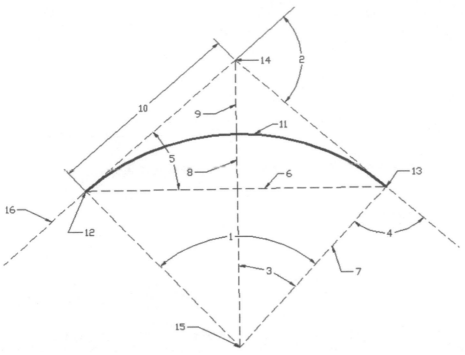

Figure 6-68

8. Name the parts of the arc shown in Figure 6-68.

What is 1?	What is 2?
What is 3?	What is 4?
What is 5?	What is 6?
What is 7?	What is 8?
What is 9?	What is 10?
What is 11?	What is 12?
What is 13?	What is 14?
What is 15?	What is 16?

9. Compute the missing values and the degree of curve for the following data. Use the formulas discussed in the chapter to solve these. Show your work.

Curve 1: R = 93.55, L = XXX.XX, Tan = 44.46, Included angle (Delta) = 50-50-38, Chord Length = 80.32

Curve 1: L = _____   Degree of Curve: _____

Curve 2: R = 52.10, L = 46.01, Tan = XX.XX, Included angle (Delta) = 50-35-50, Chord Length = 44.53

Curve 2: T = _____   Degree of Curve: _____

10. Fill in the missing blanks for the parts of the alignment (that is, PI, PC, etc.) in Figure 6-69. Note: A spiral, curve, spiral begins at 14+86.68.

What is 1? _____ What is 2? _____ What is 3? _____

What is 4? _____ What is 5? _____ What is 6? _____

What is 7? _____ What is 8? _____

What is the total length of this alignment?

11. Plot the following alignment into your CAD file. Plot the drawing at a scale of 1" =50'.

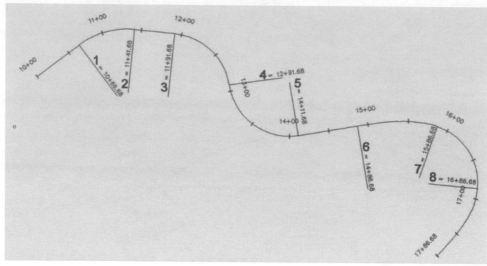

Figure 6-69

Horizontal Alignment Station and Curve Report—Alignment			
Desc. Station	Spiral/Curve Data	Northing	Easting
PI	10+00 Length: 102.81	17405.34 Course: N 34-23-28 E	14810.53
PI	11+02.81 Length: 163.49 Delta: 34-22-39	17490.18 Course: N 68-46-06 E	14868.60

Circular Curve Data				
PC	10+71.88	17464.65 17408.17	14851.13 RP 14933.65	
PT	11+31.88 Delta: 34-22-39 DOC: 57-17-45 Mid-Ord: 4.47	17501.38 Type: RIGHT Length: 60.00 External: 4.68	14897.44 Radius: 100.00 Tangent: 30.93 Chord: 59.10	Es: 4.68 Course: N 51-34-47 E
PI	12+64.43 Length: 157.56 Delta: 95-29-35	17549.39 Course: S 15-44-19 E	15021.00	

Circular Curve Data				
PC	11+81.88	17519.49 17449.58	14944.04 RP 14971.20	
PT	13+06.88 Delta: 95-29-35 DOC: 76-23-40 Mid-Ord: 24.57	17469.92 Type: RIGHT Length: 125.00 External: 36.54	15043.39 Radius: 75.00 Tangent: 82.56 Chord: 111.03	Es: 36.54 Course: S 63-29-06 E
PI	13+81.88	17397.74	15063.74	

Advanced 3D Surface Modeling

7

Chapter Objectives

- Understand the mathematics needed for Civil 3D terrain modeling.
- Compute information about terrain models and contours manually using mathematical interpolation.
- Use Civil 3D to accomplish the same functions automatically and much faster than manually.
- Understand the TIN process and the components of the TIN data.
- Understand how to analyze surface data.

INTRODUCTION

This chapter introduces terrain modeling by discussing the various algorithms and methodologies used to develop Digital Terrain Models. A Digital Terrain Model is commonly known as a *DTM*. The DTM is the basis of most of the computations that occur in Civil 3D when it comes to the third dimension. These activities include road and utility profile creation, cross sections, earthwork calculations, contour representation, and other functions. The DTM may be one of the most important components to any project.

DTM: Digital Terrain Model

Several advanced terrain problems and related solutions are also explored. Terrain models are developed and edited. Several advanced techniques are deployed to analyze the models in 3D. Surfaces, contours, breaklines, and spot shots are discussed in detail.

To begin, an engineering project, whether it is a road design job or a site development project, almost always starts with an evaluation of the existing conditions. This can be done in a number of ways—for instance, by using a traditional survey crew with total stations or by commissioning a photogrammetist to obtain aerial photographs and stereodigitizing them into a CAD file. Control would be established in either case using local monumentation or Global Positioning Systems (GPS). The existing ground data are collected, processed, analyzed, and certified for use. In addition to the horizontal aspects of that data, the DTM would likely be developed as well.

REVIEW OF FUNCTIONS AND FEATURES TO BE USED

This chapter procedurizes how to create surfaces, how to create and modify Surface Styles to control the appearance of the surface, and how to display the surface data in a variety of different ways. Surface data are computed, the surface is analyzed, and a variety of display mechanisms are taught to view the site in innovative ways.

DTM Theory

In many cases, vertical geometry is developed from an original ground surface. In the "old" days engineers would manually interpolate contours that represented certain elevations on the ground surface.

In Figure 7-1, to plot a contour for every one foot of constant elevation change, you would locate where the contour enters the data set and plot that point. You would then locate where that same contour travels as it meanders through the data set. The following sequence illustrates how to do this manually. The method parallels that of Civil 3D in that it also uses linear interpolation to compute contour locations.

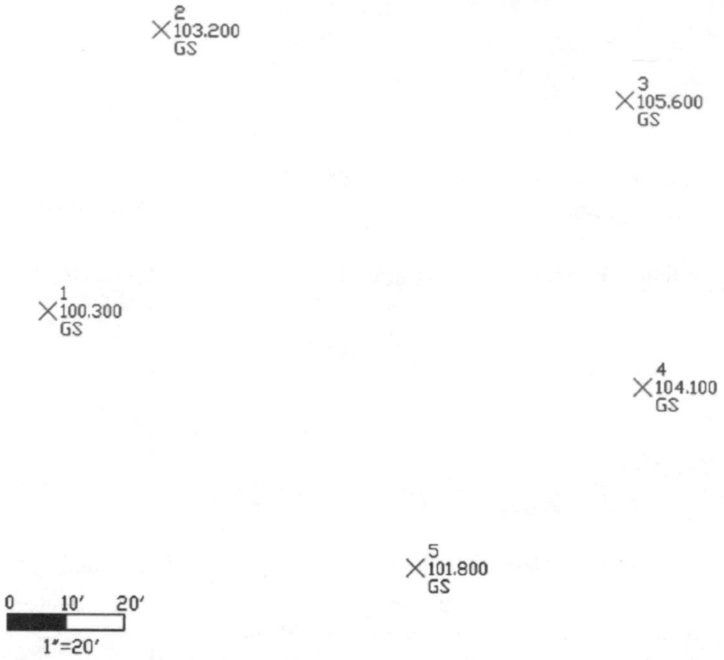

Figure 7-1   Surface spot shots

Example 7-1: Manually Compute Contour Locations

Let us identify where the 100′ contour would be. There are no data indicating that a 100′ contour exists in this data set because the lowest value is 100.3. See Figure 7-1. Therefore, locate the 101′ contour. It must be near the 100.3 ground shot, right? It appears that the 101′ contour will enter between Points 1 and 2 and exit between Points 1 and 5 (note that the direction of the contour is of no consequence to these calculations).

First compute the distance between Points 1 and 2, or because they may be on paper, scale it off the paper. This distance is 51′. Then the distance between Points 1 and 5 is scaled off. This distance is 75.4′.

Then compute the difference between the elevations of Points 1 and 2, which is 2.9′. The difference between the elevations of Points 1 and 5 is 1.5′. You now need to compute the difference from the 101′ contour to the elevation of Point 1, which is 0.7′. Compute the ratio of these elevations so that you can prorate the horizontal distance from Point 1 where the 101′ contour begins. Compute the ratio of the 101′ contour from the elevation at Point 1 with the elevation difference of Points 1 and 2. That would be 0.7/2.9, which equals 0.24. Therefore the 101′ contour begins at 24% of the total distance away from Point 1 toward Point 2. Therefore, 75.4*.24 equals 18.2′. You should scale and plot a point 18.2′ from Point 1 toward Point 2.

Let us compute the distance where the 101′ contour exits the data set. This must occur between Points 1 and 5, because no elevations exist anywhere else that would allow a 101′ contour to exit. Scale the distance from Point 1 to Point 5. You should get 75.3′. The elevation difference is 101.8 − 100.3 = 1.5. The elevation difference between Point 1 and the contour elevation of 101′

is $101 - 100.3 = 0.7$. The ratio of distance that the 101′ contour is from the 100.3 spot shot is $0.7/1.5 = 0.467$, which means that the 101′ contour is 46.67% of the distance from Point 1 to Point 5, which is $75.3*46.67 = 35.14′$.

Repeat this for any locations where the 101′ contour must pass related to the data you possess. In other words, the 101′ contour must pass between Points 1 and 3 and Points 1 and 4 on its way toward exiting between Points 1 and 5.

Continuing on with the computations in the same manner as just described, you need to be able to plot where the 101′ contour is relative to Points 1 and 3 and 1 and 4. Then you can sketch the probable path that the contour takes as it winds through the data set.

Distance from Point 1 to Point 3 = 103.48.

Positive Elevation difference between Points 1 and 3 = $105.6 - 100.3 = 5.3$.

The elevation difference between Point 1 and the 101′ contour = 0.7.

Therefore, the ratio of $0.7/5.3 = 0.13$, or 13% of the distance from Point 1 to Point 3, is established as the location of the 101′ contour, which is $0.13*103.48 = 13.67′$.

Distance from Point 1 to Point 4 = 101.18.

Positive Elevation difference between Points 1 and 4 = $104.1 - 100.3 = 3.8$.

The elevation difference between Point 1 and the 101′ contour = 0.7.

Therefore, the ratio of $0.7/3.8 = 0.184$, or 18.4% of the distance from Point 1 to Point 4, is established as the location of the 101′ contour, which is $0.184*101.18 = 18.64′$.

Now compute the location for the 102′ contour.

Distance from Point 1 to Point 2 = 51.

Positive Elevation difference between Points 1 and 2 = $103.2 - 100.3 - 2.9$.

The elevation difference between Point 1 and the 102′ contour = 1.7.

Therefore, the ratio of $1.7/2.9 - 0.586$, or 58.6% of the distance from Point 1 to Point 2, is established as the location of the 102′ contour, which is $0.586*51 = 29.89′$.

It can be seen that the 102′ contour does not exit between Points 1 and 5 because the elevation of the point is less than 102′. It must exist between Points 5 and 4.

Distance from Point 5 to Point 4 = 49.1.

Positive Elevation difference between Points 5 and 4 = $104.1 - 101.8 = 2.3$.

The elevation difference between Point 5 and the 102′ contour = 0.2.

Therefore, the ratio of $0.2/2.3 = 0.086$, or 8.6% of the distance from Point 5 to Point 4, is established as the location of the 102′ contour, which is $0.086*49.1 = 4.26′$

Distance from Point 1 to Point 3 = 103.48.

Positive Elevation difference between Points 1 and 3 = $105.6 - 100.3 = 5.3$.

The elevation difference between Point 1 and the 102′ contour = 1.7.

Therefore, the ratio of $1.7/5.3 = 0.32$, or 32% of the distance from Point 1 to Point 3, is established as the location of the 102′ contour, which is $0.32*103.48 = 33.19′$

Distance from Point 1 to Point 4 = 101.18.

Positive Elevation difference between Points 1 and 4 = $104.1 - 100.3 = 3.8$.

The elevation difference between Point 1 and the 102′ contour =1.7.

Therefore, the ratio of $1.7/3.8 = 0.447$, or 44.7% of the distance from Point 1 to Point 4, is established as the location of the 102′ contour, which is $0.447*101.18 = 45.26′$.

Now compute the location for the 103′ contour.

Distance from Point 1 to Point 2 = 51.

Positive Elevation difference between Points 1 and 2 = $103.2 - 100.3 = 2.9$.

The elevation difference between Point 1 and the 102′ contour = 2.7.

Therefore, the ratio of 2.7/2.9 = 0.93, or 93% of the distance from Point 1 to Point 2, is established as the location of the 102' contour, which is 0.93*51 = 47.48'.

It can be seen that the 103' contour exits between Points 5 and 4.

Distance from Point 5 to Point 4 = 49.1.

Positive Elevation difference between Points 5 and 4 = 104.1 − 101.8 = 2.3.

The elevation difference between Point 5 and the 103' contour = 1.2.

Therefore, the ratio of 1.2/2.3 = 0.52, or 52% of the distance from Point 5 to Point 4, is established as the location of the 103' contour, which is 0.52*49.1 = 25.6'.

Distance from Point 1 to Point 3 = 103.48.

Positive Elevation difference between Points 1 and 3 = 105.6 − 100.3 = 5.3.

The elevation difference between Point 1 and the 103' contour = 2.7.

Therefore, the ratio of 2.7/5.3=0.509, or 50.9% of the distance from Point 1 to Point 3, is established as the location of the 103' contour, which is 0.509*103.48 = 52.7'.

Distance from Point 1 to Point 4 = 101.18.

Positive Elevation difference between Points 1 and 4 = 104.1 − 100.3 = 3.8.

The elevation difference between Point 1 and the 102' contour = 2.7.

Therefore, the ratio of 2.7/3.8 = 0.71, or 71% of the distance from Point 1 to Point 4, is established as the location of the 103' contour, which is 0.71*101.18 = 71.89'.

Exercise 7-1: Manually Compute Contours

Compute the locations for where the 104' and 105' contours exist in the data set.

ANSWER TO EXERCISE 7-1

Distance from Point 2 to Point 3 = 78.8.

Positive Elevation difference between Points 2 and 3 = 103.2 − 105.6 = 2.4.

The elevation difference between Point 2 and the 104' contour = 0.8.

Therefore, the ratio of 0.8/2.4 = 0.33, or 33% of the distance from Point 2 to Point 3, is established as the location of the 104' contour, which is 0.33*78.8 = 26.26'.

Distance from Point 1 to Point 3 = 103.48.

Positive Elevation difference between Points 1 and 3 = 105.6 − 100.3 = 5.3.

The elevation difference between Point 1 and the 104' contour = 3.7.

Therefore, the ratio of 3.7/5.3 = 0.698, or 69.8% of the distance from Point 1 to Point 3, is established as the location of the 104' contour, which is 0.698*103.48 = 72.2'.

Distance from Point 1 to Point 4 = 101.18.

Positive Elevation difference between Points 1 and 4 = 104.1 − 100.3 = 3.8.

The elevation difference between Point 1 and the 104' contour = 3.7.

Therefore, the ratio of 3.7/3.8 = 0.97, or 97% of the distance from Point 1 to Point 4, is established as the location of the 104' contour, which is 0.97*101.18 = 98.14'.

It can be seen that the 104' contour exits between Points 5 and 4.

Distance from Point 5 to Point 4 = 49.1.

Positive Elevation difference between Points 5 and 4 = 104.1 − 101.8 = 2.3.

The elevation difference between Point 5 and the 104' contour = 2.2.

Therefore, the ratio of 2.2/2.3 = 0.956, or 95.6% of the distance from Point 5 to Point 4, is established as the location of the 104' contour, which is 0.956*49.1 = 46.9'.

Distance from Point 2 to Point 3 = 78.8.

Positive Elevation difference between Points 2 and 3 = 103.2 − 105.6 = 2.4.

The elevation difference between Point 2 and the 105′ contour = 1.8.

Therefore, the ratio of 1.8/2.4 = 0.75, or 75% of the distance from Point 2 to Point 3, is established as the location of the 105′ contour, which is 0.75*78.8 = 59.1′.

Distance from Point 3 to Point 4 = 47.8.

Positive Elevation difference between Points 3 and 4 = 105.6 − 104.1 = 1.5.

The elevation difference between Point 3 and the 105′ contour = 0.6.

Therefore, the ratio of 0.6/1.5 = 0.4, or 40% of the distance from Point 3 to Point 4, is established as the location of the 105′ contour, which is 0.40*47.8 = 19.1′. See Figure 7-2.

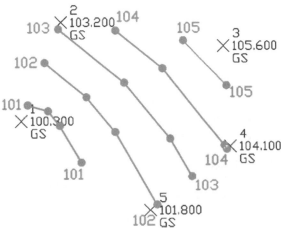

Figure 7-2   Hand-drawn contours

Today, many engineers use a computer and its software to perform this interpolation. Computers create and use Digital Terrain Models (DTM). The source data for this DTM can be composed of various types of data ranging from spot shots or ground shots, breaklines, and contours. A DTM is a digital approximation (that is, a model) of the data collected to represent the 3D conditions of the site. At various stages, assumptions, interpolations, and computations occur to prepare the "terrain surface." The user must study and understand what the software is trying to do in order to interact with the model. The user may make changes to override interpolations and assumptions made by the system, if desired.

The DTM TIN algorithm is based on Delauney's criteria, which create triangular planes that define the terrain surface. This is typically the method most manufacturers use and is one in which a triangle is created between the closest three points in the site. The triangle is a planar face from which computations can be performed. For instance, a profile of a roadway centerline can be computed from a TIN using linear interpolation. A new and increasingly used methodology for developing DTMs is topologically triangulated networks, or TTNs. This algorithm enables the user to segregate the data used as source data for the TIN processing.

Once a TIN is prepared, computations can be "sampled" or calculated from it. These might produce spot elevations interpolated from the triangle face, contours, a profile, or a cross section. A profile is the graphical intersection of a vertical plane, along the route in question, with the Earth's surface. Profiles are covered in detail in Chapter 8.

Cross sections are shorter profiles made perpendicular to the route in question. Two types of cross sections are often used: one for roadways or corridors and the other for borrow pits, landfills, and detention ponds.

THE TIN PROCESS

Figure 7-3 shows four spot shots, Figure 7-4 shows a resulting TIN, and Figure 7-5 shows contouring and depicts a hill or a rise. How do you know this is not a stream or ditch? If the algorithm had placed the interconnecting TIN line so that it connected the 100′ elevations, there would be a different condition to be solved.

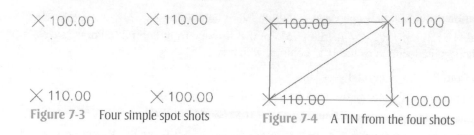

✕ 100.00   ✕ 110.00

✕ 110.00   ✕ 100.00

Figure 7-3   Four simple spot shots

Figure 7-4   A TIN from the four shots

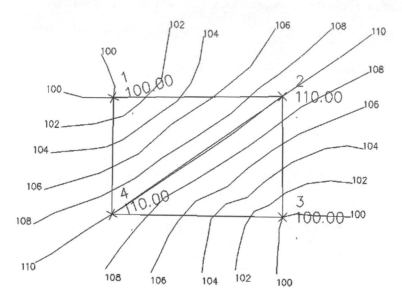

Figure 7-5   Contours from the TIN

This example shows that the software can easily produce a seriously incorrect interpretation of the data, if controls are not put into place to prevent it. The contours generated in Figure 7-6 differed by almost 90 degrees from those in Figure 7-5! Only a technician who knew that the area contained a swale would be able to estimate contours properly for the data given. Of course, the software had no way of knowing whether to connect the points to produce a swale or a highpoint (ridge) condition. That information was not available from the data set of points alone. This situation typically occurs in low areas, hilltops, and ridges. The answer is to place breaklines at the

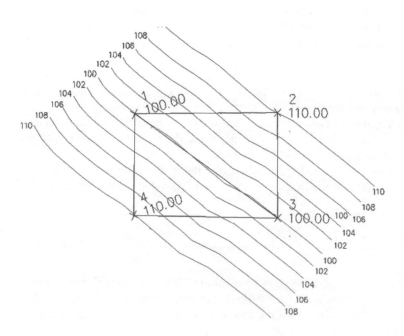

Figure 7-6   Same TIN, different contours

tops of ridges and in the centerlines of swales, at the tops of banks and in the toes of slopes, and every place a "break" exists that must be retained.

GROUND INFORMATION

A contour is a linestring that represents a single elevation along a surface. It is a coplanar object that always has a consistent elevation at each vertex of the object. It is an imaginary linestring that connects points of equal elevation.

Contours usually have a primary interval and a secondary interval. Some call these index and intermediate, whereas others call them high and normal contour intervals, respectively. Some typical intervals might be 2′ and 10′ intervals where the 10′ intervals' linework is designated as a more dominant lineweight and perhaps a different linestyle than the 2′ contours. In high terrain areas, the interval might jump to 5′ and 25′ intervals. In flat areas, the interval might be 1′ and 5′ intervals, whereas metric projects may use .5 m and 2.5 m intervals.

The interval is important so that enough data are shown to convey an understanding of the site. Some interesting facts about contours follow. Refer to Figure 7-7.

- Contours were first introduced in 1729 by a Dutch surveyor named Cruquius in connection with depth soundings of the sea. Laplace then used the concept to represent terrain in 1816.
- Water flows perpendicular to the contour.
- Contours bend or point upstream when they cross creeks or rivers.
- Evenly spaced contours represent a fairly uniform or constant slope condition.
- Closed contours that end on an intermediate elevation should be identified with hachures or spot shots to indicate whether the ground is rising or dropping.

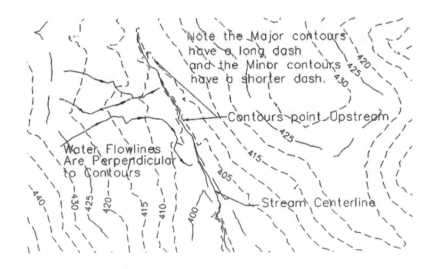

Figure 7-7   Contours speak to us

WHAT METHOD IS USED TO CALCULATE THE CONTOURS FOR THE SITE?

Let us review the contouring processing. In a particular set of data, the contours may be drawn as shown next. Please note that the algorithms for calculating contour lines vary from manufacturer to manufacturer. One general means for generating contours is straight-line interpolation from the TIN surface.

The calculations interpolate where the desired contour crosses the TIN line. In this manner, you can find out where the contour enters and leaves the triangle. As can be seen in Figure 7-8, this kind of processing is quite exact. Notice the 105′ contour. It must touch the 105′ spot shot.

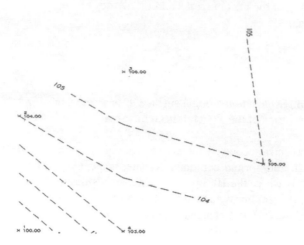

Figure 7-8 An accurate contour

However, because the ground tends to roll in natural conditions, the contour must usually be "smoothed" to represent this rolling. When the software smoothes a contour, it adds error to it. See Figure 7-9.

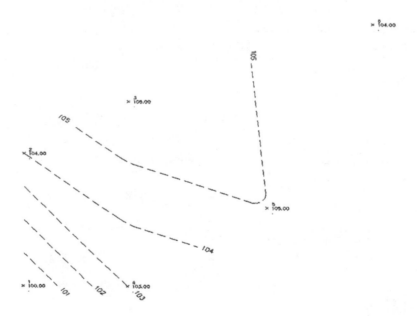

Figure 7-9 A smoothed contour

This error can be noticed in Figure 7-9 because the 105′ contour no longer touches the 105′ spot shot. The smoothing process sacrifices the sharp vertices while trying to retain the shape and location of the remaining contour. This is only one of several variations that can occur in contour generation.

The data in Figure 7-10 show a 140-acre site with breaklines and mass points. Breaklines represent a break in the surface where one plane changes slope from the plane adjacent to it. Mathematically, the breakline serves the TIN creation algorithm in that no triangle will ever be allowed to cross a breakline. This rule allows the user to control how a TIN is developed. This is more efficient than depicting it with contour data. The contour file for this project was around 20 MB whereas this file is less than 1 MB. The resulting contours for this site are shown in Figure 7-11.

With the accuracies attained by breaklines and mass point data, you can compute profiles and sections with more precision than that which is possible with contours.

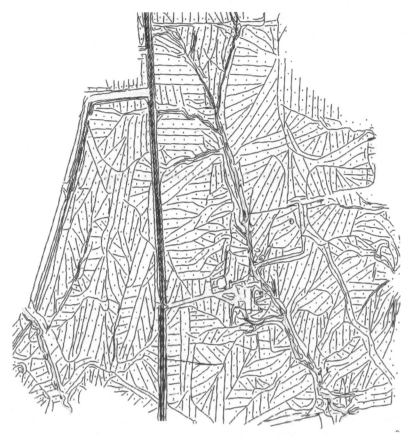

Figure 7-10   Breaklines and mass points

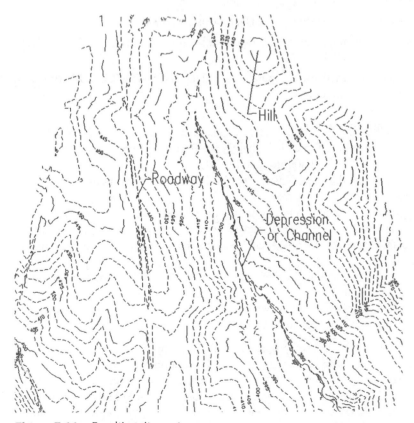

Figure 7-11   Resulting site contours

Civil 3D has the industry's leading terrain modeling capabilities. Now that the theories and algorithms involving DTMs have been discussed, you now explore how Civil 3D handles these computations.

Surfaces in Civil 3D

Next you run through an exercise that sets some basic settings, and then you create an Existing Ground Style and generate a surface. The **Surfaces** pull-down menu, Figure 7-12, contains the following commands:

Figure 7-12   The Surfaces pull-down menu

Create Surface... allows for the user to create and name a new surface and choose its surface type, TIN, Grid, and Volume.

Create Surface from DEM... allows for creating a surface from a Digital Elevation Model. These are available from several sources, including the U.S. Geological Survey at www.usgs.org.

Create Surface from TIN... allows for importing a TIN from Land Desktop. It requires a .tin and its associated .pnt file.

Edit Surface offers many options for surface editing.

Add Surface Labels allows for labeling the surface or its contours.

Add Legend Table... allows for bringing in a legend table for a variety of surface analyses that can be generated in Civil 3D.

Utilities is where you perform volume computations and use the **WATER DROP** command to check for drainage flow directions.

Exercise 7-2: Open Drawing and Inspect Source Data

To access student data files, go to www.pearsondesigncentral.com.

1. Launch Civil 3D and open the file called Chapter-7-DTM.dwg. Type **V** for **View**, select the view called **DTM-A**, hit **Set Current**, and hit **OK**.
2. Notice that there are breaklines and mass points in the file. The mass points are actually AutoCAD blocks floating at the correct elevation. The breaklines were developed by an aerial photogrammetist using stereodigitizing techniques. The breaklines are three-dimensional and have elevations at each vertex. The mass points are placed in the data set to densify the surface data. Together the breaklines and mass points represent the existing ground conditions.
3. Click on a breakline somewhere in the file and notice the grips. Place your cursor in one of the grips, but do not click it. Simply look at the lower left corner of the screen and observe that the X, Y, Z coordinates are shown for the grip. Notice the Z coordinate or elevation has a value representing the elevation of the surface at that location.

Now that you have observed the data set, prepare a Civil 3D surface for existing ground. First you must inspect some important surface-related settings. The first one you change is the **Precision of the Contour** label. Because you are labeling even contours that are multiples of 2, there is no need to have thousandths place precision on the annotation when whole numbers suffice. The precision is unneeded, and the extra decimal places tend to clutter up the drawing. Additionally, you create a layer for the annotation to reside on.

Exercise 7-3: Develop Surface Settings

1. Go to the **Toolspace**. Click on the **Settings** tab.
2. In the **Master View**, expand **Drawings**. Then expand **Surface**. Then expand **Label Styles**.
3. Choose the **Contour** label style, and note that one exists called **Standard**.
4. Click on the **Standard** label style, right-click, and choose **Edit....**
5. The **Label Style Composer** dialog box displays. Click on the **Information** tab and observe the contents of the panel. Click on the **General** tab and observe the contents of the panel.
6. Click the **Layout** tab. Several properties exist in the **Property** column.
7. Click on **Text**; expand **Text**. Choose **Contents** and then refer to the **Value** column. Click on the value for **Contents**. Choose the button with the ellipsis (...).
8. This brings up the **Text Component Editor—Contents**.
9. Click in the **Preview** window on the right side of the dialog box; highlight the data there and erase them so that the window is blank.
10. Click on **Precision** in the **Modifier** column.
11. The value for the **Precision** is **0.001**, which is not appropriate for your contour label because you do not wish to have decimal points on even contours. Click on **0.001** and select **1** from the pop-down window in the **Value** column.
12. Then click the **arrow** at the top of the dialog box to populate the **Preview** window with the new data settings.
13. Look on the **Preview** window and see some code indicating that new settings exist. Hit **OK**.
14. In the **General** tab for the **Layer** property, click on the value where it shows **Layer 0** and notice that a button with an ellipsis (...) exists. Choose the button, and a **Layer Selection** dialog box appears. Choose **New**. In the **Create Layer** dialog box, click on the value for **Layer** property where it says **Layer 1** and type in a new layer name of **C-Topo-Labl**. Hit **OK**, and hit **OK** again.
15. In the **Label Style Composer-Standard** dialog box under the **General** tab, there is a property for **Plan Readability**. Set **Flip Anchors with Text**; set it to **True**.
16. Hit **Apply** and **OK**.

You need to set one more setting. When executing the procedure to label contours, several technicalities are established by the software that will provide benefits later on. One of those has to do with a Contour Label Control Line. This linework appears in the center of the contour label and can be placed on its own layer so it will be nonintrusive to the user when plotting or negotiating through the drawing.

Exercise 7-4: Set Up a Surface

Now allocate a surface for the project. Develop a surface name and set the type of surface you will have.

1. From the Civil 3D pull-down menu, choose **Surfaces**.
2. Select **Create Surface....**
3. The **Create Surface** dialog box appears.
4. Several types of surfaces can be created: a TIN surface, a Grid surface, and two types of Volume surfaces. The Volume surfaces are created during earthwork take-off computations. The Grid surface is used when a surface of evenly spaced rectangular data whose elevations are interpolated from the data is desired.
5. You want a **TIN** surface. In the window is the informational item that includes the name of the surface. Click on the **Value** column for the **Surface** name.
6. The **Surface** name is incremental so the first surface will be **Surface 1**, the second surface is **Surface 2**, and so on. Click in this field and type **Existing Ground** as your name or select the ellipses (...) to bring up the **Name Template** dialog box.
7. To the right of the type is the **Surface layer** field. Select the button on the right side of the dialog box for **Surface layer**. An **Object Layer** dialog box appears. Where it says **Base layer name**, choose the button on the right for **Layer**, and the **Layer Selection** dialog box opens.
8. Hit the button for **New** layer and enter **C-Topo** in the field for **Layer 1**, hit **OK**, hit **OK** again. Then where it says **Modifier**, select **Suffix** from the pop-down window.

9. When the field to the right becomes available, type in a dash and an asterisk (-*). This creates a layer with the name of the surface as a suffix to the layer name. You should get a layer called **C-Topo-Existing Ground**, as can be seen in the **Preview**. Hit **OK**.
10. Type **Existing Ground** for the **Description** also.
11. Leave all else as default and hit **OK**.
12. Next go to the **Toolspace** and choose the **Prospector** tab.
13. Look under **Open Drawings** for your drawing. Expand **Surfaces** to show the new surface you just created for Existing Ground.

Exercise 7-5: Build a Surface

The next step is to identify the 3D surface data and build the surface.

1. Expand the **Existing Ground Surface** item. You see an item for **Definition**.
2. Expand **Definition**, and you see all the data types that can go into the preparation of the surface. These include **Breaklines, Contours, DEM Files**, and **Drawing Objects**.
3. Your data set contains breaklines and blocks, as discussed earlier. Therefore, use the commands for adding **Breaklines** and use **Drawing Objects** to add the blocks.
4. Begin by clicking on **Breaklines**, then right-click on **Breaklines** and select **Add....**
5. A dialog box for **Add Breaklines** displays. Add a **Description** of **EG**.
6. Use **Standard** breaklines as the type of breakline but notice that other choices exist in the pop-down list. The choices allow for **Proximity breaklines**, **Wall breaklines**, **Breaklines from a file**, and **Non-destructive breaklines**.

TIP Proximity breaklines are 2D polylines that have points with elevations at each vertex in the polyline. The software uses the point elevations in creating 3D breaklines from the 2D polylines. The **Wall breakline** option is used to represent vertical components of surfaces. In actuality they are not truly vertical as this would cause issues in the software relating to a divide by zero in the denominator for various slope computations. Therefore, the software allows for Wall breaklines that contain wall height data, but the top of the wall is slightly offset from the bottom of the wall to avoid the vertical computational issue. Another choice is to bring in breaklines from an external text file.

You use **Standard** breaklines, which are the 3D polylines in the file. The last setting is a **Mid-ordinate distance** field, which is available for creating 3D breaklines from 2D polylines that have curves in them. In this case if you use the default of 1′, a 3D polyline would be created so that small chords simulate the curve but do not deviate from the arc by more than 1′.

7. Hit **OK**, and the command prompt instructs you to `Select objects:` Place a window around the data. Do not worry if there are points mixed in with the selection set of breaklines because the software filters anything that is not a breakline.
8. A **Panorama** dialog box may appear that indicates there are two crossing breaklines. Coordinates are displayed so the user can check the severity of the issue. In this case, you have determined that this will not harm your surface integrity and so continue on. Click the checkmark in the top right of the **Panorama** to continue. On completion of this function, the software creates the surface as can be seen by a yellow boundary.
9. Now in the **Prospector**, choose **Drawing Objects** under **Surfaces >> Definition** area. Right-click and choose **Add....**
10. For the **Object type**, choose **Blocks**.
11. Type **EG** as the **Description** field in the dialog box and hit **OK**.
12. `Select objects:` Place a window around the data. Do not worry if there are breaklines mixed in with the selection set of points because the software filters out the unnecessary data.
13. On completion, the yellow surface boundary is updated to include the blocks.

Now that the surface is created, you typically want to view contours representing the surface.

Exercise 7-6: Develop Contours for the Surface

1. In the **Toolspace**, choose the **Settings** tab. Choose **Surface >> Surface Styles >> Standard**. Right-click on **Standard** and choose **Edit....**
2. In the **Surface Style** dialog box, choose the **Display** tab.
3. With the view direction in the pop-down window set to **Plan**, click **On** the lightbulb to turn on the **Major** and **Minor contours** and turn **Off** the lightbulb for **Border**. Note the colors are preset and can be changed here if so desired. Hit **Apply** then hit **OK**.
4. On leaving the dialog box, the contours in Civil 3D are automatically updated to show the contours as defined in the Style.
5. The next step is to create contour labels on the contours. From the Civil 3D pull-down menu, choose **Surfaces >> Add Surface Labels >> Contour-Multiple at Interval**.
6. `Select a surface:` Pick on surface. Existing Ground, `Pick first point:` Place a point at the top of the site and place a second point to the bottom and outside of the site.
7. `Interval along contour <100.000'>:` **500 <Enter>**. On completion of the command, zoom in and inspect the data and the contour labels every 500' across the site.
8. Save your file to a name with your initials as the suffix of the name, Chapter-7-DTM-YourInitials.dwg.

TIP Use the contour labeling as often as is needed to obtain coverage across the site for all the desired contours that you wish to be labeled.

Job skills will benefit in that the drawing labels can be customized. If you have duplicate labels, notice that you can delete the **Contour Label Control Line** to delete the label. Notice also that you can move this **Contour Label Control Line** to relocate the label.

Congratulations! You have created a surface, displayed its contours, and labeled them. Note that you can also add other labels, as shown in Figure 7-13.

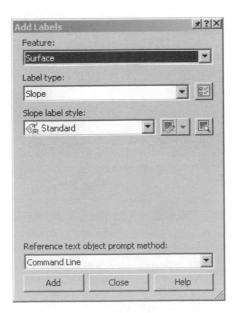

Figure 7-13 Add Labels dialog box

Exercise 7-7: Create a Surface from DEM Data

Now use another Civil 3D command to build a surface based on DEM data. A DEM is a Digital Elevation Model data set. DEM data can be found in a number of locations, but one source is the USGS.org website. This exercise uses a DEM data set for Norfolk-E, Virginia.

To access student data files, go to www.pearsondesigncentral.com.

1. Launch Civil 3D and open the file called Chapter-7-DEM.dwg.
2. Under the **Surfaces** pull-down menu, choose the option for **Create Surface From DEM....**
3. When prompted, select the file called **Norfolk-E.dem**. This file was downloaded from the USGS.org website with the filename Norfolk-E.gz, which is a WinZip file that produces a file called Norfolk-E. It was renamed to a .DEM file prior to using it in this exercise. No scaling or geoedetics have been applied to the file, and it is being used directly as it was downloaded from the USGS.org website.
4. At this point, the software reads the file, prepares the surfaces, and generates the contours for the area.
5. Use **ZOOM EXTENTS** to see the results on completion.

Exercise 7-8: Importing a Surface from Land Desktop

Now use another Civil 3D command to import a TIN surface from a Land Desktop project. This file, specifically the .TIN file, can be found in the DTM folder of a Land Desktop project.

Note:
You must have the associated OSI-INTX.PNT file for this to work. It is provided but is not requested in the process.

To access student data files, go to www.pearsondesigncentral.com.

1. Launch Civil 3D and open the file called Chapter-7-importtin.dwg.
2. Under the **Surfaces** pull-down menu, choose the option for **Create Surface from TIN....**
3. When prompted, select the file called **OSI-INTX.TIN**.
4. At this point, the software reads the file, prepares the surface for Civil 3D usage, and displays it based on the Style in effect.
5. Use **ZOOM EXTENTS** to see the result on completion.

Exercise 7-9: Surface Labeling

This exercise explores some of the surface labeling features in Civil 3D. Zoom into the side road in the file you just imported. Let us evaluate the slopes of the roadway. See Figure 7-14.

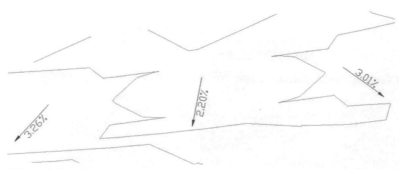

Figure 7-14 Roadway contours with labels

1. Under the **Surfaces** pull-down menu, select **Add Surface Labels** and choose the option for **Add Surface Labels....**
2. A dialog box appears requesting information on the type of label you want to create.
3. Use a **Surface Feature;** the **Label type** will be a slope (as opposed to a spot elevation label), and you use a **Standard** slope label style. Hit the **Add** button.
4. The prompt requests you to choose whether you want a one-point or two-point label.

TIP

A one-point label computes the slope at the point you pick based on the triangle slope of the TIN triangle. The two-point option allows you to pick two points where it computes the elevations of the two points, the distance between the two points, and the average slope between them.

5. Hit **<Enter>** for **One Point** and pick points inside the surface of the side road. Slope labels appear, and you can repeat this as often as needed.

Surface Analysis

The next item of discussion is how to perform analyses on the surface. Civil 3D has many types of analyses that can be computed. They include:

Contour renders surface triangles according to the range into which a contour falls.

Directions renders surface triangles according to the direction they face.

Elevations renders surface triangles according to the elevation range into which they fall.

Slopes renders surface triangles according to the slopes they have.

Slope Arrows places directional vector arrows based on the flow direction that a triangle has.

User-Defined Contours draws the location for user-specified contour elevations.

Watersheds draws the perimeters of drainage divides.

Exercise 7-10: Performing Slope Analysis

Quite often, there is concern with the slopes occurring across a site, so it is important to perform a slope analysis. Perform a slope analysis of the roadway as in Figure 7-15.

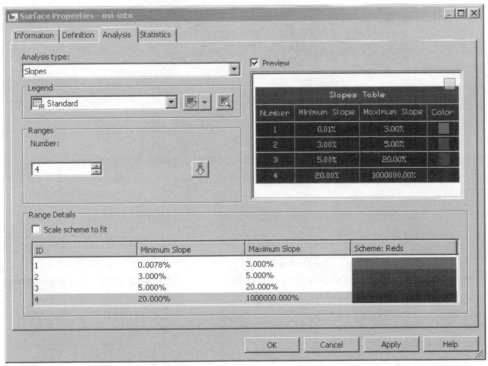

Figure 7-15   Surface analysis

1. Select the surface in the file. Right-click and choose **Surface Properties....**
2. A **Surface Properties** dialog box appears. Set the **Analysis** type to **Slopes**.
3. Set the **Number** of **Ranges** to **4**.

4. Turn off the **Scale scheme to fit** option. Click the **gray down** arrow.
5. For ID1, set the **Maximum Slope** to **3%**.
6. For ID2, set the **Minimum Slope** to **3%** and the maximum slope to **5%**.
7. For ID3, set the **Minimum Slope** to **5%** and the maximum slope to **20%**.
8. For ID4, set the **Minimum Slope** to **20%** and the maximum slope to **10000000%**. Hit **Apply** and **OK**.
9. The system sets the surface to display these data once the Style is set to do so.
10. Click on a contour and right-click. Choose **Edit Surface Style....**
11. Under the **Display** tab, turn **Off** the **Contour** components and turn **On** the **Slopes**. Hit **OK**.
12. The surface should display with red-colored faces.
13. Now from the **Surfaces** pull-down menu, choose **Add Legend Table....**
14. `Enter table type [ Directions/Elevations/Slopes/slopeArrows/Contours/ Usercontours/Watersheds] :` Type **S** for **Slope**.
15. `Behavior [ Dynamic/<Static>] :` Hit **<Enter>** for **Dynamic**.
16. `Select upper left corner:` Pick a point below and out of the way of the surface data, and a table of the statistics appears. See Figure 7-16.

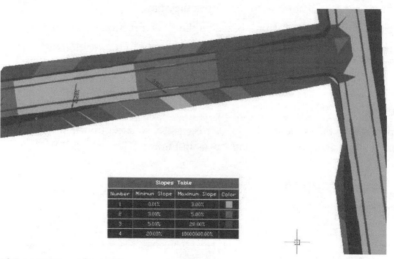

Figure 7-16   A Legend

Exercise 7-11: How to Edit a Surface

Now explore surface editing a little. You have identified that a low spot for an inlet is needed at the intersection of these roads. Add that low spot by editing the surface and dropping the desired location by 1'.

1. Start by selecting the surface, right-click, and choose **Edit Surface Style....**
2. In the **Display** tab, turn **On** the **Contours** and **Points** and turn **Off** the **Slopes** from the last exercise.
3. Hit **OK** to see the contours for the surface.
4. Type **V** for **View**, select a view called **DTM-B**, hit **Set Current,** hit **OK**. This places your view near the intersection of the two roads.
5. In the **Prospector**, expand your drawing file. Expand the **Surfaces** item. Expand the surface called **osi-intx**. Expand **Definition**. Right-click on **Edits**, and a menu displays Surface editing commands.
6. Choose **Modify Point**, shown in Figure 7-17.
7. `Select points:` Type **15700,18843.5** and hit **<Enter>** twice.
8. `New elevation:` Type **441.8**.
9. Notice that a new contour appears immediately at the intersection of the roads, indicating that the point has dropped 1', thereby creating a new contour. That new contour shows up just above the cursor in Figure 7-18.

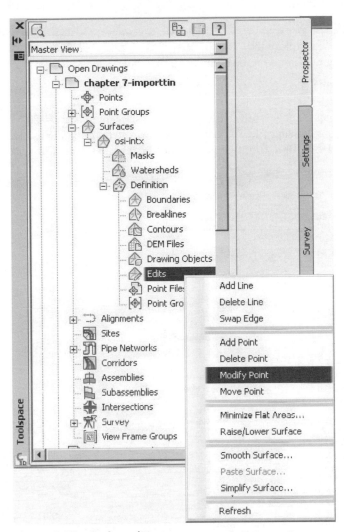

Figure 7-17   Surface editing

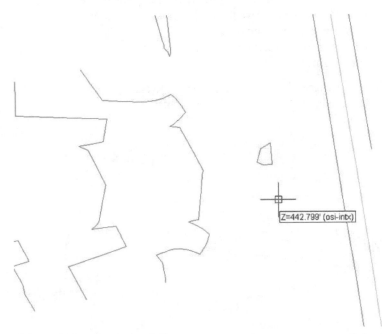

Figure 7-18   Contour updating

Exercise 7-12: Adding Surface Boundaries

In the last surface-related exercise, you explore the concept of surface boundaries. Boundaries allow you to curtail surface computations based on the boundaries that you define.

1. Zoom into the view of the same file where you imported the **osi-intx** surface of the two roads. Zoom into the side road.
2. Draw a polyline around the outside edge of the side roadway, as shown in Figure 7-20.
3. In the **Prospector**, expand your drawing file. Expand the **Surfaces** item. Expand the surface called **osi-intx**. Expand **Definition**. Right-click on **Boundaries** and select **Add...** as in Figure 7-19.

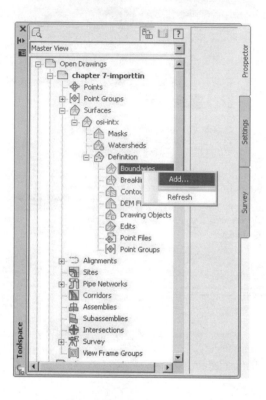

Figure 7-19   Add Boundary

4. When the **Add Boundaries** dialog box appears, type **B1** for the name of the boundary.
5. Choose **Outer** for the type of boundary. Leave the mid-ordinate distance at **1.0′**. Hit **OK**.
6. `Select object(s):` Pick the polyline you drew.
7. The surface is instantly reduced to exist within the boundary drawn. Notice that the adjacent road is now gone. See Figure 7-20.

To continue exploring with the surfaces features, take some time to change the **Surface Styles** and turn on or off various items to change how the surface can display itself.

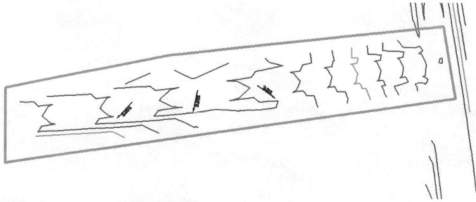

Figure 7-20   Effect of surface boundary

CHAPTER SUMMARY

This chapter introduced terrain modeling and discussed the mathematics needed to develop Digital Terrain Models. The DTM is the basis of most Civil 3D three-dimensional computa-tions, including road and utility profile creation and contour rep-resentation. Terrain models were developed and edited, and sev-eral advanced techniques were used to analyze models in 3D.

CHAPTER TEST QUESTIONS

Multiple Choice

1. Which of the following acronyms pertain to surface models?
   a. TIN
   b. DTM
   c. TTN
   d. All of the above

2. A DTM can represent which of the following?
   a. Caves and escarpments
   b. Existing and finished ground surfaces
   c. Roadway profiles
   d. None of the above

3. DTMs can be created by using the following as source data:
   a. Points, breaklines
   b. Roadway profiles and alignments
   c. DEMs combined with utility data
   d. All of the above

4. The following computations usually use surface data:
   a. Profiling
   b. Earthworks
   c. Cross sections
   d. All of the above

5. Contour intervals can be which of the following?
   a. 1' and 5' intervals
   b. 2' and 10' intervals
   c. 5' and 25' intervals
   d. All of the above

6. The following information items are attributed to contours:
   a. Laplace used the concept to represent terrain in 1816.
   b. Water flows perpendicular to the contour.

   c. Contours bend or point upstream when they cross creeks or rivers.
   d. All of the above.

7. What method is used to calculate the contours for a site?
   a. Straight-line interpolation from the TIN surface
   b. Slope analysis
   c. Delauney's method
   d. None of the above

8. Surfaces in Civil 3D can be:
   a. TIN surfaces
   b. Grid surfaces
   c. Volume surfaces
   d. All of the above

9. Proximity breaklines are:
   a. Breaklines near other breaklines
   b. Polylines that have points with elevations near their vertices
   c. Breaklines that are in the proximity of mass points
   d. None of the above

10. Civil 3D can analyze surfaces according to which of the following:
    a. Triangle direction
    b. Slope
    c. Elevation
    d. All of the above

True or False

1. True or False: A DTM stands for Digital Terrain Method-ology.

2. True or False: A contour with a value of 101.5 can never be a legitimate contour elevation.

3. True or False: A DEM is a legitimate source data type for a surface.

4. True or False: Contours can be used in conjunction with spot shots to develop surfaces.

5. True or False: The TIN theory is based on Descartes' methods.

6. True or False: Most of the computations for the third di-mension emanate from the surface model.

7. True or False: Cross sections are usually computed or-thogonally from the centerline.

8. True or False: The TIN algorithm computes triangle ver-tices based on the closest three points.

9. True or False: A contour is a linestring that represents a single elevation along a surface.

10. True or False: Contours may have primary and secondary intervals.

CHAPTER EXERCISES

1. Draw the 5′ contours where they fall on this map of spot elevations shot by a surveyor in the field (Figure 7-21). The tick marks designate where the actual spot shot is located. Use manual interpolated techniques to determine where the contours fall.

X 427.52 X 422.27 X 430.02 X 429.44 X 428.53 X 430.36 X 431.70 X 425.28 X 414.89 X 407.92 X 402.45

X 422.40 X 418.86 X 428.16 X 427.08 X 424.56 X 427.98 X 430.27 X 426.69 X 417.42 X 406.51 X 401.28

X 417.91 X 420.07 X 425.48 X 422.56 X 422.33 X 426.26 X 428.90 X 425.74 X 416.24 X 407.08 X 401.63

X 415.39 X 412.61 X 420.19 X 417.10 X 419.57 X 425.70 X 428.31 X 427.93 X 421.14 X 410.72 X 401.71

X 410.87 X 409.28 X 410.60 X 413.67 X 421.79 X 426.95 X 431.14 X 427.78 X 417.31 X 407.78 X 406.03

X 405.04 405.48 X 407.95 X 415.10 X 421.30 X 426.62 X 431.22 X 430.56 X 421.27 X 411.25 X 411.57

X 399.67 X 409.32 X 415.52 X 420.04 X 424.90 X 429.92 X 433.73 X 429.64 X 419.44 X 415.3 X 415.49

X 404.7 X 409.59 X 415.65 X 420.97 X 426.32 X 425.35 X 432.04 X 431.25 X 424.36 X 422.29 X 419.74

Figure 7-21   Surface Data—spot shots

2. Show the drainage for the site in Problem 1. Draw six arrows representing the drainage across the site.
3. Circle the high and the low points on the site in Problem 1.
4. What is the slope in Figure 7-22 from the 434 contour to the 424 contour, the 426 to the 424 contour, and the 422 contour to the 420 contour?
5. How many 2′ contours would exist on the side sloping of a retention pond if the top of the pond elevation were at 500′ elevation, the side sloping were at 3:1 down, and the existing ground tie-out were at 485?

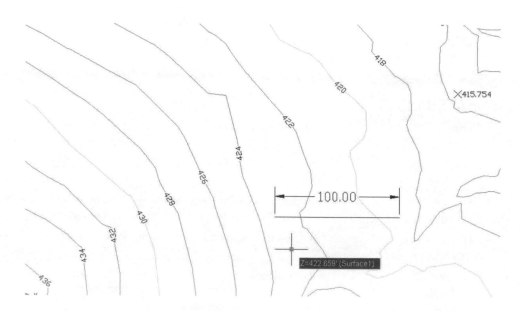

Figure 7-22   Computing slope from contours

Advanced Profiles and Sections

8

Chapter Objectives

- Understand the algorithms and formulas involved in computing existing and proposed profiles.
- Understand how profiles and sections build on what was learned in the previous chapter on surfaces.
- Understand how existing ground profiles and cross-sectional data are associated with horizontal alignments.
- Design, label, and edit a proposed vertical alignment.
- Produce, label, and edit sections.

INTRODUCTION

This chapter begins with some of the theory involved in designing roads, moving you into the third dimension with creating roadway profiling; developing vertical tangents, vertical curves, and vertical alignments; and the editing and labeling of these. Roadway vertical tangents, vertical curves, vertical alignments (profiles), and profile views are discussed in detail. Cross sections are also covered in this chapter because they are closely related to profiles.

REVIEW OF FUNCTIONS AND FEATURES TO BE USED

There are three main requirements for designing a roadway. The first is the development of an alignment, covered in Chapter 6. The second is the roadway profile, covered in this chapter. The third is the road's cross-sectional *template*, to be discussed in Chapter 9 on corridor design. Here you learn how to produce existing ground profiles, how to place them into profile views, and how to develop *proposed profiles* and annotate them. This chapter explores the link between horizontal alignments, existing ground profiles, and cross sections and how they are updated when modifications are made to the data. Similar material will be procedurized for section-based views of the roadway as well.

    In some locations across the country, road design can be accomplished with the alignment, the profile, and a simple cross-sectional detail outlining the typical cross section for the road. The contractor follows the alignment for horizontal control, the profile for vertical control, and then inputs the cross-sectional data into the paving machinery.

template: A template consists of one or more typical examples of how the roadway will appear for varying conditions, such as a roadway with a curb and gutter at the edge of the pavement or perhaps a shoulder treatment at the edge of the pavement. It is shown in a cross-sectional view and shows the road from left to right looking into the profile grade line (PGL).

proposed profile: The vertical alignment for the roadway as defined by the proposed vertical tangents and vertical curves.

THEORY OF VERTICAL ALIGNMENTS

Before getting into the Civil 3D approach for developing profiles, some of the rudimentary mathematics involved with the vertical alignments for roadways must be discussed.

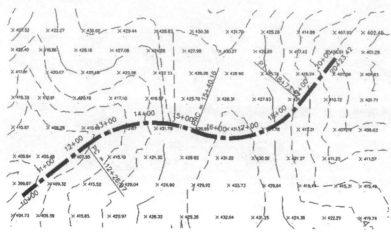

Figure 8-1   A horizontal alignment

Profiles are created by sampling the elevation at intervals along a horizontal alignment (see Figure 8-1). The existing profile is shown as the heavy line in Figure 8-2. For tangent sections, this is often accomplished by computing the elevation wherever the alignment crosses the TIN lines in the terrain model. In curved locations, a chord-based system is often used to simulate the curve. The location of the chord is where the computation occurs as it crosses TIN lines in the model. Figure 8-2 shows an alignment lying on the terrain model.

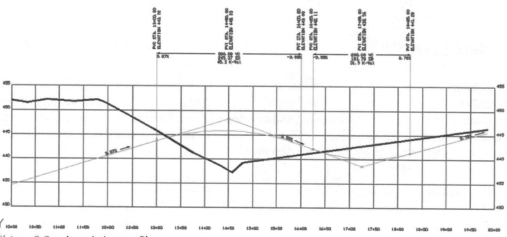

Figure 8-2   An existing profile

PVI: The Point of Vertical Intersection of the incoming and outgoing vertical tangents. This is also referred to as the *VPI* for Vertical Point of Intersection.

PVC: The Point of Vertical Curvature where the vertical curve begins and departs the tangent. Also called *BVC* for Begin Vertical Curve.

PVT: The Point of Vertical Tangency where the vertical curve ends and returns to the tangent. Also called *EVC* for End Vertical Curve.

The proposed vertical alignment, shown as the light linework in Figure 8-2, is comprised of vertical tangents and vertical curves. Two tangents meet at a *PVI (Point of Vertical Intersection)*. Usually if there is a grade break between the two longitudinal tangents that is considered slight, a vertical curve is not required. Slight differences between agencies may range from 0.5% to 2.5%. Anything beyond these values requires a vertical curve to smooth out the transition between the tangents. Figure 8-2 shows a dark, thick existing ground line, a light thin line for proposed tangents, and vertical curves. There are elevations on the vertical axis, and it is usually exaggerated to show vertical detail. There are stations along the horizontal axis that match the alignment. There are three proposed tangents and two vertical curves. The tangents are denoted by a beginning station and elevation and a grade. It ends at the *PVC (Point of Vertical Curvature)*, where the vertical curve begins. The curve ends at the *PVT (Point of Vertical Tangency)*. A short tangent exists, and then another PVC begins the next curve.

In Figure 8-3, a vertical curve is shown emboldened with annotation for the PVC and the PVT. The PVI is shown as a triangle. The back tangent is before the curve, and a forward tangent occurs after the curve. Once these are known, the only other criterion is the length of the curve because a parabolic equation governs the remaining computations.

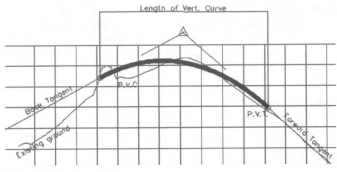

Figure 8-3   A vertical curve

In Figure 8-4, criteria are identified with the curve data. A completed proposed profile shows the incoming tangent slope is 5.44%, the outgoing is −9.15%, and the vertical curve length is 400′.

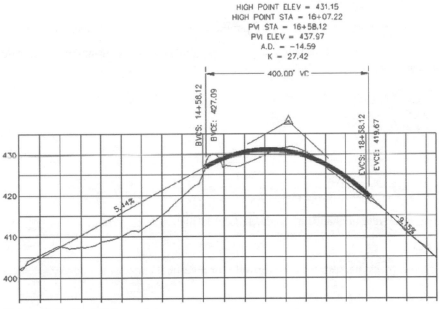

Figure 8-4   Vertical Curve data

THE PROPERTIES OF PARABOLIC CURVES

Following are the properties of parabolic curves:

- A curve's elevation at the midpoint of the curve is halfway from the elevation at the PVI to the elevation at the midpoint of a straight line from the PVC to the PVT.

- The tangent offsets vary as the square of the distance from the points of tangency.

- For points spaced at equal horizontal distances, the second differences are equal, which is useful when checking the vertical curve computations. The differences (or subtractions) between the elevations at equally spaced stations are called first differences. The differences between the first differences are called the second differences.

The design of a vertical alignment is usually specified in terms of a maximum grade and the minimum length for the vertical curve. The maximum allowable grade is a parameter that considers whether the service vehicles can negotiate the grade easily and safely. In other words, trucks would have considerable difficulty in climbing a road with a 12% grade. It would be clearly unsafe for trucks to be descending this grade should the brakes fail. Therefore, a highway might limit the maximum grade to 8%, so that the service vehicles (trucks and cars) could negotiate the grade safely. Because the vertical curves are parabolic, their criteria are represented as a K factor. The K factor is computed by dividing the length of the curve by the grade break at the PVI. The relationship here is that a smaller K factor means a sharper curve and a larger K factor designates a flatter curve.

Cross-sectional design criteria depend on the service classification for the roadway. Subdivision roads may have four lanes for high-density areas and two lanes for less dense areas. They may be bounded by a curb and gutter and sidewalks for drainage and pedestrian traffic. Highways, on the other hand, usually have several lanes and are bounded by shoulders. Often there is a center median to divide the bidirectional traffic.

FORMULAS USED FOR COMPUTING PARABOLIC VERTICAL CURVE DATA

Where L = the Length of curve, the PVC station = PVI station $- (L/2)$.

The PVT = PVI + $(L/2)$. The PVT = PVC + L.

The general equation for a vertical curve is a parabolic equation, which derives as follows:

$Y_p = a + bX_p + cX_p^2$, where Y_p is any point on the parabola located X_p from the origin. And a, b, and c are constants.

For a vertical curve,

$a = Y_{BVC}$
$bX_p = g_1X$
$c = (g_2 - g_1)/2L$

Therefore:

$Y = Y_{BVC} + g_1X + ((g_2 - g_1)/2L)*X^2$

A useful term is the rate of change of grade. This is defined as r. Therefore:

$r = (g_2 - g_1)/L$

Combining the expressions results in the formula for a vertical curve of a roadway:

$Y = Y_{BVC} + g_1X + (r/2)*X^2$

Example 8-1: A Manually Computed Vertical Curve Problem

With a back tangent of 2%, a forward tangent of -2.5%, and a vertical curve length of $800'$, compute the starting and ending stations of this vertical curve and its accompanying table if the PVI station is 36+70 and the PVI elevation is 813.53.

$R = (g_2 - g_1)/L \rightarrow (-2.5 - 2)/8 = -.5625\%/\text{station}$
VPI = 36 + 70
$-L/2 = 4 + 00$
BVC = 32 + 70
$+L = 8 + 00$
EVC = 40 + 70

The Elevation at BVC = 813.53 $- (2.00)(4) = 805.53$

The Elevation at EVC = $Y_{BVC} + g_1X + (r/2)x^2 = 805.53 + (2)(8) + (-.5625)(64)/2$
    $= 805.53 + 16.0 + (-18.054) = 803.53$

The Elevation at the midpoint of the chord of the curve = $(805.53 + 803.53)/2 = 804.53$

The Elevation at midpoint of curve = $(813.53 + 804.53)/2 = 809.03$

A table, such as in Table 8-1, can be established to compute the elevations along the vertical curve. You may select an interval for the information you are interested in computing, say every 20 or 25 feet. You would use Vertical Curve Property #3 described above, to ensure that you have computed the correct answers. You simply break down the formula for the vertical curve into its parts and make each part a column in the spreadsheet. The second to last column will compute the first difference between the elevations. The last column will compute the second difference (or the difference between the first differences). Note it equals r.

Table 8-1   Table for Computing Elevations Every 100' Along a Vertical Curve

Sta	X(Sta)	g_1X	$rX^2/2$	Curve Elev.	1st Diff	2nd Diff
40+70	8	16	−18	803.53		
40+00	7.3	14.6	−14.99	805.14		
39+00	6.3	12.6	−11.16	806.97	−1.83	
38+00	5.3	10.6	−7.9	808.23	−1.26	−.57
37+00	4.3	8.6	−5.2	808.93	−.7−.56	
36+00	3.3	6.6	−3.063	809.067	−.137	−.56
35+00	2.3	4.6	−1.488	808.642	.425	−.56
34+00	1.3	2.6	−.475	807.655	.987	−.56
33+00	.3	.6	−.025	806.105	1.55	−.56
32+70	0	0	805.53	.575		

The High/Low points of a vertical curve are computed as such:

$$X = g_1L/g_1 - g_2 \rightarrow -g_1/r \rightarrow -2/-.5625 = 3.555 \text{ stations} = X$$

The High point $= 32 + 70 + (3.555) = 36 + 25.5$
The Elevation $= 805.53 + 2(3.555) + (-.5625/2)(3.555)^2$
$= 805.53 + 7.11 - 3.554 = \underline{\mathbf{809.086}}$

Another method for computing vertical curves for roads is by using the K factor, where K = L/A. L is the length of the vertical curve, and A is the algebraic difference between the outgoing and incoming vertical tangents. Therefore the Length of vertical curve can be computed based on a required K minimum value such that L = KA.

Tables 8-2 and 8-3 provide examples of the American Association of State Highway Transportation Officials (AASHTO) criteria for vertical curves for both crest and sag conditions with

Table 8-2   AASHTO Stopping Sight Distances for Crest Curves

Design Speed	Minimum Stopping Distance (ft)	K Value for Crest Curve
30	200	19
35	250	29
40	305	44
45	360	61
50	425	84
55	495	114
60	570	151
65	645	193
70	730	247

| Table 8-3   AASHTO Stopping Sight Distances for Sag Curves | | |
Design Speed	Minimum Stopping Distance (ft)	K Value for Crest Curve
30	200	37
35	250	49
40	305	64
45	360	79
50	425	96
55	495	115
60	570	136
65	645	157
70	730	181

regard to being able to stop the vehicle. There must be enough sight distance for the driver to realize a problem and then apply the brakes. This information can be found in the AASHTO publication, *A Policy on Geometric Design of Highways and Streets*.

Very often designers need to design a vertical curve so that it meets a minimum K value as established by the transportation authority with jurisdiction over the design. The curve can exceed the minimum K value but must not be less than the required value. Engineers usually compute the length of curve needed to meet this condition and then round it up to the next even 50' value to make it easier for others to check the work and stake it out for construction.

Another method for determining lengths of vertical curves has to do with passing sight distance. When a driver is in a sag curve, oncoming traffic can be observed easily because both cars are in the concave portion of the curve. However, when the driver is approaching a crest curve, eyesight is obscured by the crest of the hill. Therefore, there must be enough forward sight distance for the driver to see an oncoming vehicle before making a decision to pass another vehicle. Table 8-4 provides an indication of the AASHTO passing sight distances required for a roadway.

| Table 8-4   AASHTO Passing Sight Distances | | |
Design Speed	Minimum Passing Distance (ft)	K Value for Crest Curve
30	1090	424
35	1280	585
40	1470	772
45	1625	943
50	1835	1203
55	1985	1407
60	2135	1628
65	2285	1865
70	2480	2197

Sections.   Roadway sections (Figure 8-5, showing SL-1) are similar to profiles in that they represent conditions before and after design. They are three-dimensional in what they are representing and are denoted with axes similar to profiles.

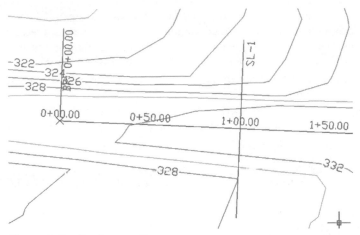

Figure 8-5   Roadway sections

There are elevations on the vertical axis, which is usually exaggerated to show vertical detail, and there are distances along the horizontal axis that equate to the length of the cross section to the left and to the right of the centerline. Typically where the centerline crosses the section is denoted with zero (0), whereas the distances are shown positive leaving the centerline to the right and negative to the left.

The section information is shown in Figure 8-6 for the existing ground section.

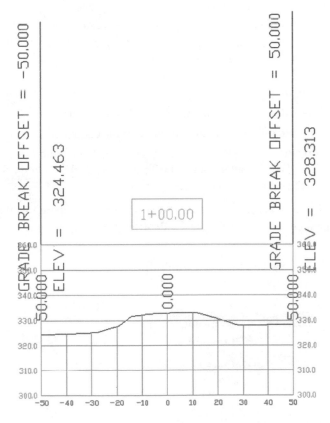

Figure 8-6   An existing ground section

APPLICATIONS USING CIVIL 3D FOR PROFILING

Profiles and sections in Civil 3D are intelligent objects, similar to the point groups, parcels, terrain models, and alignments already discussed. Profiles and cross sections are dynamically linked to horizontal alignments and surfaces. When the horizontal alignment is edited, the profile and cross section associated to it automatically update. If the surface is modified, the profile and cross-sectional data also update automatically. The related annotation updates as well, thereby saving time in drafting functions. Styles in Civil 3D are defined to control the display of this profile and cross-sectional data as well as the related annotation. These Styles represent the standards of your company or agency or your client. They are developed and stored in prototype Civil 3D drawings and within the project drawings.

In Civil 3D, existing ground profiles and cross sections are related to horizontal alignments. Changes to the alignment result in automatic updates to the profile and to the sections. This is referred to as a *dynamic model*, the *ripple-through effect*.

The process to be followed in the next steps is:

1. Compute the data and plot existing ground profile data in a **Profile View**. The **Profile View Style** controls the display of the profile grid, the title, and the horizontal and vertical axes annotation for stations and elevations. The **Profile View Label Styles** control the display of the annotation inside the **Profile View**.

A step-by-step procedure for designing a road right through profiles and sections and then sending it to construction would involve the following tasks:

1. Create and, if needed, edit the horizontal alignment.
2. Compute and plot the existing ground profile in the **Profile View**.
3. Develop and, if needed, edit the vertical alignment.
4. Compute and analyze the existing ground cross sections.
5. Develop roadway template(s) or assemblies.
6. Process the Corridor.
7. Plot the proposed roadway design cross sections. Repeat Steps 1 through 7 as needed.
8. Develop construction stakeout information for traditional staking, or 3D digital data for 3D Machine Control using Trimble Link, Carlson Connect, or Leica XChange. Compute earthwork takeoffs.

2. Develop the finished ground profile using vertical tangents and vertical curves.

3. For the cross sections, compute and plot the existing ground cross-sectional data.

4. Civil 3D simplifies the modification process for existing ground profiles and cross sections due to the dynamic link to the horizontal alignment. To experience this, modify the source data and again observe the ripple-through effect.

You will begin by opening a drawing that has a surface and an alignment prepared so that your profiling activities can be expedited. Then you will use the **Profiles** pull-down menu, shown in Figure 8-7, with its commands described.

Create Profile from Surface... allows you to develop a profile of an alignment from the surface object, normally Existing ground.

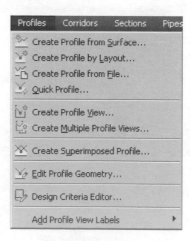

Figure 8-7   The Profiles pull-down menu

Create Profile by Layout... opens the **Layout** toolbar for designing profiles using criteria.

Create Profile from File... allows the creation of a profile from an external file with data in it.

Quick Profile... creates a temporary profile view for a selected object such as a feature line.

Create Profile View... allows for creating a **Profile View** for use later.

Create Multiple Profile Views... allows for split profiles so they fit on multiple sheets.

Create Superimposed Profile... allows for superimposing multiple profiles into a **Profile View**.

Edit Profile Geometry... invokes the **Layout** toolbar for editing design profiles criteria.

Design Criteria Editor... allows making modifications to the design criteria XML file.

Add Profile View Labels allows for adding specific profile labels.

Exercise 8-1: Create Profile from Surface Data

1. Launch Civil 3D and open the file called Chapter-8-a.dwg.
2. Type **V** for **View** and select the view called **Plan-A**, hit **Set Current**, then hit **OK**.
3. From the **Profiles** pull-down menu, select the command **Create Profile from Surface...**. See Figure 8-8. Please note that although you are working with Chapter 8 drawings the alignments refer to Chapter 6 that were created for a previous textbook.

To access student data files, go to www.pearsondesigncentral.com.

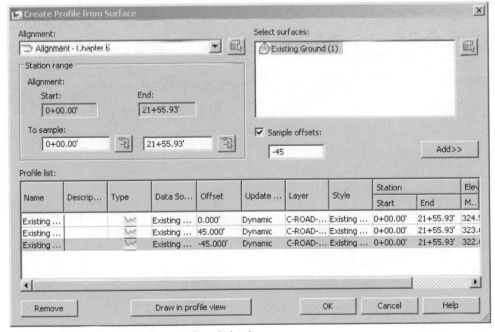

Figure 8-8   Create Profile from Surface dialog box

4. The **Alignment** of **Alignment—Chapter 6** should be set. Now select the **Existing Ground** under the **Select surfaces** window and hit the **Add>>** button.
5. Then turn on the **Sample offsets**, type **45** into the **Sample offsets** field, and hit **Add>>**. In the **Profile list** window at the bottom, click on the second row where the offset of **45**

exists and double-click on the value in the **Style** column. The **Pick profile style** dialog box appears. From the selection options, choose **Existing Ground BRL Right** for the style of this offset profile (because 45 is positive and therefore to the right). You want to differentiate it from the centerline so as not to confuse it with the centerline profile.

Job skills benefit in that it is often desired to compute and draw the profile for the BRL (Building Restriction Line), so the reviewer can see what the ground is doing where a structure might be built.

6. Then type **−45** into the **Sample offsets** field and hit **Add>>**. In the **Profile list** window at the bottom, click on the third row where the offset of **−45** exists and double-click on the Value in the **Style** column. From the selection options, choose **Existing Ground BRL Left** for the style of this offset profile. Again, you want to differentiate it from the centerline and the other BRL linework so as not to confuse it. The values should appear as indicated in Figure 8-8.

7. Click on the button that says **Draw in profile view**.

8. Then the **Create Profile View** dialog box displays, as shown in Figure 8-9.

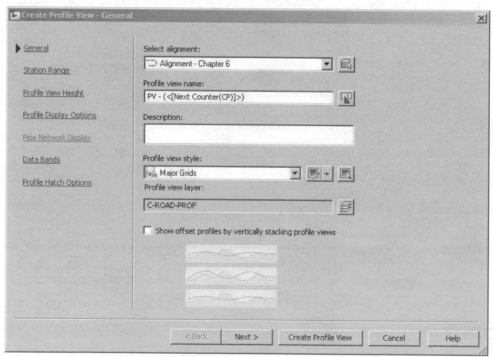

Figure 8-9   The Create Profile View dialog box

9. In the dialog box, check the name of the **Profile view name** field. Accept the automatic naming **PV - (<[Next Counter(CP)]>)**, which is 1. Provide a description of Chapter 8. From the **Alignment** pop-down window, **Alignment—Chapter 6** should be selected. Notice the profiles you computed in the previous box are shown.

10. As you have done several times in the previous chapters, create a layer for the **Profile View** called **C-Road-Prof-View**. Hit **Create Profile View** and place the location of the view to the right of all of the plan view data, say, at a coordinate of **18800,19500**.

Now you have an existing ground profile for your alignment. It also shows left and right offset profiles, which are often required by reviewing jurisdictions so they can observe the ground activity near where buildings might be constructed. The centerline profile should be red, the left profile is green, and the right profile is blue. The engineer also uses this information to analyze the impact that a proposed roadway or corridor might have near the BRL line.

Exercise 8-2: Develop a Finished Grade Profile

The next task is to develop a proposed profile for the roadway. Use the Civil 3D commands to execute the formulas discussed earlier in this chapter. Create vertical tangents with PVIs between them and vertical curves at these PVIs. To begin, open a drawing containing the existing ground profile.

1. Launch Civil 3D and open the file called Chapter-8-b.dwg.
2. **Zoom** in to view the profile.
3. From the **Profiles** pull-down menu, select the command **Create Profile by Layout…**.
4. The prompt asks you to select the **Profile View** in which you will be working. Select the grid of the profile.
5. A **Create Profile** dialog box displays, requesting information about your profile. Set it up as shown in Figure 8-10, with a **Description**, a new layer for the proposed profile, and a style called **Design Style**. Use the **Complete Label Set** for the **Profile label set**. Hit **OK**.

To access student data files, go to www.pearsondesigncentral.com.

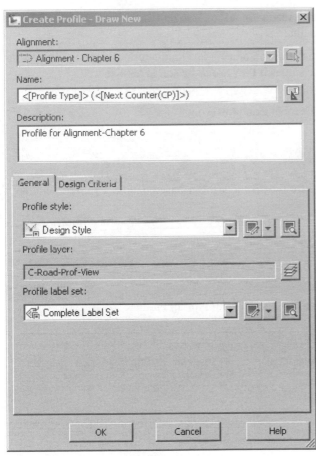

Figure 8-10   Profile information

PROFILE LAYOUT TOOLBAR

On hitting **OK**, the **Profile Layout Tools** toolbar displays. It is shown in Figure 6-11 and a description of the commands follows.

Figure 8-11   The Profile Layout Tools toolbar

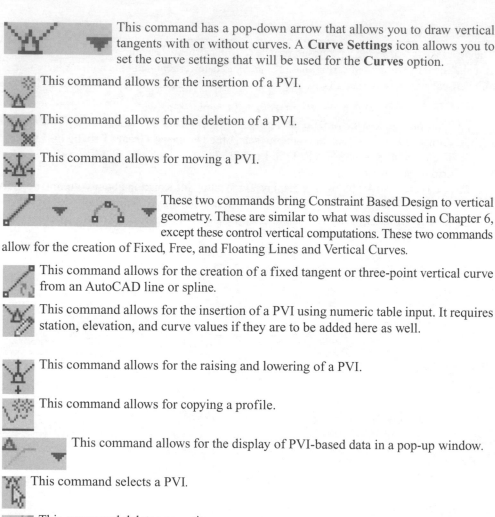

This command has a pop-down arrow that allows you to draw vertical tangents with or without curves. A **Curve Settings** icon allows you to set the curve settings that will be used for the **Curves** option.

This command allows for the insertion of a PVI.

This command allows for the deletion of a PVI.

This command allows for moving a PVI.

These two commands bring Constraint Based Design to vertical geometry. These are similar to what was discussed in Chapter 6, except these control vertical computations. These two commands allow for the creation of Fixed, Free, and Floating Lines and Vertical Curves.

This command allows for the creation of a fixed tangent or three-point vertical curve from an AutoCAD line or spline.

This command allows for the insertion of a PVI using numeric table input. It requires station, elevation, and curve values if they are to be added here as well.

This command allows for the raising and lowering of a PVI.

This command allows for copying a profile.

This command allows for the display of PVI-based data in a pop-up window.

This command selects a PVI.

This command deletes an entity.

This command allows for editing best-fit data for all entities.

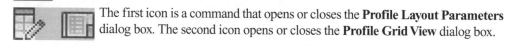

The first icon is a command that opens or closes the **Profile Layout Parameters** dialog box. The second icon opens or closes the **Profile Grid View** dialog box.

Exercise 8-3: Create a Proposed Profile

So, continuing on using the **Profile Layout Tools** toolbar that appears, create a proposed profile. The software prompts you to `Select a command:` from the **Layout** tools.

1. Using the pop-down arrow for the first icon, select the **Curve Settings...** command.
2. The **Vertical Curve Settings** dialog box displays, as shown in Figure 8-12. In the **Select curve type** drop-down window, use **Parabolic**, although circular and asymmetrical curves are available. Use a curve length of **400′**, so set the sag and crest curve lengths to **400**. Hit **OK**.

A crest curve goes over a hill whereas a sag curve goes into a depression.

3. From the **Profile Layout Tools** toolbar, choose the first icon from the left to **Draw Tangents With Curves**. The software prompts you to select a start point for the vertical tangents with curves. `Specify start point:` Use the **Endpoint** snap to pick the left edge of the red existing ground centerline profile. It should be around 0+00 and elevation 324.5.
4. `Specify end point:` it is asking for the end of the tangent segment.

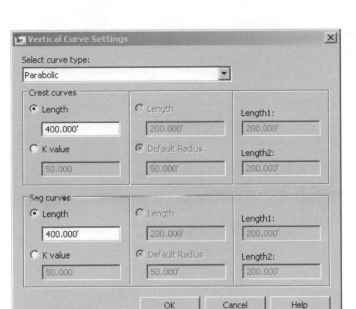

Figure 8-12   The Vertical Curve Settings dialog box

TIP Notice that as you move the cursor around the profile, the cursor tip will appear, telling you the SZ of the point where you are. The SZ is the station and elevation of your current location.

5. Locate the station of 9+00 and an elevation near 339.0 by reading the axis information. When you find that approximate location, use the **Nearpoint** snap and pick it on the vertical gridline.
6. `Specify end point`: Locate the station of 15+00 and an elevation near 327.0 by using these cursor tips. When you find that approximate location, use the **Nearpoint** snap and pick it on the gridline.
7. `Specify end point`: Locate the end of the **red** existing ground profile and use the **Endpoint** snap to pick it, thereby completing the development of the vertical tangents. This should be close to 21+56 and elevation 343.0. Feel free to **Zoom** in when needed to snap to these locations.

It is usually a smart move to place your PVIs at even stations to make it easier for surveyors or contractors to build the road without having to worry about odd station numbers. Nice, even 25, 50, or 100' stations accommodate this.

8. **Zoom** out to view the profile and notice that curves exist automatically at the PVIs. Guess what the curve lengths are?
9. Take a moment to inspect the profile. Notice that the vertical tangents are one color whereas the curves are another color. This is to help you visualize when lines end and curves begin.

Exercise 8-4: Re-create Profile with Different Styles

Now let us assume that this profile is ready for plotting. Re-create this profile view with a different set of styles to make it more appropriate for a plot.

1. From the **Profiles** pull-down menu, choose **Create Profile View....** The **Create Profile View** dialog box appears, as shown in Figure 8-13. Provide the **Description** shown in the figure.

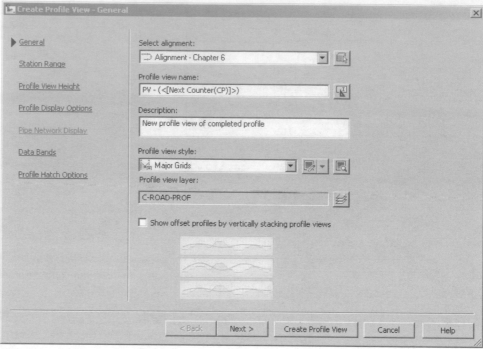

Figure 8-13   The Create Profile View dialog box

2. Click on **Data Bands** and change the **Band set** to **Profile Data & Geometry**.

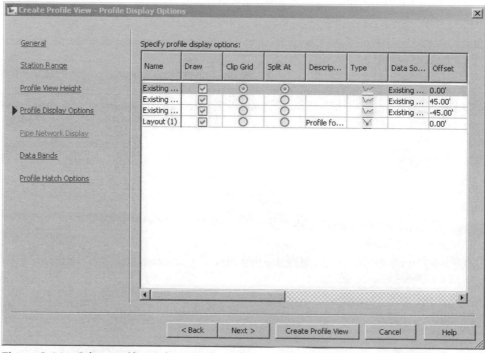

Figure 8-14   Select profiles to draw

3. Click on **Create Profile View**, the software prompts for a point to place the new profile. Pick a point somewhere well above the original profile.

TIP

Notice that if you do not want to draw a particular profile, you can turn off the check mark in the **Create Profile View** properties dialog box using the **Profile Display Options** tab as shown in Figure 8-14.

4. Inspect the profile when it comes in and notice that curves are labeled and data bands come in at the bottom. Notice that one shows the horizontal geometry relative to the profile. This is a wonderful analysis tool to compare the horizontal and vertical geometries.
5. In order to acquire some additional experience in editing these Styles, notice that there is a band of information at the bottom representing the existing ground that is too verbose and unneeded. Now if this represented the finished ground, that could be useful in seeing that the vertical geometry is a single rapid observation.
6. Click on a grid for the **Profile View**. Right-click and select **Profile View Properties....** You can also access the **Profile View Properties** from the **Prospector**, as shown in Figure 8-15.

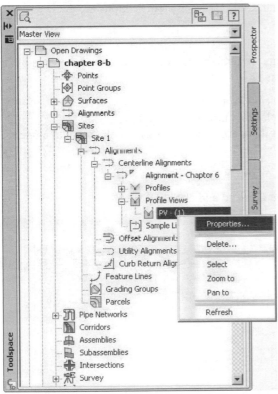

Figure 8-15   Access the Profile View Properties from the Prospector

7. Choose the **Bands** tab and select the **Vertical Geometry** item in the **Band type** pop-down window..
8. In the column labeled **Profile 1**, set the value to **Layout (1)** so it knows to display graphics for the finished ground profile. Hit **OK**.
9. Next, delete the first **Profile View** used to construct the profile. Open the **Toolspace** and go into the **Prospector**.
10. Expand the items for the Current Drawing, **Sites**, **Site 1**, **Alignments, Centerline Alignments, Alignment-Chapter 6**, and **Profile Views**. Right-click on **PV – 1** and select **Delete...** to remove it from the project and drawing. Click **Yes** to the confirmation. Notice that when it is complete, the second "final" **Profile View** remains while the first is removed.

TIP You can also just simply delete the graphics of the **Profile View** in AutoCAD.

This exercise illustrates how to develop an Existing Ground profile, what the **Profile Views** offer, how to alter the **Profile View Styles**, and how to develop a proposed roadway profile and alter its appearances and display capabilities.

Job skills will benefit from reviewing the bands showing the horizontal and vertical geometry so that an engineer or manager can easily review the design data without having to hunt through the profile or alignment data.

The next exercise explores what happens in Civil 3D when modifications are made.

Exercise 8-5: Modify the Label Style

You may have noticed that the vertical tangents are not labeled. Add these now as they and other labels can be affected on the fly or from the start.

To access student data files, go to www.pearsondesigncentral.com.

1. Launch Civil 3D and open the file called Chapter-8-c.dwg.
2. Notice that the previously developed plan and profile are visible.
3. **Zoom** into the **Profile** and notice that there are no grade labels on the vertical tangents. You want to add those to the **Profile**.
4. In the **Toolspace**, click on the **Settings** tab. Expand the **Profile** item, the **Label Styles** item, and the **Line** item.
5. Right-click on the label style **Finished Ground** and choose **Edit...**.

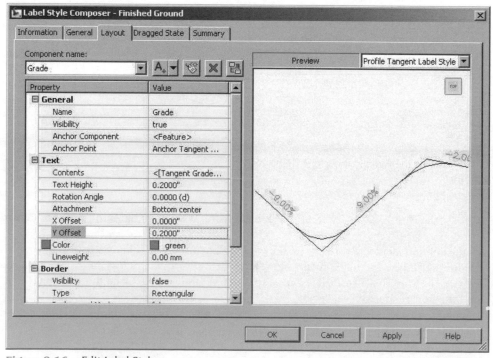

Figure 8-16   Edit Label Styles

6. In the **Layout** tab, change the **Text Height** to **0.2** and the **Y Offset** to **0.2**. Set the color to **green**. See Figure 8-16. Hit **OK** to exit.

7. Next, select the blue proposed profile linework in the Profile View, right-click, and choose **Edit Labels...**.

8. The **Profile Labels** dialog box appears.

9. Under the **Type** pop-down, choose **Lines**.

10. Under **Profile Tangent Label Style**, choose **Finished Ground**.

11. Then hit the **Add>>** button. It should appear as shown in Figure 8-17.

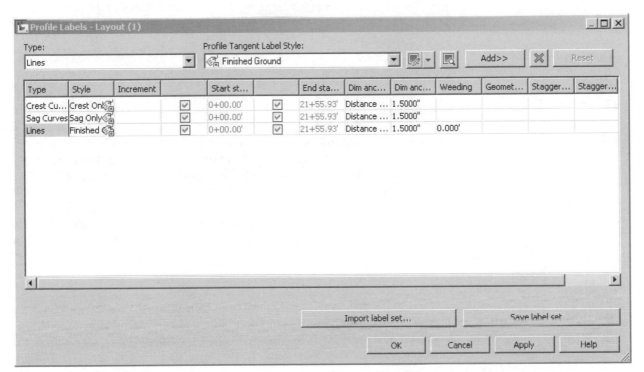

Figure 8-17   Profile Labels

12. Hit **OK** and notice that you now have grade labels on the vertical tangents.

THE RIPPLE-THROUGH EFFECT

Civil 3D has state-of-the-art capabilities in updating the design model. Because many of the objects are linked, they sense whether modifications have been made to the data that affect their display and computations.

Exercise 8-6: Try the Ripple-Through Effect

Next you open a drawing and make some changes to the data to observe how the ripple-through effect works and its potential to save enormous time and effort on the project.

1. Continuing on in the same drawing Chapter-8-c.dwg, discussion will concern making modifications.

2. **Zoom** into the beginning of the profile and notice that the existing ground elevation is around **324.5**.

3. Now type **V** for **View**, select the view called **Plan-A**, hit **Set Current**, and hit **OK**. Notice some contour activity and the alignment.

4. Select the alignment with the mouse. Notice that grips show up. Square grips appear on tangents, circular grips show up on the curves, and triangular grips appear on the **Pls (Points of Intersection)**.

To access student data files, go to www.pearsondesigncentral.com.

5. Using **Grip-edit** features, select the grip at station 0+00 and move it to another location within the contoured surface, say, near an *X*, *Y* of 14600,18750. The alignment relocates, recomputes, and redrafts its annotation.
6. Now type **V** for **View** and select the view called **Profile-A**, hit **Set Current**, and hit **OK**. Notice that the **red** Existing ground linework has changed up to around elevation 320, which is where the alignment now begins.
7. If you **Zoom** out to see the whole profile, notice that it actually became longer to compensate for the increased length created when the beginning of the alignment was moved. Normally, the proposed profile would need to be "stretched" to relocate its beginning and endpoints. This would be accomplished using the grip-edit features of the profile in exactly the same manner that you just moved the alignment.

In order to expand your skills, an optional exercise is to relocate the proposed profile using this method.

8. When you are finished experimenting, either open this drawing again, without saving it, or type **U** for **Undo** and repeat until the alignment returns to its original location.
9. Now type **V** for **View** and select the view called **Profile-A**, hit **Set Current**, and hit **OK**. Notice that the **red** Existing ground linework has changed back to what it was, around elevation 324.5.
10. This is a major feature of the Civil 3D software, which we call the *ripple-through effect*.
11. Feel free to experiment with this file and save it as another name so you can return to it in the future.

Job skills benefit from this feature in that "value engineering" can be performed in identifying the best design for the issues at hand. By experimenting with various design alternatives, the engineer can focus on the most cost-effective solution. Many firms are now offering value engineering to their clients as an added benefit to their services.

Exercise 8-7: Numerical Editing of Profiles

The next function you explore is the numerical editing of a profile. Sometimes designers feel it is advantageous to edit a profile using a tabular view that allows them access to the elevations, slopes, and grades. Civil 3D allows for this in addition to visual or graphical edits.

To access student data files, go to www.pearsondesigncentral.com.

1. Launch Civil 3D and open the file called Chapter-8-d.dwg. It opens with the profile in the view.
2. From the **Profiles** pull-down menu, choose **Edit Profile Geometry**. When prompted, select somewhere on the **blue** proposed profile. The **Profile Layout Tools** toolbar displays.

Note that you can also simply grip the proposed profile, right-click, and select **Edit** to achieve the same result.

3. Pick the command near the end of the toolbar called **Profile Grid View.** This will display the **Panorama** with all of the profile data in it, shown in Figure 8-18.
4. The fields that cannot be edited are screened back and inaccessible. Fields that can be altered are accessible by double-clicking in the cell.
5. For PVI 2, change the **Profile Curve Length** to **500**. Hit **<Enter>** and close the **Panorama**.
6. Then **Zoom** into PVI 2 and notice the annotated curve length is now 500. The graphics and text have been automatically updated.

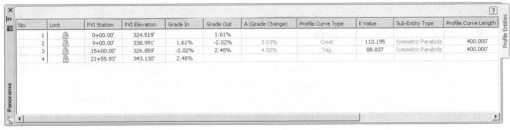

No.	Lock	PVI Station	PVI Elevation	Grade In	Grade Out	A (Grade Change)	Profile Curve Type	K Value	Sub-Entity Type	Profile Curve Length
1	🔒	0+00.00'	324.519'		1.61%					
2	🔒	9+00.00'	338.991'	1.61%	-2.02%	3.63%	Crest	110.195	Symmetric Parabola	400.000'
3	🔒	15+00.00'	326.859'	-2.02%	2.48%	4.50%	Sag	88.837	Symmetric Parabola	400.000'
4	🔒	21+55.93'	343.130'	2.48%						

Figure 8-18   Profile Panorama

Exercise 8-8: Delete a Profile Component

Sometimes it is necessary to use an asymmetrical vertical curve that occurs when there is not enough incoming or outgoing tangent length to accommodate a symmetrical curve. For instance, you might be required to have a 500′ curve; however, there is only 200′ of incoming tangent available. Therefore, an asymmetrical curve where the first portion of the curve is 200′ and the second portion of the curve is 300′ would satisfy the overall length requirement. You will now perform an example of this. Begin by deleting the second curve and notice how Civil 3D automatically drafts it up. Follow that up by adding an asymmetrical curve to that same PVI.

1. In the same file called Chapter-8-d.dwg, choose **Edit Profile Geometry...** from the **Profiles** pull-down menu. When prompted, select somewhere on the **blue** proposed profile. The **Profile Layout Tools** toolbar displays.
2. Choose the fourth button from the right, the command to **Delete Entity**.
3. `Select subentity:` select the second vertical curve at station 15+00.
4. Hit **<Enter>** to complete the sequence.
5. Notice that the curve is gone, but the PVI remains.

Exercise 8-9: Create an Asymmetrical Curve

Now add in an asymmetrical curve.

1. In the same file called Chapter-8-d.dwg, choose **Edit Profile Geometry...** from the **Profiles** pull-down menu. When prompted, select somewhere on the **blue** proposed profile. The **Profile Layout Tools** toolbar again displays.
2. Choose the command **More Free Vertical Curves >> Free Asymmetrical Parabola (PVI Based)** from the pop-down arrow in the toolbar. It is associated with the sixth button from the left.
3. `Pick point near PVI or curve to add curve:` Pick a point near the PVI at station 15+00.
4. The software asks you to specify **Length 1** of the asymmetrical curve. Type **200**.
5. The software asks you to specify **Length 2** of the asymmetrical curve. Type **300**.
6. Hit **<Enter>** then **<Esc>** to complete, and notice the new curve and the related annotation, shown in Figure 8-19. Notice the center of the curve does not exist at the PVI as it would for a symmetrical curve. This asymmetrical curve can be very useful in road design.

To access student data files, go to www.pearsondesigncentral.com.

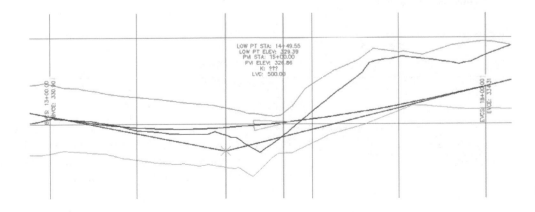

Figure 8-19   Curve data

Asymmetrical vertical curves are often used as a last resort in road design. They might be used in situations in which a standard symmetrical vertical curve just does not work. For example, let us say you are designing a curve near an intersection and there is a PVI that requires a vertical curve approaching that intersection. The prevailing DOT code may require a vertical curve length of, say, 600'. It could be that you have only 200' to the left of the PVI before you enter the intersection, but you have plenty of space to the right side of the PVI. This is where you might place an asymmetrical curve such that 150' occurs to the left side of the PVI and 450' occurs to the right side. In this fashion, you have accommodated the requirement to establish a 600' curve without encroaching on the intersection.

SUPERIMPOSING PROFILES

Another powerful feature within the profiling functions of Civil 3D is the ability to superimpose one profile into another. This is useful when you wish to compare how one profile relates to another.

Exercise 8-10: Superimpose One Profile onto Another

To access student data files, go to www.pearsondesigncentral.com.

1. Launch Civil 3D and open the file called Chapter-8-e.dwg. There is an additional alignment and another profile in this file. They were prepared in the same manner as the one you just completed and are included here in order to expedite this command usage.
2. **Zoom** into the two profiles so they can be seen.
3. From the **Profiles** pull-down menu, choose **Create Superimposed Profile....** `Select source profile:` select the red linework in the shorter profile.
4. `Select destination profile view:` select a gridline in the longer **Profile View**.
5. The **Superimpose Profile Options** dialog box appears. You can restrict the length of the profile to be computed if you wish or just hit **OK**.
6. The superimposed profile appears in the longer profile.
7. Notice that it is longer than it was in the source profile. That is because the profile is projected into the destination orthogonally. The source alignment is not parallel to the destination alignment.
8. **Zoom** into the plan view and inspect how the source alignment is drawn. It is on the **C-Road** layer.

CIVIL 3D SECTIONS

The last part of this chapter delves into sections. As discussed earlier, sections are typically, but not always, orthogonal to the alignment and are created at intervals that travel along the alignment. Sections provide you with more information on what is occurring adjacent to your alignment. Civil 3D develops cross-sectional data in **Sample Line Groups**, and, as we have seen already, Styles control the appearance of the **Sample Line Groups**. Next you will use the **Sample Line Tools** toolbar, Figure 8-20.

Figure 8-20   Sample Line Tools toolbar

The window on the left side of the **Sample Line Tools** toolbar provides the ability to name the sample lines. The icon to its right brings up a dialog box that allows you to change the template naming, which is automatic and sequentially increments the name.

The pop-down window near the center of the toolbar displays the current **Sample Line Group** with which the sample line is associated. The icon to its right allows you to create or modify the **Sample Line Group**. The options within this icon include **Create sample line group, Edit group defaults, Delete current group**, or you can be prompted to select a group from the drawing, which then becomes the current Sample Line Group.

 The fifth button from the right displays the various sample line creation methods used to create the sample line(s). The pop-down arrow allows for other actions such as creating sample lines **By range of stations...**, along the alignment. In this case, a perpendicular transient graphic appears in Civil 3D that you can move along the alignment to witness the current location. The other methods for creating sample lines include **At a station, From corridor stations**, **Pick points on screen**, and **Select existing polylines**.

 The fourth button from the right prompts you to select a sample line from the screen.

The third button from the right toggles the select or edit sample line functionality. When the button is down, the **Edit Sample Line** dialog box is displayed.

The last two buttons are **Undo** and **Redo**.

Exercise 8-11: Create Sample Lines for Sections

Next you explore the abilities of sections.

1. Open a file called Chapter-8-f.dwg.
2. From the **Sections** pull-down menu, select **Create Sample Lines...**. When prompted, select the **Alignment** in the plan view.
3. The **Create Sample Line Group** dialog box opens, as shown in Figure 8-21. Hit **OK**.

To access student data files, go to www.pearsondesigncentral.com.

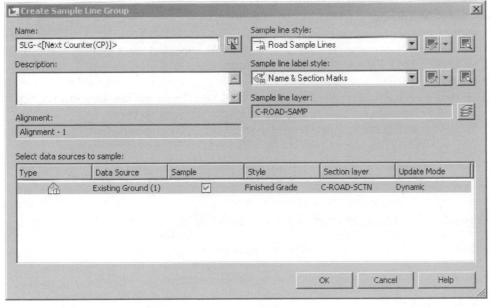

Figure 8-21   The Create Sample Line Group dialog box

4. The **Sample Line Tools** toolbar displays.
5. Using the pop-down arrow associated with the fifth button from the right, select the **By range of stations** icon. The **Create Sample Lines—By Station Range** dialog box appears. See Figure 8-22.

Property	Value
⊟ **General**	
Alignment	Alignment - 1
⊟ **Station Range**	
From alignment start	true
Start Station	0+00.00'
To alignment end	true
End Station	21+55.93'
⊟ **Left Swath Width**	
Snap to an alignment	false
Alignment	Alignment - 1
Width	50.000'
⊟ **Right Swath Width**	
Snap to an alignment	false
Alignment	Alignment - 1
Width	50.000'
⊟ **Sampling Increments**	
Use Sampling Increments	true
Increment Along Tangents	50.000'
Increment Along Curves	25.000'
Increment Along Spirals	25.000'
⊟ **Additional Sample Controls**	
At Range Start	true
At Range End	true
At Horizontal Geometry Points	true
At Superelevation Critical Stations	true

Figure 8-22   The Create Sample Lines—By Station Range dialog box

6. Notice that by default the cross-sectional data are sampled 30′ to the left and right of the alignment and data are sampled at 50′ increments along the alignment.
7. Change the **Left** and **Right Swath Width** to **50′**.
8. Change the **Increment Along Curves** and **Spirals** to **25′**.
9. For the **Additional Sample Controls**, turn all the options to **True**. So, **At Range Start and End**, **At Horizontal Geometry Points**, and **At Superelevation Critical Stations** are all marked **True**. This way you obtain additional sections at these locations as well.
10. Hit **OK**.
11. `Specify station along alignment:` hit **<Enter>**. Notice that sample lines appear along the alignment with 50′ lines on tangents and 25′ lines on curves.
12. You will notice in the **Prospector**, under **Sites**, **Site 1**, **Alignments**, **Center Alignments Alignment 1**, and **Sample Line Groups** that a number of sections now appear.

TIP   Note that in the **Plan View**, linework has shown up illustrating where the sections were cut.

Exercise 8-12: Create Sections

In the next steps, you create existing ground cross section views for each of these locations. In order to view these cross sections to evaluate what is occurring to the side of your alignment, you need to develop cross section views, similar to profile views.

1. From the **Sections** menu, click **Create Multiple Section Views...**, which displays the **Create Multiple Section Views** dialog box, as shown in Figure 8-23. In the **General** tab, change the **Group plot style** to **Plot All** and hit **Create Section Views**.

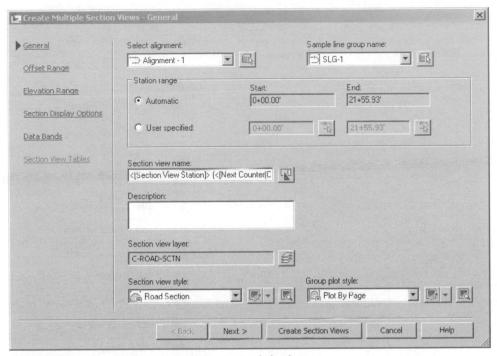

Figure 8-23   The Create Multiple Section Views dialog box

2. When prompted to identify the *section view* origin, pick a point to the right of the profile for the cross sections to be placed, say at **21000,21000**. **Zoom** in and notice that Section sample lines are shown on the alignment in Figure 8-24 and sections should be in your drawing similar to those shown in Figure 8-25.

section view: A Civil 3D term for the location in Civil 3D where sections are displayed. Each section view must be related to an alignment. The section view displays new or existing sections.

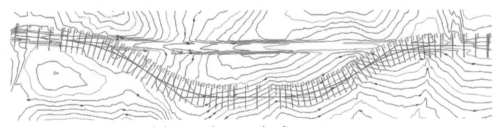

Figure 8-24   Section sample lines are shown on the alignment

These cross section views are objects that are dynamically linked to the horizontal alignment in much the same manner that the profile view was when you were making modifications. If the horizontal alignment is relocated, the existing ground cross-section views automatically update to reflect those modifications.

3. **Zoom** into one section (Figure 8-26) and notice that there is too much information for the grade breaks of the existing ground. You do not really need this density of data, so turn it off.
4. Click on the gridline for a section, right-click, and select **Section View Properties...** to invoke the dialog box.
5. Select the **Sections** tab. In the **Labels** column, select the cell for the grade breaks where it says **<Edit...>**.
6. A **Section Labels** dialog box appears. Click on the grade breaks row and hit the button with the red **X** to delete. Hit **OK**. Hit **OK** again. The labels are gone and the section is easier to read.

Figure 8-25 Plotted sections

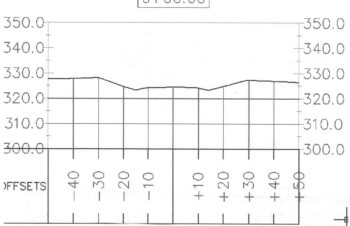

Figure 8-26 One section

To turn these off prior to computing the sections and to effect this change on all sections, you can access the settings in the **Toolspace Settings** tab. Go to the **Section View** parameter and right-click. Select **Edit Feature Settings...** to access the **Edit Feature Settings** dialog box. Expand **Default Styles**, click on **Section Label Set**, click on the value of **EG Section Labels.** This allows you to select the button for the **Value**. This invokes the **Section Label Set** dialog box. Click on the middle icon and choose **Edit Current Selection** from the pop-down arrow. The same dialog box appears and you can hit the same red **X** to delete the grade breaks as you did earlier. Import your sections again to see the results.

CHAPTER SUMMARY

This chapter addressed the theory involved in designing roads, then moved into creating roadway profiles. You learned how to develop and annotate your proposed profiles. The chapter explored the link between horizontal alignments, existing ground profiles, and cross sections, looking at how they are updated when modifications are made to the data. Next we look at corridor design.

CHAPTER TEST QUESTIONS

Multiple Choice

1. There are three main requirements for designing a roadway. They are:

   a. Alignments, sections, and templates (or assemblies)
   b. Profiles, sections, and earthworks
   c. Alignments, corridors, and parcels
   d. Alignments, profiles, and a proposed section

2. Proposed vertical alignments can be developed from:

   a. Horizontal tangents, curves, and spirals
   b. Vertical tangents and vertical curves that do not exceed 8%
   c. Vertical tangents and vertical curves
   d. None of the above

3. Which of the following vertical curve properties are true?

   a. A tangent ends at the PVC, and a vertical curve begins at a PVC.
   b. A vertical curve begins at a PVT, and a vertical tangent begins at a PVT.
   c. Two tangents meet at a PVC.
   d. None of the above

4. Which of the following are properties of a vertical curve?

   a. The tangent offsets vary as the square of the distance from the points of tangency.
   b. For points spaced at equal horizontal distances, the second differences are equal.
   c. A curve's elevation at the midpoint of the curve will be halfway from the elevation at the PVI to the elevation at the midpoint of a straight line from the PVC to the PVT.
   d. All of the above

5. The design of a vertical alignment is usually specified in terms of:

   a. A maximum grade and the minimum length for the vertical curve
   b. A minimum grade and the minimum length for the vertical curve
   c. A maximum grade and the maximum length for the vertical curve
   d. Always being dictated by the State Department of Transportation

6. Civil 3D has a ripple-through effect:

   a. Where profiles and cross sections are dynamically linked to horizontal alignments and surfaces
   b. If the surface is modified, the profile and cross section data also update automatically
   c. Where related annotation updates as changes are made
   d. All of the above

7. A proposed profile can be edited using which of the following features?

   a. By graphically selecting grips for PVIs
   b. By using the numerical editor in the **Edit Profile** toolbar
   c. By graphically selecting grips for vertical tangents
   d. All of the above

8. Which of the following modifications can be accomplished by using the **Edit Profile** commands?

   a. Inserting and deleting PVIs
   b. Inserting and deleting alignment segments
   c. Inserting and moving PVIs, but not deleting them
   d. All of the above

9. Which of the following vertical curves are supported?

   a. Parabolic
   b. Circular
   c. Asymmetrical
   d. All of the above

10. Cross sections can be created in the AutoCAD drawing in which of the following ways?

    a. Individually
    b. By sheet
    c. All sections can be imported at once
    d. All of the above

True or False

1. True or False: Profiles are created by sampling the elevation at intervals along a horizontal alignment.

2. True or False: Profiles computed along tangent sections usually sample the elevation wherever the alignment crosses the TIN lines in the terrain model.

3. True or False: A profile cannot be developed if the alignment has horizontal curves or spirals.

4. True or False: A PVI is the intersection of two vertical tangents.

5. True or False: A PVC is the intersection of two vertical curves.

6. True or False: Sometimes a grade break may occur that does not require any vertical curve at all.

7. True or False: A vertical curve is usually parabolic with an ever-changing radius.

8. True or False: The K value for profile computations is derived from empirical results of roadway friction factors.

9. True or False: Roadways are designed for safety and never use subjective parameters such as passing sight distances or stopping sight distances.

10. True or False: In Civil 3D, profiles are linked to the alignment and can react to changes made to the alignment.

CHAPTER EXERCISE

1. With a back tangent of −2%, a forward tangent of 1.6%, and a vertical curve length of 800′, compute the starting and ending stations of this vertical curve and its accompanying table if the PVI station is 87+00 and the PVI elevation is 743.24.

Advanced Corridor Development 9

Chapter Objectives

- Understand corridor design, in which the proposed section or template for the roadway is created.
- Develop assemblies.
- Customize subassemblies.
- Create and edit simple roadways.
- Create multiple assembly roadways.
- Understand a safety technique used by engineers to assist motorists in handling curves called superelevating the roadway.
- Create multiple baseline roadways.

INTRODUCTION

This chapter commences with discussions and algorithms for roadway superelevations and then moves into corridor development. Civil 3D offers state-of-the-art capabilities for developing roadways and corridors in general.

At this point the text has discussed developing alignments, existing, and proposed profiles, and cross sections. This chapter covers corridor design, which is the creation of the proposed section or template for the roadway. The objectives should be generalized because a corridor can include not only roadways but many other projects as well. If a project has a beginning, an end, limitations to the right and left, and standardized cross-sectional components, it may be a corridor. Think of stream improvements and railroads as examples of this, perhaps even tunnels and aqueducts. The chapter also delves into a safety technique used by engineers to assist motorists in handling curves called superelevating the roadway.

REVIEW OF FUNCTIONS AND FEATURES TO BE USED

This chapter provides instruction in the functions for corridor design. These include using **Tool Palettes** to access subassemblies and how to configure them for use in almost any scenario. These subassemblies are used to build assemblies for the sections to be designed. The discussion then walks through examples of how to build both simple and sophisticated corridors. The chapter also covers viewing the resulting cross sections of the design and various outputting strategies.

CORRIDOR THEORY

Once the section is developed, considerations are then made for safety as the driver negotiates curves in the road. According to the laws of mechanics, when a vehicle travels on a horizontal curve, it is forced outward by centrifugal force. Therefore, engineers use a method called *superelevation*

superelevation: Refers to the cross slope introduced into a cross section of a roadway in order to compensate for the centrifugal forces created by horizontal curves. According to the laws of mechanics, when a vehicle travels on a curve it is forced outward by centrifugal force. On a superelevated roadway, this force is resisted by the vehicle weight component parallel to the superelevated surface and the side friction between the tires and pavement. The pavement is essentially tilted to counter the forces described above.

by which they tilt the pavement lanes to counteract the centrifugal force. The two figures presented here indicate a template in normal conditions (along the tangent of a road) in Figure 9-1 and in the superelevated condition (around a curve, in this case, turning to the left) in Figure 9-2.

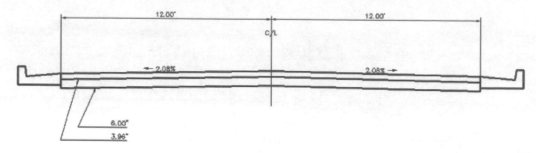

Figure 9-1 A normal template

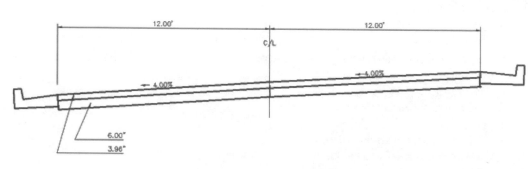

Figure 9-2 A superelevated template

Civil 3D performs DOT-level highway design because it allows for corridors with multiple baselines and multiple assemblies, all operating under a variety of conditions. Many subassemblies are included for roadway, curb, and sidewalk design.

SUPERELEVATION OF ROADWAYS—BASIC CRITERIA

On a superelevated highway, this centrifugal force is resisted by the vehicle's weight parallel to the superelevated surface and the friction between the tires and pavement. Centrifugal force cannot be balanced by superelevation alone, because for each curve radius a specific superelevation rate must be selected for a particular driving speed. In other words, the ***rate of superelevation*** varies based on the radius of the curve. Any side thrust must be offset by side friction. If the vehicle is not skidding, these forces are in equilibrium. Figure 9-3 illustrates the trigonometry involved in computing superelevation problems. Refer to the *AASHTO Green Book: A Policy on Geometric Design of Highways and Streets,* 5th Edition, for an authoritative reference on this subject.

> **rate of superelevation:** The rate of banking a roadway. AASHTO (American Association of State Highway and Transportation Officials) provides examples of design superelevation rates based on the design speed, the radius of curve, and the superelevation rate.

Variables and terms for superelevations include:

e = Superelevation slope

e_{max} = Maximum superelevation rate for a given condition

R = Curve radius

v = Velocity

$P = mv^2/R$

B = Horizontal lane width

A maximum superelevation (SE) is required when the radius (R) is a minimum:

$\tan(a) = P/mg \quad \tan(a) = (mv^2/R)/mg \quad \tan(a) = v^2/gR$

$SE = B*\tan(\alpha) \quad SE_{max} = Bv^2/gR$

This model is theoretical and is usually guided by the state DOT or AASHTO.

Superelevation transitions are used to define the pavement rotation up to a maximum super-elevation and are also used to bring a superelevated section back to the normal crown state. At a reverse curve, the section is often flat at the **PRC** as the superelevation in one direction transitions to the other direction.

PRC: Point of Reverse Curvature

Two components make up the total transition for a superelevated section: the Tangent runout and runoff (Figure 9-4). The Tangent runout defines the length of highway needed to bring a normal crown section to a section where the outside lane has a zero percent slope instead of normal crown. The superelevation runoff defines the distance needed to bring a section from flat to fully superelevated, or vice versa.

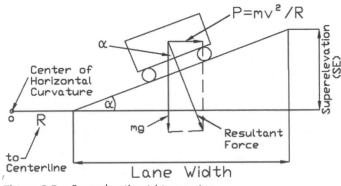

Figure 9-3   Superelevation trigonometry

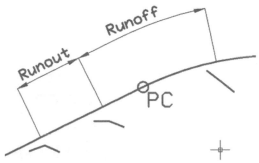

Figure 9-4   Tangent runout and runoff

TIP

The superelevation criteria for entering a curve are usually mirrored as the driver leaves a curve.

Figure 9-5 shows how the edge of pavement rises and drops based on the tilting of the road before and after the **PC** or **PT** of a curve.

PC: Point of Curvature

PT: Point of Tangency

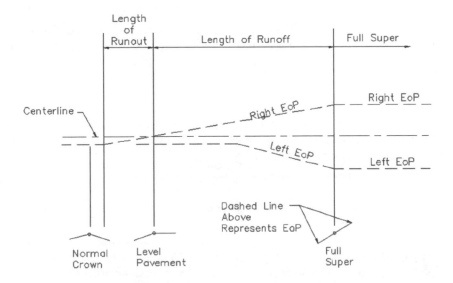

Figure 9-5   The edge of pavement in superelevation

Standard superelevation rates are usually provided by the Department of Transportation that oversees roadway design in the jurisdiction. A typical chart from which to obtain these values, shown in Figure 9-6, comes from the Virginia Department of Transportation (VDOT). For a specific curve radius and a design speed, the superelevation rate can be easily determined. For example, for a 3000′ radius curve and a design speed of 40 mph, the state requires a minimum of 2.5% superelevation rate.

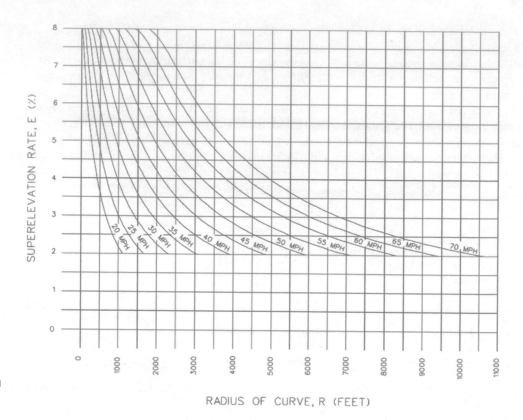

Figure 9-6   Superelevation rates for VDOT

For more information on design standards for roadway design, the American Association of State Highway and Transportation Officials (AASHTO) studies and recommends criteria to engineers. It can be located at www.aashto.org. Consult with your local state, county, or city DOT for its respective requirements as well.

Now that sections and superelevations have been discussed, you will use Civil 3D to develop a corridor.

CREATE A CORRIDOR FOR A ROAD

Remember that a corridor is a Civil 3D object and as such is linked to the horizontal and vertical alignments, surfaces, and assemblies that were used to create it. If one or more of these components are altered, the corridor is correspondingly modified.

TIP
For the rebuild to be automatic, you must right-click on the corridor and select **Rebuild-Automatic**. Otherwise, a rebuild can be executed at your choice by right-clicking on the corridor and selecting **Rebuild**.

The next step is to modify subassembly properties for design criteria, create an assembly from the subassemblies, and then create the Corridor model.

Subassemblies are the primitive components of assemblies, and they instruct the software on how to handle lanes, curbs, guardrails or shoulders, related side sloping, and tie-out. Civil 3D provides many subassemblies to begin with, which you can access from the **Tool Palettes**. The assemblies, on the other hand, are stored in the drawing and can be accessed from the **Project Toolspace** under **Assemblies**. They contain the definition of the typical section being designed and are developed by piecing together subassemblies.

This corridor has the following design requirements: The road will be a crowned section with a pavement width of 12′. The cross slope of the lane is −2.0% from the crown. A 6″ curb and 2′ gutter are used, located at the edge of pavement. Add on a 2′ grass strip, a 4′ sidewalk, and another 2′ grass strip, respectively. Then the side sloping will be 3:1 until it hits existing ground.

The **Corridors** pull-down menu is shown in Figure 9-7.

Create Assembly... allows you to develop a roadway template, now called an assembly. It is constructed from subassemblies selected from the **Catalog** or **Tool Palettes**.

Add Assembly Offset allows you to develop a controlling offset on an assembly. This is used for roads that have other paths that will define the design, such as a service road.

Create Subassembly from Polyline allows you to develop new subassemblies from polylines that you draw in AutoCAD.

Subassembly Tool Palettes allows you to open the **Tool Palettes** window where you can access subassemblies.

Subassembly Catalog... allows you to access catalogs of metric and imperial tools.

Create Simple Corridor... designs the corridor from an alignment, a profile, and an assembly.

Create Corridor designs a corridor for a sophisticated roadway including such items as station frequency and controlling offsets, multiple baselines, and regions.

View/Edit Corridor Section allows you to view the corridor sections and edit them interactively.

Utilities allows you several options for creating objects and importing subassemblies.

Exercise 9-1: Set Up Toolspace and Subassembly Settings

1. Open the drawing called Chapter-9a.dwg.
2. Under the **General** pull-down menu, click on the **Tool Palettes** window command. See Figure 9-8 for an example of the **Tool Palettes**. Choose the **Imperial-Basic** tab.

To access student data files, go to www.pearsondesigncentral.com.

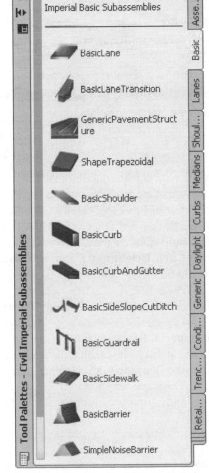

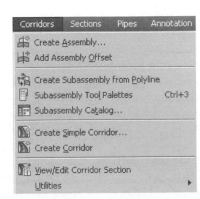

Figure 9-7 The Corridors pull-down menu

Figure 9-8 The Tool Palettes window

3. Note that right-clicking at the bottom of the tabs brings up a list of the many **Tool Palettes** available.

MODIFY SUBASSEMBLIES FOR THE ROAD

This **Tool** palette can be used to develop the roadway corridor, and it will remain in place for future jobs as well.

You will now modify the properties of the subassemblies needed for the road. The modifications occur as the subassemblies are placed into the assembly. These include the **BasicLane**, the **BasicCurbandGutter**, the **BasicSidewalk**, and the **DaylightStandard** subassemblies.

You can create the assembly from the subassemblies on the **Tool Palette**. The assembly contains the design control for the proposed typical section of the road.

Exercise 9-2: Create the Assembly

1. Type **Z** for **Zoom** at the command prompt and hit **<Enter>**. Type **C** for **Center** and type **17000,20000**. When asked for a height, type **50**.
2. This has placed you in a location where you can create the assembly. There is nothing special about this location; it is simply out of the way and zoomed to a height of 50′.
3. From the **Corridors** pull-down menu, select **Create Assembly....** The **Create Assembly** dialog box opens.
4. Accept the default name and set the name of the layer to **C-Road-Assm.** Leave the remaining settings as default and hit **OK**.
5. `Specify assembly baseline location:` Pick a point in the middle of the screen and a small symbol with a **red** line shows up. This indicates the assembly location to which you will attach subassemblies.

If you look in the **Prospector** and expand the tree for **Assemblies**, you see the assembly name. You now attach the subassemblies to both the left and right sides of the assembly location.

Exercise 9-3: Attach Subassemblies to an Assembly

1. From the **Imperial-Basic** tool palette, click the **BasicLane** subassembly. The properties for the subassembly can be altered at that time. Look in the **Properties** palette under **Advanced Parameters** and ensure that the parameter for **Side** is set to **Right**. Set the **Depth** to **0.67**. Ensure that the **Width** is set to **12.0** and the **%Slope** is **−2.0**.
2. `Select marker point within assembly:` Pick the assembly baseline location, which is the circular symbol in the middle of the assembly that you created. The lane should show up on the right side of the assembly marker.
3. From the **Imperial Basic** tool palette, click the **BasicCurbandGutter** subassembly. Look in the **Properties** palette under the **Advanced Parameters** and ensure that the parameter for **Side** is **Right**. Change the **Gutter width** to **2.0**. Change the **Gutter %Slope** to **−2.0**. Change the **Curb Height** to **0.5** and the **Curb Width** should be **0.5** as well. The **Curb Depth** should be **1.5**.
4. `Select marker point within assembly:` Click on the upper right circle of the lane you just placed and the **BasicCurbandGutter** subassembly appears connected to the lane.
5. From the **Imperial Basic** tool palette, click the **BasicSidewalk** subassembly. Look in the **Properties** palette and ensure that the parameter for **Side** is **Right**. Change the **Width** to **4.0**. Change the **Depth** to **0.33**, and change both of the **Buffer widths** to **2.0**.
6. `Select marker point within assembly:` Click on the upper right circle of the **Basic-CurbandGutter** subassembly, and the sidewalk appears connected to the back of the Curb.
7. Now repeat this process, but select the parameter for **Side** being **Left**, place the left side of the assembly, and connect it up as you did the right side.
8. When finished, the assembly should have a left and right travel lane, curb and gutter, and a sidewalk on both sides.

9. Next, you handle the tie-out of the road to the existing conditions. Using the **Imperial-Daylight** tab in the **Tool Palette**, click the **DaylightStandard** subassembly. Check the **Properties** dialog box and ensure that the side is **Right**, the **Ditch width** is **0.0**, the **Flat Cut Max Height** is **5.0**, the **Flat Cut Slope** is **6.0**, the **Flat Fill Max Height** is **5**, and the **Flat Fill Slope** is **6.0**.

10. Place it on the top rightmost circle on the sidewalk. Repeat for the left side by setting the **Side** parameter to **Left**.

11. Press **<Enter>** twice to finish the command.

You have now created the assembly. Figure 9-9 shows how it should appear.

Figure 9-9 A completed assembly

Job Skills benefit in that the designer can build the right side independently of the left if he or she chooses. The assembly does not have to be symmetrical.

The assembly for the Access Road is now complete. Save the file. You now move forward to create the roadway. In this task, the pieces to the corridor puzzle come together. You have all the components for the corridor. Let us summarize. The primitive geometry for the alignment is developed, and a completed alignment is defined. The **Profile View** is established with an existing ground profile. From there a finished ground profile (or *PGL*) was developed for the corridor. Then you set the settings for some subassemblies and created an assembly.

PGL: The profile grade line is the proposed profile.

TIP   Note that you can edit any particular subassembly by selecting it, right-clicking, and choosing **Subassembly Properties...** from the menu. Parameters can be altered as needed. You now create the corridor and the finished design surface.

Exercise 9-4: Create a Corridor

1. Open the drawing called Chapter-9b.dwg. Notice the assembly.
2. Restore a presaved view to place the view around the centerline.
3. Type **V** for **View** at the command prompt to obtain the **View** dialog box. Select the **Plan** view, hit **Set Current**, then hit **OK**. You are placed at the centerline of the Access Road. A view is set up for the profile as well in the event that you need it.
4. From the **Corridors** pull-down menu, select **Create Simple Corridor....**
5. Accept the default name and hit **OK**.
6. `Select a baseline alignment:` Pick the **red** centerline in the view.
7. The command prompt then asks you to `select a profile <or press enter key to select from list>:`
8. Hit **<Enter>**, and the **Select a Profile** dialog box appears. Choose **Layout (5)** and hit **OK**. Note that the other options are the offsets created in a previous chapter.
9. The command prompt then asks you to `select an assembly <or press enter key to select from list>:` Hit **<Enter>** and select **Assembly 1**.
10. A large window of data displays for **Target Mapping**.

To access student data files, go to www.pearsondesigncentral.com.

If you recall from Chapter 2, **Target Mapping** is a technical way of assigning the particular alignments, profiles, and surfaces required by the subassemblies to create the complete assembly. For instance, the **DaylightStandard** subassembly needs to know to which surface to compute, and so the **Target Map** for this would be the **Existing Ground** surface. See Figure 9-10.

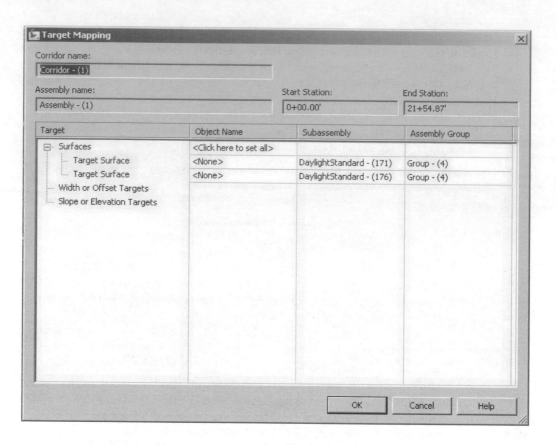

Figure 9-10 The Target Mapping dialog box

11. In the second column and in the row for **Surfaces** is a cell that says **<Click here to set all>**.
12. When you click on the cell, a dialog box called **Pick a Surface** displays. Choose the **Existing Ground** and click **OK**. You see the **Target Surface** is now **Existing Ground**. Click **OK**, and the corridor generates.
13. Close the **Panorama** if it appears and inspect the results of the processing. A Corridor model is evident in the drawing.

Let us learn how to control the appearance of the corridor data.

14. Click and select the roadway corridor. Then right-click and choose **Corridor Properties...** shown in Figure 9-11.
15. In the **Surfaces** tab, click the button on the left to **Create a corridor surface**.
16. After you choose this button, a **Corridor (1)** is created and appears in the window below.
17. In the **Data type** pop-down window, select **Links** if it is not already selected.
18. In the **Specify code:** pop-down window, choose **Top**. Then hit the + button to the right to add it to the matrix. The **Top** surface then appears under the **Name** column.
19. In the **Surface Style** column, click on the style that defaults, typically **Borders & Contours**.
20. A **Pick Corridor Surface Style** dialog box displays with a pop-down menu. Select **Borders & Contours**. Click on the pop-down arrow to the right of **Borders & Contours** and select **Edit Current Selection**. A **Surface Style** dialog box appears. Select the **Contours** tab. Set the **Contour interval** to **2** and **10** for the intermediate and index contours, respectively. Hit **OK**. Hit **OK**.
21. Now choose the **Boundaries** tab at the top.
22. Right-click on **Corridor (1) Surface (1)**. Choose **Add Automatically**.
23. Select **Daylight** from the menu that displays.
24. The **Name** column now shows a boundary item. Hit **OK**.
25. You should see contours for the corridor in AutoCAD when it is finished processing.

Civil 3D automatically creates a surface object upon creating a Corridor surface. You can see it in the **Prospector** under **Surfaces**.

Let us continue controlling the appearance of the corridor data and visualize it with faces and shading. To set the data up so they can be viewed in 3D, perform the following exercise.

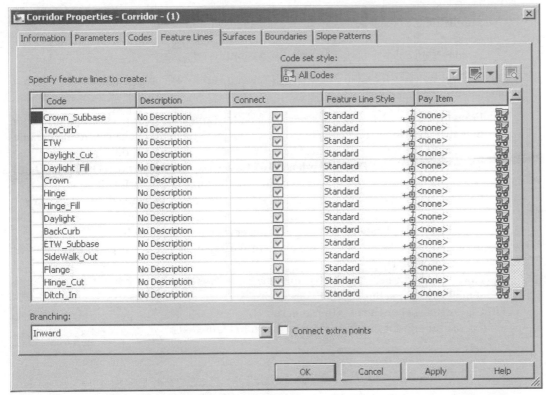

Figure 9-11   Corridor Properties

Exercise 9-5: Set Up Corridor for 3D Shading

1. Click and select the roadway corridor. Then right-click and choose **Corridor Properties....**
   A **Corridor Properties** dialog box appears. Select the **Surfaces** tab.
2. In the **Surface Style** column, click on the style that defaults, typically **Borders & Contours**.
3. A **Pick Corridor Surface Style** dialog box displays with a pop-down menu. Select **Borders & Triangles and Directions**. Hit **OK**.
4. Use AutoCAD's **3DOrbit** command to view the corridor in a bird's-eye perspective to help you see the road in 3D. In the event it is not rendered, while in the **3DOrbit** command, right-click, choose **Visual Styles**, and select **Conceptual** shading to shade the view. You see the road is 3D, complete with representation of the gutters and sidewalks.
5. If you have already left the **3DOrbit** command and the view is not shaded, use the **View** pull-down menu, and select **Visual Styles** and **Conceptual** shading.
6. Type **PLAN <Enter> <Enter>** to return to the plan view when you are finished viewing.
7. Save and close the file.

SUPERELEVATING A ROADWAY

The next step is to walk through a procedure for superelevating a roadway. Civil 3D has some excellent and very easy-to-use tools for computing superelevations. You will open another file and create a different template, which is for a more sophisticated highway condition. The specifications for this roadway are as follows: 12′ pavement lane, a curb and gutter, a sidewalk with a slope to drain into the roadway, and a multiple side slope configuration for tying out to daylight. There are multiple subgrade surfaces on this template for a base and subbase situation. You use AASHTO's superelevation criteria, and should the roadway design violate these criteria, the software provides a warning.

Exercise 9-6: Create an Assembly for Superelevations

1. Open the drawing called Chapter-9c.dwg.
2. Restore a presaved view to place your view around a location where you build a new corridor assembly.
3. Type **V** for **View** and select the view called **Assembly**, hit **Set Current**, then hit **OK**.

To access student data files, go to www.pearsondesigncentral.com.

4. Under the **Corridors** pull-down menu, choose **Create Assembly....** When the **Create Assembly** dialog box appears, accept the defaults by hitting **OK**.
5. `Specify assembly baseline location:` Choose a point in the middle of the screen. Notice that a marker appears for **Assembly—1**.

Using the **Tool Palettes** for **Civil 3D**, you will select a variety of subassemblies from which to create the overall assembly.

6. From the **Imperial-Lanes** tab, select the icon for **LaneOutsideSuper**. Before placing it, note that the **Properties** dialog box opens, allowing you to make changes to the parameters. Make the following changes: Select **Right** because you will do the right side first. The width is **12'**. The **Pave1 Depth** is **0.167** for a 2″ asphalt top surface. The **Pave2 Depth** will be **0.0**. The **Base Depth** will be **0.33'**, and the **Sub-base Depth** will be **1'**.
7. `Select marker point within assembly:` Pick a point on the right side of the circle on the assembly marker. A pavement lane with subgrades appears.
8. Look back in the **Properties** dialog box and change the side to **Left**.
9. Pick a point on the left side of the circle of the assembly marker. A pavement lane with subgrades appears.
10. Now pick the **Imperial—Curbs** tab in the **Tool Palettes**. Notice many structures for assembly creation in this area.
11. Choose the **UrbanCurbGutterGeneral**.
12. Set the settings for this dialog box as shown in Figure 9-12.

TIP   Note that if you click on any of the settings in the dialog box for **Dimension A—G** an explanation of what these dimensions represent will appear.

13. Do the left side of the template first.
14. Once these parameters are set, click a point on the upper left **Edge of Pavement** circle of the pavement.
15. Change the **Properties** dialog box to the **Right** side, and place the curb and gutter on the circle at the top right of the **Edge of Pavement**.
16. You now see curb and gutter on the left and right of the template.
17. Now, choose the **UrbanSidewalk** from the **Imperial—Curbs** tab in the **Tool Palettes**.
18. Note in the **Properties** dialog box that settings now exist for the sidewalk. Set the **Side** to **Right**. Set the **Inside boulevard width** to **2'**. Set the **Sidewalk width** to **4'**. Set the **Outside boulevard width** to **1'**. Set the **Slope** to **2%**. Set the **Depth** to **0.33'**.
19. Now pick a point on the circle at the upper right, top, back of curb. You see a sidewalk. Change the **Properties** setting for **Side** to **Left** and select a point on the circle at the upper left, top, and back of curb. Sidewalks now exist on both sides of the template.
20. Now, choose the **DaylightStandard** from the **Imperial—Daylight** tab in the **Tool Palettes**. Set the settings as shown in Figure 9-13.
21. Then pick a point on the circle at the left edge of the sidewalk extension. A cut/fill subassembly appears.
22. Change the **Side** to **Right** in the **Properties** dialog box and place the subassembly on the right side as well.

This completes your assembly development. The assembly should appear as shown in Figure 9-14. Save your file.

Exercise 9-7: Establish Superelevation Criteria

You must now set the superelevation characteristics for the roadway. To do this, you inspect the alignment properties. You will now run through this procedure and set alignment properties for superelevations.

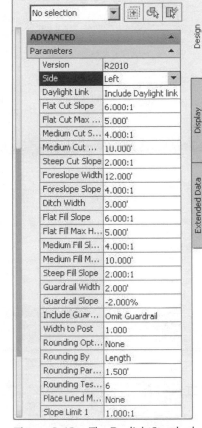

Figure 9-12   Urban Curb Gutter General settings

Figure 9-13   The DaylightStandard subassembly parameters

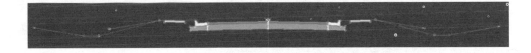

Figure 9-14   Completed assembly

1. Open the drawing called Chapter-9d.dwg.
2. Restore a presaved view to place your view around the centerline.1
3. Type **V** for **View** and select the view called **Plan**, hit **Set Current**, then hit **OK**.
4. Select the roadway and right-click. Choose **Alignment Properties...** from the menu.
5. Go to the **Design Criteria** tab and click the button labeled **Add Design speed....**
6. Click in the **Design Speed** cell for that station number **1** and type **45** for the speed.
7. Then click on the **Superelevation** tab to the right. See Figure 9-15 and notice that there are three buttons on the upper left side of the box. Click on the third button, labeled **Set Superelevation Properties**.
8. The **Superelevation Specification** dialog box appears, as shown in Figure 9-16. Hit **OK**.
9. The superelevation rate table can be changed for the eMax rate, whether the roadway is two or four lanes, whether the roadway is crowned or planar (such as in a divided highway). Take a moment to address the other parameters to see how they can be selected. Hit **OK**.
10. See Figure 9-16 where each curve is broken into regions that can be addressed individually.
11. Any grayed-out items cannot be changed because they are set elsewhere, such as the design speed. Other parameters can be changed simply by selecting the item.
12. When finished inspecting, hit **OK**.

The computations occur for the superelevation data. Refer to Figure 9-15 showing the computations. All the critical and most often needed stations are computed and shown in the table.

To access student data files, go to www.pearsondesigncentral.com.

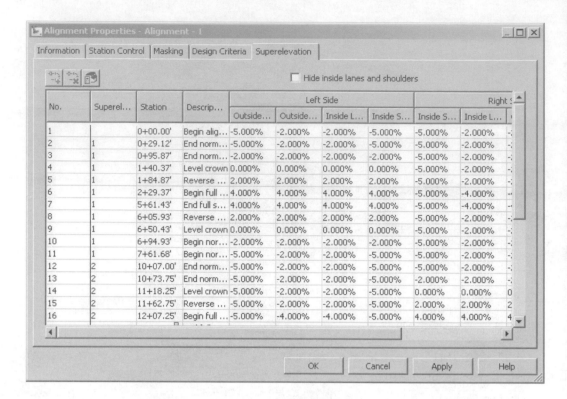

Figure 9-15 Alignment Properties

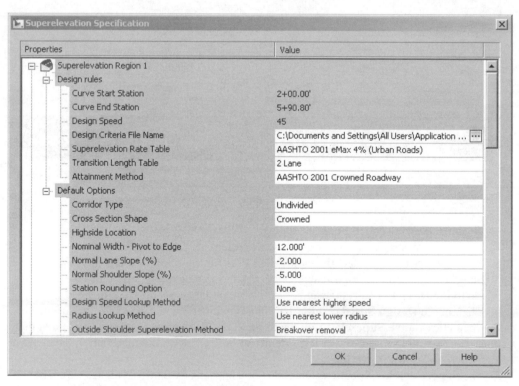

Figure 9-16 Superelevation specifications

Civil 3D computes these data. If there are any errors or notifications of which the user needs to be aware, they appear in the **Panorama**. These might include warnings that curve radii are not up to par. Close the **Panorama** when you are through inspecting its contents.

Exercise 9-8: Build a Simple Corridor

1. Select **Create Simple Corridor...** from the **Corridors** pull-down menu.
2. The **Create Simple Corridor** dialog box appears and requests a name for the corridor. Hit **OK** for the default name and layer.

3. `Select a baseline alignment:` Click on the centerline for the road.
4. `Select a profile:` **Zoom** out and select the proposed profile in the profile view in the upper right part of the drawing.
5. `Select the Assembly:` Pick the **Assembly** marker in the assembly you created.
6. The **Target Mapping** dialog box shown in Figure 9-17 then appears so that Civil 3D can identify which surfaces are involved in the computations.

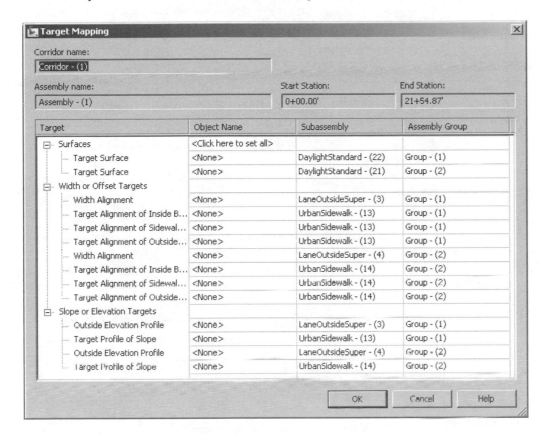

Target	Object Name	Subassembly	Assembly Group
⊟ Surfaces	<Click here to set all>		
├ Target Surface	<None>	DaylightStandard - (22)	Group - (1)
└ Target Surface	<None>	DaylightStandard - (21)	Group - (2)
⊟ Width or Offset Targets			
├ Width Alignment	<None>	LaneOutsideSuper - (3)	Group - (1)
├ Target Alignment of Inside B...	<None>	UrbanSidewalk - (13)	Group - (1)
├ Target Alignment of Sidewal...	<None>	UrbanSidewalk - (13)	Group - (1)
├ Target Alignment of Outside...	<None>	UrbanSidewalk - (13)	Group - (1)
├ Width Alignment	<None>	LaneOutsideSuper - (4)	Group - (2)
├ Target Alignment of Inside B...	<None>	UrbanSidewalk - (14)	Group - (2)
├ Target Alignment of Sidewal...	<None>	UrbanSidewalk - (14)	Group - (2)
└ Target Alignment of Outside...	<None>	UrbanSidewalk - (14)	Group - (2)
⊟ Slope or Elevation Targets			
├ Outside Elevation Profile	<None>	LaneOutsideSuper - (3)	Group - (1)
├ Target Profile of Slope	<None>	UrbanSidewalk - (13)	Group - (1)
├ Outside Elevation Profile	<None>	LaneOutsideSuper - (4)	Group - (2)
└ Target Profile of Slope	<None>	UrbanSidewalk - (14)	Group - (2)

Figure 9-17 The Target Mapping dialog box

7. In the **Object Name** column, in the first row it says to **<Click here to set all>**. Click in that cell and choose the **Existing ground** surface. That will be the surface to which you tie out. Hit **OK**. Hit **OK** to execute.

Exercise 9-9: Use View/Edit Corridor Sections

The corridor is now complete. Let us inspect it. If you **Zoom** back to your centerline, it should appear as shown in Figure 9-18.

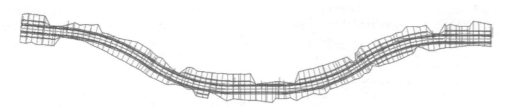

Figure 9-18 Completed corridor

1. The daylight limits are shown around the perimeter of the site.
2. To inspect the cross section of the proposed road, choose **View/Edit Corridor Section** from the **Corridors** pull-down menu. You are prompted to Select a corridor, pick the corridor object.
3. A **Section Editor** tab appears at the top of the screen. Click on it and choose the **Parameter Editor** command. A table appears showing all the pertinent data for the cross section at station 0+00. Refer to Figure 9-19.
4. Take a moment to review this information. It should reflect a normal cross slope for the road.

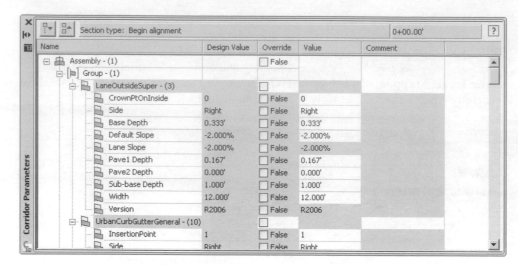

Section type: Begin alignment				0+00.00'	?
Name	Design Value	Override	Value	Comment	
⊟ 🏛 Assembly - (1)		☐ False			
⊟ [▣] Group - (1)					
⊟ 🗎 LaneOutsideSuper - (3)		☐			
🗎 CrownPtOnInside	0	☐ False	0		
🗎 Side	Right	☐ False	Right		
🗎 Base Depth	0.333'	☐ False	0.333'		
🗎 Default Slope	-2.000%	☐ False	-2.000%		
🗎 Lane Slope	-2.000%	☐ False	-2.000%		
🗎 Pave1 Depth	0.167'	☐ False	0.167'		
🗎 Pave2 Depth	0.000'	☐ False	0.000'		
🗎 Sub-base Depth	1.000'	☐ False	1.000'		
🗎 Width	12.000'	☐ False	12.000'		
🗎 Version	R2006	☐ False	R2006		
⊟ 🗎 UrbanCurbGutterGeneral - (10)		☐			
🗎 InsertionPoint	1	☐ False	1		
🗎 Side	Right	☐ False	Right		

Corridor Parameters

Figure 9-19 View/Edit Corridor Section Tools

5. A view of the road section also appears in AutoCAD. **Zoom** and **pan** freely to inspect it visually. See Figure 9-20.

Figure 9-20 A view of the road section

6. In the **Section Editor**, use the pop-down arrow for stations and select other stations, for instance, 2+50. Notice that the roadway is now superelevated.
7. A view of the superelevated roadway is also displayed in AutoCAD. See Figure 9-21.

When through inspecting the sections, terminate the command by closing the toolbar.

Figure 9-21 A view of the superelevated roadway

CODES AND FEATURE LINES

Two additional items that should be mentioned with regard to corridor design are codes and feature lines.

Codes represent specific three-dimensional locations on the Corridor model that are identified with descriptions. They are defined with the subassemblies and are used to create and organize the assemblies. Codes can be exported for the corridor as point objects and uploaded to data collectors, or made available to 3D Machine Control for automated construction. Corridor section labeling is supported through the introduction of Code, Point, Link, and Shape label styles. Corridor assemblies and sections can be annotated with the new label styles.

Exercise 9-10: Review These Codes

1. In the same drawing, look in the **Prospector**. Expand **Corridors** and right-click on **Corridor - (1)**. Choose **Properties** from the menu. When the dialog box appears, select the **Codes** tab. Refer to Figure 9-22.
2. Change the **Code set style** to **All Codes**.
3. Look through the **Name** column and note that there are **Link** codes, **Point** codes, and **Shape** codes. Hit **OK** when finished observing.

A brief explanation of these items follows:

Link codes are the codes assigned to each of the links that are part of the assembly definitions for the roadway. A link is a straight-line segment between endpoints on any cross section.

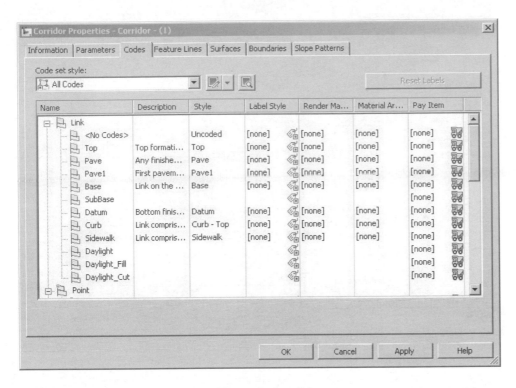

Figure 9-22   Corridor Codes

Shape codes are closed cross-sectional areas created by the subassembly. Shape codes can be used to visualize different materials within the assembly, in order to view the assembly more clearly.

Feature lines represent the linear elements of corridors such as centerlines, edge of pavement, ditch components, and daylight cut/fill lines. These can be used for visualizing the corridor but can also be exported as alignments or as **Grading Feature Lines**.

Exercise 9-11: Change the Aesthetics of the Corridor

This next procedure walks you through how to assign a feature line style for an element of the corridor.

1. In the same drawing, look in the **Prospector**. Expand **Corridors** and right-click on **Corridor - (1)**. Choose **Properties...** from the menu. When the dialog box appears, select the **Feature Lines** tab.
2. Look through the **Code** column and note that there are descriptions for items such as **Top_Curb**, and so on.
3. Click on the **Top_Curb**, look in the **Feature Line Style** column, and you see it defaults to **Ditch**. Click on the icon in the cell for that row. Refer to Figure 9-23.
4. A **Pick Feature Line Style** dialog box with a drop-down menu appears. Select the **Curb Line** style in the drop-down menu.
5. There is a button just to the right of the **Curb Line** item in the drop-down menu. Click on the triangle and select **Edit Current Selection**. A **Feature Line Style—Curb Line** dialog box displays. Click on the **Display** tab and note that you can control how this item appears in AutoCAD. In **Model**, it appears as a magenta color. Hit **OK** when finished observing. Hit **OK** and you are in the **Corridor Properties** dialog box again.
6. Click on **Daylight_Fill** and change the **Feature Line Style** for this to **Daylight Line—Fill**.
7. Click on **Daylight_Cut** and change the **Feature Line Style** for this to **Daylight Line—Cut**.
8. Hit **OK** to exit.
9. The corridor recomputes. When it is complete, **Zoom** in and notice that the corridor shows a magenta line where the **Top of Curb** exists. Look just outside of the flowline for the curb.
10. Also observe that the **Daylight Lines** for **Cut** and **Fill** have changed color.

The next powerful feature is to export these items to AutoCAD for additional functionality. This linework can be sent to AutoCAD in 2D or 3D, which allows for customization.

11. Look in the **Corridors** pull-down menu and select the **Utilities** command.

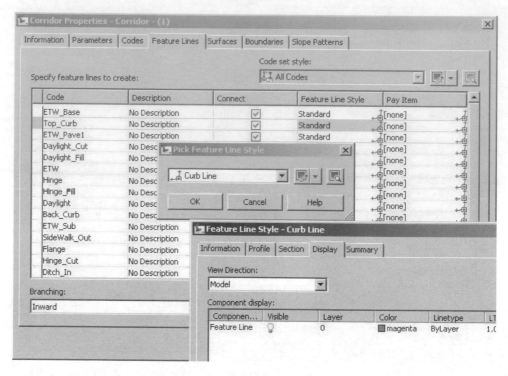

Figure 9-23 Corridor Properties, Feature Line Styles

12. You can export these objects as Polylines, Feature Lines, Alignments, or Profiles. Select **Create Grading Feature Line from Corridor**.
13. `Select a corridor feature line:` **Zoom** in and select the magenta **Top of Curb** object. A **Create Feature Line from Corridor** dialog box appears. Hit **OK**.
14. `Select a corridor feature line:` **Zoom** out and select the **Cut/Fill** linework. **Select a Feature Line** dialog box appears. Hit **OK**. Hit **<Enter>** to complete.
15. When finished, notice that these objects are now in AutoCAD as separate entities and in three dimensions!

One more concept to explore has to do with a major transportation corridor. This area of engineering warrants its own independent textbook; however, it needs to be touched on here.

The Civil 3D **Corridors** pull-down menu has another function for creating corridors called **Create Corridor** You have used the **Create Simple Corridor** up to this point. The **Create Corridor** command is for high-level roads that have multiple alignments, ramps, gores, multiple assemblies, and so on. It is in this function that multiple assemblies are assigned and act together in roadway design.

MULTIPLE BASELINES

The software makes more in-depth use of regions in this methodology. Although you have already seen regions used in the design of superelevations, these regions are used to expand that functionality.

Exercise 9-12: Multiple Baselines

To access student data files, go to www.pearsondesigncentral.com.

1. Open the file called Chapter-9-e.dwg. It has the same alignment and profile you have been working with but has two assemblies. One is a four-lane, rural assembly with a shoulder, and the other is a two-lane urban assembly with curb and gutter. A wide, white boundary is drawn for a surface to be created later. Type **V** for **View** and select the **Assembly** view, hit **Set Current**, then hit **OK**. **Zoom** out a little, and you see both assemblies.
2. Look in the **Corridors** pull-down menu and select the **Create Corridor** command.
3. Select **Alignment—1** when asked by hitting **<Enter>** to access the library of alignments.
4. Select **Profile—Layout (5)** when asked by hitting **<Enter>** to access the library of profiles.
5. Select **Assembly—(1)** when asked by hitting **<Enter>** to access the library of assemblies.
6. A **Create Corridor** dialog box appears, showing that the software already assumes a **Region 1**.
7. For **Baseline 1—Region 1**, change the ending station to **1000** for the use of **Assembly—(1)**.

8. Then right-click on **Baseline 1**, and a shortcut menu appears allowing you to **Add Region...**.

9. First a **Create Corridor Region** dialog box appears, asking you to select the appropriate assembly for the second region. Select **Assembly—(2)**. See Figure 9-24.

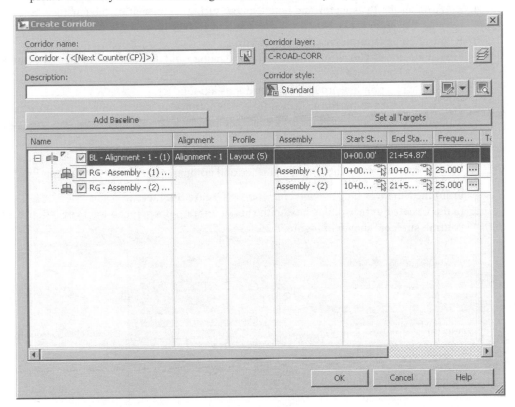

Figure 9-24 Multiple Baselines—Corridor Properties

10. Now change the starting station to **1000** for **Region 2**.

11. Click the button at the top right of the dialog box that says **Set all Targets**; a **Target Mapping** dialog box appears. Click on **Surfaces <Click here to set all>**. Select **Existing Ground** and hit **OK**.

12. Hit **OK** and the system reprocesses the corridor.

13. When it is finished, click on the corridor, right-click, and select **Corridor Properties...** or choose your corridor from the **Prospector.**

14. In the **Surfaces** tab, click the button on the left to **Create a corridor surface**.

15. After you choose this button, a **Corridor—(1) Surface—(1)** is created and appears in the window below.

16. In the **Data Type** pop-down window, select **Links** if it is not already selected.

17. In the **Specify Code** pop-down window, choose **Top**. Then hit the + button to the right. The **Top** surface appears under the **Name** column.

18. In the **Surface Style** column, click on the style that defaults, typically **Borders & Contours**.

19. A **Pick Corridor Surface Style** dialog box displays with a pop-down menu. Select **Borders & Contours** as the style. Click on the pop-down arrow to the right of **Borders & Contours**. Choose **Edit Current Selection** and go to the **Contours** tab. Set the **Contour interval** to **2** and **10** for the intermediate and index contours, respectively.

20. You should see contours for the corridor in AutoCAD when it is finished processing.

21. Zoom in and identify station 10+00 and notice that the software has built a corridor using the multiple assemblies. It has transitioned between the urban template and the rural template along the common edges, that is, the pavement. A 336′ contour runs through the transition between 10+00 and 10+25.

Exercise 9-13: Create a Corridor Surface

The next option to discuss is creating a corridor surface that will be evident in the **Surfaces** area of the **Prospector**.

1. In the same file, look under the **Corridors** pull-down menu. Select **Utilities >> Create Detached Surfaces from Corridor....**

2. Pick your corridor if requested.
3. A **Create Corridor Surfaces** dialog box displays, confirming your surface naming and the styles to use. Use the defaults or change them here and hit **OK**.
4. Look under the **Prospector** and notice a new surface representing the corridor.
5. Expand **Corridor—(1)**, **Surface—(1)**. Expand **Definitions**.
6. Right-click on **Boundaries** and select **Add....**
7. Give it a name of **Corridor Boundary** in the name field that displays in the **Add Boundaries** dialog box. Hit **OK**.
8. Pick the white polyline around the corridor as a boundary.
9. This can be used to perform surface-related functions such as pasting it into the existing ground to create a monolithic surface and the like.

Exercise 9-14: Earthworks on a Corridor Surface

Let us perform earthworks on the corridor surface and compare it to the existing ground surface.

1. From the **Surfaces** pull-down menu, choose **Create Surface....**
2. In the **Create Surface** dialog box, in the upper left pop-down menu for **Type**, choose **TIN volume surface**, shown in Figure 9-25.

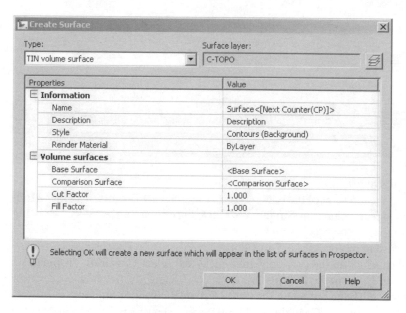

Figure 9-25 Create Surface dialog box

3. Under the **Value** column for the **Name** field, provide a name of **TIN Volume EG vs. Corridor**.
4. In the **Volume surfaces** field, there are fields for selecting the comparison surfaces.
5. Select **Existing Ground** for the **Base Surface** and select **Corridor (1)—Surface (1)** for the **Comparison Surface**. Hit **OK**.
6. Look in the **Prospector** and you see a surface called **TIN Volume EG vs. Corridor**. Right-click on it and select **Surface Properties....**
7. Choose the **Statistics** tab in the dialog box for **Surface Properties** and expand the **Volume** item. Volumes are automatically computed for the two surfaces. See Figure 9-26. Your results may differ.
8. If these two surfaces change, the volumes recompute if the **Rebuild—Automatic** item is checked in the surface parameters.

Exercise 9-15: Corridor-Related Quantity Takeoffs

Now let us use the **Quantity Takeoff** commands under the **Sections** pull-down menu to compute some quantities from the corridor.

This task is often used due to the requirement to estimate the costs for providing certain quantities of material for a project. Contractors and engineers must be able to ascertain the cost of the project before it goes to construction.

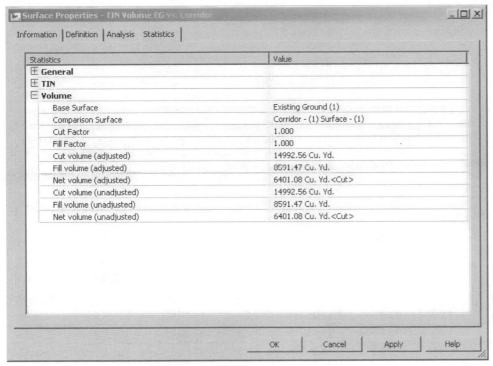

Figure 9-26 Quantities from surface calculations

1. Open Chapter-9-f.dwg; you will notice that the **Sample Line Group** has already been created as discussed in the earlier chapter on **Sections** in order to expedite this exercise. Right-click on **Corridor 3** to rebuild it.

2. Look under the **Sections** pull-down and select **Compute Materials....**

3. A dialog box will display called **Select a Sample Line Group**; select the SLG-1 group. The **Compute Materials** dialog box then displays.

4. In the top left of the dialog box is a pop-down window; select the option called **Earthworks**.

5. For the **EG Criteria**, **Object name**, select **Existing ground (1)**.

6. For the **Datum**, select **Corridor (3) Corridor (3)—Surface (1)**.

7. Hit **OK**.

8. Look under the **Sections** pull-down and select **Generate Volume Report....**

9. The **Report Quantities** dialog box will display. Use **Alignment—1**, **SLG-1**, **Material List—1** and the **Earthwork** style sheet. See Figure 9-27. Hit **OK**.

10. A volume report is generated and should appear similar to that in Table 9-1. Your results may differ.

To access student data files, go to www.pearsondesigncentral.com.

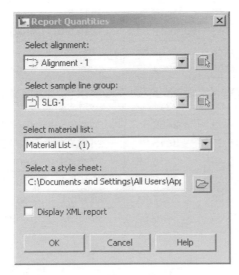

Figure 9-27 Report Quantities dialog box

Table 9-1 Volume Report

Project: chapter 9-f.dwg   Alignment: Alignment—1   Sample Line Group: SLG-1
Start Sta: 0+00.000   End Sta: 21+54.874

Station	Cut Area (sq. ft.)	Cut Volume (cu. yd.)	Re-usable Volume (cu. yd.)	Fill Area (sq. ft.)	Fill Volume (cu. yd.)	Cum. Cut Vol. (cu. yd.)	Cum. Reusable Vol. (cu. yd.)	Cum. Fill Vol. (cu. yd.)	Cum. Net Vol. (cu. yd.)
0+00.000	230.93	0.00	0.00	12.77	0.00	0.00	0.00	0.00	0.00
0+50.000	249.93	445.24	445.24	19.05	29.47	445.24	445.24	29.47	415.77
1+00.000	237.50	451.33	451.33	24.24	40.08	896.57	896.57	69.55	827.02
1+50.000	149.15	358.01	358.01	29.75	49.99	1254.58	1254.58	119.53	1135.05
2+00.000	23.37	159.74	159.74	62.78	85.67	1414.32	1414.32	205.20	1209.11
2+25.000	12.87	15.88	15.88	68.78	61.40	1430.20	1430.20	266.61	1163.59
2+50.000	5.73	8.17	8.17	93.73	75.71	1438.37	1438.37	342.32	1096.05
2+75.000	4.94	4.69	4.69	88.94	85.13	1443.06	1443.06	427.45	1015.61
3+00.000	4.28	4.03	4.03	90.46	83.70	1447.09	1447.09	511.15	935.94
3+25.000	0.26	1.99	1.99	93.74	85.58	1449.08	1449.08	596.73	852.36
3+50.000	0.88	0.51	0.51	115.93	97.19	1449.59	1449.59	693.92	755.67
3+75.000	0.34	0.53	0.53	164.63	129.83	1450.12	1450.12	823.74	626.38
4+00.000	0.00	0.15	0.15	226.89	181.29	1450.27	1450.27	1005.03	445.24
4+25.000	0.00	0.00	0.00	313.84	249.79	1450.27	1450.27	1254.82	195.45
4+50.000	0.00	0.00	0.00	392.70	325.78	1450.27	1450.27	1580.60	−130.33
4+75.000	0.00	0.00	0.00	402.37	368.14	1450.27	1450.27	1948.74	−498.47
5+00.000	0.02	0.01	0.01	446.26	394.79	1450.28	1450.28	2343.53	−893.25
5+25.000	0.00	0.01	0.01	424.96	404.87	1450.29	1450.29	2748.39	−1298.10
5+50.000	0.00	0.00	0.00	372.11	369.68	1450.29	1450.29	3118.07	−1667.78
5+75.000	0.25	0.12	0.12	352.70	336.44	1450.42	1450.42	3454.51	−2004.10
5+90.799	0.01	0.08	0.08	327.22	199.01	1450.50	1450.50	3653.52	−2203.02
6+00.000	0.00	0.00	0.00	333.64	112.50	1450.50	1450.50	3766.02	−2315.52
6+25.000	0.00	0.00	0.00	256.94	272.76	1450.50	1450.50	4038.78	−2588.28
6+50.000	2.44	1.05	1.05	191.42	207.30	1451.55	1451.55	4246.08	−2794.53
6+75.000	7.60	4.33	4.33	136.95	152.02	1455.88	1455.88	4398.10	−2942.21
7+00.000	0.30	3.41	3.41	69.75	96.36	1459.30	1459.30	4494.46	−3035.16
7+25.000	9.11	4.55	4.55	14.39	39.40	1463.84	1463.84	4533.86	−3070.02
7+50.000	105.75	52.55	52.55	2.55	7.93	1516.39	1516.39	4541.79	−3025.39
7+75.000	119.49	102.62	102.62	1.34	1.86	1619.01	1619.01	4543.65	−2924.64
8+00.000	126.91	112.51	112.51	0.16	0.72	1731.52	1731.52	4544.37	−2812.85
8+25.000	205.70	152.86	152.86	0.00	0.08	1884.37	1884.37	4544.44	−2660.07
8+50.000	251.87	211.86	211.86	0.00	0.00	2096.24	2096.24	4544.44	−2448.21
8+75.000	212.69	215.08	215.08	0.00	0.00	2311.32	2311.32	4544.45	−2233.13
9+00.000	161.94	171.23	171.23	4.43	2.11	2482.55	2482.55	4546.56	−2064.01
9+25.000	141.41	136.40	136.40	28.53	15.66	2618.95	2618.95	4562.22	−1943.27
9+50.000	126.50	119.50	119.50	69.13	46.48	2738.45	2738.45	4608.70	−1870.26
9+75.000	114.29	107.19	107.19	81.12	71.59	2845.64	2845.64	4680.29	−1834.65
9+77.881	113.05	11.67	11.67	82.87	9.03	2857.31	2857.31	4689.32	−1832.01
10+00.000	105.83	89.66	89.66	89.62	70.65	2946.97	2946.97	4759.97	−1813.01

Station	Cut Area (sq. ft.)	Cut Volume (cu. yd.)	Re-usable Volume (cu. yd.)	Fill Area (sq. ft.)	Fill Volume (cu. yd.)	Cum. Cut Vol. (cu. yd.)	Cum. Reusable Vol. (cu. yd.)	Cum. Fill Vol. (cu. yd.)	Cum. Net Vol. (cu. yd.)
10+50.000	111.45	201.19	201.19	146.94	219.04	3148.15	3148.15	4979.01	−1830.86
11+00.000	80.40	177.64	177.64	218.61	338.47	3325.79	3325.79	5317.48	−1991.69
11+50.000	0.00	74.44	74.44	337.46	514.87	3400.23	3400.23	5832.36	−2432.13
11+77.881	0.03	0.01	0.01	411.42	386.66	3400.25	3400.25	6219.02	−2818.77
12+00.000	3.63	1.41	1.41	349.49	315.25	3401.65	3401.65	6534.27	−3132.62
12+25.000	68.19	31.24	31.24	297.95	302.94	3432.90	3432.90	6837.20	−3404.31
12+50.000	93.19	70.44	70.44	199.92	234.39	3503.34	3503.34	7071.59	−3568.25
12+75.000	124.56	95.33	95.33	103.30	144.29	3598.67	3598.67	7215.88	−3617.21
13+00.000	161.55	125.55	125.55	71.53	83.39	3724.22	3724.22	7299.27	−3575.05
13+25.000	165.57	144.57	144.57	42.22	54.33	3868.79	3868.79	7353.60	−3484.81
13+50.000	170.90	150.11	150.11	32.50	35.93	4018.89	4018.89	7389.53	−3370.63
13+75.000	164.95	150.21	150.21	39.50	34.70	4169.11	4169.11	7424.23	−3255.12
14+00.000	154.41	141.83	141.83	54.28	44.93	4310.93	4310.93	7469.16	−3158.22
14+25.000	146.96	132.16	132.16	64.48	56.67	4443.10	4443.10	7525.83	−3082.74
14+50.000	137.18	124.11	124.11	71.30	64.89	4567.20	4567.20	7590.72	−3023.52
14+75.000	131.24	117.92	117.92	77.86	71.27	4685.12	4685.12	7662.00	−2976.87
15+00.000	113.28	107.56	107.56	67.47	69.18	4792.69	4792.69	7731.18	−2938.49
15+25.000	85.00	87.11	87.11	149.85	103.33	4879.80	4879.80	7834.51	−2954.71
15+50.000	55.72	61.52	61.52	165.29	148.59	4941.31	4941.31	7983.09	−3041.78
15+66.536	83.55	40.22	40.22	91.67	79.73	4981.53	4981.53	8062.82	−3081.29
15+66.537	83.55	0.00	0.00	91.67	0.00	4981.53	4981.53	8062.82	−3081.29
15+75.000	103.49	30.84	30.84	64.06	23.89	5012.37	5012.37	8086.71	−3074.35
16+00.000	211.75	151.20	151.20	2.13	29.93	5163.56	5163.56	8116.64	−2953.08
16+25.000	390.31	281.89	281.89	0.00	0.94	5445.45	5445.45	8117.58	−2672.13
16+50.000	516.35	420.90	420.90	0.00	0.00	5866.36	5866.36	8117.58	−2251.23
16+75.000	630.68	530.89	530.89	0.00	0.00	6397.25	6397.25	8117.58	−1720.33
17+00.000	621.03	580.18	580.18	0.00	0.00	6977.42	6977.42	8117.58	−1140.16
17+25.000	588.40	563.78	563.78	0.00	0.00	7541.21	7541.21	8117.58	−576.38
17+50.000	533.25	524.78	524.78	0.00	0.00	8065.99	8065.99	8117.58	−51.59
17+75.000	470.20	469.74	469.74	0.00	0.00	8535.73	8535.73	8117.58	418.15
18+00.000	411.09	411.08	411.08	0.00	0.00	8946.81	8946.81	8117.58	829.22
18+25.000	317.45	341.69	341.69	0.34	0.15	9288.50	9288.50	8117.73	1170.76
18+50.000	263.18	275.74	275.74	18.36	8.29	9564.23	9564.23	8126.02	1438.21
18+75.000	204.76	223.36	223.36	49.05	29.65	9787.59	9787.59	8155.67	1631.92
19+00.000	160.84	174.42	174.42	45.20	41.30	9962.01	9962.01	8196.97	1765.04
19+25.000	153.34	149.21	149.21	34.24	34.92	10111.22	10111.22	8231.90	1879.32
19+50.000	162.22	149.78	149.78	25.34	26.34	10261.00	10261.00	8258.24	2002.76
19+54.873	163.99	30.23	30.23	22.97	4.16	10291.23	10291.23	8262.40	2028.83
20+00.000	133.33	248.46	248.46	22.59	38.08	10539.70	10539.70	8300.48	2239.22
20+50.000	275.76	378.79	378.79	10.66	30.79	10918.49	10918.49	8331.26	2587.22
21+00.000	218.93	458.05	458.05	8.29	17.55	11376.54	11376.54	8348.81	3027.73
21+50.000	153.64	344.97	344.97	19.36	25.61	11721.51	11721.51	8374.42	3347.09
21+54.874	0.00	13.87	13.87	0.00	1.75	11735.37	11735.37	8376.16	3359.21

In computing earthworks, a section-based method is used whereby the amount of cut and fill is computed between each section of the corridor. The volume of cut between station 0+00 and station 0+50 is 445.24 c.y. and the volume of fill between those same stations is 29.47 c.y. The difference between those two figures is 415.77 c.y., which is referred to as a Net Volume of 415.77 c.y. cut. Notice that the entire amount of cut and fill is assumed to be reusable, such that the earth cut from one area of the project can be used to fill another area.

The entire project's volumes are shown in the last row of Table 9-1. In the last row, the fourth column from the right shows the accumulated amount of cut removed from the existing ground. It is 11,735.37 c.y. of earth. The second column from the right shows the accumulated amount of fill needed to achieve the proposed conditions above existing ground. It is 8,376.16 c.y. of fill. Therefore, the entire project must dispose of 3,359.21 c.y. of the earth that was cut; hence, there is a net volume of 3,359.21 c.y. of cut. Typically it must be trucked off the site because it is excess earth. Clearly this is not a balanced site or all of the earth would have been used somewhere on the site.

ROADWAY DESIGN FOR REHABILITATION AND RECONSTRUCTION—

The next exercise delves into roadway rehabilitation and reconstruction. This part of the software is new to most Autodesk users because the Land Desktop software could not perform this function as elegantly as Civil 3D can. The idea is that not all roads are new roads; in fact, far more roads are maintained each year than built new. Civil 3D provides tools to assist engineers responsible for roadway maintenance, and these include subassemblies for asphalt overlays, median reconstruction, sidewalk rehabilitation, milling and overlaying, and curb and gutter replacements. There are parametric values that can even compute how much of a stripped material can be reused for the new overlay.

Exercise 9-16: Roadway Design for Rehabilitation and Reconstruction

To access student data files, go to www.pearsondesigncentral.com.

1. Open Chapter-9-g.dwg; notice that you have already created an alignment and an existing ground profile. A new assembly has been created called **Assembly—Rehab**. This mill and overlay subassembly was used to place a crowned surface over another, worn, existing crowned surface.
2. The method to perform these computations is to use the alignment in the drawing, which has been prepared to coincide roughly with the asphalt crown of the existing road. The profile used is the existing ground profile for the existing roadway because it already has reasonable grades on it. Then use the new assembly for rehabilitation of the new overlayed surface.
3. Select **Create Corridor** from the **Corridors** pull-down menu. Select the only **Alignment** available. Then select the existing ground profile for the proposed profile and select the **Assembly—Rehab** assembly for the new surface.
4. When the dialog box displays, choose the button for **Set all Targets** and then click in the cell for **<Click here to set all>**. Choose the **Existing Ground** surface and hit **OK**. Hit **OK** twice to compute.
5. Then **Zoom** into the plan view of the road and notice a corridor exists.
6. From the **Corridors** pull-down menu, select **View/Edit Corridor Section** and browse to stations 0+00, 4+00, and 17+00 and inspect the sections. You can choose a specific station from the pop-down window under **Select a Station.** Notice that milling and overlaying has occurred per your specifications. Refer to Figures 9-28, 9-29, and 9-30.

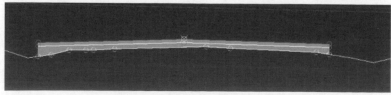

Figure 9-28   Milling and Overlaying Result 1

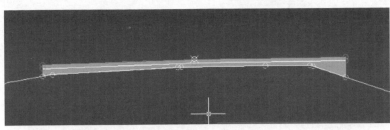

Figure 9-29   Milling and Overlaying Result 2

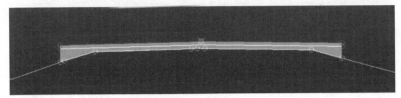

Figure 9-30   Milling and Overlaying Result 3

Exercise 9-17: Designing a Bifurcated Highway

This last roadway-related exercise explores a situation in which there are two baselines. This can occur in many projects, such as a mainlane with an off-ramp or a mainlane with a frontage or a potentially bifurcated highway.

This next design has an eastbound and westbound set of mainlanes. Although the alignments are parallel, the profiles are not the same. This is a ***bifurcated highway***. This exercise uses multiple baselines to show how a DOT-level roadway might be designed.

1. Open Chapter-9-h.dwg; notice that you have already created two alignments and two profiles. Two new assemblies have been created called **Assembly—Eastbound** and **Assembly—Westbound**. There is also a third profile called **Profile—Middle** to guide the center of the median between the two mainlanes.
2. From the **Corridors** pull-down menu, select the **Create Corridor** command. You are asked to select an alignment, so pick the **Alignment—Eastbound**, either from the screen or by hitting **<Enter>** and choosing it from the library. Then select the profile called **Layout–Rt side** from the library as well. Last, select the **Assembly—Eastbound**.
3. This displays the **Create Corridor** dialog box. Click the **Add Baseline** button in the top left of the dialog box to add a baseline to your computations. Choose **Alignment—Westbound** when prompted.
4. Then right-click on the **Baseline 2** and select **Add Region....** Select the **Assembly—Westbound** when prompted. Set the **Profile for Baseline 2** to **Layout—Left**.
5. Click the button for **Set All Targets**. See Figure 9-31.
6. Click the cell where it says to **<Click here to set all>** and select the **Existing Ground (1)** surface for any tie-outs.
7. Then in the **Target Profile** row, under **Object Name**, select **Layout middle** and hit **Add** for both of the **Target Profile** items. This guides the center of the median between the two baselines. Click **OK**. Click **OK** to compute.
8. When the processing is completed, select **View/Edit Corridor** sections from the **Corridors** pull-down menu. Notice how the center of the median now follows the **Layout middle** profile established. Refer to Figure 9-32.
9. Then feel free to establish the surface and view it using the **3DOrbit** command. You can see the two baselines interconnected, each with its own alignment and profile activity. Refer to Figure 9-33.

Exercise 9-18: Designing an Intersection

Perhaps the most requested topic during our training sessions is intersection and cul-de-sac design. Civil 3D has the ability to create integrated intersections and cul-de-sacs, but it is a somewhat advanced topic.

---

bifurcated highway: Where one direction of traffic has an independent PGL from the opposite direction of traffic. The profile may go uphill in one direction and downhill in the opposite direction.

To access student data files, go to www.pearsondesigncentral.com.

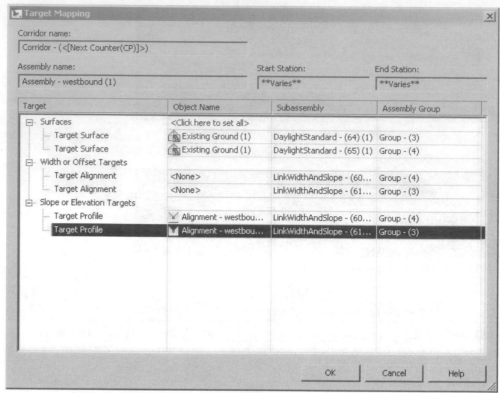

Figure 9-31   Target Mapping for a bifurcated roadway

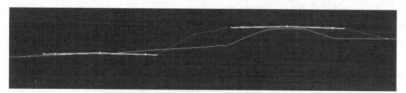

Figure 9-32   Cross section of resultant bifurcated roadway

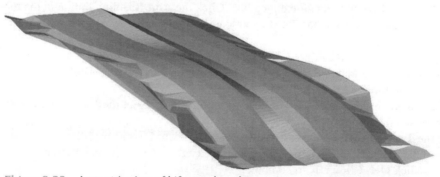

Figure 9-33   Isometric view of bifurcated roadway

roadway assembly fragments:
Pieces of cross-sectional templates that are applied to locations on alignments where they can be controlled from and then stretched to various targets elsewhere in the corridor.

The concept is to use ***roadway assembly fragments***, tie them onto one or more alignments, and allow the floating side of the fragment to stretch to any one of many targets that can be identified elsewhere in the corridor. In the simplest sense, you use a typical assembly for the portions of the corridor that are fairly uniform and standardized. At the point when nonstandard conditions occur, such as the intersection of two or more alignments or in cul-de-sac situations, then you can use this fragment methodology. This is a topic that we usually spend significant time on in the classroom; in order to abbreviate it for this text, we will analyze an existing, already designed intersection and cul-de-sac. From this information, you should be able to observe the concepts described and reproduce them on a project fairly easily.

1. Open Chapter-9-i.dwg; you will notice that you already have some alignments and profiles developed. This is a T-intersection with a cul-de-sac on the east end. The roads are called **Primary Road** and **Side Road**. You will notice that we have additional alignments. The alignment around the cul-de-sac is called **Culdesac ep**. For the intersection, the alignments are called **l-ep**, which is the left edge of pavement for the primary road; **small ep**, which is the edge of pavement directly within the intersection; **l-return**, which is the left end return of the side road as it connects with the primary road; and **r-return**, which is the right end return of the side road as it connects with the primary road.

2. Inspect these alignments by using the **Toolspace**, locating them in the **Prospector** under **Sites**, **Site 1**, **Alignments**, and **Centerline Alignments**. Right-click on each alignment and select **Zoom to** to inspect it visually.

3. Note that there are also existing ground and proposed ground profiles developed for each of the alignments. Inspect these profiles by using the **Toolspace**, locating them in the **Prospector** under **Sites**, **Site 1**, **Alignments, Centerline Alignments**, and **Profile Views** under the individual alignments. Right-click on each **Profile View** and select **Zoom to** to inspect them visually. You will see profiles for the Primary road, the Side road, the Left Ep inside the intersection (between the returns), the two curb returns, and the cul-de-sac. Refer to Figure 9-34.

To access student data files, go to www.pearsondesigncentral.com.

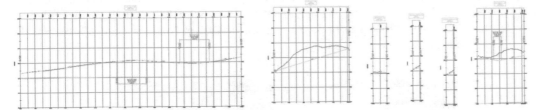

Figure 9-34   Profiles for intersection and cul-de-sac design

4. Next, notice the assemblies that have been created. **Assembly-3** is the main assembly for the primary and side roads. **CDS** is the assembly that will "spin" around the right end return of the side road as it connects. **CDS (1)** is the assembly that will "spin" around the left end return of the side road as it connects. The **CDS** is also the assembly that will be used to design the cul-de-sac and it will also be "spun" to create the pavement and tie-outs. See Figure 9-35.

Figure 9-35   Assemblies for intersection and cul-de-sac design

5. Now that you have inspected the components of the alignments, profiles, and assemblies, let us examine how they are compiled into a corridor. Notice that Corridor (1) is the Primary Road, Corridor (2) is the Side Road, Corridor (3) is the Left Curb Return (looking into the Side Road from the Primary Road), and Corridor (4) is the Right Curb Return (looking into the Side Road from the Primary Road). Notice that the cul-de-sac is part of the Primary Road. Select the Primary Road Corridor; right-click and select **Corridor Properties**. The **Corridor Properties** dialog box will display as shown in Figure 9-36.

6. Notice that the **Parameters** tab shows how to prepare the intersection for the incoming side road. The name indicates that **Assembly (3)** will be used; however, regions are established that allow differing tie-out conditions from station 0+00 up to the intersection, through the intersection, and then after the intersection. The conditions that differ are that the road will be tied to existing ground on both the left and right up to the intersection,

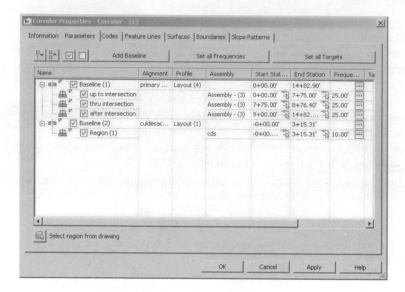

Figure 9-36 Corridor properties for primary road

only on the right through the intersection, and again on both left and right after the inter-section. Verify this by clicking the button that says **Set All Targets** in the dialog box as shown in Figure 9-37. The Target Surface whose **Object Name** is set to **<None>** is the left side through the intersection.

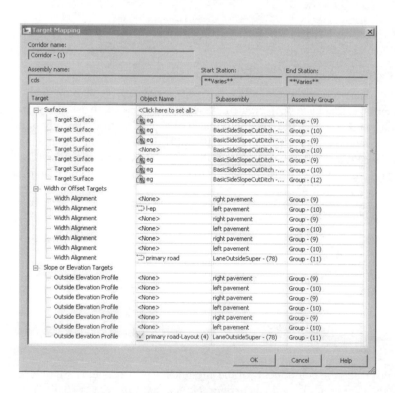

Figure 9-37 Set All Targets

7. Also examine how the cul-de-sac is developed. Notice in **Corridor Properties** for **Cor-ridor (1)** that another alignment exists in the dialog box called **culdesac** and it uses a pro-file called **Layout (1)**, which is the profile for the unwrapped cul-de-sac around the EP of the cul-de-sac. The assembly used is **CDS**, and it is applied to the entire spin-out of the cul-de-sac. To inspect the targets for just the cul-de-sac, click the button on the right side of the dialog box in the **Target** column for the **CDS** assembly. It has three dots on it. This invokes the targets for the cul-de-sac specifically, shown in Figure 9-38.

8. The Surface target shows a tie-out to existing ground on the right side of the assembly, an Alignment target of the Primary Road (where the assembly will be stretched to for hori-zontal control), and to Layout (4) (where the assembly will be stretched to for vertical

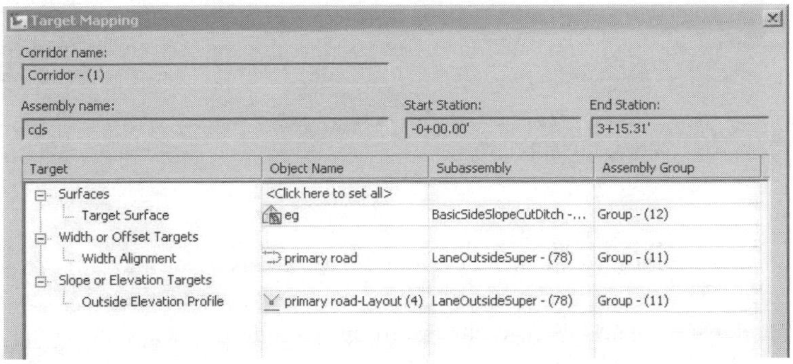

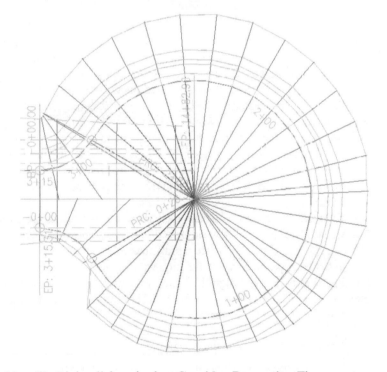

Figure 9-38   Target Mapping dialog box

control). The frequency was increased to 10' for the cul-de-sac to create a more granular computation for this smaller area.

9. In the plan view of the drawing, you can see that the assembly ties to the primary road centerline and then to the end of the centerline as it spins. Refer to Figure 9-39, where dashed linework shows the intervention of the cul-de-sac over the primary road computations.

10. For the intersection, click the side road; right-click and select **Corridor Properties**. Notice that we begin the corridor at the PC of the curb return. Close the dialog box.

Figure 9-39   Completed cul-de-sac

11. Now click the **Corridor (3)**. Right-click and select **Corridor Properties**. There are two regions: one from station 0+00 along the left EP of the Primary Road to the intersection of the Side Road with the EP of the Primary Road, and another from the intersection to and along the centerline of the Side Road.

12. Hit the button to **Set All Targets**. You will see that Surface targets is the existing ground for tie-out. The alignment targets are the Small EP for the region from 0+00 to 0+27, and the Side Road for station 0+33 to the end stationing for the curb return. The profiles are controlled by tying the target to the profile called **Small EP PGL-2** for the region from 0+00 to 0+27 and to the profile called **Sideroad PGL** for the stationing of 0+33 to the end stationing for the curb return.

13. Repeat this inspection for the right curb return and notice similar targeting there. Inspect the plan view of the intersection to see how the assemblies tie to the targets to complete the design.

You may notice that the roadway continues up to the center of the cul-de-sac. Therefore your next step might be to end the processing of that part of the road at the PC of the EP of the beginning of the cul-de-sac. Explore these possibilities.

TIP   This is certainly not the only way to prepare intersections and cul-de-sacs! Experiment with concepts and realize that everything can be placed into a single corridor, or items can be pieced together. The idea here is that by making changes to alignments, assemblies, or profiles, the entire corridor will update with new computational results.

At this point you have developed basic roads as well as a more sophisticated roadway with subgrades and superelevations. There are many more structures for building assemblies within the software, and now you have a strong foundation to explore them.

Begin to combine the concepts you have learned. For instance, a powerful feature of the software is that after a corridor is developed, very often changes occur to the design. You have already seen the ripple-through effect that occurs when modifications are made to the various object components. If the existing ground surface is modified, that change ripples through the corridor and re-develops the corridor. If the profile is changed, it ripples through the design and affects the sections. Take some time to try out these features similar to what has been accomplished in previous chapters.

New Corridor Intersection Capabilities

This is the main new feature of note (in our opinion) in the 2010 release of Civil 3D. Before this function was introduced, each roadway corridor was independent of the others. Although the corridors could have multiple baselines, it was impossible to create corridors that crossed each other as the streets would in three-way and four-way intersections.

Earlier in this chapter, we had an exercise on designing intersections. This was the method we were forced to use prior to Civil 3D 2010. Keep this example; it may still come in handy because you may still need to custom craft some corridors together using this technique.

For most corridors and intersections, however, we can use the new **CreateIntersection** wizard. This is an easy-to-use set of dialogs that walk you through the parameter setup for automatically designing these difficult 3D solutions. Intersections are a new object type in the software and can be seen in the Prospector as an intersection icon.

To invoke this routine you can type **Createintersection** or use a ribbon by selecting **Home** tab >> **Create Design** panel >> **Intersection**. If you follow the steps in the dialog, you will be able to create intersections in 3D more rapidly than ever.

In our exercise on how this function works, you will open a drawing already prepared for performing an intersection design. This simply means that two corridors have already been built. They intersect at a "T" or three-way confluence. The software can also handle four-way confluences, but this example will get the concept across.

Exercise 9-19: Creating an Intersection

To access student data files, go to www.pearsondesigncentral.com.

1. Open Chapter-9-Intersection.dwg. Type in **V** for **View** and select the view called **Intersection** to navigate to the corridors in question.
2. Type **Createintersection** at the command prompt. You can also use the ribbon by selecting the **Home** tab, **Create Design Panel**, and **Intersection**.
3. The prompt asks for the intersection. Select the intersection of the centerlines of the two corridors. Note that the intersect snap should be on already; if it isn't, turn it on. (Just to be sure you are at the correct location; the intersection X,Y coordinate is at 15941.6547, 18335.6246. Don't type the value; we are simply providing this value so you can be sure you are at the correct location.)
4. The prompt responds with `Select main road alignment <or press enter key to select from list>`: Hit **<Enter>**
5. When the Select alignment dialog displays, choose the **Horizontal Road** and hit **<Enter>**.
6. The **Create Intersection** dialog then comes up. See Figure 9-40. The intersection name will default; use the **Standard** intersection marker style, leave the layer at **0** for now, and use the **Standard** intersection label style, and the intersection corridor type will be **Primary Road Crown Maintained.** Hit **<Next>**.

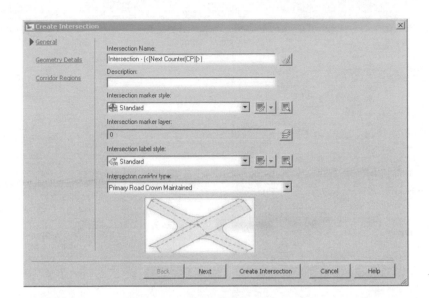

Figure 9-40

7. The next screen within the wizard displays. See Figure 9-41. Click the button for **Offset Pa-rameters** and Figure 9-42 displays. Inspect the values in the fields to observe that the primary road will be 15′ by default to the left and right of the main alignment. Change this to **12′**. Note the secondary road parameters and change these to **12′** too. Hit **<OK>**.

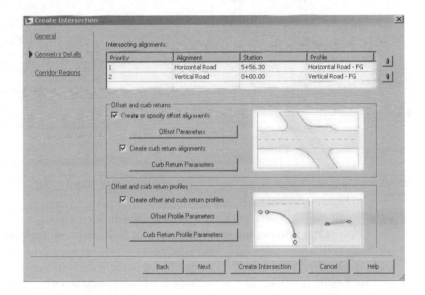

Figure 9-41

TIP

Civil 3D 2010 supports intersections with up to four quadrants. This is sufficient for three-way and four-way intersections.

8. Now click the **Curb Return Parameters** and that dialog will display as shown in Figure 9-43. Note that there is a drop-down menu for the **Intersection Quadrant** at the top of the dialog. The parameters for each quadrant can be controlled individually if needed. Click in the **Curb Return Type** drop-down and note that it supports three types of returns: chamfer, circular, and 3-centered arcs. Leave it on circular. Note that if you click the **Widen turn lane for incoming road** toggle, a new set of parameters shows up in the dialog. These would be used to set the widening criteria. Turn off the **Widen turn lane for incoming road** toggle, accept the default values, and hit **<OK>**.
9. Staying within the **Create Intersection** dialog, click on the button for **Lane Slope Parameters**. This feature allows the user to create profiles to guide the **Edge of Pavement** or

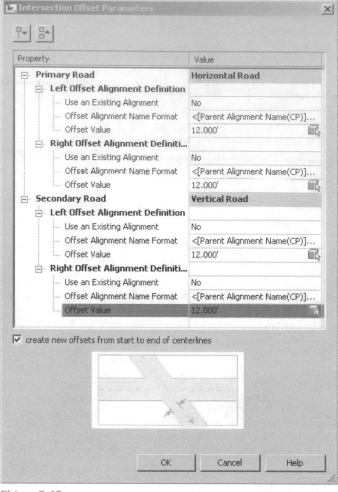

Figure 9-42

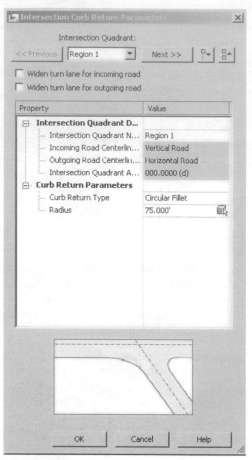

Figure 9-43

compute it based on the cross slope of the roadway. Again, we will use the defaults shown in Figure 9-44 and hit **<OK>**.

10. Again, staying within the **Create Intersection** dialog, click on the button for **Curb Return Profile Parameters** and the dialog in Figure 9-45 displays. Note how the **Regions** can be controlled separately. Following your inspection of the values, hit **<OK>**.

11. Hit **Next** in the **Create Intersection** dialog and Figure 9-46 shows. We will take the default of **Create New Corridor** in the upper left of the dialog and we will daylight to the **Surface 1 Corridor (1) Surface** in the upper right corner.

12. In the middle of the dialog is a screen with several options. The following graphics provide an idea of the options for connecting the two roadways together. Inspect your options by reviewing the figures shown here.

- Curb Return Fillets—Figure 9-47

- Primary Road Full Section—Figure 9-48

- Primary Road Part Section—Daylight Left—Figure 9-49

- Primary Road Part Section—Daylight Right—Figure 9-50

- Secondary Road Full Section—Figure 9-51

- Secondary Road Half Section—Daylight Left—Figure 9-52

- Secondary Road Half Section—Daylight Right—Figure 9-53

13. Following your observations of the **Corridor Region Section Types**, we will leave the defaults as they are; in other words, we will use **Assembly (1)**. Hit the **Create Intersection** button.

14. Upon completion notice the resulting intersection as shown in Figure 9-54. Note that this was created as a new corridor and can be viewed under **Corridors** in the **Prospector**.

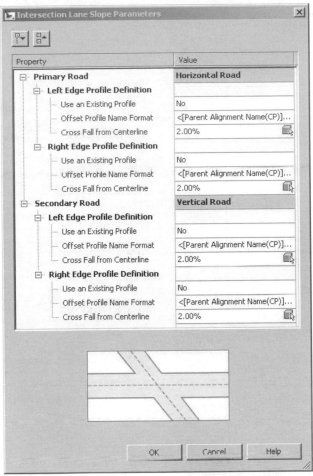

Figure 9-44

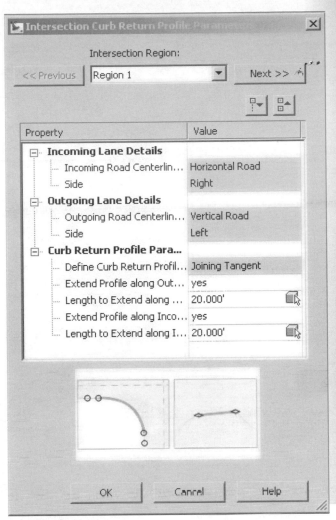

Figure 9-45

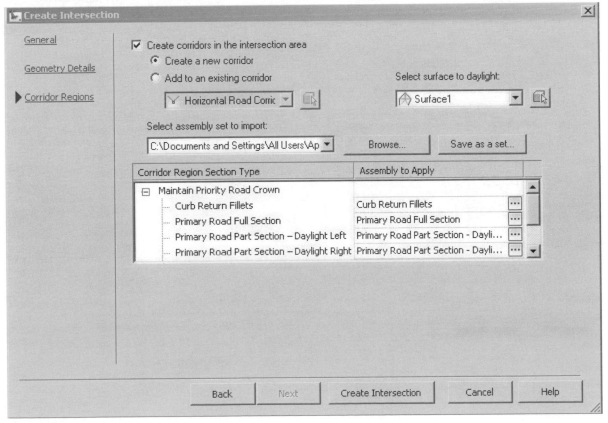

Figure 9-46

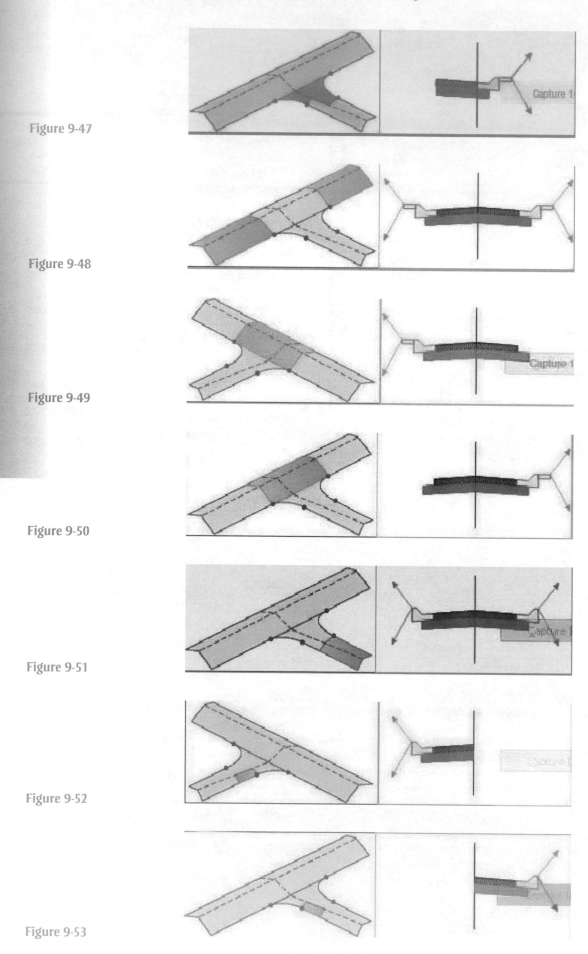

Figure 9-47

Figure 9-48

Figure 9-49

Figure 9-50

Figure 9-51

Figure 9-52

Figure 9-53

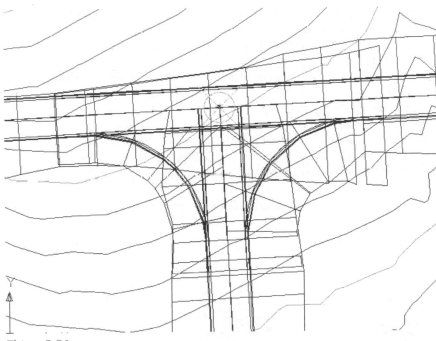

Figure 9-54

Exercise 9-20: Creating an Intersection as Part of an Existing Corridor

To access student data files, go to www.pearsondesigncentral.com.

1. Open Chapter-9-Intersection.dwg. Type in **V** for **View** and select the view called **Intersection** to navigate to the corridors in question.

2. Type **Createintersection** at the command prompt. You can also use the ribbon by selecting the **Home** tab, **Create Design Panel, Intersection**.

3. The prompt asks for the intersection; select the intersection of the centerlines of the two corridors. Note that the intersect snap should be on already, if it isn't, turn it on. (Just to be sure you are at the correct location; the intersection X,Y coordinate is at 15941.6547, 18335.6246. Don't type the value; we are simply providing this value so you can be sure you are at the correct location.)

4. The **Create Intersection** dialog then comes up. See Figure 9-40. The intersection name will default; use the **Standard** intersection marker style, leave the layer at **0** for now, use the **Standard** intersection label style, and the intersection corridor type will be **Primary Road Crown Maintained**. Hit **<Next>**.

5. The next screen within the wizard displays. See Figure 9-41. Click the button for **Offset Parameters** and the dialog displays. Inspect the values in the fields to observe that the primary road will be 15′ by default to the left and right of the main alignment. Change these values to **12′** for the primary and secondary roads as shown in Figure 9-42. Hit **<OK>**.

TIP   Civil 3D 2010 supports intersections with up to four quadrants. This is sufficient for three-way and four-way intersections.

6. Now click the **Curb Return Parameters** and that dialog will display as shown in Figure 9-43. Note that there is a drop-down menu for the **Intersection Quadrant** at the top of the dialog. The parameters for each quadrant can be controlled individually if needed. Click in the **Curb Return Type** drop-down and note that it supports three types of returns: chamfer, circular, and 3-centered arcs. Leave it on circular. Note that if you click the **Widen turn lane for incoming road** toggle, a new set of parameters shows up in the dialog. These would be used to set the widening criteria. Turn off the **Widen turn lane for incoming road** toggle, accept the default values, and hit **<OK>**.

7. Staying within the **Create Intersection** dialog, click on the button for **Lane Slope Parameters**. This feature allows the user to create profiles to guide the Edge of Pavement or compute it based on the cross slope of the roadway. Again, we will use the defaults shown in Figure 9-44 and hit **<OK>**.

8. Again, staying within the **Create Intersection** dialog, click on the button for **Curb Return Profile Parameters** and the dialog in Figure 9-45 displays. Note how the **Regions** can be controlled separately. Following your inspection of the values, hit **<OK>**.

9. Hit **Next** in the **Create Intersection** dialog and Figure 9-55 shows. Change the default from **Create New Corridor** in the upper left of the dialog to **Add to Existing Corridor** and select the **Horizontal Road Corridor**. We will daylight to the **Surface 1** in the upper right corner.

10. Hit the **Create Intersection** button.

11. Upon completion notice the resulting intersection. Note that this was created as part of the **Horizontal Road** corridor and can be viewed under **Corridors** in the **Prospector**.

Note that chapter-9-intersection-complete.dwg and chapter-9-intersection-ex-corridor-complete.dwg are the completed versions for this exercise.

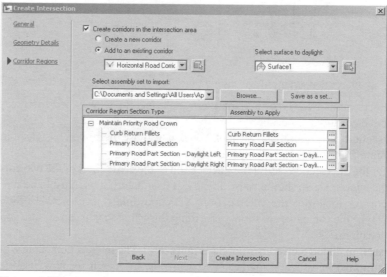

Figure 9-55

Chapter Summary

Civil 3D offers state-of-the-art capabilities for developing roadways. This chapter looked at corridor design, with algorithms for superelevations to ensure motorist safety. In corridor design, the proposed template for the roadway or corridor is completed. The chapter also covered intersection and cul-de-sac design.

Chapter Test Questions

Multiple Choice

1. According to the laws of mechanics, when a vehicle travels on a horizontal curve:

   a. It is forced outward by centrifugal force
   b. It is forced inward by centrifugal force
   c. It is unaffected
   d. None of the above

2. Engineers use which method(s) to countcract centrifugal forces that are trying to send the car off the road on curves?

   a. Superelevation where the pavement lanes are tilted
   b. Vertical curves where the pavement is curved in crests and sags

c. Tapers and widenings of pavement

d. None of the above

3. The rate of superelevation varies:

a. Based on the vertical curves in the profile

b. Based on the radius of the horizontal curve

c. Based on the tangent lengths of the alignment

d. Based on the centrifugal forces involved

4. Variables and terms for superelevations include:

a. e, e_{max}, R, V

b. R, K, L

c. PVC, PRC, PI

d. All of the above

5. A maximum superelevation (SE) is required:

a. When the radius (R) is a minimum

b. When the radius (R) is a maximum

c. In all cases

d. Never

6. At a reverse curve, the roadway section is often:

a. At e_{max} because the roadways are fluctuating the most at that point

b. Flat at the PRC as the superelevation in one direction transitions to the other direction

c. In a tangent; therefore, there is no need to address it

d. None of the above

7. The Tangent runout defines:

a. The length of highway needed to bring a normal crown section to a section where the outside lane has a zero percent slope instead of normal crown

b. The distance needed to bring a section from flat to fully superelevated, or vice versa

c. The length of vertical curve needed to negotiate the arc

d. All of the above

8. Using the Virginia DOT superelevation chart in Figure 9-6, what superelevation rate would be appropriate for a 2500' radius curve and a design speed of 60 mph?

a. 5%

b. 6%

c. 6.5%

d. 5.5%

9. Civil 3D provides subassemblies for which of the following?

a. Tunnels

b. Lanes, curbs, guardrails, and shoulders

c. Bridge trusses and cable stayed bridges

d. All of the above

10. Corridors can be checked for quality assurance using the following methods:

a. **3DOrbit**

b. View/Edit Sections

c. Surface Styles

d. All of the above

True or False

1. True or False: Horizontal alignments, profiles, and subassemblies are used to build corridors.

2. True or False: Assemblies are created by drawing polylines to represent the proposed roadway conditions.

3. True or False: Centrifugal forces act on the vehicle as it negotiates through horizontal curves.

4. True or False: Superelevated roadway sections are always used when the roadway goes through turns.

5. True or False: Superelevations are used to counter the centrifugal forces acting on vehicles as they go in and out of curves on roadways.

6. True or False: The *AASHTO Green Book* is a good reference for highway design.

7. True or False: e_{max} is the maximum to which a road can be superelevated before the car will leave the pavement on an arc.

8. True or False: Two components used in superelevating a roadway are runout and runoff.

9. True or False: Subassemblies are the primitive components of assemblies, and they instruct the software in how to handle lanes, curbs, guardrails or shoulders, related side sloping, and tie-out.

10. True or False: Civil 3D provides many subassemblies to begin with, and you access them from **Tool Palettes**.

CHAPTER EXERCISES

1. Describe the process that a superelevated roadway goes through as it moves from normal crown to a fully superelevated section.

2. If a roadway has a −2.08% cross slope, how many feet will it take to superelevate to flat or 0% if it has a superelevation rate of 6%?

3. If a roadway has a −2.08% cross slope, how many feet will it take to superelevate to a fully a superelevated roadway if it has a superelevation rate of 5%?

4. If a roadway is fully superelevated to 4% and needs to go back to a normal crown of −2.08%, how many feet will it take to reduce its superelevation to a crowned section roadway if it has a superelevation rate of 4%?

5. Using the Virginia DOT superelevation chart shown in Figure 9-6, what superelevation rate would be needed to counteract a curve radius of 5000′ and a speed of 65 mph?

6. Using the Virginia DOT superelevation chart shown in Figure 9-6, what curve radius would be appropriate for a superelevation rate of 3.0% and a design speed of 40 mph?

7. Using the Virginia DOT superelevation chart shown in Figure 9-6, what superelevation rate would be appropriate for a 3500′ radius curve and a design speed of 55 mph?

8. Using the Virginia DOT superelevation chart shown in Figure 9-6, what design speed would be allowable for a superelevation rate of 5% and a curve radius of 2800′?

Advanced Site Grading and Virtual Site Design™

10

Chapter Objectives

- Understand the grading capabilities of Civil 3D.
- Understand feature lines and gradings.
- Understand earthworks theories and applications using Civil 3D.

INTRODUCTION

This chapter discusses Civil 3D grading capabilities pertinent to site grading and subdivision design. This is often the next logical step in the design process. Once the roadway is developed, the site can be accessed, and the 3D layout of the site can be developed. The roadway usually plays a major part in the site design because the site drainage is often dictated or influenced by the roadway around it.

REVIEW OF FUNCTIONS AND FEATURES TO BE USED

It is important for you to understand some of the grading capabilities of Civil 3D. These tools can also create object-oriented entities that can perform powerful design functions that are interactive and react to the conditions about them. A large percentage of an engineering project involves grading and, for many reasons, a chief concern is drainage. Other concerns are landscaping, aesthetics, security, and safety. These functions use elevations, slopes, and grades and tie out to the natural ground conditions.

This chapter provides instruction in the functions for grading and includes feature lines, breaklines, and grading objects.

In Chapter 2 you went through the design of a basic commercial site. The discussion here covers the commands that allow you to design almost any type of site from subdivisions to commercial to landfill and retention ponds. Grading objects and feature lines are discussed in detail.

VIRTUAL (3D) SITE DESIGN™

Methods of creating proposed topographic grading data include Developing Zones of Slope Influence, Contour digitizing, Developing 3D breaklines, and Developing 3D spot shots. 3D points should be used in these designs, not so much for their ability to influence the TIN, but rather as "thinking points." Thinking points are set to locate critical locations in 3D. If you are wondering whether you can establish a drain inlet 200 feet away if you slope the ground at a −2% grade, you may set a thinking point at that location using those exact criteria. Once you see the elevation of the point, you can decide whether to use those criteria. If you do use them, you then have a 3D location from which you can traverse to other locations on the site. If you decide not to use them, you can easily erase them and try an alternative criteria set.

A Zone of Influence is a plane or group of planar objects that are set by the designer in 3D using elevations, slopes, or grades. The intent is to create a basic, fundamental base surface on which the designer would add more surface objects as the site design matures.

Figure 10-1 shows a site developed 100% in three dimensions. This site contains an underground detention pond, which sets some of the minimum proposed elevations due to hydraulic requirements. An existing roadway sets the criteria for the southern edge of the site. An adjacent property is being built to the north of the site, and its proposed elevations are considered as the existing elevations to which to tie in. The plan is to tie in to existing ground on the east and the west sides of the site. The black linework shows the 3D breaklines, and the markers shown indicate the spot elevations that "tied out" the site.

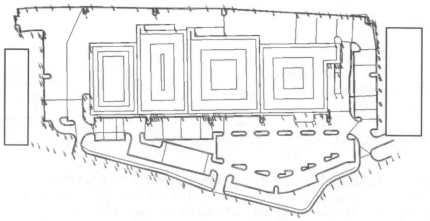

Figure 10-1   Site developed in three dimensions

Figure 10-2 shows the resulting computer-generated contours for the site.

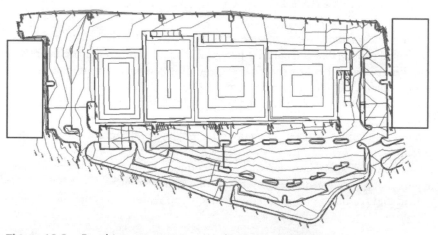

Figure 10-2   Resulting computer-generated contours for the site

Figure 10-3 shows a cross section through the site with impeccable detail. Notice the section cut through the truck loading dock, the building finish floor, and the parking lot islands.

Figure 10-3   A cross section through the site

Notice the detail in the truck loading dock and the drainage divides in the parking lot in Figure 10-4. The section below is cut through the building, the dock, the drive lane, and the curb.

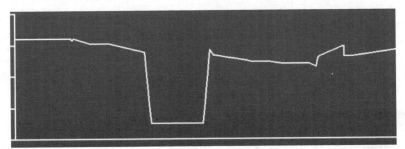

Figure 10-4   A section showing a truck loading dock

Note the renderings of the site in 3D in Figures 10-5 and 10-6. Each island, drainage divide in the parking lot, and loading dock comes to life.

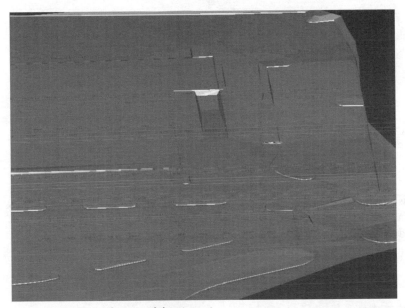

Figure 10-5   Renderings of the site—1

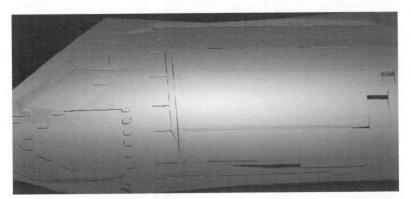

Figure 10-6   Renderings of the site—2

Requirements for quality control for this project were very high due to the visibility of the site. Drainage could not go into the street and had to be self-contained and directed into the underground storage ponds beneath the site. Notice the bird's-eye view and rendered depiction of the site. The curbs, gutters, and loading docks are all evident (see Figure 10-6).

Earthworks for the project were also accomplished using these data. Figure 10-7 shows a subdivision developed in 3D. The profile for the site had a very high level of terrain activity with roadway grades of up to 10%. Some of the residential houses had 50′ of drop from the front of the lot to the back of the lot. Preliminary and final grading design were performed for this subdivision. The plan view of a piece of the subdivision is shown here.

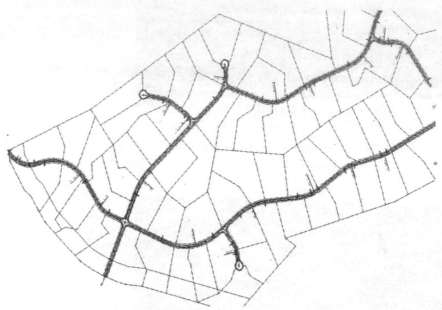

Figure 10-7   A subdivision developed in 3D

Three-dimensional houses were developed for the housing styles to be used. Examples of the houses are shown in Figure 10-8. The house on the left has no walkout basement, has a garage on the left side of the house, and can be used on lots that are fairly flat. The house on the right does have a walkout basement and a garage on the right side of the house. This can be used on lots that have a good fall toward the back of the house. Once the houses were situated, the task of designing the driveways had to be done.

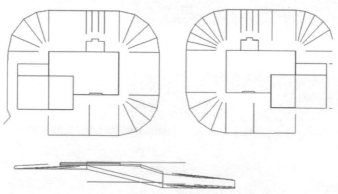

Figure 10-8   A 3D house template

This was a major component of the project because earthworks had a major impact on cost. Figure 10-8 shows the two houses in plan view: one with a walkout basement, one without. The bottom of Figure 10-8 shows the elevation view of a house template. With the road and houses laid out in 3D, it was fairly easy to design the driveways. See Figure 10-9.

Figure 10-10 shows a section of the design completed. The houses float in 3D, and the point data represent the tie-out to the existing ground. It should be noted here that the tie-out can be seen immediately when performed. The benefit here is that if the tie-out projects into the adjacent property, the designer can adjust the side slopes at that point to rectify it.

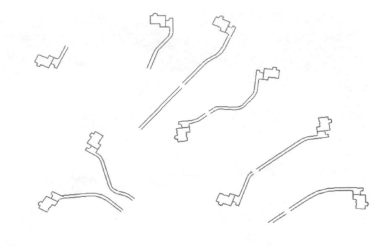

Figure 10-9   Subdivision driveways

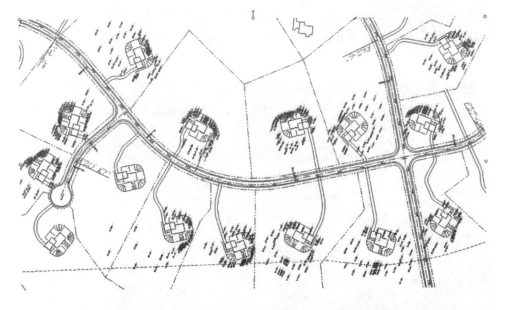

Figure 10-10   A section of the design

The graphics in Figures 10-11 through 10-15 show other sites that are readily developed as 3D models. This methodology plays very strongly into the rapidly growing 3D/GPS Machine Control market. This is a GPS-based technology by which the earthmoving equipment is located on the

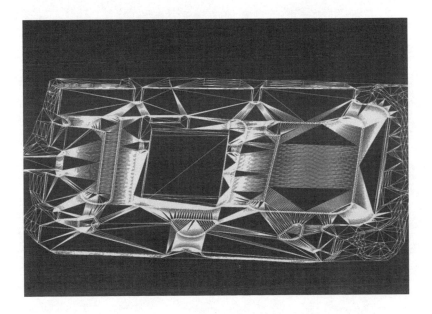

Figure 10-11   A TIN model of a commercial site

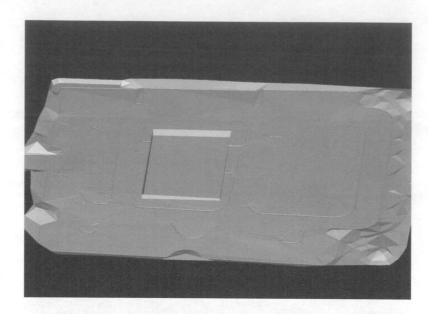

Figure 10-12   A rendered view of the commercial site

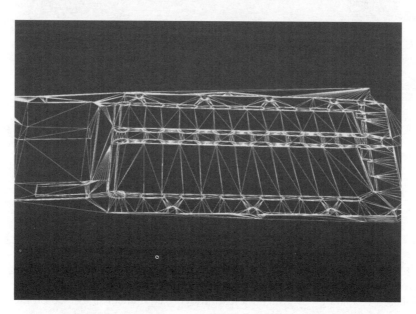

Figure 10-13   A TIN model of an office building site

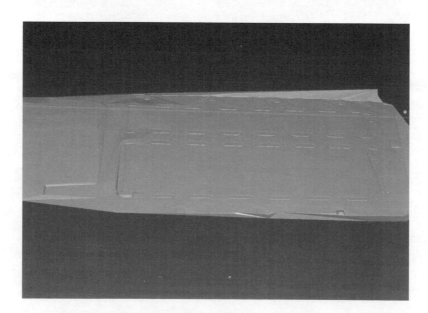

Figure 10-14   A rendered view of an office building site

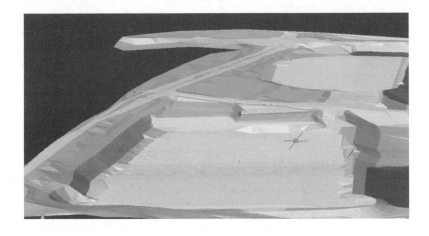

Figure 10-15   A rendered view of a "big box" site

existing ground based on GPS. An on-board computer stores the Digital Terrain Model for the proposed surface(s), which may include subgrade surfaces. Robotics handle the hydraulic movement of the earthmoving blade. This technology requires an accurate 3D model from which to operate. If engineering firms do not learn to work in 3D, they will lose more and more work to those that do work in 3D. Civil 3D provides add-on software that can convert the Civil 3D data into a formatted data conducive for use by Topcon, Trimble, and Leica equipment. They are Carlson Connect, which addresses Topcon; Trimble Link from Trimble; and Leica X-Change.

The concept of engineers designing their sites in three dimensions is called Virtual Site Design, which is designing a site in the computer using slopes, grades, and elevations. The contouring, labeling, and analyses should be computer generated from that point on. With the site in 3D, some very visual viewpoints can be established to verify quality control, and all editing of the surface would be done to the 3D elements, which consist of breaklines, points, and grading objects.

Once a designer has a surface, one of the quality assurance functions to be performed is earthworks. You need to know how much earth you are moving or cutting or filling. There are several methods for earthworks computations, some of which are explored next.

EARTHWORKS ALGORITHMS

In order to discuss the validity of results from an earthworks computation, you should know which algorithms were used in the processing because the results can vary based on the method selected. Some of the common methods are as follows:

- Section method
- Grid method
- Composite method

Each of these methods has positive and negative aspects. Please review the next set of graphics. The Section method entails computing a cross section through the existing ground and the proposed surface. The area of cut is computed as well as the area of fill for that section. Then, at some interval away, another section is computed, and the area of cut and fill in that section is computed. Then the two areas of cut are averaged together to obtain an average end area of cut. Similarly, the two areas of fill are averaged together to obtain an average end area of fill. These numbers yield a square footage of material. Then the average cut is multiplied over the interval distance yielding the cubic footage of material between the two sections. Divide that by a factor of 27 to obtain the number of cubic yards. Repeat this for each section in the project.

TIP   Divide by 27 to obtain cubic yards from cubic feet because 1 cubic yard is 3′ × 3′ × 3′.

Example 10-1: The Section Method Done by Hand

In this example problem computed by hand, refer to Figure 10-16. Here is a simple situation in which you have a road section with two 12′ lanes and 6′ of 3:1 embankment.

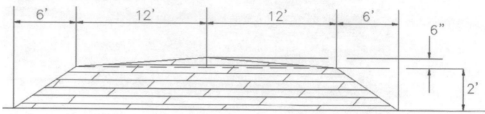

Figure 10-16   A roadway section in fill

In order to compute this earthwork, you do not need to compute the amount of cut because there is none; this entire section is in fill. Therefore, the fill area is computed using a series of triangle and rectangular area formulas as follows:
Fill in embankment:

$(6′ \times 2′)/2 = 6$ s.f.; there are two embankment areas, so the fill in the embankment is 12 s.f.

Fill under the pavement is computed using a rectangular area formula for the 2′ of fill and then a triangular area formula for the fill above the 2′ but under the grade of the road.

$12′ \times 2′ = 24$ s.f.; there are two lanes, so 24 s.f. $\times 2 = 48$ s.f.
Then: $12′ \times .5′ = 6$ s.f.; there are two lanes, so 6 s.f. $\times 2 = 12$ s.f.
Summing, we have 48 s.f. + 12 s.f. + 12 s.f. = 72 s.f. of material.

For the second section, which was cut 50′ away from the first, please refer to Figure 10-17. This section has both cut and fill. Let us compute the fill first.

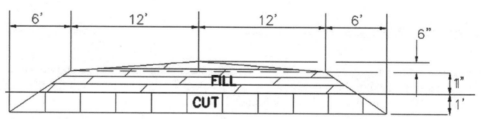

Figure 10-17   A roadway section in cut and fill

Fill in embankment:

$(3′ \times 1′)/2 = 1.5$ s.f.; there are two embankment areas, so the fill in the embankment is 3 s.f.

Fill under the pavement is computed using a rectangular area formula for the 1′ of fill and then a triangular area formula for the fill above the 1′ but under the grade of the road.

$12′ \times 1′ = 12$ s.f.; there are two lanes, so 12 s.f. $\times 2 = 24$ s.f.
Then: $12′ \times .5′ = 6$ s.f.; there are two lanes, so 6 s.f. $\times 2 = 12$ s.f.
Summing, we have 24 s.f. + 12 s.f. + 3 s.f. = 39 s.f. of material.

Now compute the amount of cut.
Cut in embankment:

$(3′ \times 1′)/2 = 1.5$ s.f.; there are two embankment areas, so the fill in the embankment is 3 s.f.

Cut under the pavement is computed using a rectangular area formula as well.

$12′ \times 1′ = 12$ s.f.; there are two lanes, so 12 s.f. $\times 2 = 24$ s.f.
Summing, we have 24 s.f. + 3 s.f. = 27 s.f. of cut for the second section.

Computing the average fill between the two sections we have

39 s.f. + 72 s.f. = 111/2 = 55.5 s.f.

Computing the average cut between the two sections we have

0 s.f. + 27 s.f. = 27/2 = 13.5 s.f.

The volume of fill between section 1 and section 2 is 55.5 s.f. × 50′ = 2775 / 27 = 102.77 c.y.

The volume of cut between section 1 and section 2 is 13.5 s.f. × 50′ = 675 / 27 = 25 c.y.

Therefore, a net fill of 77.77 c.y. exists between the two sections. (102.77 − 25 = 77.77 c.y.)

Example 10-2: The Grid Method Done by Hand

The next type of earthworks is the Grid method. In this case, a grid is identified and laid across the site. The grids are uniform, and the elevations of the proposed surface and the existing surface are computed for each corner of each grid. The difference between the proposed and existing elevations are computed for each corner. The four corners of each grid are averaged and multiplied by the area of the grid to obtain the cubic feet of material. This is then divided by 27 to obtain c.y. This example contains 4 grids, each 50′ × 50′; see Figure 10-18.

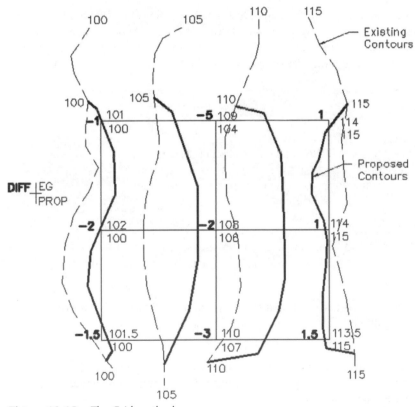

Figure 10-18   The Grid method

Beginning with the grid in the upper left, compute as follows:

−1 + −5 + −2 + −2 = −10′/4 corners = −2.5′ of average cut.
With a grid area of 2500 s.f., that grid contains 2500 × 2.5′
= 6250 c.f. of cut. Divided by 27 yields 231.5 c.y. of cut.

The grid in the upper right corner computes as follows:

−5 + 0 + −2 + 0 = −7′/4 = −1.75′ of cut. There is also some fill in this grid of
  0 + 1 + 0 + 1 = 2′/4 = .5′ fill.

Therefore, the cut for the grid is 2500 × 1.75 = 4375 s.f., divided by 27 = 162.0 c.y. of cut. The fill for the grid is 2500 × .5 = 1250 s.f. divided by 27 = 46.3 c.y. of fill. The net is 162 − 46.3 = 115.7 net cut.

The lower left grid computes as follows:

−2 + −2 + −1.5 + −3 = −8.5/4 = −2.125′ net cut. With a grid area of 2500 s.f., that grid contains 2500 × 2.125′ = 5312.5 c.f. of cut. Divided by 27 yields 196.8 c.y. of cut.

The grid in the lower right corner computes as follows:

−2 + 0 + −3 + 0 = −5′/4 = −1.25′ of cut. There is also some fill in this grid of 0 + 1 + 0 + 1.5 = 2.5′/4 = .625′ fill.
Therefore, the cut for the grid is 2500 × 1.25 = 3125 s.f., divided by 27 = 115.7 c.y. of cut. The fill for the grid is 2500 × .625 = 1562.5 s.f. divided by 27 = 57.8 c.y. of fill.
The net is 115.7 − 57.8 = 57.9 net cut.

The earthworks for the site then is:

Cut = 231.5 + 162 + 196.8 + 115.7 = 706.0 c.y.
Fill = 0 + 46.3 + 0 + 57.8 = 104.1 c.y.
The net is 601.9 c.y. of cut.

The last method is the Composite (in Land Desktop terminology) or Prismoidal method. Civil 3D uses this method for its site-based earthworks, and it is a TIN comparison-based method. It is more math intensive than the others, but Civil 3D can rapidly perform it. It produces a more accurate volume than the Average End Area or the Grid method.

Pros and Cons of Earthworks Algorithms

Section Method

- Pro: It is a traditional method, is understood by all, and produces good results.
- Con: Accuracy varies according to interval and can be enhanced by running the section computations twice, where the second run is perpendicular to the first run.

Grid Method

- Pro: It is also a traditional method, is understood by all, and produces good results.
- Con: Interpolation occurs. Hence, some loss of accuracy exists; the perimeter can be lost if the grid falls off the surface; highs and lows inside of each grid can be lost; and accuracy varies according to grid size.

Composite Method

- Pro: It is the best theoretical method, uses all surface data, and no interpolation is involved.
- Con: It seems to be sensitive to vertical faces (which you should not have anyway).

Now that grading capabilities have been discussed, let us explore some of Civil 3D's functions. The **Grading** pull-down menu (Figure 10-19) has several commands that are critical to 3D site design. These are described next.

Create Grading... invokes the toolbar for performing grading functions.

Create Grading Infill inserts a grading face with no criteria inside an area bounded by feature lines or lot lines.

Draw Feature Line allows for the creation of feature lines used in many grading functions. The options for creating them include slope, grade, and elevational data combined with horizontal distances.

Create Feature Lines from Objects allows selecting existing AutoCAD objects and converting them to feature lines.

Create Feature Lines from Alignment creates a feature line from the geometry of an alignment and the elevations of a specified profile.

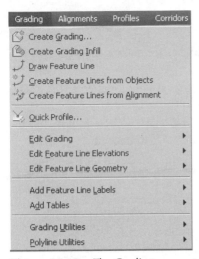

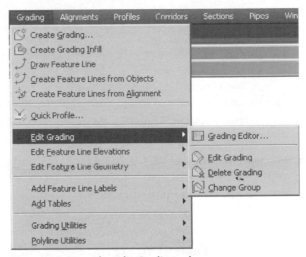

Figure 10-19 The Grading pull-down menu

Figure 10-20 The Edit Grading submenu

Quick Profile... draws a temporary profile based on linework selected and surfaces chosen. These profiles are deleted on saving and are used for quality assurance/control.

Edit Grading (see Figure 10-20) allows for a submenu that contains the following routines:

- **Grading Editor...** allows for editing grading objects in a **Panorama**.
- **Edit Grading** allows for editing the grading parameters for objects such as the **Stepped Offset** command.
- **Delete Grading** deletes a selected grading object.
- **Change Group** allows for changing the grading group that an object resides in.

Edit Feature Line Elevations (see Figure 10-21) submenu has several commands that are critical to 3D site design. These commands include:

- **Elevation Editor...** is a dialog-based command that allows for making changes to the elevations of objects.

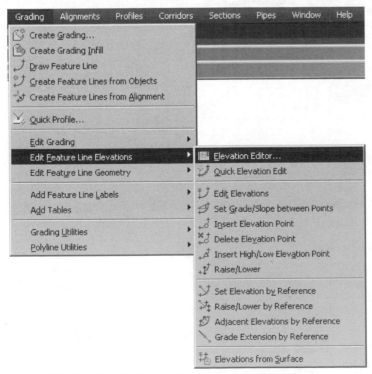

Figure 10-21 The Edit Feature Line Elevations submenu

- **Quick Elevation Edit** allows for quick, on-the-fly alterations to the slopes/grades of feature lines.
- **Edit Elevations** is a prompt–based command that allows for making changes to the elevations of objects.
- **Set Grade/Slope between Points** is a command prompt system for altering the grades and elevations of feature lines at user-selected locations.
- **Insert/Delete Elevation Point** inserts/deletes vertices. These points do not alter the horizontal geometry of the object; they affect only the third dimension.
- **Insert High/Low Elevation Point** inserts a point elevation based on the incoming and outgoing user-selected grades.
- **Raise/Lower** raises or lowers an object.
- **Set Elevation by Reference** sets the elevation based on a referenced 3D elevation from another location.
- **Raise/Lower by Reference** raises or lowers an object at a given slope/grade from a specified location.
- **Adjacent Elevations by Reference** specifies the elevations of an object based on a grade, slope, or elevation difference from points on another feature.
- **Grade Extension by Reference** specifies the elevations of an object by extending the grade of a segment on another feature.
- **Elevations from Surface** sets the elevations of feature line vertices based on surface sampling.

Edit Feature Line Geometry (see Figure 10-22)

- **Insert/Delete PI** inserts/deletes vertices. These do affect the geometry of the feature line.
- **Break** breaks a feature line or parcel line.
- **Trim** trims feature lines or parcel lines.
- **Join** joins feature lines similar to AutoCAD's PEDIT.
- **Reverse** reverses the direction of the feature line.

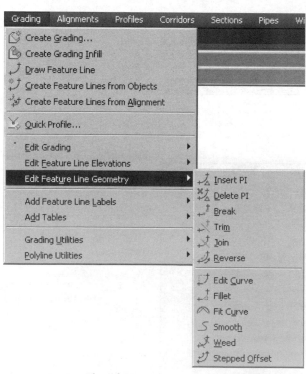

Figure 10-22   The Edit Feature Line Geometry submenu

- **Edit Curve** edits the radius of a feature line arc, parcel line arc, or survey figure arc.
- **Fillet** places a curve at the PI of a feature line.
- **Fit Curve** fits the PI with a curve similar to PEDIT's **FIT** command.
- **Smooth** smooths the PI with a curve similar to PEDIT's **SMOOTH** command.
- **Weed** deletes unneeded vertices.
- **Stepped Offset** offsets the feature line and raises or drops it. Think curb faces or retaining walls here!

Add Feature Line Labels labels slopes on feature lines.

Add Tables allows you to add tables for lines, curves, and segments.

Grading Utilities

- **Grading Volume Tools...** invokes the toolbar to adjust cut/fill volumes for grading groups.
- **Create Detached Surface...** detaches the surface from the grading group so it no longer updates.

Polyline Utilities

- **Convert 2D to 3D Polylines** converts polylines to allow them to be used to set different elevations on each vertex.
- **Convert 3D to 2D Polylines** converts polylines to flatten them.
- **Edit Polyline Elevations** edits elevations at vertices.

The Grading Creation Tools

The **Grading Creation Tools** are described next (see Figure 10-23).

Figure 10-23   The Grading Creation Tools toolbar

 Set the **Grading Group**.

 Sets the **Target Surface**.

 Sets the **Grading Layers**.

 Sets the **Criteria Set**.

 Develops **Grading** with one of five commands:

- **Create Grading** creates a grading object based on the criteria.
- **Copy Create Grading** copies the criteria and style from an existing grading and applies it to a grading you wish to create.
- **Create Transition** allows for transitions around objects.
- **Create Infill** connects the interior of grading objects such as on the top of a berm of a detention pond where one grading develops the inside of the pond and the other grading develops the outside of the pond.

 Edit Grading allows for absorbing elevations from the surface and some management commands.

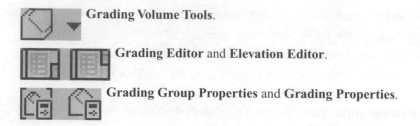

Grading Volume Tools.

Grading Editor and **Elevation Editor**.

Grading Group Properties and **Grading Properties**.

Exercise 10-1: Laying Out a Basic Parking Lot in 3D

Now explore Civil 3D and run through some procedures using the grading objects.

To access student data
files, go to
www.pearsondesigncentral.com.

1. Open Chapter-10-a.dwg.
2. Type **V** for **View**, select the **Plan** view, hit **Set Current**, then hit **OK** and you see some existing ground contours.
3. There is a white object on the **C-Site-Grad-3D** layer. Use this as the construction limits for this site.
4. Let us set it to the existing ground elevation and drape it on the existing ground in order to guarantee that no grading occurs outside these limits.
5. From the **Grading** pull-down menu, select the command **Create Feature Lines from Objects**. Choose the white polyline object on the **C-Site-Grad-3D** layer, accept the defaults in the **Create Feature Lines** dialog box, hit **OK**, and one feature line is added to **Site 1**. Turn on the **C-Topo-Grad-Flin** layer to see it.
6. From the **Grading** pull-down menu, choose the **Edit Feature Line Elevations** command and then choose **Elevations from Surface**.
7. Select the **Existing Ground** surface.
8. Turn on the toggle to insert intermediate grade break points. Hit **OK**.
9. Select the feature line and hit **<Enter>**. Notice it processes and places small markers where it has inserted intermediate breaks.
10. This object is now "draped" onto the existing ground data with a 3D vertex at each TIN crossing. Click on the feature line, and notice all the vertices that now have the elevations of the existing ground embedded into them.
11. Turn on the layer called **C-Site-Grad-Text** for the design parameters for this site.
12. These parameters indicate a Finished and Basement floor elevation for the building in the upper right of the site and a 4′ sidewalk with a 2% cross slope draining toward the parking lot. It has a 6″ high curb on it. The parking lot drains to the Southwest at −2%.

Next you will create the 3D objects that meet these specifications.

13. **Zoom** into the **cyan** building polylines and notice two lines: one representing the outside building wall and the inside linework representing the building's basement. From the **Grading** pull-down menu, select **Create Feature Lines from Objects**. Select lines, arcs, polylines or 3d polylines to convert to feature lines or [Xref]: Select the two **cyan** building polylines and hit **<Enter>**.
14. Accept the defaults in the **Create Feature Lines** dialog box, and hit **OK**.
15. Choose **Edit Feature Line Elevations >> Elevation Editor** from the **Grading** pull-down menu.
16. When asked, select the outside **green** polyline representing the building pad. This is the outermost **green** linework.
17. In the **Panorama** that displays, set the elevations to **362.0** for all vertices. Click the green checkmark.
18. Repeat the command and select the inside cyan polyline representing the building basement.
19. Set the elevations to **353.0** for all vertices.
20. Draw a **3D** polyline along the west and southern edge of the building by snapping to the edge of the finished floor of the building. This inherits the elevations of the finished floor. You might want to turn off the C-Site-Grad-3D layer to ensure snapping to the correct polyline. Turn the layer back on after the polyline is created.
21. From the **Grading** pull-down menu, select **Edit Feature Line Geometry >> Stepped Offset**. The following prompts and responses should occur:

```
Specify offset distance or [Through/Layer] : 4
```

Select an object to offset: Pick the 3D polyline you've just created.

`Specify side to offset or [Multiple] :` Pick a point outside the building.

```
Specify elevation difference or [Grade/Slope/Elevation/Variable]
<0.000>: g
```

```
Specify grade or [Slope/Elevation/Difference/Variable] <0.000>: −2
```

You can use the **<Shift> <Space>** keys to select objects on top of other objects if needed.

22. Hit **<Enter>** to terminate. This object represents the top, face of curb.
23. Repeat this command, and the following prompts and responses should occur.

    ```
    Specify offset distance or [Through/Layer] <4.0000>: .1
    ```

    Select an object to offset: Select the top, face curb.

    `Specify side to offset or [Multiple] :` Pick a point outside the face of curb.

    ```
    Specify grade or [Slope/Elevation/Difference] <−2.000>: d
    ```

    ```
    Specify elevation difference or [Grade/Slope/Elevation/Variable]
    <−0.080>: −.5
    ```

24. `Select an object to offset:` Hit **<Enter>** to terminate. This represents the flow-line of the curb.

The building and the sidewalk are established. Let us work on the parking lot now.

25. Draw a pline that represents the drainage divide in the parking lot from the edge of flowline at the northwest corner of the building diagonally to the southwest corner of the parking lot.

Be advised that when specific elevations are given in the text, your results may differ slightly.

26. Then use **Grading >> Draw Feature Line** to draw a feature line from the flowline of the curb at a **−2%** grade to the lower left corner of the parking lot designated by the **red** poly-line. Accept the defaults in the dialog box when it displays. Refer to Figure 10-24 for the location of the swale. Then the following prompts and responses should occur: `Specify start point:` Snap to the flowline of the curb near the northwest corner of the build-ing. This is shown in Figure 10-25. It should have an elevation of 361.42.

    ```
    Specify elevation or [Surface] <361.420>: <Enter>
    ```

    ```
    Specify the next point or [Arc] : Distance 426.778', Grade −84.597,
    Slope −1.182:1, Elevation 0.000'.
    ```

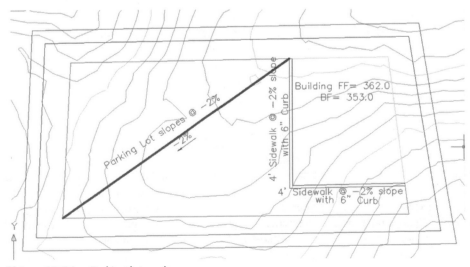

Figure 10-24   Parking lot swale

Snap to the lower left corner of the red polyline in the southwest corner of the parking lot.

```
Specify grade or [SLope/Elevation/Difference/SUrface/Transition]
<0.000>: -2
```

```
Specify the next point or [Arc/Length/Undo] : <Enter>.
```

This elevation should be 352.51 when you are finished.

27. Next draw a pline by snapping to the flowline of the edge of sidewalk, which is the same spot that Figure 10-25 indicates. Then snap to the upper left corner of the **red** polyline depicting the parking lot. Snap to the end of the swale drawn at −2% to the lower left corner of the parking lot. This will draw a polyline from the curb flowline near the northwest corner of the building around the north and west perimeter of the parking lot to the southwest corner of the parking lot.

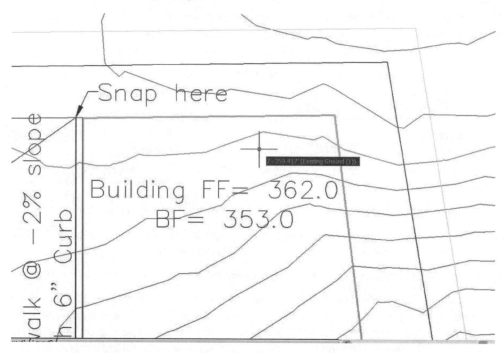

Figure 10-25   Snap location

28. From the **Grading** pull-down menu, select the command **Create Feature Lines from Objects**. Choose the **white** polyline object that you just drew around the north and west side of the parking lot, accept the defaults in the **Create Feature Lines** dialog box, hit **OK**, and one feature line is added to **Site 1**.

29. Choose **Edit Feature Line Elevations >> Elevation Editor...** from the **Grading** pull-down menu. Select the new feature line you just converted. When the **Panorama** displays, set the elevation for the second vertex to **356.387**. The three elevations for the vertices should then be **361.043**, **356.387**, and **352.508,** respectively. Close the **Panorama**. This will be the polyline shown in Figure 10-26.

Now set the perimeter of the east and southern edge of the parking lot.

Use the same command sequence to establish both grade and elevation along this object. From the flowline of the sidewalk beginning at the southeastern edge of the building, design a −1% grade drop to the southeastern corner of the parking lot, and then tie into the drainage divide in the southwest corner of the parking lot at an elevation of 352.8861.

30. Draw a pline from the flowline of the sidewalk beginning at the southeastern edge of the building to the southeastern corner of the parking lot, and then end it at the drainage divide at the southwestern corner of the parking lot. Refer to Figure 10-27 for the location of this polyline.

31. From the **Grading** pull-down menu, select the command **Create Feature Lines from Objects.** Choose the polyline object that you just drew around the east and south side of the parking lot, accept the defaults in the **Create Feature Line** dialog box, hit **OK**, and one feature line is added to **Site 1**.

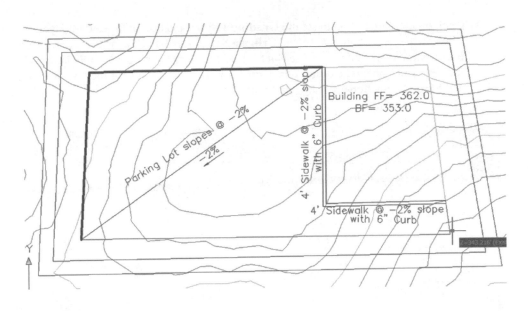

Figure 10-26   Polyline on the north and west perimeter

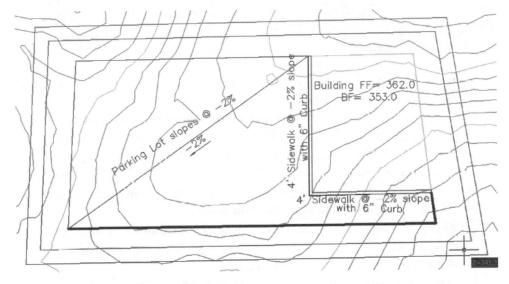

Figure 10-27   Location of south and east perimeter of parking lot

32. Choose **Edit Feature Line Elevations >> Elevation Editor** from the **Grading** pull-down menu. Select the new feature line you just converted. When the **Panorama** displays, set the grade for the first vertex to **−1.0%**. The three elevations for the vertices should then be **361.043**, **360.596**, and **352.508**, respectively. Close the **Panorama**. Save your file.

This object now represents the southern edge of the parking lot and is designed to achieve a −1% drop from the sidewalk to the southeastern corner and tie into the diagonal divide at the southwest corner.

33. Open Chapter-10-b.dwg.
34. Select **Create Grading...** from the **Grading** pull-down menu.
35. The **Grading Creation Tools** toolbar appears.
36. Move from left to right across the toolbar, setting or verifying the settings as you go.
37. Choose the first button on the left to set the **Grading Group** for the next step. A **Create Grading Group** dialog box displays.
38. Accept the default name of **Grading Group <Next Counter>**. Turn **On** the **Automatic Surface Creation**. The **Use the Group Name** toggle should be **On**. The **Surface Style** should be set to **Borders & Contours**. Accept **10.0** for tesselation spacing and **3** degrees for angle. This sets intermediate computations. Turn **Off** the **Volume base surface**. Hit **OK**.
39. When the **Create Surface** dialog box appears, hit **OK** for the defaults.
40. Next click on the second button, set the **Target Surface**, and choose the **Existing ground**.

To access student data files, go to www.pearsondesigncentral.com.

41. Click on the third button to set the **Grading Layers** and accept the default layers.
42. Click on the fourth button to set the **Criteria Set**. Select **Basic Set** as the criteria set to use.
43. In the pop-down window, choose **Surface @ 2-1 Slope**. With the **Details** button enabled (the chevron icon on the right of the toolbar), notice that details for the **Grading Method** and **Slope Projection** are shown in Figure 10-28.

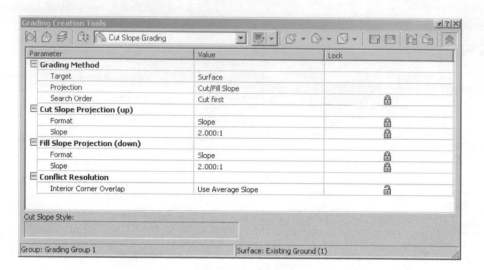

Figure 10-28 The Grading Creation Tools dialog box

44. Next choose the second button to the right of the pop-down window that says **Surface @ 2-1 Slope**. It should default to **Create Grading**.
45. `Select the feature:` Pick the feature line at the north edge of the parking lot.

    `Select the grading side:` Pick a point to the outside of the parking lot.

    `Apply to entire length?` Hit **<Enter>** for **Yes**. Grading appears along the north side of the parking lot.
46. `Select the feature:` again, assuming that you will repeat this sequence. Pick the feature line along the southern edge of the parking lot.

    `Select the grading side:` Pick a point to the outside of the parking lot.

    `Apply to entire length?` Hit **<Enter>** for **Yes**. Grading appears along the south side of the parking lot. Hit **<Esc>** to exit.
47. Pick on a contour and right-click. Select **Edit Surface Style....** In the **Contours** tab, expand the **Contour intervals** item and change the minor and major intervals to **2** and **10**, respectively.

Notice that the grading ties out to existing ground along the north, west, and southern sides. See Figure 10-29.

Now tie the north and eastern sides of the building out to the northeastern corner of the site.

48. Explode the outside cyan building feature line.
49. Use the **BREAK AT POINT** AutoCAD command to place a break on the outside cyan polyline at the northwest corner of the building. Use the same command to place a break on the outside **cyan** polyline at the southeast corner of the building. By doing this, you can project the top and right sides of the building toward the existing ground.
50. Select **Create Grading...** from the **Grading** pull-down menu.
51. The **Grading Creation Tools** toolbar displays.
52. Click on the fourth button to set the **Criteria Set**. Select **Basic** as the criteria set to use.
53. In the pop-down window, choose **Surface @ 2-1 Slope**.
54. Once again, choose the second button to the right of the pop-down window that says **Surface @ 2-1 Slope**. It should default to **Create Grading**.
55. `Select the feature:` **Zoom** in and pick the outer edge of the building that you just broke. Hit **OK** to the **Create Feature Lines** dialog box that displays.

    `Select the grading side:` Pick a point well outside of the building.

    `Apply to entire length?` Type **Y** for **Yes**. Hit **<Enter>** to accept and terminate.

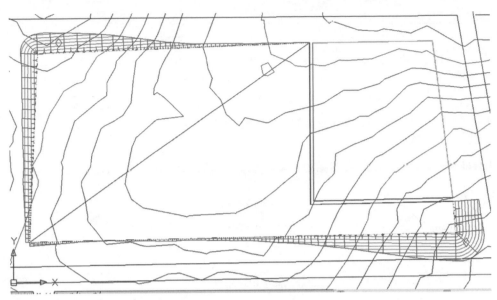

Figure 10-29   The grading tie-outs

56. Grading appears as shown in Figure 10-30, in which the entire perimeter is now tied to existing ground.

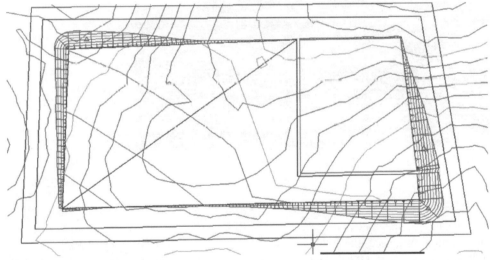

Figure 10-30   Resultant grading

57. Let us add in the sidewalk and drainage divide in the parking lot.
58. Look in the **Prospector** under **Surfaces**. Expand the surface called **Grading Group 1**. Expand **Definition**. Right-click on the **Breaklines** item and select **Add....**
59. Hit **OK** to accept all the defaults that come up in the **Add Breaklines** dialog box.
60. When asked to select objects, place a crossing window to include the sidewalk edges, basement, the left and southern edge of the building, and the drainage breakline in the parking lot.
61. If the **Panorama** appears with messages, close it.
62. You see now that the contours reflect the sidewalk and drainage divide. See Figure 10-31.
63. Using **3DOrbit**, rotate the view into a 3D bird's-eye perspective. The Surface style for 3D kicks in, and a 3D triangulation appears automatically.
64. Turn off the layer for the existing ground, **C-Topo-Existing Ground**, and you isolate the proposed parking lot. As discussed in Chapter 9 on corridors, you can select **View >> Visual Styles >> Conceptual** shading and then observe something like Figure 10-32. It shows the basement, the divide, and the sidewalk clearly.

In the next exercise, you will compute earthwork volumes for the site.

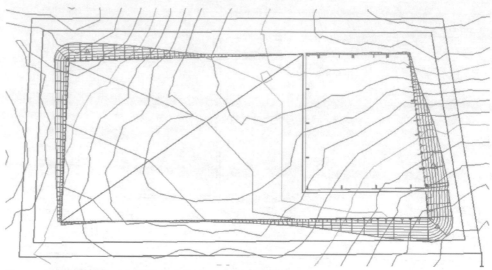

Figure 10-31   The contours reflect the sidewalk and drainage divide

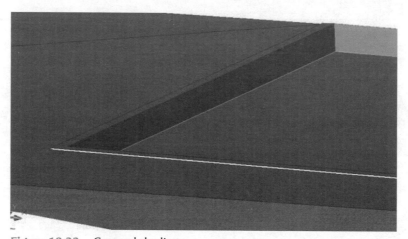

Figure 10-32   Gouraud shading

Earthwork volumes, sometimes called takeoffs, are performed on projects in order to estimate the amount of earth being moved. This is important to the engineer in that the design goal is often to produce a "balanced site." This means that the earth that is cut or dug out is then used to lift or fill the site in areas where needed. Balancing means that you have no excess cut or fill material. Consider that a dump truck might have a capacity of 10 c.y., and you can estimate how many truckloads it would take to move excess earth on the site.

Exercise 10-2: A Quick Earthworks Volume

Now you will compute the earthworks for the site.

To access student data files, go to www.pearsondesigncentral.com.

1. Open Chapter-10-c.dwg.
2. Select **Utilities** from the **Surfaces** pull-down menu. Then choose **Volumes....**
3. When the **Panorama** appears, click the first button from the left to create a new volume entry. A row of data displays in the window.
4. Click in the cell for **Base surface** where it says to **<select surface>** and choose **Existing Ground**.
5. Then click in the cell for **Comparison Surface** where it says to **<select surface>** and choose **Grading Group 1**. Click somewhere in the **Panorama** to execute the processing. It should yield almost 12,000 c.y. of material in a net fill condition.

Exercise 10-3: "Popping Up" a Curbed Parking Lot Island

In order to provide another example of the power of the **Grading** tools in Civil 3D, you will now see how to pop a curbed island out of the asphalt paving area. The curb will be 6″ high and have a slight kilter to its face so as to avoid a vertical edge on the face of curb.

1. Open Chapter-10-c.dwg or stay in the drawing from the last exercise.
2. **Zoom** into the parking area to the west of the building. You see some plines representing the flowline of some parking islands.
3. From the **Grading** pull-down menu, select **Create Feature Lines from Objects**. Select the four parking lot islands in the parking lot. Hit **OK** to the **Create Feature Lines** dialog box.
4. From the **Grading** pull-down menu, select **Edit Feature Line Elevations** and then **Elevations From Surface**. When the **Set Elevations from Surface** dialog box displays, select **Grading Group 1** as the surface to compute to. Turn on the toggle to insert intermediate grade breaks. Hit **OK**.
5. `Select object or [Multiple/Partial]` : Pick all four islands one by one, and the software computes additional elevations from the asphalt pavement over and beyond the vertices in the plines. The pline islands are now "draped" onto the parking lot surface.
6. You are now ready to pop the islands up from the surface. From the **Grading** pull-down menu, select **Edit Feature Line Geometry >> Stepped Offset**. The following prompts and responses should occur:

   `Specify offset distance or [Through/Layer] <0.1000>:` **.1**

   `Select an object to offset:` Pick an island.

   `Specify side to offset or [Multiple]` : Pick a point inside the island.

   `Specify elevation difference or [Grade/Slope/Elevation/Variable] <-0.500>:` **.5**

7. Repeat this for each island. Inspect the results when complete and notice that the interior object is 0.5′ higher than the outside object, hence achieving the top of curb.
8. Now you will add the islands into the surface of the parking lot.
9. Look in the **Prospector** under **Surfaces**. Expand the surface called **Grading Group 1**. Expand **Definition**. Right-click on the **Breaklines** item and select **Add…**.
10. Hit **OK** to accept all the defaults that come up in the **Add Breaklines** dialog box.
11. When asked to select objects, select the eight objects representing the islands.
12. If the **Panorama** appears with messages, close it. Hit **<Enter>**.
13. You see now the islands and the contours "jump" the curb as expected.
14. See Figure 10-33 for an example of the **3DOrbit** that you can perform.

To access student data files, go to www.pearsondesigncentral.com.

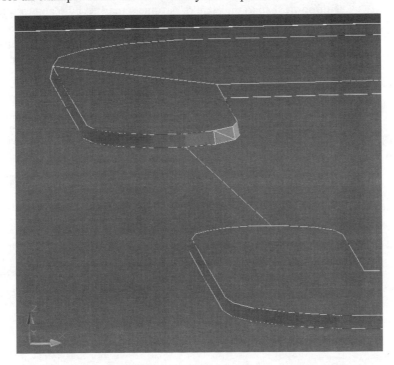

Figure 10-33 Parking lot islands

Exercise 10-4: A Brief Example of Intersection Design

One more example to introduce the gradings to readers is the age-old intersection design.

Intersections are one of the most often asked about design tasks that people want to automate. You open a file that has some edge of pavement in it. The linework is in 3D and can be achieved from the corridor design using the **Corridor >> Utilities >> Create Grading Feature Line from Corridor** command. The linework for each component of the corridor can be imported into AutoCAD. Then, using the **EXPLODE** command, explode the feature lines so that they can be trimmed, extended, or broken as needed to begin developing the desired site features. That is where the exercise begins. You add the intersection returns and illustrate an example of how intelligent feature lines can be. Note: Generalize on this example!

Note that intersections and cul-de-sacs can be graded using the **Corridor** tools as well, but these might be considered high-end skills. The approach in this chapter deals with "hand grading." Intersections have been automated in Civil 3D 2010.

To access student data files, go to www.pearsondesigncentral.com.

1. Open Chapter-10-d.dwg and note that a basic intersection has been developed as described previously. The edge of pavement and centerlines are in 3D. The **red** arcs denote where the returns are supposed to be and they are in 2D.
2. Under the **Grading** pull-down menu, select the **Create Feature Lines from Objects** command.
3. Select the four edges of pavement, identified with numbers 1, 4, 3, and 6, plus the one in the intersection between 3 and 6. Also select the two centerlines on **Layer 0**, and hit **<Enter>**. Hit **OK** for the dialog box that displays.
4. Now draw a polyline by snapping to the edge of pavement at the point marked by a number **1**. Make sure to select the **Endpoint** snap to the white edge of pavement and not the **red** arc. The **white** edge has a 3D elevation. Then type **A** for **arc** and then type **S** for **second point** (of the arc) and **Near** snap to a point on the **red** arc marked with a number **2**. Then **Endpoint** snap to the edge of pavement marked by a number **3** and terminate.
5. Repeat the **Polyline** command and perform this on the right side of the intersection. Snap to the edge of pavement at the point marked by **4**. Make sure to **Endpoint** snap to the **green** edge of pavement and not the **red** arc. Then type **A** for **arc** and then type **S** for **second point** (of the arc) and **Near** snap to a point on the **red** arc marked with a **5**. Then **Endpoint** snap to the edge of pavement marked by **6** and terminate.
6. Under the **Grading** pull-down menu, select the **Create Feature Lines from Objects** command. Select the two polylines that you just drew. Now use the **Grading** pull-down menu, and select **Edit Feature Line Elevations** and then **Edit Elevations** to check the elevations of the two arcs that you converted to feature lines. Notice that Civil 3D recognized that the plines were being connected to feature lines and automatically inherited the elevations at the endpoints.
7. From the **Surfaces** pull-down menu, select **Create Surface....** Provide a **Name** for the surface, call it **Intersection**, and use the **Borders & Contours** style.

This is a revolutionary function in case you did not realize it. This is the first time in AutoCAD history that there can be a 3D arc! Notice that there are no chords to simulate the arc as has been the case in the past using various routines.

8. In the **Prospector**, under **Surface**, expand the intersection surface that was just created. Expand **Definition** and right-click on **Breaklines** Select **Add....** Type **Intersection** in the description for the breaklines when the dialog box appears.
9. Select all the feature lines, including the edge of pavement, the arcs that you created at the intersection, and the centerlines. Do not forget the edge of pavement breakline in the intersection between the arcs.

10. A **Surface** generates showing contours inside the intersection. Use **3DOrbit** to inspect the intersection in 3D.

11. Now, generalize on this concept because if the intersection had a curb and gutter, it could be created just as easily within a minute or two. Refer to Figure 10-34 to see the contours created in the intersection.

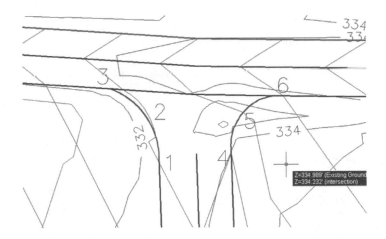

Figure 10-34 Contours are created in the intersection

You could take a lot more time performing grading features but would likely need a separate textbook to cover all the situations. In the meantime, explore these commands and find that almost any type of site can be designed in 3D.

TIP Be aware that you can create your own grading criteria. Look in the **Toolspace Settings** under the **Grading** item. Expand **Grading Criteria Sets** and notice the **Basic** grading set. Right-click on **Basic** grading and select **New...** to create your own criteria. When the dialog box appears, click on the **Criteria** tab and explore how you can customize these tools.

Congratulations! You have graded a parking lot, a building with a basement, and its related tie-outs and sidewalks. You have also added parking lot islands and computed earthworks. You have even had a taste of modeling an intersection using **Grading** commands! Enormous powers exist in the grading objects and only experimentation can yield their true powers.

CHAPTER SUMMARY

This chapter covered Civil 3D capabilities for site grading and subdivision design. Once the roadway is created, the site can be accessed and its 3D layout developed. Much of an engineering project involves grading, and one of the chief concerns is site drainage. This chapter provided instruction in the functions for grading and included feature lines, breaklines, and grading objects.

CHAPTER TEST QUESTIONS

Multiple Choice

1. When grading a site, which of the following information items are useful?
   a. Elevations
   b. Slopes
   c. Grades
   d. All of the above

2. The **Elevation Editor** can be used to perform which design tasks?
   a. Establish profiles and vertical tangents grades
   b. Set grades and elevations
   c. Establish the elevations for superelevations
   d. All of the above

3. Methods of creating proposed topographic grading data include which of the following?

    a. Developing Zones of Slope Influence
    b. Contour digitizing
    c. Developing 3D breaklines and Developing 3D spot shots
    d. All of the above

4. You would consider using "thinking points" for which of the following design tasks?

    a. Annotating parcel lines
    b. Balancing traverses
    c. Establishing pipe inverts
    d. None of the above

5. The sites developed in Civil 3D can be made ready for use by 3D/GPS Machine Control equipment by using which of the following add-ons?

    a. Carlson Connect, which addresses Topcon
    b. Trimble Link
    c. Leica X-change
    d. All of the above

6. Understanding that the concept of engineers designing their sites in three dimensions is a "must achieve" goal, then what do they rely on the computer to do for them?

    a. Assisting in designing the site in the computer using slopes, grades, and elevations
    b. Creating the contouring objects and analyses
    c. Annotating the contour, spot shot, and grade labeling
    d. All of the above

7. What are some of the methods for performing earthworks takeoffs?

    a. Section method
    b. Grid method
    c. Composite method
    d. All of the above

8. In the Section earthworks method, there are the following computations: Section 1 has a cut area of 100 s.f., Section 2 has a cut area of 200 s.f., Section 1 has a fill area of 50 s.f., and Section 2 has a fill area of 150 s.f. The distance between Section 1 and Section 2 is 50 feet. What is the net value for cut or fill for the volume between Section 1 and Section 2 in cubic yards?

    a. 278 c.y. cut
    b. 185 c.y. fill
    c. 93 c.y. cut
    d. 463 c.y.

9. Which of the following earthworks algorithm properties are true?

    a. The Grid method is a traditional method; however, some loss of accuracy can occur for a variety of reasons.
    b. The Section method is a traditional method; however, some loss of accuracy can occur for a variety of reasons.
    c. The Grid method produces good results when used properly, but highs and lows that may occur inside individual grids may not be accounted for in the computations.
    d. All of the above.

10. When working with some of the **Grading** tools, what results can be achieved?

    a. Grading objects can be created according to our design criteria.
    b. Surfaces can be automatically created as we create grading objects.
    c. Contours for the surfaces can automatically be displayed.
    d. All of the above.

True or False

1. True or False: The civil engineering field should prepare its roadway and site designs using contours because they represent the proposed site conditions better than any other data type.

2. True or False: A Zone of Influence is a method of design, not a command in Civil 3D.

3. True or False: Once a proper 3D site is created, sections can be pulled to observe extraordinary detail such as loading docks and parking lot islands.

4. True or False: Civil 3D can use 3D house templates for grading purposes.

5. True or False: There are several types of earthworks algorithms available in Civil 3D.

6. True or False: The Grid method can be performed only manually by the user.

7. True or False: To convert cubic feet of earthworks into cubic yards, you multiply by 27.

8. True or False: The Grid method gets less accurate as the size of the grid becomes smaller.

9. True or False: The Section method becomes more accurate as the size of the interval between sections becomes smaller.

10. True or False: A "balanced site" means that whatever earth is cut or dug out is then used to lift or fill the site in areas where that needs to be done.

CHAPTER EXERCISES

1. What is the difference between slope and grade in the software's viewpoint?
2. What is a "tie-out"?
3. What is daylight?
4. What types of quality control can be used to check the proposed design?
5. What type of CAD data can be used for rendering the site?
6. What is a "thinking point"?
7. How can someone perform quality control on his or her grading?
8. What do the commands **Distance @ Grade**, **Distance @ Slope**, **Relative Elevation @ Slope**, **Surface @ 2:1**, **Surface @ 3:1**, **Surface @ 6:1**, and **Surface @ Slope** do?
9. Could you use the **Distance @ Grade** tool in the **Grading Layout** toolbar to create an island with a curb?
10. Compute the earthworks for the site in Figure 10-35 based on a 100′ × 100′ grid method. Show your work.

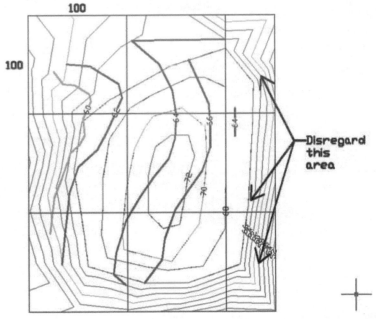

Figure 10-35

Piping for Storm Sewers and Drainage

11

Chapter Objectives

- Understand basic hydrology and hydraulic concepts.
- Perform piping layout and drafting for utilities and storm sewers.

INTRODUCTION

This chapter discusses developing storm sewer plan and profile data. This is part of a larger engineering task related to hydrology and hydraulics. Civil 3D performs some limited hydrologic computations. The hydraulics is also limited but does use object oriented piping for storm sewers on your project. It extracts the rim elevations and develops inverts based on criteria established. This feature, although not a totally complete hydraulics design tool, is a welcome addition to the software's capabilities.

The purpose of this chapter is to introduce you to some basic hydrology and hydraulic concepts and provide some basic procedures for using Civil 3D toward these purposes.

REVIEW OF FUNCTIONS AND FEATURES TO BE USED

This chapter provides instruction in the functions for producing hydrologic watersheds from the surface object as well as producing pipes in plan and profile views. These will carry into sections should they be imported as well. The features for piping are objects and react to the environment around them. These functions can be used for typical drafting purposes as well as to react to design changes and conflict resolution. The piping of multiple networks can be imported into any number of profiles or sections to test for conflicts.

HYDROLOGY

Runoff

When rain or snow falls onto the Earth, it follows the laws of gravity and conveys to the lowest point. Part of the precipitation is absorbed by the ground and replenishes the groundwater reservoirs. Most of it, though, flows downhill and is called runoff. Runoff is extremely important in site design because it changes the landscape through erosion. Engineers typically must design retention facilities to detain the amount of additional runoff their design creates when they replace natural grass-covered ground with asphalt-paved parking lots and the like. If the additional runoff were not captured and held, it would likely flood or erode downstream properties.

A Definition of Runoff. Runoff is a portion of precipitation, snowmelt, or irrigation water that flows over ground in uncontrolled, above surface streams, rivers, or sewers. Computation factors include the speed of its arrival after a rainfall or a snowmelt; the sum of total discharges during a specific period of time; and the depth to which a drainage area would be covered if all the runoff for a given period of time were uniformly distributed over it.

Meteorological Factors Affecting Runoff.   The following meteorological factors affect runoff:

- Type of precipitation such as rain, snow, sleet, and so on
- Rainfall intensity, amount, and duration
- Distribution of rainfall over the watershed
- Other meteorological and climatic conditions that affect evapotranspiration, such as temperature, wind, relative humidity, and the season

Physical Characteristics Affecting Runoff.   The computations of hydrologic study often involve the type of land use, the vegetation on the land, the soil type evident in the area, the total drainage area involved, the shape of the watershed basin, elevations, slopes, drainage patterns, topography, bodies of water, and biogeomorphism, which accounts for the impedances that may exist that could alter the flow of water in the basin.

The watershed for Front Royal, Virginia, is shown in Figure 11-1.

- Rivers and streams in this watershed: 15 (provided by EPA's River Reach File, version 1)
- Lakes in the watershed: 68; total number of acres: 679.8
- River and stream miles:

    1358.7 total river miles

    988.9 perennial river miles

    % of total rivers and streams that have been surveyed

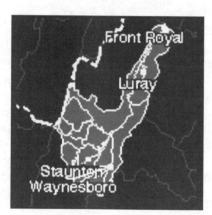

Figure 11-1   A simple watershed map

Software for Hydrologic Estimations and Computations.   Software for hydrologic estimations and computations includes TR-20—rainfall runoff calculations; HEC-1—water surface profiles; and TR-55—Technical Release 55 (TR-55). These present simplified procedures for small urbanizing watersheds to calculate storm runoff volume, peak rate of discharge, hydrographs, and storage volumes required for floodwater reservoirs.

In these computations there are some of the following items:

IDF (Intensity-Duration-Frequency) Curves.   These indicate the relationship between the intensity (I) and duration (D) of a rainfall event with a given return period (T).

The Rational Method for Predicting Runoff.   This may be used to predict the peak runoff with the equation

$q = CIA$, where:

q = Peak runoff (CFS) C = Runoff coefficient

I = Rainfall intensity (in./hr) A = Area (acres)

The method indicates that the units have been "rationalized" where 1 cubic foot per second (CFS) = 1.01 in.-acre/hr.

The rational method is dependent on the selection of C and I, where C is based on the soil, ground cover, and other factors, and I is obtained from the local IDF curve for a given return period and duration.

One of the challenges of the rational method is that of choosing the correct duration. The rational method is intended only to determine peak runoff.

SCS Storm Distributions

By studying the Weather Bureau's Rainfall Frequency Atlases, the Soil Conservation Service (SCS) determined that the continental United States could be represented by four dimensionless rainfall distributions each of a 24-hour duration. These distribution curves were developed from the same depth-duration-frequency data used for IDF curves.

The major advantage of the SCS storm distributions is that each curve contains depth information for storm events of all durations up to 24 hours. These distributions also provide the cumulative rainfall at any point in time, which makes them useful for volume-dependent routing calculations.

Determining the Time-of-Concentration

For overland flow computations related to storm activity, a time-dependent factor must be introduced in order to determine how the runoff is distributed over time. The time-of-concentration (T_c) is used for SCS methods. The T_c is usually defined as the time required for a theoretical drop of water to travel from the most hydrologically remote point in the watershed to the point of collection.

Some Important Equivalents

1 cfs = 448 gallons/minute
1 cfs-day/mi^2 = 0.03719" of runoff
1" of runoff/mi^2 = 26.89 cfs-day = 2,323,200 ft^3 = 53.33 acre-ft
1 acre = 43,560 sq. ft = 4047 sq. m = .4047 ha
1 sq. mi = 640 acres = 2.59 sq. km
Acceleration of gravity = 32.17 ft/s^2 = 9.806 m/s^2

Example 11-1: Watersheds

In Figure 11-2, delineate the watershed boundaries for the site.

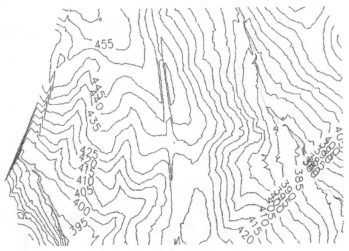

Figure 11-2   Delineate the watershed boundaries

The graphic in Figure 11-3 shows an example of watershed boundaries.

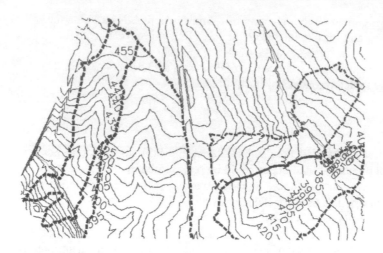

To access student data
files, go to
www.pearsondesigncentral.com.

Figure 11-3   An example
of watershed boundaries

Exercise 11-1: Civil 3D Watersheds

You now explore Civil 3D and its ability to develop watersheds from the surface model.

1. Open Chapter-11-a.dwg.
2. Type **V** for **View**, select the **Plan** view, hit **Set Current**, then hit **OK**, and you see existing ground contours.
3. These contours belong to a surface model. Watershed generation is built into every surface model. Click on and select the **Surface** in AutoCAD; right-click and select **Edit Surface Style....**
4. When the **Surface Style** dialog box comes up, click on the **Display** tab and deselect or turn **Off** the contours and border layers. Select the **Watersheds** layers and turn it **On**.
5. Then click on the **Watersheds** tab. Several types of watersheds are automatically computed as shown in Figure 11-4.

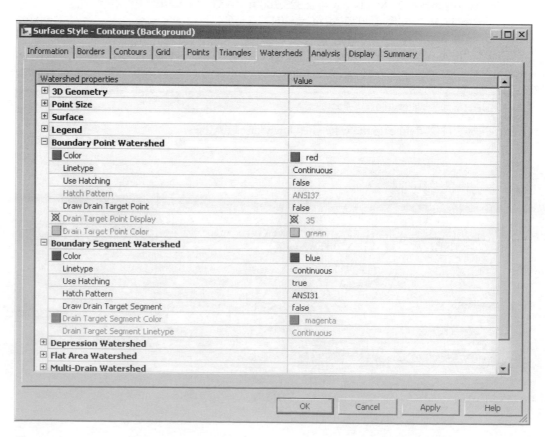

Figure 11-4   The Surface
Style dialog box

6. Hit **OK** in the **Surface Style** dialog box, and the surface immediately represents itself as a watershed analysis, as shown in Figure 11-5.

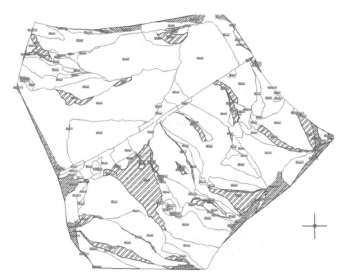

Figure 11-5   A watershed analysis

TIP

The type of watersheds automatically computed include the following.

Boundary Point, a watershed in which water leaves the shed at a single location.
Boundary Segment, a watershed in which water leaves the shed over a levee or wall type object (technically it is likely to be the side of a TIN triangle).
Depression, a watershed in which water is in a basin and has no way out.
Flat Area, a watershed that is flat (this is interesting to observe in proposed roadways because flat areas are not desirable in the paved lanes due to safety reasons because they can cause hydroplaning).
Multi-Drain, a watershed in which water has multiple ways out of the shed.
Multi-Drain Notch, a watershed in which there is a flat area between two points on the surface, reminiscent of a trapezoidal channel.

Each of these watersheds can be colored or shaded differently so that it stands apart for analysis.

HYDRAULICS

Hydraulics, like hydrology, is a huge field within civil engineering. The word *hydraulics* comes from the Greek word *hydraulikos,* meaning water. This term comes from another term meaning water pipe. Hydraulics systems, whether retaining or conveying water, are designed to deal with water at rest or in motion. This discussion is concerned with the principles and methods of planning, controlling, transporting, conserving, and using water.

Basic Concepts Related to Flowing Water

Flow is classified into two conveyances: open channel and closed conduit flow. Open channel flow occurs when the flowing stream has a free or unconstrained surface that is open to the air. Flows in channels or in pipelines with partial flow and venting are examples. In open channels, the only force that can cause flow is the force of gravity on the fluid.

Hydraulically speaking, a pipe is a closed conduit that carries water under pressure. It can be of any shape but is often round for friction purposes.

Flow occurs in a pipeline when a pressure or "head" difference exists between the ends. The discharge Q that occurs depends mainly on the amount of pressure or head difference that exists from the inlet to the outlet; the friction or resistance to flow caused by pipe length, pipe material, bends, constrictions, changes in shape and size, and type of fluid; and the cross-sectional area of the pipe.

Discharge–Area–Velocity Relationships

Flow rate or discharge, Q, is the volume of water in cubic feet passing a flow section per unit time, usually measured in cubic feet per second (ft^3/s). To get the time rate of flow or discharge, Q, in cubic feet per second, use the equation: $Q = AV$, or $V = Q/A$.

Hydraulic Mean Depth and Hydraulic Radius

An irregular flow cross section often uses a hydraulic radius and depth for computing area. The hydraulic radius, R_h, is defined as the area of the flow section divided by the wetted perimeter, P_w: $R_h = A/P_w$. The wetted perimeter times the hydraulic radius is equal to the area of irregular section flow.

Velocity Head Concept

It is known that a dropped object gains speed as it falls due to acceleration caused by gravity (g), which is equal to 32.2′ per second per second (ft/s^2). Measurements show that an object dropping 1′ reaches a velocity of 8.02′ per second (ft/s). An object dropping 4′ reaches a velocity of 16.04 ft/s. After an 8′ drop, the velocity attained is 22.70 ft/s.

If water is stored in a barrel and an opening is made in the barrel wall 1′ below the water surface, the water shoots from the opening with a velocity of 8.02 ft/s, which is the same velocity that a freely falling object reaches after falling 1′. Similarly, at openings 4′ and 8′ below the water surface, the velocity of the shooting water is 16.04 ft/s and 22.68 ft/s, respectively. Therefore, the velocity of water shooting from an opening under a given head (h) is the same as the velocity that would be attained by an object falling that same distance. The equation that shows how velocity changes with head defines velocity head: $V = \sqrt{2gh}$, which is also written as $h = V^2/2g$.

CIVIL 3D STORM SEWERS

This chapter explores Civil 3D and its ability to draft storm sewer piping using the piping objects. The main menu for piping is the **Pipes** pull-down, shown in Figure 11-6. The first thing you must do is **Set Pipe Network catalog** and select either **Imperial** or **Metric** piping. Then you select the **Create Pipe Network by Layout…** tool, this brings up the **Create Pipe Network** dialog box. Hit **OK**, this invokes the **Layout** toolbar for placing pipes and structures. Editing can occur after the system is in place. **Draw Parts in Profile View** allows the network to be automatically drawn in the profile of your choice. **Add Pipe Network Labels** can be done afterward if the labeling style chosen did not perform labeling.

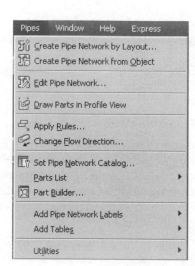

Figure 11-6   The Pipes pull-down menu

Several routines exist to aid design. They include the following:

- **Create Pipe Network by Layout...**, by which you can create a pipe network using Network Layout Tools.
- **Create Pipe Network from Object**, by which you can create pipe systems from pre-existing AutoCAD objects.
- **Change Flow Direction...**, which allows for changing the downhill flow of water.
- **Set Pipe Network Catalog...**, which allows you to set the default path for the pipe and structure catalog.
- **Parts List**, by which new pipe parts can be developed. This includes both structures and pipe types. They can be created or edited.
- **Part Builder...**, by which new graphic parts can be developed with a version of the **Dynamic Blocks Editor**.

Under **Utilities** are:

- **Create Interference Check**, by which you can visualize where conflicts exist between utilities. This allows you to solve for physical conflicts as well as tolerance conflicts. This is important for jurisdictions that have tolerance where, say, the water lines cannot be within 5′ of a sanitary line.
- **Create Alignment from Network Parts...**, by which you can create an alignment from connected pipe network parts.

Your job here is to place a storm structure network beginning at station 9+00 using a manhole. It connects with a 12″ concrete pipe to another manhole at station 12+00. Then a 12″ pipe is used to connect to a manhole at 15+00. This connects to a headwall just off the paving perpendicular to station 15+00. Use the **Network Layout Tools** toolbar (Figure 11-8) to create the network. The tools are described here:

 Pipe Network Properties, which is the first command.

 Select surface, which is used for scanning for the rim elevation.

 Select alignment if there is a need to relate the piping to a station/offset of an existing alignment.

 Parts List for pipe and structure components

 **Structure List** allows for selecting a structure.

 **Pipe List** allows for selecting a pipe type.

 Places the Pipe, Structures, or both.

 Toggle upslope/downslope changes the sloping for the pipe from downhill to uphill.

 Deletes the pipe network object.

 Displays the Pipe Network Vista, tabular editing.

Exercise 11-2: Create Pipes by Layout

1. Open Chapter-11-b.dwg.
2. Type **V** for **View**, select the **Plan** view, hit **Set Current**, then hit **OK** and you see a corridor between station 9+00, a high point, and 15+00, a low point.

To access student data files, go to www.pearsondesigncentral.com.

3. From the **Pipes** pull-down menu, Figure 11-6, select **Set Pipe Network Catalog**.
4. Choose **Imperial** for each selection item.
5. Then choose **Create Pipe Network by Layout** from the **Pipes** pull-down menu.
6. A **Create Pipe Network** dialog box displays. Set the defaults as shown in Figure 11-7, where the **Surface name** is **Corridor—(1) Surface—(1)** and the **Alignment name** is **Alignment—1**. Hit **OK**.

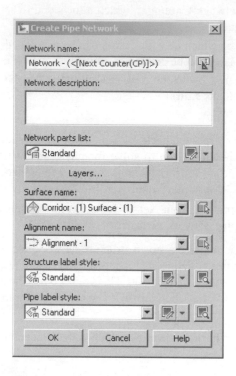

Figure 11-7   The Create Pipe Network dialog box

7. The **Network Layout Tools** toolbar displays.
8. Choose the first button on the left in Figure 11-8, **Pipe Network Properties**. It invokes a dialog box for **Pipe Network Properties**. Set the parameters for the **Layout Settings**, as shown in Figure 11-9.

Figure 11-8   The Network Layout Tools toolbar

9. Then pick the tab for **Profile**, and set the parameters for **Structure profile label style** to **Standard** and the **Pipe profile label style** to **Standard**. Hit **OK**.
10. In the pop-down **Structure List**, select **Concentric Structure 48 dia. 18 frame 24 cone 5 wall 6 floor**, from the **Concentric Cylinder Structure** item.
11. Pick **12 inch Concrete Pipe** from the **Pipe List**.
12. Pick on the command in the toolbar for **Draw Pipes and Structures,** choose **Pipes and Structures.** Specify the structure insertion point: Pick a point on the corridor near station 9+00.
13. Pick another point at station 12+00 while staying in the command.
14. Pick another point at station 15+00 while staying in the command.
15. Now in the pop-down **Structure List**, change the **Concentric Structure 48 dia. 18 frame 24 cone 5 wall 6 floor**, to a **38?6?48 inch Concrete Rectangular Headwall VH** from the **Concrete Rectangular Headwall Variable Height** item.
16. Place the last point near the end of the 3:1 side sloping (approximately 40′ right of the centerline for the corridor at station 15+00). Then hit **<Enter>** to complete the network.

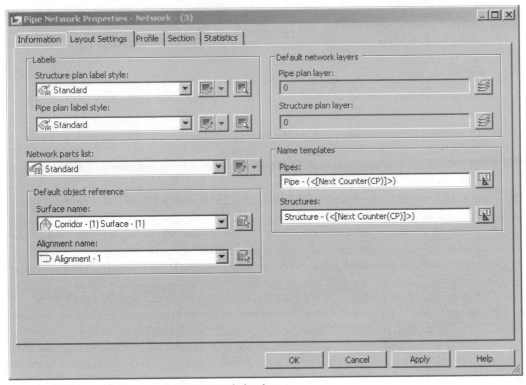

Figure 11-9   The Pipe Network Properties dialog box

On inspection, note that the piping is drawn in the plan view. Next, lay it into the profile and see how it appears. After that, move the piping around to refine it for your needs and observe how it recomputes itself.

Exercise 11-3: Create Pipes in the Profile

1. Type **V** for **View**, select the **Prof** pipe view, hit **Set Current**, then hit **OK** and you see a profile between station 9+00, a high point, and 15+00, a low point.
2. From the **Pipes** pull-down menu, select the command to **Draw Parts in Profile View**.
3. Select network(s) to add to profile view or (Selected parts only): **Zoom** out and select a pipe in the **Pipe Network** you just created and hit **<Enter>**.
4. Select profile view: **Zoom** back to the profile and select any grid line in your profile.
5. Observe your profile because the pipe system is then drawn into the profile for you. It appears something like Figure 11-10.

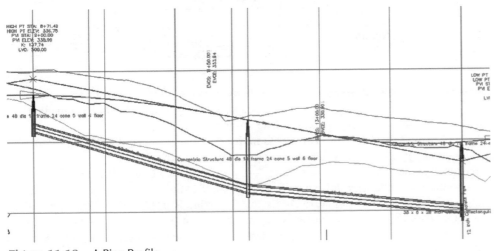

Figure 11-10   A Pipe Profile

Notice that the rim elevations are all automatically taken from the roadway's finished ground surface. The labeling appears as directed by the Standard labels selected in the styles chosen. You need to modify the label styles to reflect the way you want your plans to appear.

Exercise 11-4: Add a Structure

Take a few moments to edit and examine the system. You will add another manhole structure at station 11+00.

1. Choose **Edit Pipe Network...** from the **Pipes** pull-down menu. The **Select pipe network** dialog box appears. Choose **Network-(1)**, hit **OK**.
2. The **Network Layout Tools** toolbar displays.
3. In the pop-down **Structure List**, change the current structure to **Concentric Structure 48 dia. 18 frame 24 cone 5 wall 6 floor** from the **Concentric Cylindrical Structure** item.
4. Specify the structure insertion point:
5. **Zoom** to the plan view and use a **Nearest** snap to pick a point on the pipe near station 11+00 and notice a new structure is placed. Hit **<Enter>** to terminate.
6. From the **Pipes** pull-down menu, select the command to **Draw Parts in Profile View**.
7. Select network(s) to add to profile view or (Selected parts only): **Zoom** out and select a pipe in the **Pipe Network** you just created and hit **<Enter>**.
8. Select profile view: **Zoom** back to the profile and select any grid line in your profile. Notice that the system added the new structure at station 11+00.
9. Now adjust the labeling for the profile to add more information. Choose the **Add Pipe Network Labels >> Add Pipe Network Labels...** (Figure 11-11) command from the **Pipes** pull-down menu.

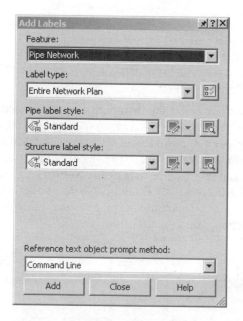

Figure 11-11   Add Pipe Network Labels dialog box

10. Change the **Standard Structure** label style by clicking on the **down arrow** next to the **Structure label style** pop-down window and selecting **Edit Current Selection** style.
11. This brings up the **Label Style Composer** (Figure 11-12).
12. In the **Layout** tab, look in the **Value** column for the **Text Property Contents**. In that cell is a button with ellipses to enter the dialog. Click that button.
13. This causes the **Text Component Editor—Contents** dialog box to display.
14. Using the **Properties** pop-down window, you will add in the following data items for labeling: **Structure Station**, **Structure Offset**, and **Insertion Rim Elevation**. Click in the black window at the end of the existing text string and hit **Enter** to move the cursor down one line. From the pop-down menu select a new data item. Hit the **gray arrow** to the right of the **Properties** pop-down window after each selection to populate the window to the right. Hit

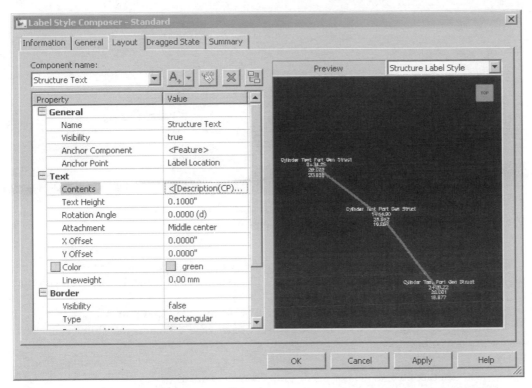

Figure 11-12   The Label Style Composer dialog box

Enter to move the cursor down one line and choose another data item. When complete as shown in Figure 11-13, hit **OK**, until the process completes. Notice that the profile labeling has already been altered.

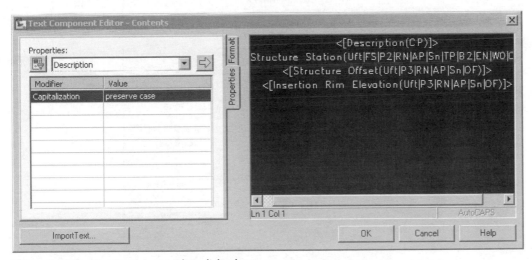

Figure 11-13   Text Component Editor dialog box

Exercise 11-5: Move Structures

Now you move the beginning structure from station 9+00 to station 8+50.

1. **Zoom** back to the plan view or type **V**, select **Plan** view, hit **Set Current**, then hit **OK**.
2. Click on the manhole structure and notice two **cyan** grips appear. See Figure 11-14.
3. Click on the square grip and stretch the grip to approximately station 8+50.
4. Notice that the structure and pipe move at the same time.
5. Now **Zoom** back to the profile, or type **V**, select **Prof** view, hit **Set Current**, then hit **OK**.
6. Notice that the pipe and structure are already relocated in the profile view.

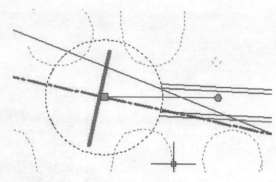

Figure 11-14   Grips on a structure

Exercise 11-6: Create Pipes by Layout

You now perform a brief exercise in identifying pipe conflicts.

To access student data
files, go to
www.pearsondesigncentral.com.

1. Open Chapter-11-c.dwg.
2. Type **V** for **View**, select the **Plan** view, hit **Set Current**, hit **OK**, and you see two piping systems in the corridor between station 10+00, a high point, and 13+00. You will now examine whether a conflict occurs here.
3. Select **Utilities >> Create Interference Check** from the **Pipes** pull-down menu.
4. `Select a part from the first network:` Select the pipe that follows the corridor centerline.
5. `Select another part from the same network or different network:` Select the other pipe on the north side of the corridor centerline.
6. The **Create Interference Check** dialog box displays. See Figure 11-15. Click on the button at the bottom of the dialog box that says **3D proximity check criteria....**

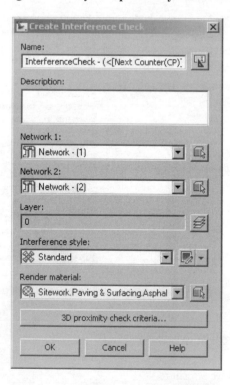

Figure 11-15   The Create Interference Check dialog box

7. When the **Criteria** dialog box appears, turn **On** the **Apply 3D Proximity Check** button.
8. Then type in **5′** for the **Use Distance** field and hit **OK**. Hit **OK**.
9. You get a response that says 1 interference was found, which is correct.
10. To see the interference, type **V** for **View**, select **Pipe Conflict**, and set it current.
11. You see a sphere indicating the conflict. Figure 11-16 shows a 2′ sphere for a 5′ conflict. This is just one way to show conflicts. Try experimenting with the settings and identify other methods on your own.

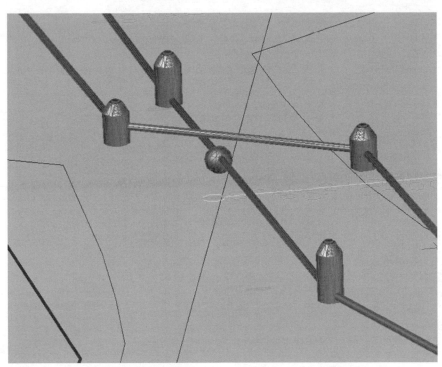

Figure 11-16   An interference of two pipes

With experimentation, you will notice that very powerful drafting features exist in the piping abilities of the Civil 3D product. The 2007 version added huge capabilities to the product, and its modeling and drafting features are unparalleled. The 2008 version added strong plan and profile drafting routines that have been much desired.

CHAPTER SUMMARY

This chapter looked at storm sewer plan development and introduced you to hydrology and hydraulic concepts. Civil 3D provides basic procedures to perform piping layout and drafting for utilities and storm sewers. The chapter also provided instruction in the functions for producing hydrologic watersheds from the surface object.

CHAPTER TEST QUESTIONS

Multiple Choice

1. Meteorological factors affecting runoff include which of the following?

    a. Type of precipitation such as rain, snow, sleet, etc.
    b. Rainfall intensity, amount, and duration
    c. Distribution of rainfall over the watershed
    d. All of the above

2. Physical characteristics affecting runoff include which of the following?

    a. Location such as the tropics, piedmonts, mountains
    b. Land use, vegetation, soil type, and total drainage area involved
    c. Shading of the watershed basin
    d. Sunlight strength

3. Various software is usually used to compute which of the following hydrological characteristics:

    a. Storm runoff volume
    b. Peak rate of discharge
    c. Hydrographs and storage volumes
    d. All of the above

4. Intensity-Duration-Frequency curves indicate which relationships?

    a. Between duration and area
    b. Between storage volumes and flows
    c. Between the intensity and duration of a rainfall event with a given return period
    d. Between erosion and siltation factors

5. The time-of-concentration is:

    a. Used for SCS methods
    b. Defined as the time required for a theoretical drop of water of water to travel from the most hydrologically remote point in the watershed to the point of collection
    c. Also called a T_c
    d. All of the above

6. Several types of watersheds are automatically computed in Civil 3D. They include:

    a. Boundary Profiles
    b. Boundary Points and Segments
    c. Weirs
    d. Low Flow Areas

7. The discharge of water depends mainly on:

    a. The amount of pressure that exists from the inlet to the outlet
    b. The friction or resistance to flow caused by pipe length
    c. Pipe material, bends, constrictions, the type of fluid, and the cross-sectional area of the pipe
    d. All of the above

8. The hydraulic radius, R_h, is defined as:

    a. The area of the flow section divided by the wetted perimeter
    b. The wetted perimeter divided by the area of the flow section
    c. $Q = AV$
    d. None of the above

9. Several terms associated with fluid flow include which of the following?

    a. Velocity head
    b. Hydraulic radius
    c. Discharge–area–velocity relationships
    d. All of the above

10. The word *hydraulics* comes from:

    a. The Greek word *hydraulikos*
    b. The English term *water*
    c. Hydrology
    d. Water at rest or in motion

True or False

1. True or False: Runoff is that part of precipitation that is absorbed by the ground, thereby replenishing our reservoirs.

2. True or False: Runoff can cause erosion.

3. True or False: Hydrologic study often involves such items as land use, vegetation, soil type, and total drainage area.

4. True or False: Meteorological factors affecting runoff include rainfall quality and contaminants.

5. True or False: As evidenced by the watershed for Front Royal, Virginia, watersheds tend to be small and usually less than one acre.

6. True or False: IDF curves can be found on the Internet and stand for Internet-Definable-Frequency curves.

7. True or False: The rational method for predicting runoff may be used to predict the peak runoff.

8. True or False: The rational method formula is $q = CIA$, where q is the peak runoff being computed.

9. True or False: Although the rational method appears straightforward, it is totally dependent on the "correct" selection of the area involved.

10. True or False: The time-of-concentration is usually defined as the time required for a drop of water to be absorbed into the ground.

CHAPTER EXERCISES

1. What is the volume of water in a full 24″ pipe if the velocity of the flow is 5 ft/s?

2. What is the velocity of water in a 48″ pipe, flowing full with a volume of 60 cfs?

3. What size of pipe is needed to convey 50 cfs at a velocity of 4 ft/s?

4. Develop a storm network in Civil 3D that uses different pipe sizes and structures as an exercise in placing the objects.

5. Edit these objects to increase, decrease, or change slopes of the pipes.

Plan Production Tools

12

Chapter Objectives

- Turn an alignment and profile into a set of sheets immediately ready for plotting
- Create Frames
- Create Sheets

INTRODUCTION

This chapter introduces Plan Production Tools to the Civil 3D user. This technology was added to the 2008 release and offers the generation of plan over profile sheet layout. This function now provides a tool that is traditionally found in civil engineering software and assists the user in preparing what are typically called Plan/Profile plot sheets. Civil 3D will use a corridor alignment and its related vertical profile information to set up, rotate, scale and cut layout frames in Layouts automatically for direct plotting.

The Civil 3D Plan Production Tools functionality includes the following abilities.

- The **Prospector's** interface has a **View Frame Groups** collection.
- The **General** menu has the option, **Plan Production Tools**. See Figure 12-1.
- Two main functions are **Create View Frames...** and **Create Sheets...**.

The purpose of this chapter is to introduce you to the routines of "cutting P&P sheets" as they are called.

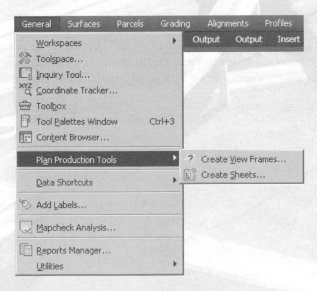

Figure 12-1 General pull-down menu

REVIEW OF FUNCTIONS AND FEATURES TO BE USED

The text provides instruction in the use of functions for generating plan and profile sheets for plotting purposes. When you lay your cursor on a tab, a preview of that layout appears.

TIP If the user adds Ortho-photos to the plan view, the resulting plot can be quite striking. Figure 12-2 shows a project where hundreds of P&P sheets were generated and aerial photos were included and set to precise geodetic coordinates.

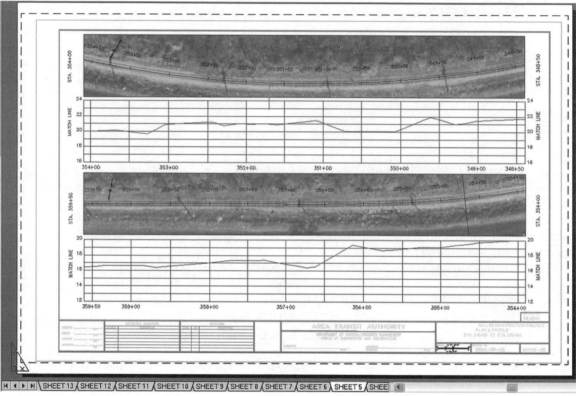

Figure 12-2   P&P sheet

Exercise 12-1: Creating a P&P Sheet

You will open a Civil 3D drawing that has an alignment and profile designed. You will then run through a procedure that will create a set of frames and then a set of sheets for plotting the P&P drawings.

To access student data files, go to www.pearsondesigncentral.com.

1. Open the drawing Chapter 12-a-start.dwg. Note that the alignment, surface, profile, corridor, and assemblies are all created.

TIP If you place your cursor in the large profile and move it left to right, you will see a visual concurrence occurring in the plan view showing the corresponding location of the cursor in the profile related to the plan view. If you lay your cursor in the plan view, you will see some visuals in the profile as well.

2. Select **General >> Plan Production Tools >> Create View Frames**. The **Create View Frames** dialog displays. Set it up as shown in Figure 12-3.

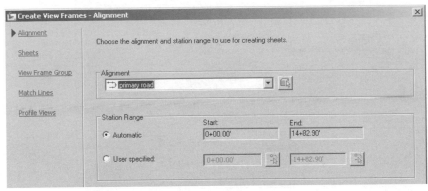

Figure 12-3   Create View Frames - Alignment dialog box

3. Then click **Next**. The next dialog box appears as shown in Figure 12-4. Select **Plan and Profile** under **Sheet Settings**.

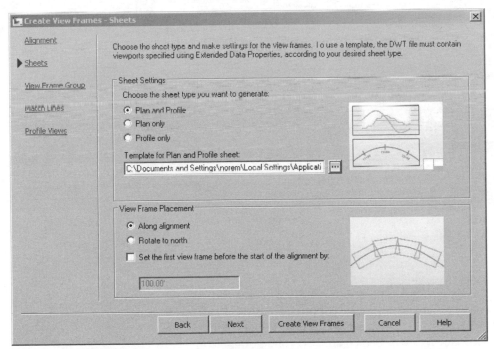

Figure 12-4   Create View Frames - Sheets dialog box

4. Select the template to use for the sheet creation as ANSI D Plan and Profile 40 Scale.
5. Select **Along alignment** under **View Frame Placement**. Hit **Next**.
6. The **Create View Frames—View Frame Group** dialog box appears, shown in Figure 12-5.
7. Set as shown in Figure 12-5 and hit **Next**. This brings up the **Match Lines** settings.
8. The **Match Lines** dialog box is shown in Figure 12-6. Set the settings as shown. Click **Next**.

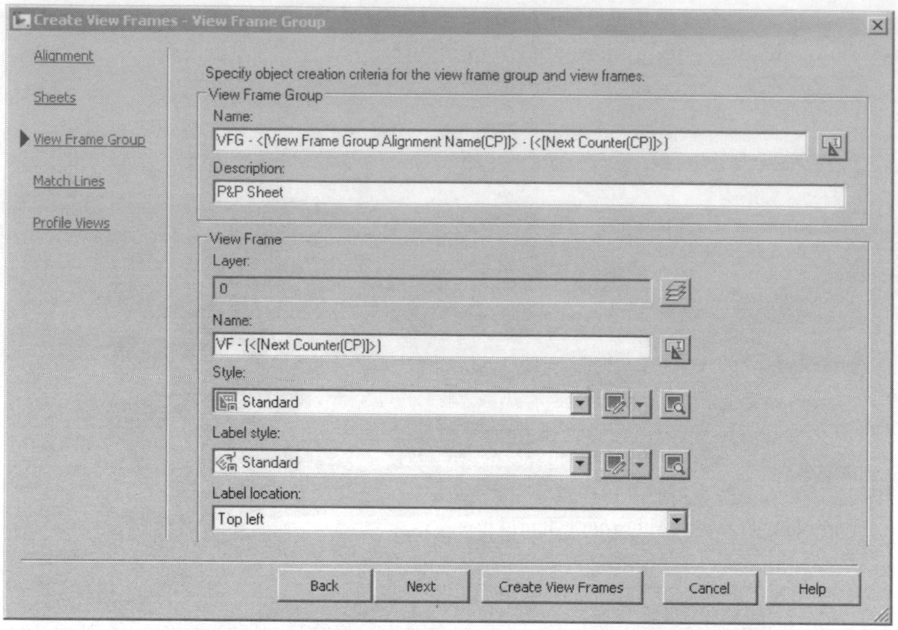

Figure 12-5 Create View Frames - View Frame Group dialog box

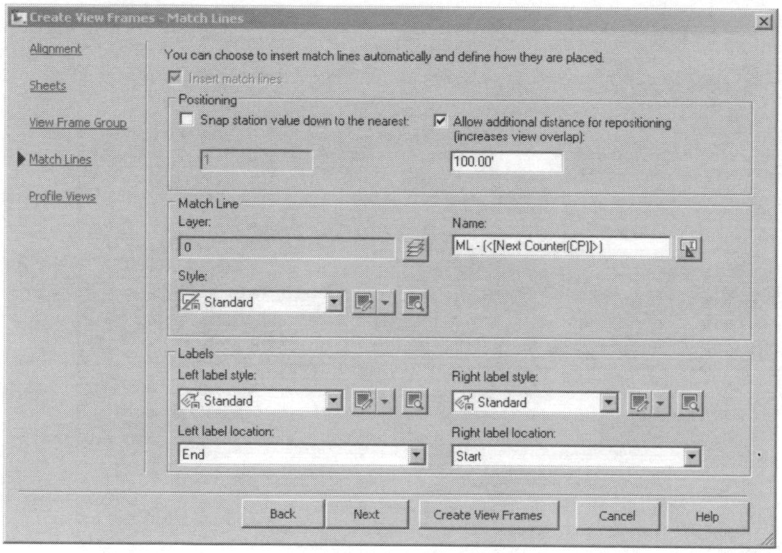

Figure 12-6 Create View Frames - Match Lines dialog box

9. When the **Create View Frames - Profile Views** dialog box appears, simply select **Standard** for the **Profile View Style** and the **Band Set** for now. Then click **Create View Frames**. See Figure 12-7 for an example of the Frames created.

10. Select from the pull-down, **General >> Plan Production Tools >> Create Sheets....** The **Create Sheets - View Frame Group and Layouts** dialog box displays as shown in Figure 12-8. Hit **Next**.

11. When the **Create Sheets – Sheet Set** dialog box appears, choose **VFG - primary road - (1)** as the new sheet set name.

12. Accept the .DST Storage location offered.

13. Accept the sheet location offered as well as the Sheet File name. Hit **Next** and the **Create Sheets - Profile Views** dialog box appears.

Note:
The software will force a Save after Step 16 so prepare yourself accordingly.

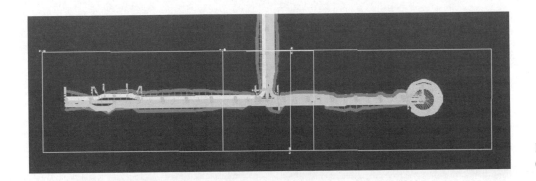

Figure 12-7 View of Created Frames

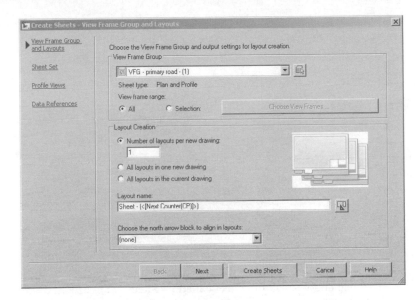

Figure 12-8 Create Sheets - View Frame Group and Layouts dialog box

14. For the **Other profile view options**, select **PV - (1)**, which is the profile you wish to have plotted. Hit **Next**, and the **Create Sheets - Data References** appears. See Figure 12-9.

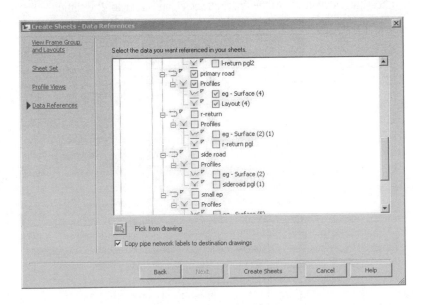

Figure 12-9 Data References

15. The primary road and its respective profiles should be selected.
16. Click on **Create Sheets**. Now you see that your current drawing will be saved. The prompt asks you to `Select profile view origin:` pick any point in your drawing.
17. The **Sheet Set** was created in your Temp folder as shown above in Step 13.

18. The **Sheet Set Manager** displays with the created sheets as shown in Figure 12-10.

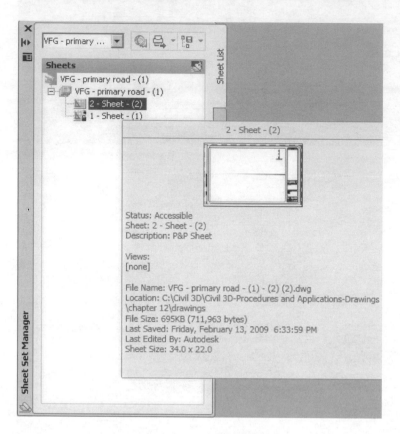

Figure 12-10   Sheet Set Manager

19. Then double-click the **Sheet** called **1 - Sheet - (1)**.
20. The file will open, and a **Plan and Profile** sheet will appear.

Sheet preparation is still a major function in the business. Note that the date, sheet number, and many other drafting items are in the drawing. See Figure 12-11 for the completed P&P sheet.
     Feel free to open the second sheet in the **Sheet Set Manager**.

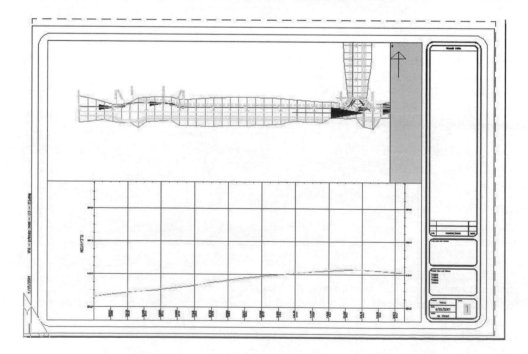

Figure 12-11   Completed P&P sheet

CHAPTER SUMMARY

This chapter introduced the Plan Production Tools to the Civil 3D user. You created Plan/Profile sheets as well as plan sheets ready for plottiing. A very important component of our business is in relaying our designs to others in a cohesive and easy to understand manner.

CHAPTER TEST QUESTIONS

Multiple Choice

1. Concerning Plan Production Tools, what does P&P stand for?
   a. Plan and profile
   b. Plan and production
   c. Profile and procedure
   d. None of the above

2. The expression "cutting P&P sheets" refers to which of the following?
   a. Creating sheets for preview purposes
   b. Generating plan and profile sheets for plotting purposes
   c. Separating drawings to export to another system
   d. None of the above

3. Why are plan and profile sheets created?
   a. To review design criteria
   b. To design an alignment and profile
   c. For plotting purposes to show the plan with the profile
   d. None of the above

4. Which of the following are the two main functions of the Plan Production Tools?
   a. **Create View Frames** and **Create Sheets**
   b. Create alignments and profiles
   c. Create the preview and layout
   d. None of the above

5. What happens when you place your cursor on a tab?
   a. A preview of the layout appears.
   b. A selection of options appears.
   c. Nothing
   d. None of the above

6. Which of the following happens when you place your cursor in the profile view and move it left to right?
   a. Only the profile view moves.
   b. Nothing
   c. You will see a visual concurrence happening in the plan view.
   d. None of the above

7. When creating P&P sheets, which of the following sheet settings are needed?
   a. **Plan** only
   b. **Profile** only
   c. **Plan and Profile**
   d. All of the above

8. Which of the following scale ratios might be more applicable to a plan profile sheet than the others?
   a. For the plan: $1'' = 10'$ horizontal,
      For the profile: $1'' = 10'$ horizontal and $1'' = 1'$ vertical.
   b. For the plan: $1'' = 10'$ horizontal,
      For the profile: $1'' = 10'$ horizontal and $1'' = 10'$ vertical.
   c. For the plan: $1'' = 50'$ horizontal,
      For the profile: $1'' = 50'$ horizontal and $1'' = 5'$ vertical.
   d. For the plan: $1'' = 1'$ horizontal,
      For the profile: $1'' = 1'$ horizontal and $1'' = 1'$ vertical.

9. Why would a designer add ortho-photos to a plot?
   a. To make it appear that more work was done than really was
   b. To add photographic detail to augment the CAD vectors in the plot
   c. To show existing conditions so a survey won't need to be done
   d. None of the above

10. Can the AutoCAD sheet manager be used with Civil 3D?
    a. Yes, but only if you leave Civil 3D and move to AutoCAD.
    b. No, a plotting module would need to be purchased.
    c. No, it is not compatible.
    d. Yes

True or False

1. True or False: Plan production tools are rarely used.

2. True or False: Plan production tools reside in the **Plotting** menu.

3. True or False: Only one tab can be created per sheet.

4. True or False: Ortho-photos cannot be used with plan and profile sheets.

5. True or False: Sheet sets need to be created in AutoCAD.

6. True or False: Sheet preparation is a critical function required in almost every project.

7. True or False: Sheet sets can only be sent to a printer.

8. True or False: Sheet sets must be created before View Frames are created.

9. True or False: Aerial photos are always needed for the creation of plan and profile sheets.

10. True or False: Once created, views cannot be altered.

CHAPTER EXERCISES

Because this chapter has only one exercise (Exercise 12-1), we suggest that you run through it again and produce two additional types of production plots.

1. Run through Exercise 12-1 again but generate Plan Only Sheets.

2. Run through Exercise 12-1 again but generate Profile Only Sheets.

Data Sharing in Civil 3D

INTRODUCTION

You have worked with Civil 3D using AutoCAD drawings and have performed your design tasks using a single AutoCAD drawing each time. In a production atmosphere, this may not always be the case. Sometimes engineers work in an environment in which they need to share data among teammates. In order to provide an understanding of how this could work, this appendix addresses data sharing for several purposes: (1) to share data with others on your team, and (2) to share data with people external to Civil 3D users.

The 2007 version added a concept called the **Vault**, which allows for securities and protections of the project data. The user is asked to log in with a password. If the password is lost or the employee who sets it leaves the organization without communicating the password to others, issues can arise. If the employee had administrator privilege, then only Autodesk can break the password. Contact Autodesk and fill out the required legal paperwork to accomplish this. Otherwise, if the employee did not have administrator access, the system administrator can gain access to the **Vault** to clear the password.

DATA SHARING

The exercises you have worked on in this text have included the use of point data, parcel data, surfaces, alignment data, profile views and profiles, corridors, and section data. The main method for data sharing has traditionally been through passing AutoCAD files back and forth. This allows others to see and manipulate the graphical data involved but does not provide strong access to the actual design data.

Civil 3D allows some very effective methods for sharing that design data. It has the ability to share the data not only with other Civil 3D users but also with non–Civil 3D users. In fact, data can be shared with others who do not even have AutoCAD as a foundation CAD platform.

Many larger projects have subconsultants working on them whereby each party contributes its own specialized expertise, or perhaps projects are multidisciplinary. In any event, data need to be shared between these groups to maximize efficiency, avoid errors, and minimize redundancies. The surveyor's base conditions need to be shared with the designers so they can develop the proposed conditions. When the proposed design conditions are finished, these must be sent back to the surveyor for quality control and preparation of stakeout or 3D/GPS Machine Control data. If machine control data are involved, they must be shared with the contractor.

This appendix covers Civil 3D's four main methods of data sharing. The first method is by simply copying the AutoCAD file and sending it to others who have Civil 3D for their use. In this case, the data are inherently available. The second method is through the use of LandXML. The third method is performed through the use of data shortcuts, and the fourth method is accomplished through the use of Civil 3D's project abilities.

Method 1: Inserting or Copying a Drawing

As discussed, Civil 3D makes it easy to incorporate data into a drawing by inserting one drawing into another drawing or by simply using **Save As....** When you wish to obtain access to data within another drawing, you just need to insert the source drawing into the active drawing or open the copy. All the object data such as terrain models, alignments, and so on are immediately available to the working session. Note that there is no live link to the source drawing when using this procedure.

Method 2: LandXML

Civil 3D includes a simple methodology called LandXML, which works similarly to the way it did in Land Desktop. This feature is a data migration tool developed to send design data across operating systems (say, from Windows XP to Unix), across different versions of CAD systems (say, between AutoCAD or Microstation), or between systems that have different CAD standards (say, between a consulting firm and the State Department of Transportation). LandXML, which is being promoted by a nonprofit group, can be accessed via the Web at Landxml.org. It is supported by a group of software manufacturers interested in making their customers' data available to others in the interest of efficiency.

The ability to import or export LandXML makes use of a file format that is open, is text based, and is not software dependent. In other words, it uses a simple definition for each data type, and each software manufacturer can read it and reassemble its respective data into its software's definition. It is also an archival facility because the data are in a generic text-based format.

Let us look at some examples of how data are stored in LandXML. The following example involves an alignment, and this is how it appears in a LandXML file.

```
<?xml version="1.0"?>
<LandXML xmlns="http://www.landxml.org/schema/LandXML-1.0"
xmlns:xsi="http://www.w3.org/2001/XMLSchema-instance"
xsi:schemaLocation="http://www.landxml.org/schema/LandXML-1.0
http://www.landxml.org/schema/LandXML-1.0/LandXML-1.0.xsd"
date="2005-06-26" time="10:42:00" version="1.0" lan-
guage="English" readOnly="false">
  <Units>
    <Imperial areaUnit="squareFoot" linearUnit="foot"
volumeUnit="cubicYard" temperatureUnit="fahrenheit"
pressureUnit="inchHG" angularUnit="decimal degrees"
directionUnit="decimal degrees"
/Imperial>

  </Units>
      <Project name="C:\Admin\prentiss-hall-civil 3d\civil
3dapplications\student files\appendix-a.dwg"
      /Project>
    <Application name="Autodesk Civil 3D" desc="Civil 3D" manu-
facturer="Autodesk, Inc." version="2007" manufact-
urerURL="www.autodesk.com" timeStamp="2005-06-26T10:42:00"
    /Application>
    <Alignments name="Site 1">
      <Alignment name="Alignment - 1" length="2154.87367186"
staStart="0." desc="Chapter 6 alignment">
        <CoordGeom>
          <Line dir="354.45437497" length="200.">
              <Start>18553.70716247
 14599.21456424</Start>
              <End>18534.37948987 14798.27847627</End>
          </Line>
            <Curve rot="cw" chord="386.34076129"
crvType="arc" delta="30.03271185" dirEnd="324.42166312"
dirStart="354.45437497" external="26.35954132"length="390.79932237"
midOrd="25.45941315" radius="745.55877333" tangent="200.">
              <Start>18534.37948987
14798.27847627</Start>
              <Center>17792.31025954
```

14726.22889691</Center>
              <End>18398.68871707 15160.00654818</End>
              <PI>18515.05181728 14997.3423883</PI>
            </Curve>
          <Line dir="296.56505118" length="0.">
              <Start>18398.68871707
15160.00654818</Start>
              <End>18398.68871707 15160.00654818</End>
          </Line>
            <Curve rot="ccw" chord="380.90154719"
crvType="arc" delta="35.55331015" dirEnd="359.97497326"
dirStart="324.42166312" external="31.2774218"
length="387.08193805" midOrd="29.78404589" radius="623.80018303"
tangent="200.">
              <Start>18398.68871707
15160.00654818</Start>
              <Center>18906.03838059
15522.94316422</Center>
              <End>18282.23825707 15522.67068898</End>
              <PI>18282.32561686 15322.67070806</PI>
            </Curve>
          <Line dir="359.97497326" length="200.">
              <Start>18282.23825707
              15522.67068898</Start>
              <End>18282.15089729 15722.6706699</End>
          </Line>
            <Curve rot="ccw" chord="383.19792514"
crvType="arc" delta="33.33121545" dirEnd="393.30618871"
dirStart="359.97497326" external="29.29379845"
length="388.65516287" midOrd="28.06330696"
radius="668.09146379" tangent="200.">
              <Start>18282.15089729
15722.6706699</Start>
              <Center>18950.24229735
15722.96249153</Center>
              <End>18391.88615615 16089.82026175</End>
              <PI>18282.06353751 15922.67065082</PI>
            </Curve>
          <Line dir="33.30618879" length="0.00099774">
              <Start>18391.88615615 16089.82026175</Start>
              <End>18391.88670402 16089.82109561</End>
          </Line>
            <Curve rot="cw" chord="382.73122679"
crvType="arc" delta="33.79240661" dirEnd="359.5137823"
dirStart="33.30618891" external="29.70487123" length="388.3352508"
midOrd="28.42259646" radius="658.43108381"
tangent="199.99900122">
              <Start>18391.88670402
16089.82109561</Start>
              <Center>17841.60420785
16451.37422662</Center>
              <End>18500.01158371 16456.96167135</End>
              <PI>18501.7087748 16256.96987144</PI>
            </Curve>
          <Line dir="359.5137823" length="200.00100003">
              <Start>18500.01158371
16456.96167135</Start>
              <End>18498.31437567 16656.95546999</End>
          </Line>
        </CoordGeom>
      </Alignment>
    </Alignments>
  </LandXML>

The next example is of a surface definition. It begins with header information and then defines the coordinates of each point involved with a reference point number. It follows that with a triangle referencing those point numbers so that the exact triangulation is honored.

```
<?xml version="1.0"?>
<LandXML xmlns="http://www.landxml.org/schema/LandXML-1.0"
xmlns:xsi="http://www.w3.org/2001/XMLSchema-instance"
xsi:schemaLocation="http://www.landxml.org/schema/LandXML-1.0
http://www.landxml.org/schema/LandXML-1.0/LandXML-1.0.xsd"
date="2005-06-26" time="10:48:52" version="1.0"
language="English" readOnly="false">
  <Units>
  <Imperial areaUnit="squareFoot" linearUnit="foot"
volumeUnit="cubicYard" temperatureUnit="fahrenheit"
pressureUnit="inchHG" angularUnit="decimal degrees"
directionUnit="decimal degrees"
  /Imperial>
  </Units>
  <Project name="C:\Admin\prentiss-hall-civil 3d\civil
3dapplications\student files\appendix-a.dwg"
  /Project>
  <Application name="Autodesk Civil 3D" desc="Civil 3D"
manufacturer="Autodesk, Inc." version="2007" manufact-
urerURL="www.autodesk.com" timeStamp="2005-06-
26T10:48:52"<</Application>
  <Surfaces>
  <Surface name="Corridor - (1) Surface - (1)" desc="">
    <Definition surfType="TIN">
  <Pnts>
    <P id="1">18492.21916265 14593.24452217 325.96527275</P>
    <P id="2">18517.37799852 14595.68726399 321.75240699</P>
    <P id="3">18520.3639572 14595.97717908 321.75240699</P>
    <P id="4">18532.30779192 14597.13683944 324.75240699</P>
    <P id="5">18533.30311148 14597.2334778 324.73240699</P>
    <P id="6">18537.28438973 14597.62003125 324.65240699</P>
    <P id="7">18539.27502885 14597.81330798 324.61240699</P>
    <P id="8">18539.68974533 14597.85357396 324.61240699</P>
    <P id="9">18539.77268863 14597.86162716 324.11240699</P>
    <P id="10">18541.76332775 14598.05490389 324.27907366</P>
    <P id="11">18553.70716247 14599.21456424 324.51907366</P>
    <P id="12">18565.65099719 14600.3742246 324.27907366</P>
    <P id="13">18567.64163631 14600.56750132 324.11240699</P>
    <P id="14">18567.72457961 14600.57555452 324.61240699</P>
    <P id="15">18568.13929609 14600.61582051 324.61240699</P>
    <P id="16">18570.12993521 14600.80909723 324.65240699</P>
    <P id="17">18574.11121345 14601.19565068
    324.73240699</P>....
... </Pnts>
  <Faces>
    <F>679 117 116</F>
    <F>369 281 280</F>
    <F>735 73 734</F>
    <F>783 126 127</F>
    <F>693 131 130</F>
    <F>519 391 392</F>
    <F>693 3 2</F>
    <F>688 125 124</F>
    <F>690 5 4</F>
    <F>690 6 5</F>
    <F>689 7 6</F>
    <F>737 70 71</F>
    <F>687 8 7</F>
```

```
<F>229 174 175</F>
<F>685 122 684</F>
<F>528 403 404</F>
<F>739 68 69</F>
<F>741 65 66</F>
<F>317 227 228</F>
<F>683 119 682</F>
<F>742 64 65</F>
<F>681 118 117</F>
<F>675 674 21</F>
<F>230 175 176</F>
<F>707 34 706</F>
<F>716 56 715</F>
<F>682 13 12</F>
<F>463 357 356</F>....
```

By inspecting these data, one can see why this is a generic, simple, and text-based method for data sharing that can easily cross platform lines, CAD system lines, or CAD standards lines.

One company can send its LandXML data to another, and each organization's CAD system can invoke its respective CAD standards when the data are imported into the design software.

You can import the LandXML information using your own native CAD standards and be unaffected by the graphics used to generate the data because LandXML exports only design data, not the graphical appearance of it. The importation process then creates the data with the aesthetics or properties of the CAD system performing the import. The critical aspect of this process is maintaining the design data integrity.

Method 3: Data Shortcuts

Civil 3D provides a data collaboration tool called data shortcuts, which allows you to externally reference objects that are either inside or outside a project. Data shortcut users are one of the following types. Either they have the source object's drawing open and produce the data shortcut (which is an external XML file that contains the AutoCAD.DWG filename, path, and object name), or they are the users of the data shortcut. If they are the users, they can create a reference to the object or read it and obtain ownership of the copy of the object. The referenced object initially has read-only geometry properties and takes up less file space when the drawing is saved, because it is only referenced.

Data shortcuts can be used for obtaining access to surfaces, alignments, and profiles. Alignment and profile data shortcuts are closely tied to each other because a profile data shortcut's source drawing must be the same as the profile's alignment data shortcut.

One last note is that data shortcuts are visible and accessible to the next method of Civil 3D projects for data sharing.

Method 4: Civil 3D Projects

A method provided in Civil 3D to allow sharing of data between Civil 3D users that is somewhat similar to that used by Land Desktop users is the project method. The person who has the source data available attaches the drawing to a project and makes data available to the project. Other users can then obtain access to these data through a Check Out/Check In system.

The project object cannot be modified directly. To modify it, the object has to be checked out. Changes are made, and the object is then checked back in to the project. If you try to modify a local copy of the data without first checking it out, it cannot be checked back in to the project. The modifications made will exist only in the drawing in which they were made.

The next task is to perform some exercises using methods 2 through 4.

Exercise A-1: Using LandXML

1. Open the file called Appendix-a.dwg. There are several data types in this file including points, a corridor, surfaces, and a pipe network.
2. From the **File** pull-down menu, select the **Export>>Export to LandXML...** command. The **Export to LandXML** dialog box appears so that you can check one or more of the

To access student data files, go to www.pearsondesigncentral.com.

items for export. There is a **Pick from drawing** button at the bottom, which allows you to select an object directly from the AutoCAD file.

3. Check the **All Points** toggle under the **Point Groups** category as shown in Figure A-1. Check the **Alignment - 1** in the dialog box under **Site, Site 1, Alignments**, and all the individual profiles check automatically. Hit **OK**.

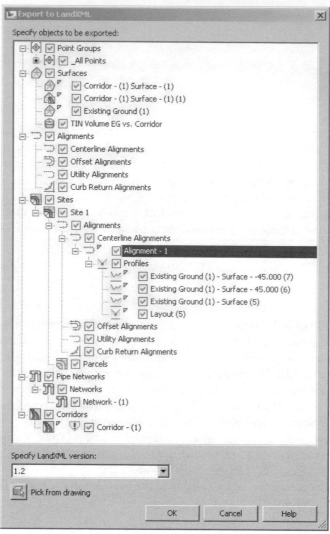

Figure A-1   Export to LandXML dialog box

4. Provide a name for the file in a location that you can locate later. Hit **Save**.
5. When that process is complete, select **File** from the pull-down menu, choose **New**, and create a new Civil 3D file, using the Autodesk **_AutoCAD Civil 3D (Imperial) NCS Base.dwt** file as a template.
6. From the **File** pull-down menu, select the **Import >>Import LandXML...** command. Locate the .xml file you just created and hit **Open**. The **Import LandXML** dialog box in Figure A-2 displays.
7. Accept that all the data are checked for import, and hit **OK**. You may get a **Panorama** box.
8. **Zoom Extents**, and you see the alignment and points in the new file.
9. Look in the **Prospector** and note that the alignment and points are visible here as well. If they are not, ensure that the button at the top left of the dialog box is toggled on. Right-click on **Alignments** and check the **Show Preview** option. Then right-click on **Alignment-1**. See Figure A-3.
10. The only thing that is left to be done is to set the **Styles** for the objects imported.

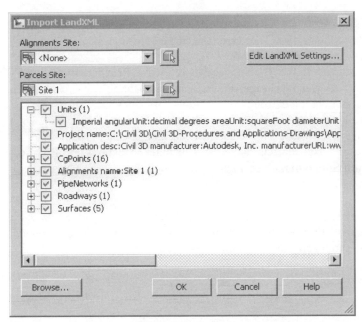

Figure A-2   Import LandXML dialog box

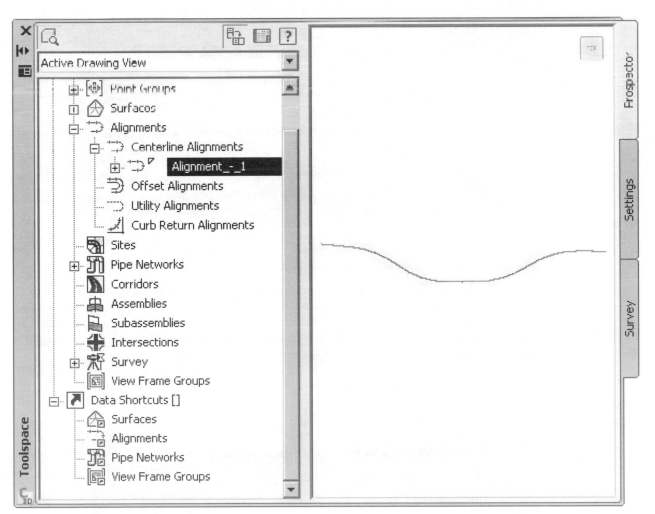

Figure A-3   Alignment in the Prospector

Exercise A-2: Using the Data Shortcuts Method

To access student data
files, go to
www.pearsondesigncentral.com.

1. Open the file called Appendix-a.dwg. There are several data types in this file including points, a corridor, surfaces, and a pipe network.
2. Set a new working folder using the **Toolspace, Master View, Prospector** tab, right-click **Data Shortcuts**. Click **Set Working Folder...** and select the folder you want.
3. Then create a new data shortcut folder using the **Toolspace, Master View, Prospector** tab, again right-click **Data Shortcuts**. Click **New Data Shortcuts Folder....** In the **New Data Shortcuts Folder** dialog box, provide a name and text description. Click **OK**.
4. The next step is to create a data shortcut using the **Toolspace, Master View, Prospector** tab, right-click **Data Shortcuts**. Click **Create Data Shortcuts...** The **Create Data Shortcuts** dialog box will display.
5. Click an object type to include in the new data shortcut. In the dialog box, select the object that you want to reference in other drawings. The data shortcut is created.
6. Note that the **Surface** and **Alignment** shortcuts in the dialog box now can be expanded. Expand them and they should appear as in Figure A-4.

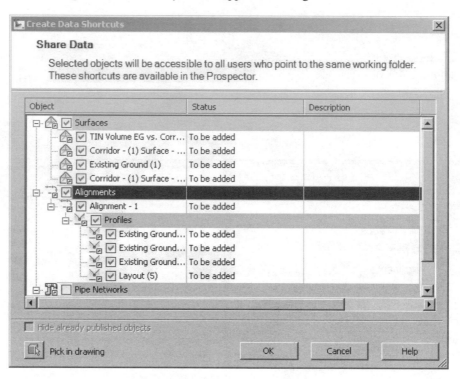

Figure A-4 The Create Data Shortcuts dialog box

You have created a data shortcut and saved it for use by others. Now let us explore how you or others who are on the project team can use these shortcuts.

7. From the Civil 3D pull-down menu, click **File** and then **New** and create a new drawing. Use the **_AutoCADCivil 3D (Imperial) NCS Base.dwt** template to create the new file.
8. Save it as a properly named AutoCAD file of your choosing. While in the new file, look at the **Prospector, Master View, Data Shortcuts**, and you will see the shortcuts available.
9. To create a reference in the new file, right-click on the **Corridor-(1)Surface (1)** shortcut and click **Create Reference....** See Figure A-5.

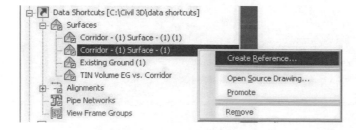

Figure A-5 Create Reference

10. Hit **OK** to the **Create Surface Reference** dialog box, taking the defaults. See Figure A-6.
11. Perform a **Zoom Extents** on the drawing, and you should see the contours for the corridor surface.
12. In the **Prospector**, right-click on the **Alignment 1** item. Click **Create Reference...**, and a **Create Alignment Reference** dialog box appears. Again, you do not really "own" this alignment but can use it and display it. See Figure A-7.

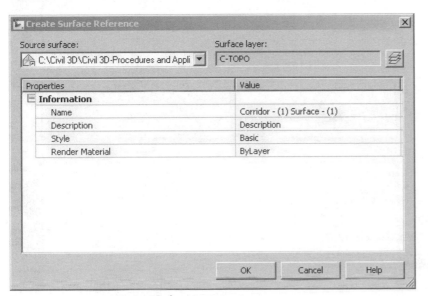

Figure A-6   Create Surface Reference dialog box

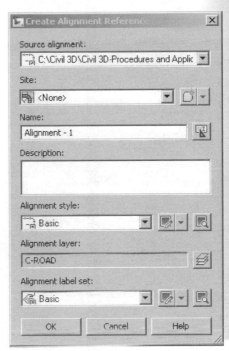

Figure A-7   Create Alignment Reference dialog box

13. Accept the defaults as shown in the figure, and hit **OK**. If a **Panorama** appears saying the alignment was created, close it.
14. You see the alignment in the file now.

> **TIP** If you click on the alignment and right-click, you see the typical commands to edit the alignment or the Style. If you select **Alignment Properties**, notice that nothing can really be modified because it is referenced. The Style, however, can be altered as needed.

15. While in the new file you created, in the Prospector under **Data Shortcuts** select **Alignment 1**. Right-click and choose **Open Source drawing....** The original file from which the data shortcut was created opens.
16. Click on the **Alignment** in the drawing, right-click, and choose **Edit Alignment Geometry....** When the toolbar displays, click on the **Alignment Grid View** on the right side of the toolbar. The **Panorama** opens with the numeric alignment data in it.
17. Scroll to the right until you can see the radius for the first curve in the alignment. Change it to **500**, hit **<Enter>**, and close the panorama. The alignment radius is now 500' for the first curve.
18. Save the file.
19. Using the **Window** pull-down menu, switch to the new drawing.
20. When you do, the **Data Shortcuts** pop-up window will display, telling you that the data shortcut has been altered and you need to synchronize it.

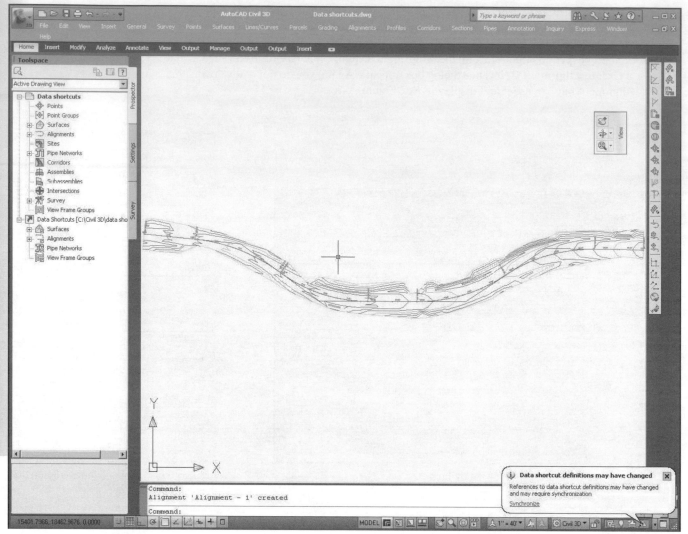

Figure A-8 Synchronize

21. Click on the **blue** hyperlink where it says **Synchronize**, shown in Figure A-8.
22. The command prompt notifies you that Alignment 'Alignment-1' created. **Alignment Alignment-1** is now up to date. **Surface Corridor-(1) Surface-(1)** is now up to date.

If you wish to take complete control of the data shortcut, then you can promote it. This detaches it from its source.

23. Click on the **Alignment**, right-click, and select **Promote**. The command prompt tells you that **1 Data References** successfully promoted.
24. Click on the **Alignment** now, and notice that grips appear, which allow you to edit the alignment, because you now "own" it.

This example shows how data shortcuts can be used. These shortcuts can be placed on a server for each member of the team to use in referencing the data that is in your drawing. They can be used to compute profiles, to change the appearances of data for different uses, or for report creation.

Exercise A-3: Using the Projects Method

To access student data files, go to www.pearsondesigncentral.com.

1. Open Appendix-a-projects.dwg.
2. Check in the **Toolspace Prospector,** and notice that there is a **Projects** item when the **Master View** is showing. See Figure A-9.
3. Right-click on **Projects** and you can **Set Working Folder....** This means that you can set the project path wherever you wish. Under the project path will reside the individual projects that you create.

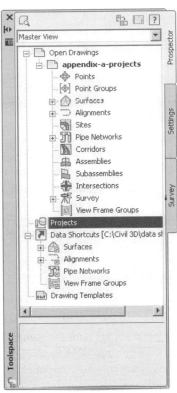

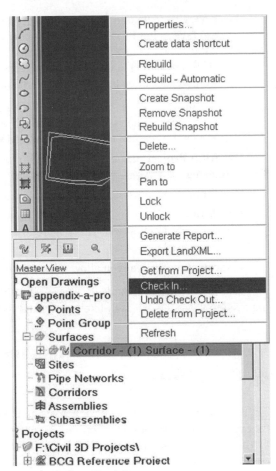

Figure A-9   A projects item in the
Toolspace Prospector

Figure A-10   Check In

4. The system defaults to **\Civil 3D Projects**, and you can switch that to a more desired location for this exercise if you like.

5. In **Prospector**, right-click on the drawing name, select **Add to Project...** If the software asks you to log in to the **Vault**, do so.

6. Next, expand the drawing, expand **Surfaces** so you can see the **Corridor—(1) Surface—(1)**. Right-click on the **Corridor—(1) Surface—(1)**, and you see an option to **Attach to Project**. Select **Add to Project**.

7. An **Add to Project** dialog box displays, allowing you to attach the surface to the project, but it needs to know under what terms you are attaching it. The default is **Check in.** Click in the pop-down window where it says **Check in**. The other options are **Check in** and **Keep Checked in** and **Check in** and **Protect**. Leave the default. Hit **OK**. See Figure A-10.

8. You now see the **Corridor—(1) Surface—(1)** under the **Surfaces** item in the **Projects** area of the **Prospector**. It can now be used by others on the project team. You will see how in the next part of the exercise.

Close the file you are in. There is no need to save it.

9. Click **File >> New** and create a new drawing. Use the **_AutoCADCivil 3D (Imperial) NCSBase.dwt** template to create the new file.

10. Save it as a properly named AutoCAD file of your choosing.

11. In the **Prospector**, right-click on your AutoCAD file, and select **Attach to Project**.

12. Choose the project called **My Project**.

13. In the **Prospector**, expand **Surfaces**, and you will see the **Corridor—(1) Surface—(1)**. Right-click on the **Corridor—(1) Surface—(1)**, and you are able to **Check Out, Get from Project**, or **Protect the surface**. Choose **Check Out**.

14. **Zoom Extents** and you see the corridor surface in the default style. You also see the **Surface** in the **Prospector** under your file's **Surfaces**.

15. After using it or making modifications to the surface, you can right-click on the **Corridor— (1) Surface—(1)** in the **Prospector** under your file's **Surfaces** and choose **Check it In**.

16. Comments can be added and a log of who checked it in/out is maintained.

Check Out means that you can create an accessible read/write copy of a project object in your drawing. When you check an object out, it then overwrites equivalent objects in your file, thereby keeping the drawing updated with the project.

Get from Project means that you can create a read-only copy of the project object in your drawing.

Protect prevents others from checking out and changing a project object.

Check In means that you can update the project with changes you made to that object while it was checked out by you. This feature locks the local copy of the object in the drawing. See Figure A-10.

Unprotect means that you allow others to check out and change a project object.

These are the main methods for sharing data in Civil 3D. As the use of the software matures, the need to share the data will likely arise, and these exercises will assist in accomplishing that.

SHARING DATA WITH CONTRACTORS FOR 3D/GPS MACHINE CONTROL

Three software add-ons assist designers using Civil 3D in developing their 3D data for contractors using robotic earthmoving devices, commonly known as machine control. This technology has been growing very rapidly and can decrease the amount of time contractors need to construct a project. As a result, contractors increasingly want the data that engineers create, and they want them in 3D!

Autodesk has recognized this need and typically offers three manufacturer's add-ons into the Civil 3D software: Carlson Connect, which addresses Topcon, Trimble Link from Trimble, and Leica X-change. Topcon, Trimble, and Leica are the three main suppliers of machine control equipment in the world. These add-ons are of no cost to the user.

Carlson Connect

Carlson Connect (Figure A-11) is another solution that offers a collection of routines for transferring and converting data between Autodesk Land Desktop or Autodesk Civil 3D and several popular data collectors. Carlson Connect runs inside Civil 3D and uses the current project data.

Once engineers or designers have created their data in 3D, say, for a roadway or a site grading project, there will be a surface involved. By using the **Carlson Connect** pull-down menu and choosing the **Topcon** command and then **Export Surface to Topcon TN3 File**, the surface can

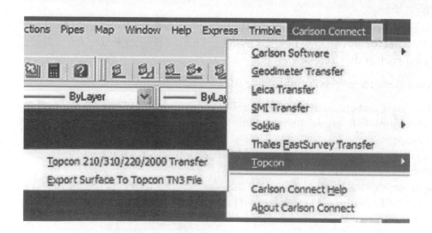

Figure A-11 Carlson Connect

be formatted into the appropriate binary file for Topcon equipment. The TN3 file can be copied to a flashcard for insertion directly into the equipment on site.

Trimble Link

Trimble's equivalent routine would be in two parts. The first is **Export Surface** file for Sitevision for sending your Civil 3D surfaces. The second is for roadway data whereby you would use **Export Road** file for Sitevision. See Figure A-12.

Figure A-12   Trimble Link

Leica X-change

Leica Geosystems released the Leica X-change for Autodesk Civil 3D, which is a group of tools running inside Autodesk Civil 3D that allows the import of data from and the export of data to a Leica System 1200 job. Points, lines, and areas as measured in the field with System 1200 (TPS and GPS) can be directly imported into an Autodesk Civil 3D drawing. Conversely, points created in Civil 3D can be exported to a System 1200 job for later usage in the field. The benefit for the user is seamless data transfer betwcen the System 1200 and Autodesk's Civil 3D software, thereby eliminating intermediate conversion steps, avoiding loss of data, and taking full advantage of the linework capabilities of the System 1200.

SHARING CIVIL 3D CONFIGURATION DATA

Before leaving this topic of sharing data, the last to discuss is sharing data among fellow project teammates. Civil 3D shares its CADD standards, Styles, and assemblies using AutoCAD files. The product configuration largely is performed in an AutoCAD file in which the environment variables and profiles can be established like normal.

Then the Styles and assemblies should be configured for Civil 3D. The Styles are stored in the AutoCAD template for dissemination to other users. The assemblies can be simply placed inside the AutoCAD file or dropped into **Tool Palettes**.

Labeling in Civil 3D 2010 **B**

This appendix briefly discusses labeling methods. One of the main tools is the ability to label simple lines and curves. Many types of objects can be labeled automatically by choosing the **Add labels...** function available under several menu pull-downs. In the **Add Labels** dialog box that will appear, under the **Feature:** option you can select **Line and Curve**. Choose the label type of either **Single** or **Multiple** segment. Then select the style by which you want to label, and hit the **Add** button to perform the function.

To access student data
files, go to
www.pearsondesigncentral.com.

Another labeling tool is the **Notes** function. This can be performed by choosing the **Add labels...** function available under several menu pull-downs. In the **Add Labels** dialog box that will appear, under the **Feature:** option you can select **Note**. The label type is **Note**. Then select the style by which you want to label, and hit the **Add** button to perform the function. You will be asked to **Pick label location:** and then pick in the drawing where you wish the new label to be placed.

> **TIP** The Note is a free-form label whose main properties are that it will resize and rotate as described by the Style when plotted.

This example shows how to create an expression and use it for augmenting the labeling capabilities of the software. Note: This exercise has worked in previous versions of the software. It has been retained here to inform you that Autodesk Civil 3D can build custom expressions. The Delta Angle Expression found in the example is not currently found in the expressions of the 2010 version. To proceed, you will need to type in **Delta Angle**.

Exercise B-1: Expressions

Another important labeling function is the ability to add expressions to the labeling. A quick example follows.

1. Open a file such as chapter 2-k-complete.dwg. Expand the **Toolspace Settings**, and look under **Alignment, Label Styles**, and **Curve**. You see an option called **Expressions** in all the labeling style areas. Expressions can be created for all the labeling styles. They are then attached during Style creation.
2. Right-click on **Expressions** and select **New....**
3. Provide a name for your expression; call it **Half-Delta**.
4. Just to the right and below the **Expression** window is a button called **Insert Function**. Click it and select the function called **RAD2DEG**.
5. Then click in the **Expression** window to the right of the parenthesis. Now click on the **Insert Property** button just below the **Expression** window.
6. Select the **Delta Angle** property.
7. Then click in the **Expression** window and add another parenthesis to the right side of the {Delta Angle} term. Then type **/2** after the expression to divide the value in half.
8. It should say **RAD2DEG({Delta Angle})/2** on completion.
9. Hit **OK**.

10. Now right-click on the **Curve** style called **Standard**. Choose **Edit....**
11. In the **Label Style Composer** dialog box, choose the **Layout** tab.
12. Under the pop-down window called **Component name:** select **Delta**.
13. Now under the **Text Contents Value** field, click the button to the right of the field with the dots on it to enter the editing facility.
14. Click before the $\Delta =$ in the **Preview** window and hit **<Enter>** to open a blank line.
15. Move to the blank line and type **Half-Delta=**.
16. Now click under the **Properties** pop-down window, and select the property called **Half-Delta** that you just created.
17. Hit the **gray arrow** to the right to send it into the **Preview** window. Hit **OK** and you see the half delta in the **Preview** window of the **Label Style Composer**. Hit **OK** again to leave.
18. Now in Civil 3D, draw an arc by typing **Arc** and selecting three points somewhere on the screen. Type **PE** for **PEdit** and convert the arc to a **Pline**.
19. Then choose the **Alignment** pull-down menu, select **Create Alignment from Polyline**, choose the arc, and accept the defaults when creating the alignment.
20. Then choose **Alignments >> Add Alignment Labels >> Add Alignment Labels....**
21. An **Add Labels** dialog box appears.
22. Select **Alignment** for the **Feature:**.
23. Select **Single Segment** for **Label type:**.
24. Click the **Add** button and choose the **arc**. A label appears showing the Length, Radius Delta, and Half-delta for the arc. Mission accomplished

Software and Hardware Versions

C

SOFTWARE VERSIONS AND SPECIFICATIONS

The software discussed in this text is Autodesk Civil 3D 2010.
Some of the major Civil 3D 2010 enhancements comprise the following items.

- Ribbons are a new interface tool that provides a new method for accessing Civil 3D commands.
- Users now have the ability to create alignments from objects, not just Plines.
- New alignment-based solutions:
- Alignments can now have "Types." Types include centerline, offset, utility, and curb return.
- Create offset alignments that are dynamic to the parent alignment.
- Create rule-based non-parallel offsets for bus turnouts and lane widenings.
- New corridor solutions:
- New tools for managing corridor data, the ability to edit a Region, geometric override cleanup tools, a new automated method of creating boundaries for corridors with multiple baselines, and creating a shrinkwrap boundary around the entire corridor.
- A new Create Intersection wizard automates roadway intersection design, including curb returns and widening, from specified main and side road alignments. This is currently limited to a four-way crossing.
- Hydrology improvements include the ability to launch the Hydraflow from within Civil 3D and support for metric units.
- Improved data sharing with Revit.
- Drafting improvements:
  - Masking of contour labels has been added.
  - Profile and section labels can be staggered to avoid overlaps.
- Draw and label projected objects in profile and section views.
- New parcel commands for Sliding Side Line and Swing Line layouts. These are similar to the old Land Desktop tools in function. Parcel previews can now be observed to see how a change will affect the parcels.
- Piping can now handle multiple pipe networks. HGL and EGL can now be computed and labeled. New pipe/structure part types are now available for Circular pipes such as: Corrugated Metal, High Density Polyethylene (HDPE), Corrugated HDPE, and Ductile Iron. For Elliptical pipes, Concrete Arch Pipes are now supported. And for Structures (Inlet\Outlet), Flared End Section, Trench Drain, Winged Headwall, Flexible Metal Rectangular End Section for Arc Corrugated Metal Pipe (CMP), and Flexible Metal Rectangular End Section for Round CMP. Additionally, several new sizes have been added to existing part families.
- A new Quantity Takeoff ability was added. You can access master pay item lists and assign pay items to drawing objects or closed areas.
- New Surface-related routines include a better memory management schema for large data sets. Although introduced in 2009, this feature maintains 2 million points in RAM.

Beyond this figure, however, the points are then sent to a paging file on the hard disk. The only limit here is practicality and hard disk size.

- Survey features include a new data import wizard for various data sources and a linework definition file for field collection.

Civil 3D 2009 enhancements comprise the following items: A hydraulic solution called Hydraflow from Intellisolve, a new **SIMPLIFY SURFACE** command that allows you to remove extra points from a surface without sacrificing accuracy, including points that are in an external point file or database, Breakline weeding, Expansion or compaction factors for volume computations, the ability to locate observation tolerance errors for angle, drawing settings support of International Foot or US Survey Foot for units in a drawing that are displayed in feet, a translate survey database tool, support for AASHTO criteria for design and analysis for alignments and profiles, and a new Design Check setting that allows for managing design criteria that are expressed as formulas. It also adds a variety of fixed, floating, and free linework to the constraint-based design tools, station tracking in multiple viewports, the ability to Mirror template subassemblies, better sharing of assemblies and four new subassemblies, the ability to generate labels from Civil 3D objects that exist within an Xref, a new wizard that improves the process of creating single or multiple section views, an external editor for data shortcuts, an improved eTransmit that includes Vault references and data shortcuts, render materials that can be displayed in Google Earth, and a changed status bar that shows a link to Vault and the addition of Survey Link Extension version 7.5.5 (from TDS).

Civil 3D 2008 added Plan Production tools as the main feature. Other enhancements comprised the ability to do more with Sub-Entities, added the old Land Desktop **Lines/Curves** menu, and the ability to extract AutoCAD objects from the Civil 3D objects. The Civil 3D 2007 version added significant labeling enhancements, corridor design improvements, new subassemblies, new piping tools, and an entire survey solution for data collectors and traverses. The Civil 3D 2006 version added the following enhancements to its feature set: corridor design enhancements, additional data sharing, and utility pipe drafting. The previous version, Civil 3D 2005, was the second iteration (but the first public release) of the Civil 3D solution and added Autodesk VIZ to the solution suite. The first version, a "pre-release" version called Civil 3D, was actually a preview of what was to come. The marketing philosophy of Autodesk was to release the software to its current clients in advance of it being made available to the public. In this fashion, Autodesk's goal was to build interest in the user population and persuade them to become acclimated to the revolutionary philosophies required to use the software successfully. It also wanted the customer to have time to consider the implementation expenses and compare them with the productivity improvements.

The Civil 3D software is provided to Autodesk Land Desktop users who have subscriptions for the Civil Design add-on as part of the subscription service. In 2005, it was formally introduced for sale to the general public.

HARDWARE SPECIFICATIONS

This section is included because very often an information technology department does the purchasing for the organization. These departments usually buy generic desktop PCs and laptops with little regard for the applications being used. CADD systems and visualization software are some of the most hardware-intensive applications available, and they deserve to be budgeted for accordingly.

Note: Always check with the software manufacturer before making final decisions as specifications may change.

Autodesk Recommended System Requirements for AutoCAD Civil and AutoCAD Civil 3D

The following recommended configuration for Civil 3D 2009 is taken from the Autodesk website. There were no 2010 specifications available at the time of this writing, so it is assumed that the general architecture requirements have stayed about the same as they were for 2009.

- Intel® Pentium® 4 (3 GHz or higher); AMD Athlon™; multiple processors supported, dual-core supported
- 32-bit only: Microsoft® Windows Vista® Ultimate/Business/Enterprise, Microsoft® Windows XP (SP2)

Note: Windows XP 64 and Windows Vista 64 are supported in 32-bit compatibility mode only.

Note: Windows XP 64 and Windows Vista 64 are supported in 32-bit compatibility mode only.

- 3 GB RAM
- 5 GB free disk space for installation
- 1,280 × 1,024 display with true color, 1,600 × 1,200 or greater recommended (OpenGL® accelerator with full OGL ICD support not required)
- Microsoft® Internet Explorer® 6.0 (SP1 or later)
- DVD drive

Recommended Vault Server Components.   The Autodesk® Vault server components can be installed on the same computer as AutoCAD Civil or AutoCAD Civil 3D 2009 if the computer complies with these recommended requirements:

- 3 GHz or higher: Intel Pentium 4, Intel® Xeon®, AMD Athlon 64, AMD Opteron™
- 32-bit: Microsoft Windows XP Home Edition (SP2), Microsoft Small Business Server 2003 Standard/Premium (SP2), Microsoft Small Business Server 2003 R2 Standard/Premium (SP2)
- 32-bit and 64-bit: Microsoft Windows XP Professional (SP2), Microsoft Vista Home Basic/Premium (SP1), Microsoft Vista Ultimate/Enterprise/Business (SP1), Microsoft Server 2003 Standard/Enterprise (SP2), Microsoft Server 2003 Standard/Enterprise R2 (SP2), Microsoft Server 2008 Standard/Enterprise
- 2 GB RAM
- 60 GB free disk space for installation
- Microsoft Internet Explorer 6.0 (SP1 or later)
- DVD drive

Identify the Civil Engineering Industry

Now that the software used in this text as well as the suggested hardware have been identified, discussion follows on the work you will be doing, the business of civil engineering, and the kinds of projects that would be appropriate to apply Civil 3D toward.

The types of work falling into an industry that provides civil engineering design typically include services such as Planning, Preliminary Design, Surveying, Final Design, Value Engineering, Plans Preparation and Construction Document Preparation, and Site Data Preparation. The goal is to define which industries can make use of the Civil 3D product at this time.

Civil engineering projects are generally performed for two types of clients: public clients and private clients. Public clients include governmental agencies such as municipal, county, state, and federal agencies. Private clients include landowners, developers, and industrial, commercial, and legal organizations.

The projects performed for the *public sector* often include corridor design such as roads, tunnels, channels, and aqueducts; construction management; environmental engineering; transportation (which includes traffic flows, evacuation planning, signage, and signalization); airport engineering; bridge design; waste management; wetlands delineation and mitigation; water supply (which includes treatment, distribution, and pump stations); sewage networks (which includes collection and effluent treatment); and water resources.

The project types performed for the *private sector* may be comprised of design of subdivisions, roads, commercial sites, and industrial sites. They may also include design, analysis, and study of waste management, wetlands, water supply and distribution, sewage systems, and water resources. Additional work is performed as part of construction management on projects as well as the legal and real estate professions.

Civil 3D provides for some hydraulic tasks but does use object technology in its pipe networks. Significant control using the pipe style exists for laying out the pipe network and making modifications to it. The seed for formulas can be observed in some of the settings and portends the things to come.

Civil 3D does not provide tools that directly apply to bridge design. Neither does it support tools for some surveying tasks such as data collection and GPS computations.

Of the projects mentioned here, Civil 3D is a *primary solution* for corridors, airports, waste management, subdivision, road, commercial site, and industrial site design. Of the projects mentioned here, Civil 3D is a *strong supporting solution* for a variety of drafting and analyses functions for construction management, environmental engineering, water systems, sewage and storm networks, transportation, wetlands delineation and mitigation, water resources, and the legal and real estate fields.

public sector: The area within civil engineering that provides funding for projects that emanate from tax revenues. This includes federal, state, county, city and town governmental entities, their associated agencies, and PUDs and MUDs.

private sector: The area within civil engineering that provides funding for projects that emanate from private sources. This includes land developers, homeowners, and professionals.

IDENTIFY THE BREAKDOWN AND FLOW OF ENGINEERING TASKS AND HOW CIVIL 3D CONTRIBUTES TO THE WORK EFFORT

By recognizing the tasks performed and the project requirements for each project type identified, it is possible to distinguish which tasks within these civil engineering projects benefit most by applying Civil 3D functionality to them.

Although the Civil 3D software is a revolutionary product and performs many worthwhile and industry leading functions, it would be beneficial to point out where the software offers extraordinary assistance to the user. The first step in accomplishing this task is to break down the types of projects that an engineer might undertake. The purpose here is to identify immediately project areas that are out of the scope of this text, identify project types that are strong candidates for use of Civil 3D as the primary solution, and identify those areas that can use Civil 3D as a supporting tool.

The second step is to identify the functionality that Civil 3D offers in performing computations or drafting assistance of those engineering tasks. The tasks are identified as well as how Civil 3D can provide improved productivity and functionality to those who use it.

The following listing provides a step-by-step description of each project's requirements. **The tasks that benefit most from the use of Civil 3D are denoted in bold type.** <u>Those tasks that can make important use of Civil 3D as a supporting tool are underlined.</u> Those tasks in normal type are outside the current feature set of Civil 3D. The functionality that Civil 3D offers is shown using the following key:

(1) Uses all Civil 3D functionality including alignments, parcels, corridor and grading tools, profiles, and sections

(2) Uses Civil 3D's modification benefits where the changes ripple through the design

(3) Uses alignments capabilities

(4) Uses parcels capabilities

(5) Uses corridor and/or profiles and sections capabilities

(6) Uses terrain modeling, surfaces, and grading capabilities

(7) Uses Civil 3D's drafting and labeling functions

(8) Uses built-in rendering engine

(9) Uses MAP 3D tools

(10) Utility/storm sewer piping

(11) Surveying capabilities for traverse development and data collection

For the Public Sector

The public sector has the following projects and can be DOTs, city, county, state agencies, public utility districts (PUDs), or municipal utility districts (MUDs). They are shown with the workflow milestones they involve.

Corridor Design.   See Figure D-1.

Figure D-1   Corridor design

- **Preliminary planning and alternative layout creation: (1), (2)**
- Communication with decision makers
- **Preliminary engineering: (1), (2)**
- Project funding and approval and notice to proceed

- Surveying activities including property research, zoning issues, ownership, determination of existing site conditions: (7), (11)
- **Terrain modeling: (1), (2), (6)**
- Determination of subsurface and geological conditions: (7)
- Wetlands determinations: (7)
- **R.O.W. determinations: (4)**
- **Curvilinear 2D geometry development, easements, alignments, parcels: (3), (4), (7)**
- **Drafting and labeling: (1)**
- **Corridor profile, section and corridor creation and analysis, roadway design, intersection ramp and gore development: (5)**
- Paving requirements: (7)
- **Intersection and cul-de-sac design: (5), (6), (7)**
- Utilities crossings, relocations, and conflict resolutions: (7)
- Drainage improvements, storm water piping, and retention: (10)
- Landscape design plans: (7)
- Irrigation design plans: (7)
- **Signage, electrical, and striping plans: (7)**
- **Erosion and siltation control design plans: (7)**
- Submit review plans
- **Make modifications based on review comments: (2)**
- **Construction plan development: (7)**
- Quantity takeoffs and cost estimations: (6), (7)
- **QA/QC and survey stakeout: (6), (7), (11)**
- **Public communication and public hearings with potential for visual renderings: (8)**

Construction Management.   See Figure D-2.

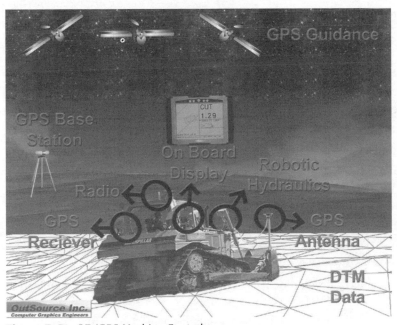

Figure D-2   3D/GPS Machine Control

- Obtain RFP, verifying plans, analyze design documents: (1)
- Quantities, earthworks takeoffs, and cost estimates: (6), (7)
- Proposal preparation: (8)

- Project awarded and notice to proceed
- Surveying activities including establishing project control, verify existing site conditions: (6), (7), (11)
- **Making design changes based on change orders and for constructability: (2)**
- **Curvilinear 2D geometry development: (1)**
- Quantity takeoffs and cost estimations: (6), (7)
- **Terrain modeling for existing and proposed conditions: (6)**
- **Earthworks computations: (6)**
- **Build/rebuild project data for road grading: (2), (5)**
- **Build/rebuild site grading data: (2), (5)**
- Build/rebuild utilities: (6), (7)
- **QA/QC of design plans and construction approaches: (2), (7)**
- **Generate stakeout information and/or GPS Machine Control: (1), (2)**
- **Format for machine control usage: (1), (2)**
- **Construction plan development: (1), (2)**
- Pavement design and analysis as-built surveying and plan generation: (6), (7)
- Project operations and maintenance: (6), (7)

Environmental Engineering

- **Curvilinear 2D geometry development for property lines, Planimetrics, etc.: (1), (2), (7)**
- **Terrain modeling and analysis: (3), (4), (6)**
- Proposed impact studies
- Data collection of above and below ground conditions, chemicals, species, etc.
- Subsurface water analysis, conditions, modeling: (6)
- Air quality conditions, analysis, modeling
- GIS development and mapping: (6), (7), (9)

Water Supply (Which Includes Treatment, Distribution, and Pump Stations)

- **Curvilinear 2D geometry development for waterline trunks, distribution systems: (3), (4)**
- Elevated storage: (6), (7)
- **Planimetrics, etc.: (7)**
- **Terrain development and analysis for waterline depth and conflict resolution: (1), (2), (6)**
- Water pressure analysis, demand loading, etc.
- Location of elevated storage, lift stations, capacities, etc.: (6), (7)
- Water treatment plants and processes (see Industrial Projects): (6), (7), (10)

Sewage Networks (Which Include Collection and Effluent Treatment)

- **Curvilinear 2D geometry development for trunkline, vacuum sewers and collection system, Planimetrics, etc.: (3), (4)**
- Location and design of collection system, lift stations, capacities, etc.: (6), (7)
- **Mapping and GIS tasks: (6), (8), (7)**
- **Drafting and labeling: (7)**
- **Terrain development and analysis of gravity flow systems: (1), (2), (6)**
- System capacity analysis

- Location and design of collection systems from main trunks to treatment facilities: (6), (7)
- Wastewater treatment plants and processes (see Industrial Projects): (6), (7)

Transportation (Which Includes Traffic Flows, Evacuation Planning, Signage, and Signalization).   See Figure D-3.

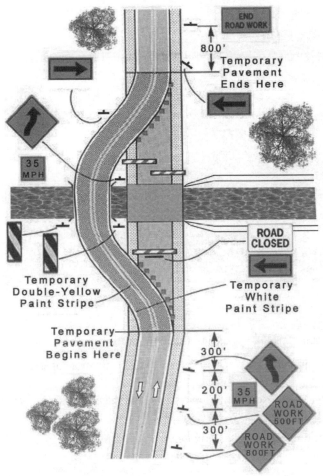

Figure D-3   Transportation

- **Geometry development: (1), (2)**
- **Planimetrics: (7)**
- Data collection, traffic counts
- Signalization
- HOV development plans and GIS studies: (6), (7)
- Data collection, traffic counts
- **Mapping and GIS tasks: (6), (7), (9)**
- Pavement design and analysis: (6), (7)
- **Drafting and labeling: (7)**

Wetlands

- Delineation, classification, and mitigation: (7)
- **Curvilinear 2D geometry development for wetlands and other boundaries, property lines, treelines, Planimetrics, etc.: (1), (2)**
- **Mapping and GIS tasks: (6), (7), (9)**

- **Drafting and labeling: (7)**
- Data collection and reduction
- **RTK/GPS and traditional surveying: (11)**

Water Resources.   See Figure D-4.

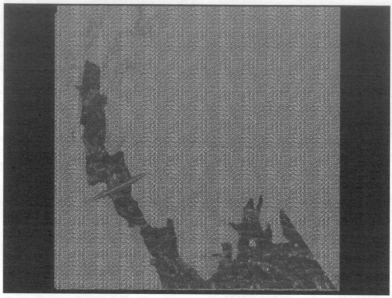

Figure D-4   Water resources

- **Preliminary planning: (1), (2)**
- Project funding and approval and notice to proceed
- Surveying activities including property research, ownership, determination of existing site conditions: (6), (7), (11)
- Determination of subsurface and geological conditions, flows, and magnitudes: (6), (7)
- Surface and groundwater water analysis
- Design/analysis of wells, water transfer systems, irrigation
- Hydrology and water supply
- River conditions and forecasts
- Water quality
- Weather forecasts
- Flood emergency information
- Water use, conservation, and planning
- Design and analysis of dams
- **Geometry development for Planimetrics: (1), (7)**
- Rainfall determinations
- Flood studies
- Wetlands determinations: (6), (7)
- Stormwater analysis and piping
- **Erosion and siltation control design: (6), (7)**
- Landscape analysis: (7)
- Chemical analysis
- **Development of maps: (6), (7), (9)**
- Report generation
- **QA/QC: (2)**
- **Public hearings with potential for visual renderings: (8)**

Airport Engineering.   See Figure D-5.

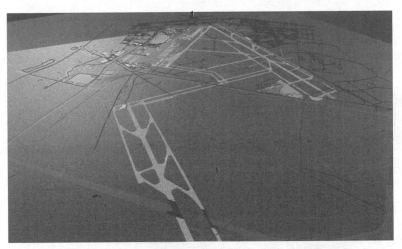

Figure D-5   Airport engineering

- Obtain FAA and local grants
- **Preliminary planning and alternative layout creation: (1), (2)**
- Communication with decision makers
- **Preliminary engineering: (1), (2)**
- Project funding and approval and notice to proceed
- Surveying activities including property research, zoning issues, ownership, determination of existing site conditions: (11)
- **Terrain modeling: (1), (2), (6)**
- Determination of subsurface and geological conditions: (6), (7)
- **Curvilinear 2D geometry development, runway/taxiways, FAA obstruction/clearance plans, parking lots, service industry access roads: (1), (7)**
- Security considerations: (6), (7)
- **Planimetrics, etc.: (1), (7)**
- FAA and state regulations compliance
- **FAA height contours, clearance analysis, etc.: (1), (7)**
- Pavement design and analysis: (6), (7)
- Runway and taxiway profiles and sections or corridors: (1), (2), (6), (7)
- **Drafting and labeling: (6), (7)**
- **Drainage improvements: (10)**
- Storm water retention: (6)
- Underground retention facilities: (6), (7)
- **Rough grading, finished grade development: (2), (6)**
- **Erosion and siltation control design: (2), (6)**
- **Final design engineering, pad siting for hangars and services: (1), (2), (6)**
- Landscape design: (6), (7)
- Irrigation design: (6), (7), (10)
- **Easement determinations: (4)**
- **Value engineering and review: (2)**
- **Engineering modifications: (2)**
- **Construction plan generation: (1)**
- **Quantities and cost estimates: (6), (7)**

- **QA/QC and survey stakeout: (1), (2), (7)**
- Obtain FAA and local construction grants
- **Public hearings with potential for visual renderings: (8)**

The Legal Field.   See Figure D-6.

Figure D-6   The legal field

- <u>Rezoning issues: (4)</u>
- <u>Study, research, analysis: (1)</u>
- <u>Legal, forensic graphics: (8)</u>
- Expert witness

Bridge Design.   See Figure D-7.

Figure D-7   Bridge design

- **Preliminary planning and alternative layout creation: (1), (2)**
- Communication with decision makers
- **Preliminary engineering: (1), (2)**

- Project funding and approval and notice to proceed
- Surveying activities including property research, zoning issues, ownership, determination of existing site conditions: (6), (7)
- **Terrain modeling: (1), (2), (6)**
- Determination of subsurface, underwater, and geological conditions: (6), (7)
- Wetlands determinations: (6), (7)
- **ROW determinations: (4), (7)**
- **Curvilinear 2D geometry development, easements, alignments, parcels: (3), (4), (7)**
- **Drafting and labeling: (1)**
- **Approach design, corridor profile, section and corridor creation and analysis, roadway design, intersection ramp and gore development: (5)**
- Structural requirements for beams, bents, columns, decks, etc.
- Paving requirements: (6), (7)
- **Intersection and cul-de-sac design: (5), (6), (7)**
- Utilities crossings, relocations, and conflict resolutions: (7)
- Drainage improvements: (10)
- Storm water retention: (6)
- Noise abatement design plans: (7)
- Landscape design plans: (7)
- Irrigation design plans: (7)
- **Signage, electrical, and striping plans: (7)**
- **Erosion and siltation control design plans: (7)**
- Submit review plans
- **Make modifications based on review comments: (2)**
- **Construction plan development: (7)**
- Quantity takeoffs and cost estimations: (6), (7)
- **QA/QC and survey stakeout: (6), (7)**
- **Public communication and public hearings with potential for visual renderings: (8)**

For the Private Sector

Subdivision Design.   See Figure D-8.

- **Preliminary planning and alternative layout creation: (1), (2)**
- Communication with decision makers
- **Preliminary engineering: (1), (2)**
- Project funding and approval and notice to proceed
- Surveying activities including property research, zoning issues, ownership, determination of existing site conditions: (7), (11)
- **Terrain modeling: (1), (2), (6)**
- Determination of subsurface and geological conditions: (7)
- Wetlands determinations: (7)
- **Refined site layout, park, and greenspace requirements**
- **Curvilinear 2D geometry development, easements, alignments, parcels: (3), (4), (7)**
- **Roadway design: (3), (5)**
- Paving requirements: (6), (7)
- **Intersection and cul-de-sac design: (5), (6), (7)**
- **Corridor profile, section, and corridor creation and analysis: (5), (6), (7)**

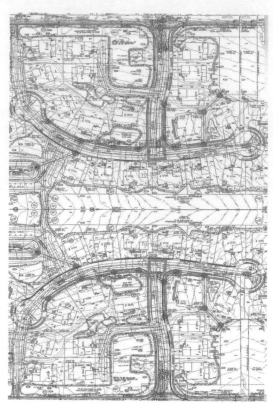

Figure D-8   Subdivision design

- **Drafting and labeling: (7)**
- **Rough grading, overlot, and finished grade development: (6)**
- **Drainage improvements: (10)**
- Storm water retention: (6)
- Sanitary sewer design plans and profiles: (5), (6), (7), (10)
- Waterline design plans and profiles: (5), (6), (7)
- Landscape design plans: (6), (7)
- Irrigation design plans: (6), (7)
- **Erosion and siltation control design plans: (2), (6)**
- Submit review plans
- **Make modifications based on review comments: (2)**
- **Construction plan development: (7)**
- Quantity takeoffs and cost estimations: (6), (7)
- **QA/QC and survey stakeout: (6), (7)**
- **Public communication and public hearings with potential for visual renderings: (8)**

Environmental Engineering

- **Curvilinear 2D geometry development for property lines, Planimetrics, etc.: (1), (2), (7)**
- **Terrain modeling and analysis: (3), (4), (6)**
- Proposed impact studies
- Data collection of above and below ground conditions, chemicals, species, etc.
- Subsurface water analysis, conditions, modeling: (6)
- Air quality conditions, analysis, modeling
- **GIS development and mapping: (6), (7), (9)**

Water Supply (Which Includes Reticulation Distribution and Pump Stations)

- **Curvilinear 2D geometry development for waterline trunks, distribution systems: (3), (4)**
- Elevated storage: (6), (7)
- **Planimetrics: (7)**
- **Terrain development and analysis for waterline depth and conflict resolution: (1), (2), (6)**
- Water pressure analysis, demand loading, etc.
- Location of elevated storage, lift stations, capacities, etc.: (6), (7)
- Water treatment plants and processes (see Industrial Projects): (6), (7), (10)

Sewage Networks (Which Include Collection, Not Treatment)

- **Curvilinear 2D geometry development for trunkline, vacuum sewers and collection system, Planimetrics, etc.: (3), (4)**
- **Mapping and GIS tasks: (6), (8), (7)**
- **Drafting and labeling: (7)**
- **Terrain development and analysis of gravity flow systems: (1), (2), (6)**
- System capacity analysis
- Location and design of collection systems up to main trunks or lift stations: (6), (7)

Transportation (Which Includes Traffic Flows for Commercial and Large Subdivision Impact)

- **Geometry development: (1), (2)**
- **Planimetrics: (7)**
- Data collection, traffic counts
- **Mapping and GIS tasks: (6), (7), (9)**
- Pavement design and analysis: (6), (7)
- **Drafting and labeling: (7)**

Wetlands Delineation and Mitigation

- Delineation, classification, and mitigation: (7)
- **Curvilinear 2D geometry development for wetlands and other boundaries, property lines, treelines, Planimetrics, etc.: (1), (2)**
- **Mapping and GIS tasks: (6), (7), (9)**
- **Drafting and labeling: (7)**
- **Data collection and reduction: (11)**
- **RTK/GPS and traditional surveying: (11)**

Commercial Design.   See Figure D-9.

- **Preliminary planning and alternative layout creation: (1), (2)**
- Communication with decision makers
- **Preliminary engineering: (1), (2)**
- Project funding and approval and notice to proceed
- Surveying activities including property research, zoning issues, ownership, determination of existing site conditions: (7)
- **Terrain modeling: (1), (2), (6)**
- Determination of subsurface and geological conditions: (7)
- **Access requirements: (4), (7)**
- **Site layout, parking space requirements, curvilinear 2D geometry development, easements, BRLs, parking lots, parcels, Planimetrics: (4), (7)**

Figure D-9   Commercial design

- Paving requirements: (7)
- **Drafting and labeling: (7)**
- **Drainage improvements: (10)**
- **Stormwater retention: (6)**
- Underground retention facilities: (7)
- **Rough grading, finished grade development: (6)**
- **Erosion and siltation control design: (7)**
- **Final design engineering, pad siting: (6)**
- Environmental considerations, oil/water separators, etc.: (7)
- Pavement design and analysis: (7)
- Water and sanitary plans and profiles: (7), (10)
- **Erosion and siltation control plans: (7)**
- Landscape design: (7)
- Irrigation design: (7)
- **Easement determinations: (4)**
- **Value engineering and review: (2)**
- **Engineering modifications: (2)**
- **Construction plan generation: (1)**
- **Quantities and cost estimates: (6), (7)**

- **QA/QC and survey stakeout: (1), (2), (7)**
- **Public hearings with potential for visual renderings: (8)**

Industrial (and Waste Management) Site Layout.   See Figure D-10.

Figure D-10   Industrial (and waste management) site layout

- **Preliminary planning and alternative layout creation: (1), (2)**
- Communication with decision makers
- **Preliminary engineering: (1), (2)**
- Project funding and approval and notice to proceed
- Surveying activities including property research, zoning issues, ownership, determination of existing site conditions: (7), (11)
- **Terrain modeling: (1), (2), (6)**
- Determination of subsurface and geological conditions: (7)
- **Public and staff access requirements: (7)**
- **Site layout, parking space requirements, curvilinear 2d geometry development, easements, BRLs, parking lots, parcels, Planimetrics: (3), (4), (7)**
- **Drafting and labeling: (1)**
- Environmental engineering analyses and considerations
- **Drainage improvements: (10)**
- Storm water retention, underground retention facilities: (6)
- **Rough grading, finished grade development: (2), (6)**
- **Erosion and siltation control design: (2), (6)**
- **Final design engineering, pad siting: (1), (2), (6)**
- Environmental considerations, oil/water separators, etc.: (7)
- Pavement design and analysis: (6), (7)
- Water and sanitary plans and profiles: (1), (2), (6), (7), (10)
- **Erosion and siltation control plans: (6), (7)**
- Landscape design: (7)
- Irrigation design yard piping design for plant activities: (7)
- EPA requirements for spill and containment: (7)

- Disaster and evacuation plans: (7)
- **Easement determinations: (4), (7)**
- **Value engineering and review: (1)**
- **Engineering modifications: (2)**
- **Construction plan generation: (1)**
- Quantity takeoffs and cost estimations: (6), (7)
- **QA/QC and survey stakeout: (6), (7)**
- **Public hearings with potential for visual renderings: (8)**

Hydrology and Water Resources: Surface Water Analysis, Groundwater Analysis, Wells, Water Transfer, Irrigation.   See Figure D-11.

Figure D-11   Surface water analysis

- **Preliminary planning, project funding and approval, and notice to proceed: (1), (2)**
- Surveying activities including property research, ownership, determination of existing site conditions: (7), (11)
- Determination of subsurface and geological conditions, flows, and magnitudes: (7)
- **Geometry development for Planimetrics: (4), (7)**
- Rainfall determinations
- Flood studies
- Wetlands determinations: (7)
- Storm water analysis
- **Erosion and siltation control design: (2), (6)**
- Landscape analysis: (6), (7)
- Chemical analysis
- **Development of maps: (6), (7), (9)**
- Report generation: (1)
- **QA/QC: (1), (2), (7)**
- **Public hearings with potential for Visual Renderings: (8)**

The Legal Field.   See Figure D-12.

- Rezoning issues: (4)
- Study, research, analysis: (1)

Figure D-12   Rezoning issues, shadow studies

- Legal, forensic graphics: (8)
- Expert witness consulting

Civil 3D's Visualization Capabilities

E

Appendix
Objectives

- Understand the art of visualizing your designs for display to the public.
- Have an awareness of a variety of examples in which renderings helped projects succeed through public hearings.

INTRODUCTION

This chapter provides you with a brief introduction on the art of visualizing your designs for display to the public. Visualizations can develop stunning and photorealistic computer renderings of projects. The objective here is simple: to introduce visualization to Civil 3D users. This feature should be explored by the user whenever the opportunity presents itself and may actually warrant its own textbook. This chapter commences with some examples of where these renderings might be used in the civil engineering business. Indeed, the examples provided were extracted from some of Harry Ward's actual projects.

In today's very visual society, communicating designs is a paramount necessity for engineers and designers. Civil engineers seem to lag behind other disciplines when it comes to visualizations, and the reason probably goes back to the idea that most engineers do not design in 3D. That is why Civil 3D could cause a paradigm shift in the way engineers work if it assists them in moving into three dimensions.

SAMPLES OF RENDERINGS

Some examples of renderings of projects that Harry Ward has performed include the following.

Figure E-1 shows a 3D model and rendering of a Virginia high school to depict it at night with lighting. It was developed for public hearings for new construction at the school.

The site pictured in Figure E-2 was a 1.5-square-mile model developed for public hearings on the new road and bridge. The graphic is a computer rendering of the site.

The roadway and bridge were cut from this model and overlayed geographically into a photograph of the site to create the photomontage in Figure E-3. The existing conditions can be viewed in the upper right of the photomontage.

Figure E-1 A rendering of a Virginia high school sports field

Figure E-2 A 1.5-square-mile model of a road and bridge for public hearings

Figure E-3 Photorealistic photomontage

The rendering in Figure E-4 was done for a local parks organization for public hearings to show that a quality structure and related grounds were to be built in its neighborhood.

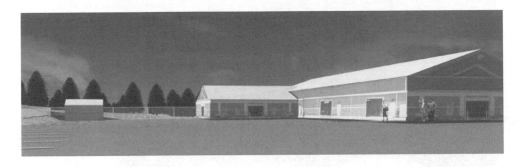

Figure E-4   Golf course maintenance building

The site in Figure E-5 was developed as a 3D model and rendered for use in a litigation case. It had to do with zoning issues and included several scenarios of waivers that might be applicable.

Scenario 4 - Iso Viewpoint, Allowable Height Under Proposed Design Regulations With 30% Waiver

Figure E-5   Zoning issues and shadow studies

The model and photomontage in Figure E-6 were done for a DOT project to show how a lane widening would appear. The lane on the left with its respective shoulder did not exist when this rendering was done.

Figure E-6   Photorealistic photomontage

The rendering and 3D model in Figure E-7 were done for a DOT project and include a new bridge and entrance monument with decorative lighting. The existing conditions are shown in the upper right of the photomontage.

Figure E-7   A new gateway to Annapolis

The 3D model in Figure E-8 was built for an international airport and displayed within the state legislature to show the legislators how the airport would look after construction in the year 2010. New interstate highways, railway spurs, and overhead taxiways were all part of the project. New parking and concession facilities were in the model as well as expanded service areas.

Figure E-8   An international airport

In the model pictured in Figures E-9 and E-10, lighting was a factor, and the office building and parking are depicted with both daytime and nighttime lighting. Everything is done to engineering specifications including parking lot drainage, cross slopes on sidewalks, and so forth.

The example in Figure E-11 is of another airport but shows a 3D model with an orthophoto draped onto it. Some relatively simple structures were placed on the model depicting planned expansion.

Figure E-9   A commercial office building—daylight

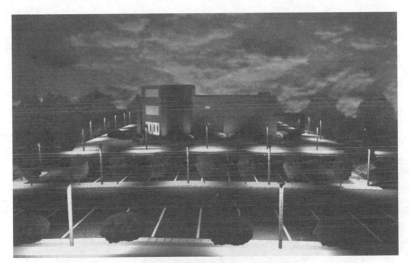

Figure E-10   A commercial office building—night lights

Figure E-11   Orthophoto draping

The project shown in Figure E-12 included improvements to both the site as well as the building for this V.A. hospital. It was shown to the directors of the hospital prior to construction so they could visualize what the plans indicated.

Figure E-12 V.A. hospital improvements

The last 3D model and rendering (Figure E-13) was performed for public hearings to allow for a roadway extension to be built. The model was projected into photographs of the site to show a photorealistic view of the project.

Figure E-13 Public hearing presentation for a roadway extension

This exercise has worked in previous versions of the software. Although the author had issues in applying multiple masks in the 2010 version of the software, he felt it important to retain this exercise to inform you that Civil 3D can build masks on surface objects for rendering purposes.

Exercise E-1: Civil 3D Example

You will now take a short trip into the visualization world by opening a file you have worked on and viewing it in a 3D perspective.

Civil 3D has visualization built in. In order to expedite the lesson, once you open the file, also notice that some closed polylines have been drawn on the **C-Mask** layer. The surface modeling in Civil 3D allows for masks to be placed on the data, which can affect several things, including rendering. The green masks represent grass-covered areas, the blue masks represent sand areas, the red areas indicate gravel drives, and the black mask indicates the paved road. There are five grass areas, three sand areas, two gravel areas, and one paved road.

1. Let us begin by opening Appendix-E-a.dwg. You see the surface you have been dealing with in various parts of this text as well as the masks.

2. In the **Toolspace**, under the **Prospector** tab, expand **Surfaces** to see the **Existing ground**.
3. Expand **Existing ground**, and you see an item for **Masks**. Right-click on **Masks** and select **Create Mask....**
4. When prompted, select the **green** colored masks to apply to the grass material.
5. The **Create Mask** dialog box appears, as shown in Figure E-14.

Figure E-14   The Create Mask dialog box

6. Accept the name as the default; enter **Grass** for the description. Click on the **Value** for **Mask type** and select **Inside**. Change the **Mid-ordinate distance** to **3′**, and select **Sitework.Planting.Grass.Thick** for the **Render Material Surface**. Hit **OK**.
7. Right-click on **Masks** and select **Add....**
8. The **Create Mask** dialog box appears.
9. Accept the name as the default; enter **Sand** for the description. Click on the **Value** for **Mask type** and select **Inside**. Change the **Mid-ordinate distance** to **3′**, and select **Sand** for the **Render Material Surface**. Hit **OK**.
10. When prompted, select a **blue** colored mask to apply to the sand material.
11. Repeat steps 7 through 10 for the additional two sand areas.
12. Right-click on **Masks** and select **Add....**
13. The **Create Mask** dialog box appears.
14. Accept the name as the default; enter **Gravel-Mixed** for the description. Click on the **Value** for **Mask type** and select **Inside**. Change the **Mid-ordinate distance** to **3′**, and select **Gravel-Mixed** for the **Render Material Surface**. Hit **OK**.
15. When prompted, select a **red** colored mask to apply to the gravel material.
16. Repeat steps 12 through 15 for the additional gravel area.
17. Right-click on **Masks** and select **Add....**
18. The **Create Mask** dialog box appears.
19. Accept the name as the default; enter **Asphalt** for the description. Click on the **Value** for **Mask type** and select **Inside**. Change the **Mid-ordinate distance** to **3′**, and select **Asphalt** for the **Render Material Surface**. Hit **OK**.
20. When prompted, select a **black** colored mask to apply to the asphalt material. Save the file.

Because the file is developed, you now view it in 3D.

21. Type **V** for **View**, select the view called **Corridor ISO**, hit **Set Current**, and hit **OK**.
22. Turn on all layers and thaw them out.
23. Then select **Visual Styles >> Realistic** from the **View** pull-down menu.
24. Use the **Zoom** command to zoom out and observe the view, and you should see grass, sand, gravel, and asphalt, as shown in Figure E-15.

We are now in a new world and that is 3D modeling and visualizations!

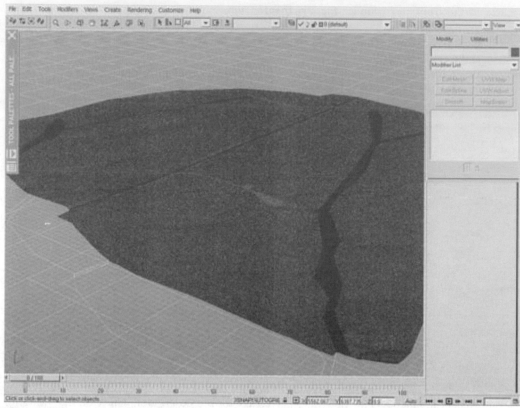

Figure E-15   Materials are applied

SUMMARY

The art of visualizing your designs is an important ability, and this chapter provided a brief introduction to using Civil 3D to do that. With visualizations, you can develop stunning computer renderings of projects. Being able to communicate your designs is paramount for engineers and designers, and this appendix gave examples of renderings.

Glossary

Alignment A series of two-dimensional curvilinear geometry elements, used to represent features such as road centerlines where it is beneficial to understand the relationship that these elements have to each other.

Assemblies Objects that manage collections of subassemblies; used for the basic structure of a corridor object.

Azimuth The North azimuth measures angles from the North axis, in a clockwise direction to 360°.

Bearing/bearing intersect Set points at the intersection of two bearings.

Bearing A point of latitude and longitude that measures a heading and are broken into four 90° quadrants: North, South, East, and West.

Bifurcated highway Where one direction of traffic has an independent PGL from the opposite direction of traffic. The profile may go uphill in one direction and downhill in the opposite direction.

Breaklines 3D polylines representing breaks in the planar slopes of the terrain. A breakline causes the mathematics of the terrain modeling to avoid building triangles that would cross a breakline. The triangle thus has a side adjacent to the breakline but does not cross it.

BRL Building restriction lines indicate the limits for construction of structures inside a property. They ensure that structures aren't built too close to other structures.

Broken back curve An alignment that has a linear segment either coming into or leaving an arc that is not tangent to the arc. This is usually not allowed in most jurisdictions.

CAD Computer aided drafting.

CADD Computer aided design/drafting.

Cartesian A word variation relating to the French mathematician René Descartes.

Civil 3D The short term used in this text for the software package officially called Autodesk Civil 3D.

COGO Software geared toward solving coordinate geometry problems.

Contour A linestring of a constant elevation on the site. It can be open or closed.

Control survey Sets the "monumentation" for the project. All survey shots and references typically come from or tie back to this monumentation.

Corridor A structure that allows passage or conveyance of people or things.

Cross section The cross section for the roadway is defined as an orthogonal view of the terrain model as it crosses the alignment and is draped onto the existing ground terrain model. Users determine the length of the section depending on how far to the left and right they would like information computed and displayed. Sections are usually computed at regular intervals, say, every 20′ along the entire length of the alignment. They can also be computed at irregular or user-defined locations to accommodate pertinent events that might interest the engineer such as driveway locations, cross streets, utility crossings, and the like. There are also occurrences where sections may be computed that are not orthogonal such as stream crossings or utility crossings.

Curvilinear objects These include arcs and spirals. Arcs or circular curves have a constant radius from beginning to end. Spirals have constantly changing radii from start to end.

Daylighting Represents where the slope grading intersects with the existing ground surface.

Description key sets A library of codes that control how points are created, where they are created, and what they represent.

Distance/distance intersect Set points at the intersection of two circles defined by their center points and respective radii distances.

DTM Digital terrain model.

Ellipsoid A mathematical surface that best fits the shape of the geoid.

Existing ground The natural ground conditions of the site before development.

Existing ground profile The vertical alignment for the roadway as defined by the location of the horizontal alignment draped onto the existing ground terrain model.

External data references Additional data files that can augment how point data is stored.

Feature line An object that the grading commands can work with. It represents breaks in the surface features. For example, the edge of pavement, ditches, or daylighting could be feature lines. Their appearance is controlled by feature line styles.

Finished ground The improved conditions for the site.

Geodetic datum A mathematical representation of the Earth.

Geodetic direction and distance Computing a point using a geodetic datum, a geodetic azimuth, and a distance along the mathematical face of the Earth for that part of the country. For instance, 1000′ along the face of the Earth is less than 1000′ horizontally because the Earth is curved.

Geoid Surface that is equal to sea level if it is not impeded or disturbed by any land masses.

GIS Geographic information system.

GPS Geographic positioning system.

Grade A change in elevation over a horizontal distance, usually described in percent (%).

Grading The grading object created in Civil 3D. It is dynamic and interacts with its environment.

Greenspace An area dedicated to the preservation or replacement of vegetation that may be reduced as a result of construction. Planning professionals often ensure that requirements for greenspace are met for a project.

Paradigm shift A fundamental change in how processes are performed.

Parcel A plot of land, usually a subdivision of a larger, quantified area.

PC Point of curvature

PGL The profile grade line is the proposed profile.

Point file formats Preformatted definitions for importing or exporting points.

Point groups A Civil 3D object representing a collection of points grouped by a relationship such as utility points, property points, terrain points.

Point styles A definition of how the point should appear.

PRC Point of reverse curvature

Private sector The area within civil engineering that provides funding for projects that emanate from private sources. This includes land developers, homeowners, and professionals such as doctors and attorneys.

Profile An object containing elevation data that is related to a horizontal alignment. It can apply to existing conditions or proposed conditions. The information within the profile is typically referred to by stations and elevations.

Profile view A Civil 3D term for the location in Civil 3D where profiles are displayed. Each profile view displays new or existing profiles and offsets for one horizontal alignment. Although you can create profiles without displaying them on a profile view, when a profile view is created, the complete list of profiles for the alignment is displayed so that a profile can be selected for display in the profile view.

Proposed profile The vertical alignment for the roadway as defined by the proposed vertical tangents and vertical curves.

PT Point of tangency

Public sector The area within civil engineering that provides funding for projects that emanate from tax revenues. This includes federal, state, county, city, and town governmental entities; their associated agencies; and PUDs and MUDs.

Pull-down menus, toolbars, pop-downs, and **dialog boxes** Interface items.

PVC The point of vertical curvature where the vertical curve begins and departs the tangent. also called *BVC* for begin vertical curve.

PVI The point of vertical intersection of the incoming and outgoing vertical tangents. This is also referred to as the *VPI* or vertical point of intersection.

PVT The point of vertical tangency where the vertical curve ends and returns to the tangent. Also called *EVC* for end vertical curve.

Rate of superelevation These values vary, but numbers on the order of 0.06 ft/ft and 0.04 ft/ft are often observed. AASHTO (American Association of State Highway and Transportation Officials) provides examples of design superelevation rates based on the design speed, the radius of curve, and the superelevation rate. The website for AASHTO is http://www.transportation.org/aashto/home.nsf/FrontPage. Note that these values represent a rate of change, say, 0.04 ft/ft. Thus for a typical template with a 2% cross slope, the edge of pavement will rise 0.04 feet for every linear foot of highway. In this case, it will take 50 linear feet for a 2% cross slope to rise to 0% or flat (example: 2.0/0.04 = 50.0).

Real numbers Expressed by allowing decimals that have an infinite sequence of digits to the right of the decimal point.

Right of way (ROW) The property typically owned by a government agency and usually dedicated for roadway usage. The roads must be built inside the state ROW so that they are not running across private property.

Ripple-through effect A term coined to describe the dynamic modeling characteristics of Civil 3D in performing automatic updates to data.

Roadway assembly fragments Pieces of cross-sectional templates that are applied to locations on alignments where they can be controlled from and then stretched to various targets elsewhere in the corridor.

Rubber sheeting Stretches objects from one set of points to a new set of points, often used to correct scans and to compensate for map distortions.

Secant A line that intersects a circle twice. An external secant is the part of the secant that is outside the circle or arc.

Section view This is a Civil 3D term for the location in Civil 3D where sections are displayed. Each section view must be related to an alignment. The section view displays new or existing sections. You can also create sections by displaying them on a section view, but when you create a section view for an alignment, a complete list of sections is displayed and can be selected for display in the section view. Section views can be created for existing ground, or multiple section views can be developed. The display style of a section view can be altered, and labels and bands can be added as needed.

Slope A change in elevation over a horizontal distance, usually described by a ratio (3:1).

Slope distance The distance measured from point *A* to point *B* along an incline. It will always be longer than the horizontal distance when the slope is not horizontal or vertical.

Station A distance along a horizontal alignment that is usually divided by 100′. Therefore 12 stations is 1200′. In metric, this might represent kilometers such that station 10 is 10 kilometers.

Stationing Distance along a baseline. It is measured in units of 100 feet in Imperial units and, typically, 1000 meters in metric. Therefore, 1 station = 100′ and is illustrated as 1 + 00.

Subassembly The fundamental building blocks used to create assemblies. It defines the geometry of a component used in a corridor section and includes predeveloped components for such things as travel lanes, curbs, side slopes, and ditches. It has intelligent behavior built into it and can automatically adapt to design conditions comprising superelevations and cut or fill requirements.

Superelevation Refers to the cross slope introduced into a cross section of a roadway in order to compensate for the centrifugal forces created by horizontal curves. According to the laws of mechanics, when a vehicle travels on a curve it is forced outward by centrifugal force. On a superelevated roadway, this force is resisted by the vehicle weight component parallel to the superelevated surface and the side friction between the tires and pavement. The pavement is essentially tilted to counter the forces described above.

Table styles A library of styles for constructing tables that report on point information.

Tangent A line that intersects a circle once. A tangent line is perpendicular to the radius drawn to the point of tangency (or point of contact with the arc or circle). If a line is perpendicular to a radius at its outer endpoint, then it is tangent to the circle.

Template A template consists of one or more typical examples of how the roadway will appear for varying conditions, such as a roadway with a curb and gutter at the edge of the pavement or perhaps a shoulder treatment at the edge of the pavement. It is shown in a cross-sectional view and shows the road from left to right looking into the profile grade line (PGL).

3D Three dimensions, characterized by the use of the X-, Y-, and Z-axes in the Cartesian coordinate system resulting in real-world models.

3D-GPS machine control An emerging technology that allows construction equipment to obtain their earthmoving information from on-board computers with 3D data sets of the site. GPS receivers locate the vehicle, compare it to the data set, and automatically adjust the earthmoving blade to the appropriate height and angle to accomplish those goals.

TIN Triangulated irregular network representing the surface.

2D Two dimensions, characterized by the use of the X- and Y-axes in the Cartesian coordinate system resulting in planar material.

Vertical curves Parabolic curves located around a PVI to smooth the road as it transitions from one tangent grade to another. These curvilinear three-dimensional components of the vertical alignment denoted by a PVI and a length of curve are typically parabolic with an ever-changing radius.

Vertical tangents Linear objects in the profile representing a grade between PVIs. These are linear three-dimensional components of the vertical alignment denoted with a grade usually in percentage (%).

Visualization In the context of CADD, it is used to produce an image of something that does not exist so that the viewer can better understand the project or model being discussed.

Index

To access all student files and figures for this section of the textbook, go to the companion website, http://ups.prenhall/chet_madsen_civildrafting_7

Part II Contents

Chapter **9**

CONTOUR LINES   635

Chapter **10**

HORIZONTAL ALIGNMENT LAYOUT   671

Chapter **11**

PROFILES   683

Chapter **12**

EARTHWORK   709

Introduction to Civil Drafting Technology

Learning Objectives

After completing this chapter, you will be able to:

- Define civil drafting and civil engineering.
- Identify the purpose of civil engineering companies.
- Describe the schooling required to be a civil drafter.
- Define terms related to maps and civil drafting.
- Identify a variety of map types.
- Draw lines typically used in civil drafting.
- Generate words using typical civil drafting text styles.
- Create general and specific notes.
- Discuss workplace ethics.
- Identify professional organizations.
- Explain the purpose of intellectual property.

Key Terms

Civil drafting
Civil engineering
Ethics
Intellectual property
Maps
Title block
Cartography
Aeronautical chart
Contour lines
Cadastral map
Quadrangle map
Engineering map
Geographical map
Hydrologic map
Military map
Nautical chart
Photogrammetric map
Topographic map
Planning map
Digital elevation model (DEM)
Geologic map
Line work
Text
General notes
Field
Specific notes

To access all student files and figures for this section of the textbook, go to the companion website, http://ups.prenhall/chet_madsen_civildrafting_7

Introduction to Civil Drafting

This chapter describes general civil drafting and map concepts. Information about civil drafting and map drafting requirements and employment opportunities is also covered.

Topics include:

- Civil engineering companies
- Schooling
- Maps
- Computer-aided design and drafting (CADD)
- Basic civil drafting techniques
- Text
- General and specific notes

Civil drafting is drafting performed for civil engineering projects. **Civil engineering** is the branch of engineering relating to the design and building of projects such as highways, bridges, waterworks, harbors, railroads, canals, and building sites. The land site or subdivision upon which your house, condominium, or apartment is located was probably designed and drafted by a civil engineering company. Generally, anything that has to do with the design of the land for construction projects involves civil drafting. While civil drafting also involves designing and drafting structures such as bridges, this textbook focuses on land-related projects such as roads and building construction sites. For this reason, much of the content covers the theory and drafting of maps and related applications.

Civil Engineering Companies

Civil engineering is the oldest form of engineering known, after military engineering. It spans the surveying and alteration of the land, to the planning, design, construction, and maintenance of structures. A student wanting to become a civil engineer must complete four or five years of college and graduate with a bachelor of engineering or a bachelor of science degree. Students can specialize in one of the wide variety of subdisciplines in the final years of study. Students who desire to work as CADD drafters/designers for a civil engineering firm should complete a one-year certificate or a two-year associate of science degree, with studies in civil drafting and geographic information systems (GIS).

Civil engineering companies are located nationwide in most cities. Some of these companies specialize in certain aspects of the industry, while others are quite diversified. The following is a list of some of the tasks that civil engineering companies may take part in:

- Land planning and subdivision
- Transportation
- Flood control
- Irrigation and drainage

- Sewage and water treatment
- Municipal improvements
- Environmental studies
- Land and construction surveys
- Construction inspection
- Refuse disposal
- Map-making
- Power plants
- Hydrologic studies
- Foundation work and soil analysis
- Agribusiness

A complete directory of consulting engineers is available from the American Council of Engineering Companies (**www.acec.org**).

Drafting salaries of workers at civil engineering firms are usually competitive with those in other technologies. Working conditions vary but are usually excellent. Companies have a wide range of employee benefits. Check your local area regarding salary ranges and schooling requirements for entry-level drafters. Areas of the country differ in these concerns.

Schooling

Technical schools and community colleges throughout the United States and Canada have drafting programs. Schools may provide a specific drafting education in mechanical, architectural, civil, piping, structural, technical illustration, sheet metal, or electrical drafting. Other schools provide students with a more general CADD curriculum that may have courses in a variety of drafting areas. Often, a school focuses on the industry needs of the immediate area. The best thing to do is to identify the school program that will best serve your specific goals. Civil drafting is offered in many technical schools and community colleges.

Your specific goals in civil drafting may include learning one of several available CADD software programs. Most, if not all, technical schools and community colleges offer CADD classes in conjunction with drafting classes, and some places of employment provide additional industry- or company-specific CADD instruction to their employees who do drafting. While drafting with the aid of a computer is a skill in itself, your sound background and competence in essential drafting knowledge, technique, and standards are necessary to your success as a CADD operator. It is preferable that you combine drafting theory with your studies of CADD so that basic drafting skills are not overlooked. Therefore, if you are interested in civil drafting as a career, in addition to learning CADD, your schooling should include the development of some of these fundamental skills:

- Drafting theory and national standards
- Sketching techniques and skills
- Use of bearings and azimuths
- Use of the engineer's scale

- Scale conversion
- Conversion of surveying field notes
- Drawing of contour lines
- Use of mapping symbols
- Interpretation of legal descriptions
- Preparation of a plat and site plan
- Development of plans and profiles
- Layout of highways, centerlines, curves, and delta angles
- Drawing of cuts and fills
- Basic use and knowledge of surveying equipment
- Math through basic trigonometry

Professional Organizations

The American Design Drafting Association (ADDA), **www.adda.org**, is a nonprofit professional organization dedicated to the advancement of design and drafting. The ADDA sponsors the following programs and activities for the design drafting profession:

- Leadership
- Curriculum certification
- Student chapters
- National design drafting conference and contest
- Drafting examination review
- The *U.S. Department of Labor's Occupational Outlook Handbook* as a free download
- Employment center
- Drafter certification program
  - According to the ADDA Web site, Drafter Certification (CD) is an international program that allows drafters to indicate their knowledge of drafting concepts and internationally recognized standards and practices. ADDA developed the examination to elevate an individual's comprehension of the professional standards related to design drafting. Certification allows drafters to demonstrate professional capabilities and helps employers in identifying quality employees. The test does not cover software specific to CADD.
  - The ADDA Drafter Certification Examination is open to all individuals, regardless of experience and formal education. Membership in the ADDA is not required to take the test or become certified.
  - Becoming a Certified Drafter reflects your proven knowledge of drafting. Certification enhances your credibility as a professional, improves your opportunities for promotion and pay increases, and gives you a competitive edge in a highly technical job market.
  - When employers hire an ADDA Certified Drafter, they know that the new employee meets certification criteria and has demonstrated initiative and pride in the profession by becoming certified. Thus, certification can serve as one

criterion for differentiating among candidates in the selection process. Certification serves educators as a supplementary measurement of a student's performance on a nationally recognized level.

The American Council of Engineering Companies (ACEC), **www. acec.org**, is a national organization devoted to the business and support of engineering companies.

The American Society for Engineering Education (ASEE), **www. asee.org**, is a nonprofit member association dedicated to promoting and improving engineering and technology education.

The American Society of Civil Engineers (ASCE), **www.asce.org**, is a professional organization that provides important value to members, member careers, partners, and the public by developing leadership, advancing technology, advocating lifelong learning, and promoting the civil engineering profession.

National Computer-Aided Design and Drafting (CADD) Standards

Two CADD Standards are recognized nationally. The National Council for Advanced Manufacturing (NACFAM) publishes the *Computer-Aided Drafting and Design (CADD) Skill Standards*. This publication provides the skills needed for beginner CADD users. While this standard is not related specifically to civil drafting, it contains valuable content for beginning CADD drafters, professionals, and educators. The NACFAM Web site is **www.nacfam.org**.

The *U.S. National CAD Standard* was created by The CADD/GIS Technology Center, the American Institute of Architects (AIA), the Construction Specifications Institute (CSI), the U.S. Coast Guard, the Sheet Metal and Air Conditioning Contractors National Association (SMACNA), the General Services Administration (GSA), and the National Institute of Building Sciences (NIBS) Facilities Information Council. This standard is related to the drafting done for architecture, engineering, and construction, of which civil drafting is a part. This standard is discussed in detail in Chapter 2. The NIBS Web site is **http://nibs.org**. The U.S. National CAD Standard Web site is **www. nationalcadstandard.org**.

Workplace Ethics

Ethics are the rules and principles that define right and wrong conduct. A code of ethics is a formal document that states an organization's values and the rules and principles that employees are expected to follow. In general, codes of ethics contain these main elements:

- Be dependable
- Obey the laws
- Be honest
- Have integrity
- Treat others with respect

- Build teamwork through trust
- Be a good citizen
- Have good customer relations

Intellectual Property Rights

The success of a company often relies on the integrity of its employees. Products are often the result of years of research, engineering, and development. This is referred to as the intellectual property of the company. Protection of intellectual property can be critical to the success of the company in a competitive economy. This is one reason why it is very important for employees to help protect design ideas and trade secrets. You will often find proprietary notes on drawings that inform employees and communicate to the outside world that the information contained in the drawing is the property of the company and cannot be used by others without permission.

Map Basics

Maps are defined as graphic representations of part or all of earth's surface, drawn to scale on a plane surface. Constructed and natural features can be shown by using lines, symbols, and colors. Maps have many different purposes, depending on their intended usage. A map can accurately provide distances, locations, elevations, best routes, terrain features, and much more.

There are hundreds of different types of maps. Some maps are used to show construction sites for new homes or commercial projects, while other maps show the geography of the world. Civil engineering companies primarily prepare maps that fall into the first category, which include construction site plans and maps relating to the civil projects previously described. The chapters covered in this textbook provide you with basic information to continue a more in-depth study or on-the-job training of mapping and civil drafting.

Some maps, such as aeronautical and nautical maps, are more commonly referred to as *charts*. This distinction is shown in the following discussion about types of maps.

Map Title Block and Legend

When you use or read a map, the first place to look is the title block and *legend*. The information given here will tell immediately if you have the correct map. Other valuable information about map scales, symbols, compass direction, and special notes will also be given. Figure 1–1 provides examples of various title block and legend data.

Cartography

Cartography is the art of making maps and charts. A *cartographer* is a highly skilled professional who designs and draws maps. Cartography is considered an art. The cartographer is a master in the

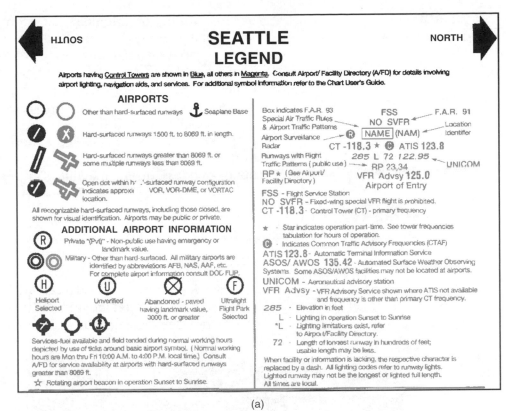

(a)

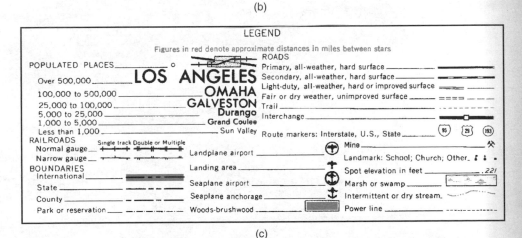

(b)

(c)

(d)

Figure 1–1. A variety of map title block and legend information examples.

(a. Courtesy of National Aeronautical Charting Office, Federal Aviation Administration, www.naco.faa.gov; c. Courtesy of U.S. Geological Survey, www.usgs.gov)

use of a variety of graphic media, computer software, mechanical and digital lettering methods, and artistic illustration.

Civil drafting and cartography are quite similar in that both professions deal with the making of maps. However, civil drafting is generally concerned with maps and plans for construction and other civil-related projects. Cartography requires that the technician use more graphic skills in the preparation of printed documents and maps. Often the job title "cartographer" requires four years of education, with emphasis on civil engineering, geography, navigation, optics, geodesy, digital imaging, and cartography.

Types of Maps

Aeronautical Charts

Aeronautical charts are used as an aid to air travel. These charts indicate important features of land, such as mountains and outstanding landmarks (see Figure 1–2). Commonly prepared in color and with

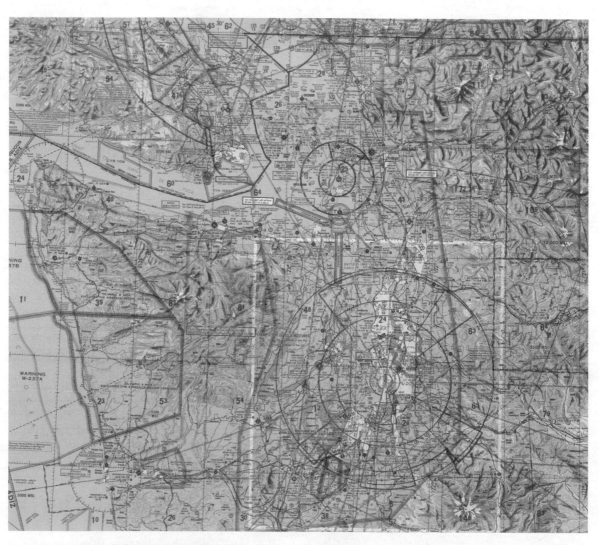

Figure 1–2.   **A typical aeronautical chart.**
(Courtesy of National Aeronautical Charting Office, Federal Aviation Administration, **www.naco.faa.gov**)

relief-shading methods, aeronautical charts are a very descriptive representation of a portion of the earth's surface. Contour lines are often provided with 200- to 1000-ft intervals. Contour lines are discussed in detail in Chapter 9 and covered in other chapters as related to the specific content. Aeronautical charts provide a comprehensive amount of information regarding air routes, airport locations, types of air traffic, radio aids to navigation, and maximum elevation of features. Look at Figure 1–2, and you can see all the detail shown in an aeronautical chart.

Cadastral Maps

Cadastral maps are large-scale maps that accurately show the features in a city or town. These types of maps are often used for city development, operation, and taxation. Figure 1–3 provides an example of a cadastral map.

Quadrangle Maps

A quadrangle map is a type of cadastral map that shows the division of land into grids known as sections. This type of map, shown in Figure 1–4, is used in the rectangular survey system discussed in Chapter 8.

Engineering Maps

Construction projects of all kinds are detailed to show the complete layout in an engineering map. The information provided on engineering maps can include:

- Property lines and boundary information
- Existing and proposed structures
- Roads
- Parking areas
- Drainage ways
- Utilities, such as sewer, water, electrical, and gas
- Landscape layout
- Contour lines
- Dimensions for location and sizes

Figure 1–5 provides two examples of civil engineering maps.

Engineering maps can also include plats. *Plats* are carefully surveyed and detailed maps of construction projects such as the subdivision with building lots as shown in Figure 1–6. The engineering map of an individual construction site is called a *plot* or *site plan*. An example of a residential site plan is shown in Figure 1–7. Plats and site plans are discussed in detail in Chapter 8.

Geographical Maps

Geographical maps are usually prepared at a small scale. These maps commonly show large areas of the earth, depicting continents,

Figure 1–3. **A typical CAD cadastral map.**
(Courtesy of Tri-Met, Tri-County Metropolitan Transportation District of Oregon)

countries, cities, rivers, and other important features. A map of the world and maps of individual countries or states are considered geographical maps. Figure 1–8 represents a typical geographical map.

Hydrologic Maps

Hydrologic maps accurately show the hydrographic boundaries of major river basins. In the United States, these maps are prepared by the U.S. Geological Survey in cooperation with the U.S. Water Resources Council. Hydrologic maps, which are used for water and land resource planning, are published at a scale of 1:500,000 (1 in.

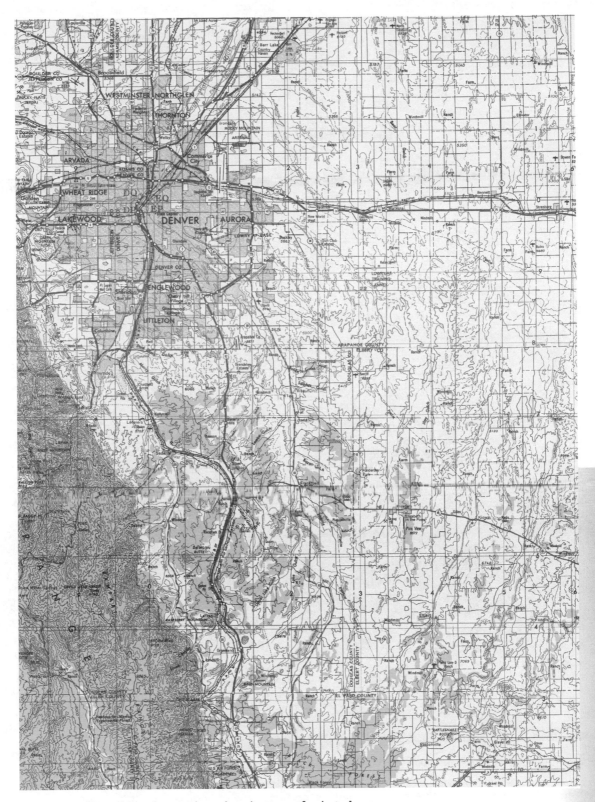

Figure 1-4.   The quadrangle map shown here is a type of cadastral map.
(Courtesy of the U.S. Geological Survey, www.usgs.gov)

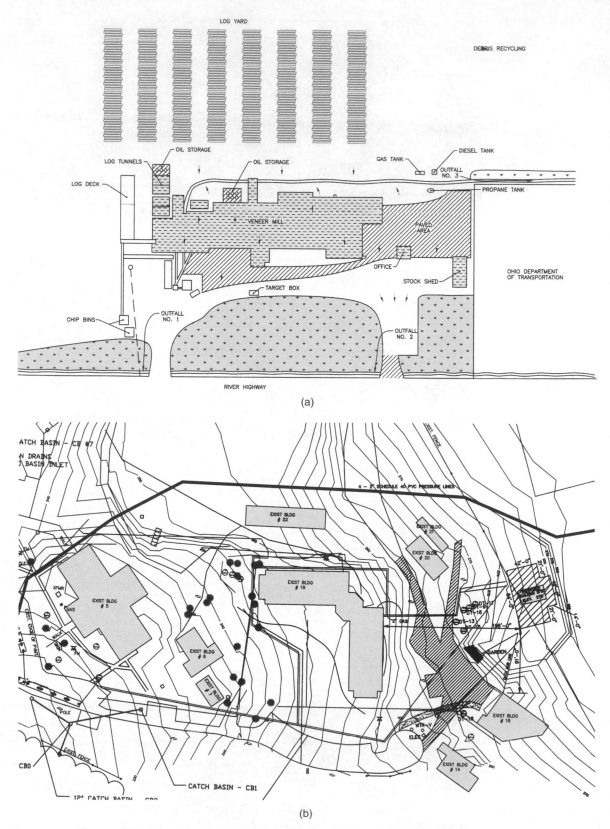

Figure 1–5. Two typical engineering site plans.

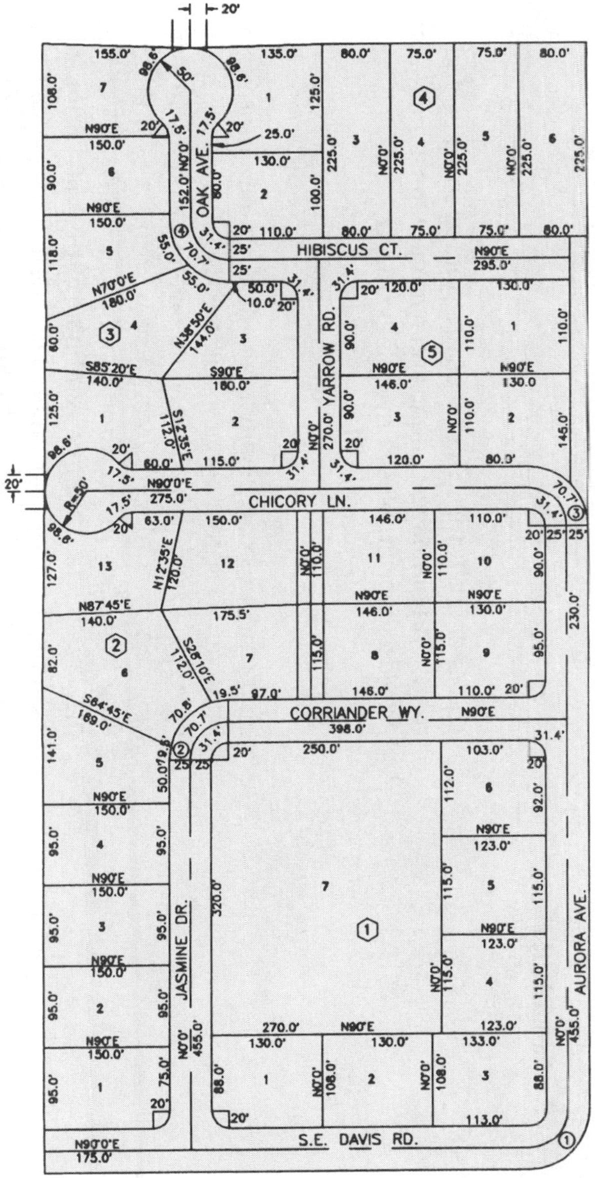

EICHOLAN ESTATES

A PART OF THE NE 1/4 OF THE NW 1/4 OF SEC. II
T.2S.,R.2E.,W.M.
CLACKAMAS COUNTY, OREGON

PREPARED BY: TANZER & ASSOC. SHEET 1 OF 5 SHEETS

	LOT	ANGLE	RADIUS	ARC LENGTH	CHORD	CHORD BEARING
BLK ①	1	90°	20.00'	31.42'	28.28'	N45°00'W
	3	90°	20.00'	31.42'	28.28'	N45°00'E
	6	90°	20.00'	31.42'	28.28'	N45°00'W
	7	90°	20.00'	31.42'	28.28'	S45°00'W
BLK ②	1	90°	20.00'	31.42'	28.28'	N45°00'E
	5	16°	70.00'	19.55'	19.48'	N8°00'E
	6	58°	70.00'	70.86'	68.87'	N45°00'E
	7	16°	70.00'	19.55'	19.48'	N82°00'E
	9	90°	20.00'	31.42'	28.28'	N45°00'E
	10	90°	20.00'	31.42'	28.28'	N45°00'W
	13	51°	20.00'	17.80'	17.22'	N64°30'W
	13	113°	50.00'	98.61'	83.39'	N83°30'W
BLK ③	1	113°	50.00'	98.61'	83.39'	N83°30'E
	1	51°	20.00'	17.80'	17.22'	N64°30'W
	2	90°	20.00'	31.42'	28.28'	N45°00'E
	3	90°	20.00'	31.42'	28.28'	N45°00'W
	4	45°	70.00'	54.98'	53.57'	N67°30'W
	5	45°	70.00'	54.98'	53.57'	N22°30'W
	7	51°	20.00'	17.80'	17.22'	N25°30'W
	7	113°	50.00'	98.61'	83.39'	N6°30'E
BLK ④	1	113°	50.00'	98.61'	83.39'	N6°30'W
	1	51°	20.00'	17.80'	17.22'	N25°30'E
	2	90°	20.00'	31.42'	28.28'	S45°00'E
BLK ⑤	2	45°	70.00'	54.98'	53.57'	S22°30'E
	3	90°	20.00'	31.42'	28.28'	N45°00'W
	4	90°	20.00'	31.42'	28.28'	N45°00'E
	℄					
	①	90°	45.00'	70.68'	63.64'	N45°00'E
	②	90°	45.00'	70.68'	63.64'	N45°00'E
	③	90°	45.00'	70.68'	63.64'	N45°00'W
	④	90°	45.00'	70.68'	63.64'	N45°00'W

Figure 1–6. A typical subdivision with building lots.

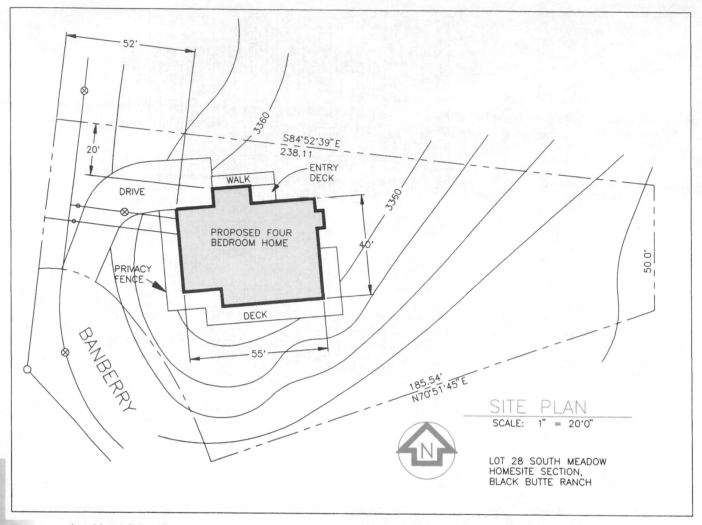

Figure 1–7. A residential site plan.

equals about 8 mi). The maps are printed in color and contain information on drainage, culture, and hydrographic boundaries. Figure 1–9 provides two samples of hydrologic maps.

Military Maps

Military maps can be any maps that contain information of military importance or that serve a military use. A military map can be used by a soldier in the field and can have information about terrain, concealment, and cover. It can also be a map of a large geographical area that can be used for military planning. Military maps often display special military symbols that signify military activity. For example, blue symbols represent friendly forces, while red symbols represent enemy forces. Distance on military maps is measured in meters, and angle is measured in mils. Mils is the abbreviation for milliradian. For example, bomb and gun sight settings are expressed in mils, which is an angular measurement, where 1° is equal to 17.45 mils. Military maps are also designed to be read using a red light during dark conditions. A section from a military map is shown in Figure 1–10.

Figure 1–8. A typical geographical map.
(Courtesy of the U.S. Geological Survey, www.usgs.gov)

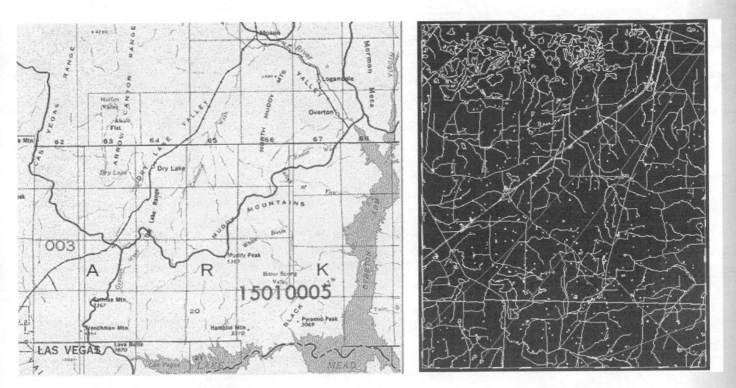

Figure 1–9. Two forms of typical hydrologic maps.
(Courtesy of the U.S. Geological Survey, www.usgs.gov)

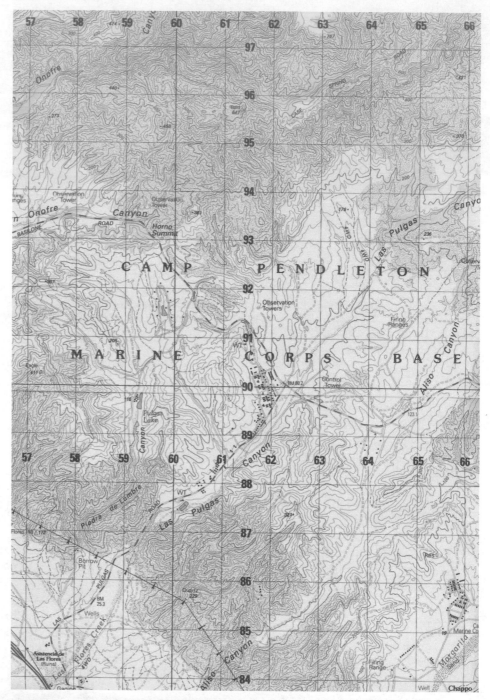

Figure 1–10.   A military map may look very similar to a quadrangle map, but it uses different units and displays military significant information, symbols, and colors.
(Courtesy of the U.S. Geological Survey, www.usgs.gov)

Nautical Charts

Nautical charts are special maps used as aids to water navigation. These charts provide such information as water depths, bridge clearances, and overhead cables. They also show navigation lanes, lighthouses, beacons, and buoys. Figure 1–11 shows a sample nautical chart.

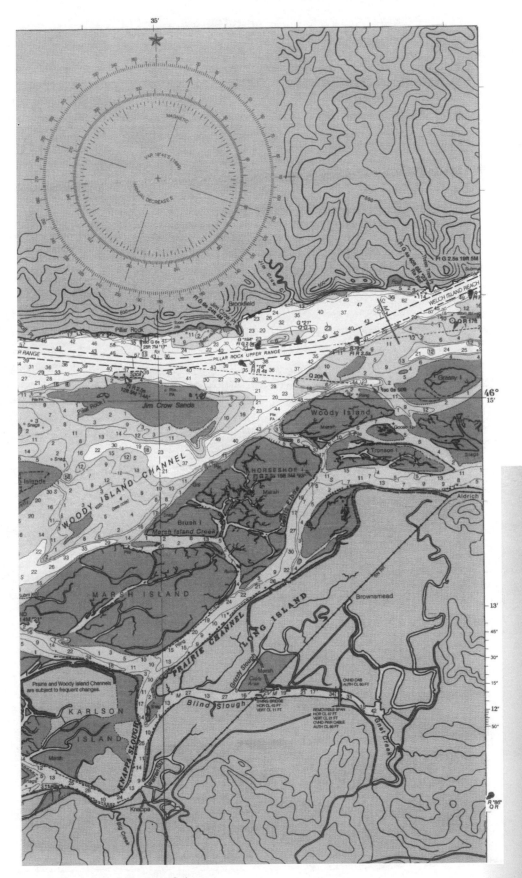

Figure 1–11. A typical nautical chart.
(Courtesy of the Office of Coast Survey, National Oceanic and Atmospheric Administration, **www.noaa.gov**)

Photogrammetric Maps

Aerial photographs are used to make photogrammetric maps. This process is the most widely used method of preparing maps. Aerial photos, known as orthophotos, are taken at certain intervals and are controlled by base stations on the earth's surface. Aerial photos can be accurately scaled and are easily read and transferred to paper using special stereoscopic instruments. Figure 1–12 shows an aerial photograph.

Compare the map in Figure 1–13 to the aerial photograph in Figure 1–12, and you can see how a map can be created from an aerial photograph.

Topographic Maps

Topographic maps accurately show the shape of the earth by the use of contour lines. Contour lines represent all the points on the ground of equal elevation above sea level. The spacing of contour lines is determined by the grade of the land. On very steep terrain, the lines are close together because changes in elevation come quickly. On terrain that slopes gradually, the contour lines are farther apart, as it takes longer to reach a change in elevation. The contour lines are drawn at equal changes in elevation, such as every 2, 5, or 10 ft. Usually, at least every fifth contour is broken along its length, and the elevation is inserted.

Topographic maps are typically drawn using a variety of colors that represent different map features. Contour lines are often drawn in

Figure 1–12. **A typical aerial photograph.**
(Courtesy of the U.S. Geological Survey, www.usgs.gov)

Figure 1–13.   A photogrammetric map created from the aerial photograph shown in Figure 1–12.
(Courtesy of the U.S. Geological Survey, www.usgs.gov)

brown, while streams, lakes, and rivers are blue. Woodland features are represented in green, and items constructed by people, such as buildings and roads, are usually shown in black.

Most of the types of maps previously discussed may often use the elements of a topographic map. Construction projects involving shape, size, location, slope, or configuration of land can be aided by the use of topographic maps. There are probably thousands of varied uses for these maps. Figure 1–14 shows a topographic map.

You can view and download U.S. Geological Survey (USGS) topographic maps at no charge at the USGS Web site, at **http://store.usgs. gov** (select "Maps").

Planning Maps

Maps used by planners can include aeronautical charts, cadastral maps, quadrangle maps, site plans, geographical maps, hydrologic maps, nautical charts, aerial photographs, photogrammetric maps, and topographic maps, depending on their needed application. A planning map may have a photogrammetric or topographic base map overlaid with appropriate information, such as zoning boundaries, urban growth boundaries, or population density. This type of map may then be used with hydrologic maps or engineering maps to show existing conditions and to plan for improvements. Planning maps that use different layers or levels from digitally recorded and produced data are relatively easy to compile and have a wide variety of uses. CADD *layers* are discussed in detail in Chapter 2. The term *digitally recorded and produced data* refers to information gathered and used by computers.

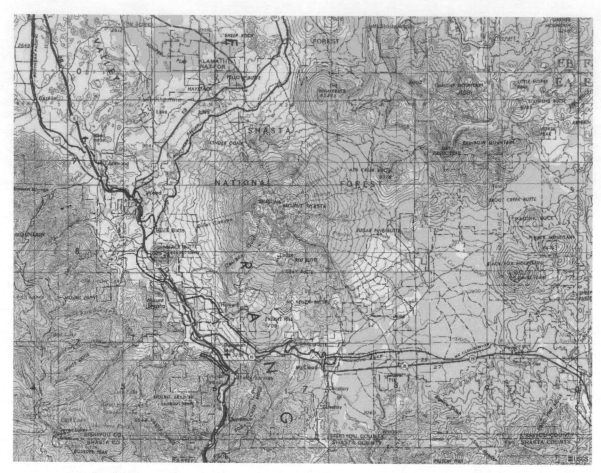

Figure 1–14. **A typical topographic map.**
(Courtesy of the U.S. Geological Survey, **www.usgs.gov**)

Computer-aided drafting applications used in conjunction with a GIS are discussed in Chapter 13. Depending on the specific need, planning maps are often produced in color and may be either large or small scale. Figure 1–15 shows a planning map.

Maps from Digital Elevation Model Data

A variety of maps can be produced from digital elevation model (DEM) data. DEM files contain a large amount of data, based on a grid of elevation points. DEMs can describe a wide variety of information about land surface, including the topography, vegetation covering, and underground aquifers. The type of DEM that provides information about the earth's surface is referred to as a *digital terrain model* (DTM). *Terrain* is a feature of land. An *aquifer* is any water-bearing rock or stratum. Figure 1–16 shows a three-dimensional DTM map of Mt. St. Helens in Washington state before and after the May 18, 1980, eruption.

DEM data can be used to produce very realistic and easily understandable maps and images. Different viewpoints of a site can be observed with the use of a CADD software program, and the vertical scale can be magnified to display minute elevation changes at sites that are relatively flat. Additional information and graphics can

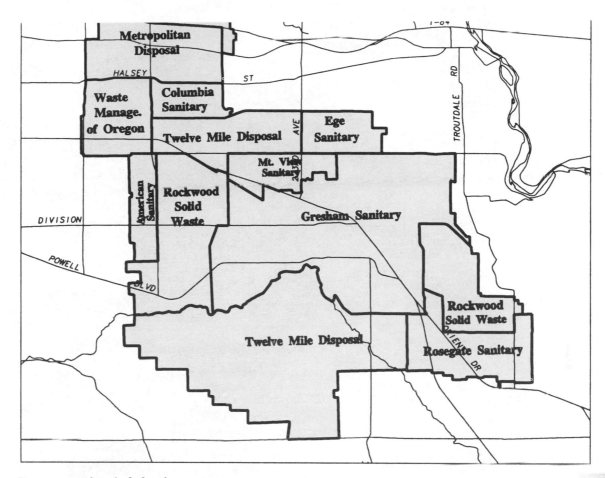

Figure 1–15.   A typical planning map.
(Courtesy of the City of Portland, Tri-Met, and Metro of Portland, OR)

Figure 1–16.   A digital terrain model (DTM) of Mt. St. Helens before and after the May 18, 1980, eruption.
(Courtesy of the U.S. Geological Survey, www.usgs.gov)

be applied to DEM maps, including photorealistic rendering and topographic map overlays. DEM maps are helpful in slope analysis and in determining hydrographic boundaries, as well as in planning of highways, subdivisions, and underground utilities that rely on gravity flow. Analyzing such models helps engineers find flaws or problem areas long before the final project is ever built. Figure 1–17 and 18 show additional examples of maps generated using DEM technology.

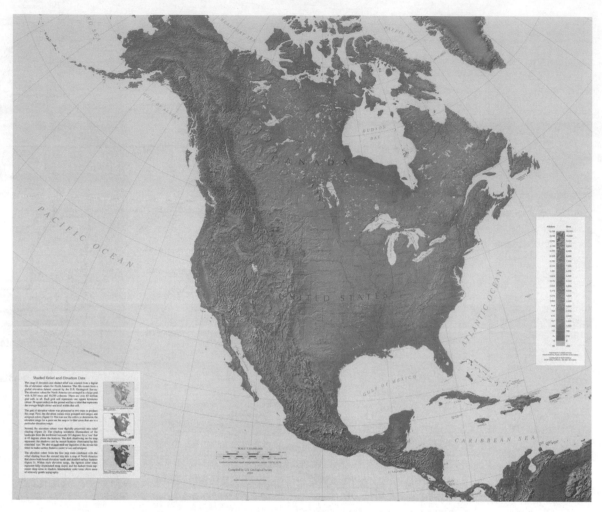

Figure 1–17.   **A color-shaded elevation map created using DEM data.**
(Courtesy of the U.S. Geological Survey, **www.usgs.gov**)

Geologic Maps

A geologic map describes the location, type, and extent of geologic features such as rock formations and edges of earth movement. A geologic map is usually created by adding geologic information to an existing map, typically a topographic map. Geologic maps contain a variety of lines, shapes, and symbols, and colors are used to describe most geologic information. Every color on a geologic map represents a different rock type and age. For example, an area made of a certain rock of a specific age might be purple in color, while an area made of the same type of rock but of a different age might be pink in color. Usually additional information is also provided, including the name of the rock type. Figure 1–19 shows an example of a geologic map.

Geologic maps have a multitude of purposes. Scientists and engineers use geologic maps when they need to understand information about the surface of the earth. The following are some of the data geologic maps help provide:

- Locations of acceptable building sites or agricultural areas
- Identification of areas prone to earthquakes, volcanoes, floods, and other dangers

Figure 1–18. **A three-dimensional map created using DEM technology.**
(Courtesy of the U.S. Geological Survey, www.usgs.gov)

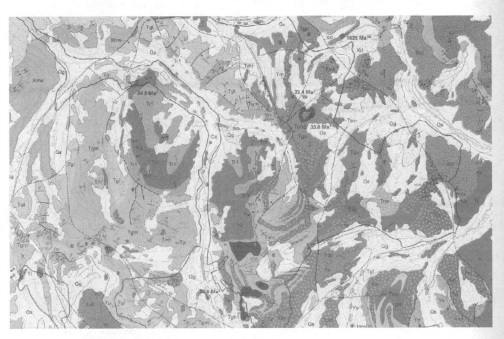

Figure 1–19. **A typical geologic map.**
(Courtesy of the U.S. Geological Survey, www.usgs.gov)

■ Locations of beneficial natural resources, such as natural gas, oil, groundwater, precious minerals, and gravel, or dangerous products such as asbestos

Remote Sensing

Remote sensing refers the detection of information about an object or experience, without actually contacting the object or experience. For example, when you read this textbook, you are remotely sensing the words, figures, and even the paper that make up the book, without touching or otherwise contacting the book. In reference to maps, the term *remote sensing* has been applied to the use of highly sophisticated instruments carried by ships, aircraft, spacecraft, and satellites that collect information about the surface of the earth. The data obtained by these instruments, which include aerial photography, radar, and multi-spectral and infrared imagery, can be used by scientists and engineers to generate numerous maps and images, especially of large areas. Applications for remote sensing range from mapping previously inaccessible areas to the creation of accurate thematic maps. *Thematic maps* are designed to provide information about specific topics, or themes, such as the amount of vegetation on the surface of the earth, observing the effects of wildfires, and plotting human population patterns, just to name a few. Figure 1–20 shows an example of a thematic map generated using satellite images. The purpose of this particular map is to show the variety and distribution of land cover in Florida.

Basic Civil Drafting Techniques

Maps and plans consist of a variety of lines, shapes, symbols, and words. When these items are effectively put together, they produce drawings that are used in the construction of highways, bridges, building sites, and other civil engineering projects. As you will learn, there are many techniques and standards associated with the creation of quality engineering drawings, including line work and text. It is the responsibility of drafters and engineers to use and interpret these techniques and standards to produce the best possible drawings.

Drafting has evolved from *manual drawing* skills to a primarily computer-based activity. Manual drawing is drafting done using traditional tools to create drawings by hand with pencil or ink on paper or other media. The need for precise hand line work, inking skills, and lettering has almost disappeared from the workplace, though occasionally the need to modify old, archived drawings does arise. However, technical sketching and CADD has become the focus rather than the use of manual drafting equipment.

As you study and work with civil drawings, you will become familiar with a variety of plan and map formats and materials, including electronic soft copies and physical hard copies. A drawing created using CADD exists as soft and hard copy forms. A *soft copy* is

Figure 1–20. A land cover thematic map created using satellite images. (Courtesy of the U.S. Geological Survey, www.usgs.gov)

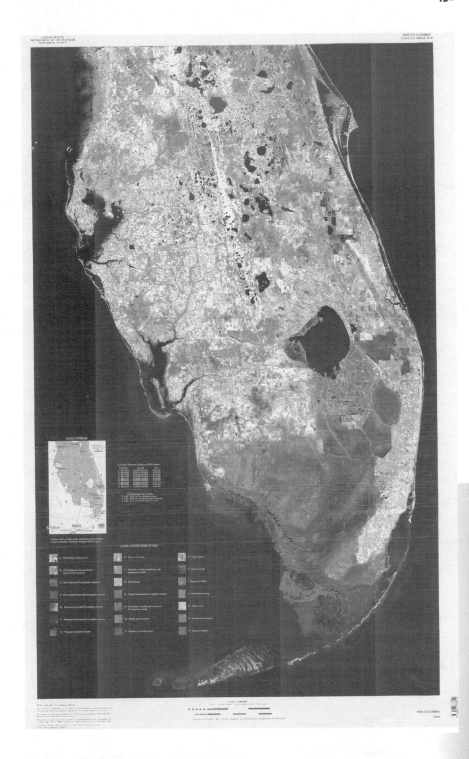

the computer version of a drawing, or the drawing that you see on the computer screen. When a soft copy is printed or plotted, the physical drawing product is known as a *hard copy*. Hard copies are typically plotted on *vellum*, bond paper, or other media. Vellum provides a readily reproducible original at minimal cost. Companies requiring a more durable original may use *polyester film*. Polyester film, commonly referred to by its trade name Mylar, reproduces better than vellum but is more costly. A more detailed description of drafting materials can be found in most basic drafting textbooks.

Line Work

Line work refers to the placement and correct use of lines, shapes, and symbols on a drawing. Typically, line work represents the majority of information on a plan or map. Line work in civil drafting is done using a number of techniques, depending on the purpose of the map and the civil engineering company. For example, one company might create very simple site plans on small sheets, while another company might produce very complex contour maps on large sheets.

CADD makes drawing lines easy and provides consistently uniform line thicknesses. However, regardless of the method used to make the lines, lines should be dark, crisp, and easy to reproduce, and they should convey the correct information. Figure 1–21 shows a sampling of lines used in civil drafting. Many more line types are introduced throughout this text. The recommended line width is given in inches and millimeters. Notice that the major boundary lines and proposed structures are drawn thicker than property lines and existing structures.

Text

The words on a drawing are referred to as text when created using CADD, or *lettering*, when applied using manual drafting methods. The otherwise time-consuming task of lettering on a drawing is as easy as typing at a keyboard when CADD is used. The quality of CADD text is uniform and easy to read. Adding text using CADD is generally many times faster than using manual lettering, and additional productivity is gained when changes are needed. Most CADD systems make a variety of text styles and fonts available, depending on the application, as shown in Figure 1–22. A *font* is all the uppercase and lowercase letters and numerals of a particular letter face design.

The style of text used on civil drawings varies, depending on the type of project or the company making the drawing. Though there is

Figure 1–21. **Lines commonly used in civil drafting.**

LINE TYPE	PEN NO	IN	MM
CITY, COUNTY, OR STATE BOUNDARY	4	.047	1.40
SUBDIVISION BOUNDARY AND PROPERTY LINE	4	.047	1.40
PROPERTY LINE AND LOT LINE	1	.020	0.50
EASEMENT LINE	0	.014	0.35
CENTER LINE	0	.014	0.35
PROPOSED WATER	2.5	.028	0.70
PROPOSED SEWER	3	.031	0.80
EXISTING WATER	0	.014	0.35
EXISTING SEWER	0	.014	0.35

Figure 1–22. Samples of CADD text fonts.

ROMANS

ABCDEFGHIJKLMNOPQRSTUVWXYZ
1234567890

ROMAND

ABCDEFGHIJKLMNOPQRSTUVWXYZ
1234567890

TIMES NEW ROMAN

ABCDEFGHIJKLMNOPQRSTUVWXYZ
1234567890

STYLUS BT

ABCDEFGHIJKLMNOPQRSTUVWXYZ
1234567890

Figure 1–23. A typical civil drafting text style.

DES MOINES ADDITION
LOT 7, BLOCK 2, DES MOINES, WASHINGTON
ELEV. MAIN FL. 101.8'
ELEV. BSMT. FL. 92.8'

PROPOSED
3 BEDROOM
HOME

Figure 1–24. An architectural text style sometimes used in civil drafting.

no particular form of text that must be used on civil plans and maps, a plain vertical text is most common, such as the Romans font style shown in Figure 1–23. Vertical or inclined text can be applied, but usually one or the other is recommended. The typical slant for inclined text is 68° from horizontal. In addition, text on a drawing is normally uppercase, though lowercase letters are used in some instances, and numbers in dimensions and notes are the same height as standard text. The lettering on some civil drafting projects used in the construction industry is an architectural style. Architectural text, such as the StylusBT font style shown in Figure 1–24, is more artistic in nature than the traditional lettering previously described.

Text height varies, depending on the purpose of the text and company standards. In general, dimensions and notes should be .12 in. or .125 in. (3 mm) high. Text any smaller than .12 in. is difficult to read. Titles, headings, and certain other notes are often .24 in. or .25 in. (6 mm) high to easily distinguish them from other text. Text should be uniform and consistent throughout a drawing. Most drawings need only two or three different text heights. All text of the same group—for example, all dimensions and notes—should have the same text height.

Placing Notes on a Drawing

Notes on a drawing provide written information—such as a comment, explanation, or specification—that is best displayed apart from other drawing content, including views and dimensions. The two types of notes are general and specific.

General notes apply to an entire drawing. General notes are typically placed in the lower-left or lower-right corner of the drawing but can be placed anywhere in the field of the drawing, depending on company standards. The field is any open area that surrounds the main views or plans displayed on the drawing. General notes should not be placed closer than 1/2 in. (13 mm) from the drawing border. A general note is shown in Figure 1–25.

Specific notes relate to specific features or instructions within the drawing, such as the elevation at a particular location. Specific notes are also referred to as *local notes* because they identify isolated items. Specific notes are often connected to the feature using a leader line, as shown in Figure 1–26. Specific notes can also be placed directly next to the feature without using a leader. Specific notes that are too complex or take up too much space can be placed with the general notes and keyed to the drawing with a short identification, such as SEE NOTE 3, or NOTE # 3. A number or letter with a symbol can also be used to key a note to the drawing, such as Note 3 with a triangle in Figure 1–25. This is referred to as a *delta* or *key note*. Circles, hexagons, or squares can also be used as the key note symbol.

Written *specifications* are separate notes that identify the quality, quantity, type of material used, workmanship, and other detailed information about an entire project. Specifications are generally prepared in a format that is different from standard drawing sheets. Specifications can be printed in a format that categorizes each phase of construction and indicates the exact methods and materials to be used. Specifications often follow the guidelines of the individual engineering firm, although a common format has been established by the Construction Specifications Institute (CSI), **www.csinet.org**, and

Figure 1–25. General notes apply to an entire drawing. General notes are typically placed in the lower-left or lower-right corner of a drawing but can be placed anywhere in the field of the drawing, depending on company standards. Some specific notes that are too complex or take up too much space can be placed with the general notes and keyed to the drawing with a symbol, such as Note 3 with a triangle. This is referred to as a delta or key note. Circles, hexagons, or squares can also be used as the key note symbol.

NOTES:
1. CONTRACTOR SHALL RESTRICT CONSTRUCTION ACTIVITY TO WITHIN EXISTING 10 FOOT PUBLIC RIGHT OF WAY AND 12 FOOT EASEMENT.
2. COMPACT ALL FILL MATERIAL TO 1200 PSI.
 CONSTRUCT INSIDE DROP CONNECTION, SEE STD PLAN 4–27–9 IN SPECIAL SPECIFICATIONS.

Figure 1–26. Specific notes relate to specific features or instructions within a drawing, such as the elevation at a particular location. Specific notes are often connected to the feature using a leader line, as shown here.

Leader line

CONNECT TO EXISTING MAINTENANCE HOLE

Construction Specifications Canada (CSC), **www.csc-dcc.ca**. The specifications are organized in what is called the MasterFormat. The MasterFormat is a list of numbers and titles that is created for the organization of information into a standard sequence that relates to construction requirements, products, and activities.

Throughout this text, you will learn and explore multiple civil drafting techniques, concepts, and standards. Additional information regarding specific CSI and CSC standards is covered when applicable, including the U.S. National CAD Standard.

TEST

Part I

Define or describe the following. Use your best hand lettering technique or access this test on the Student Web site and follow the instructions to respond electronically.

1-1   Civil drafting

1-2   Civil engineering

1-3   Map

1-4   Contour lines

1-5   Aerial photos

1-6   Plats

1-7   Site plan

1-8   General notes

1-9   Specific notes

1-10   Specifications

1-11   Text

1-12   Font

1-13 Line work

1-14 Cartography

1-15 Digital elevation model

1-16 Delta notes

1-17 Workplace ethics

1-18 Intellectual property

1-19 Field

1-20 Professional organizations

Part II

Multiple choice: Circle the response that best describes each statement or access this test on the Student Web site and follow the instructions to respond electronically.

1-1 Small-scale maps that commonly show large areas of earth, depicting continents and countries, are called:

a. Aeronautical charts
b. Cadastral maps
c. Geographical maps
d. Nautical charts

1-2 Maps that accurately show the shape of the earth through the use of contour lines are called:

a. Photogrammetric maps
b. Topographic maps
c. Engineering maps
d. Geographic maps

1-3 Maps that accurately show the boundaries of major river basins are called:

 a. Geographical maps
 b. Nautical charts
 c. Cadastral maps
 d. Hydrologic maps

1-4 Maps that are detailed to show the layout of a construction project are called:

 a. Geographical maps
 b. Cadastral maps
 c. Engineering maps
 d. Topographic maps

1-5 Large-scale maps that accurately show the features in a city or town are called:

 a. Engineering maps
 b. Geographical maps
 c. Cadastral maps
 d. Topographic maps

1-6 Maps that are two- or three-dimensional maps that have been digitally recorded and produced using a grid of elevation points are called:

 a. Geologic maps
 b. Digital elevation model
 c. Thematic maps
 d. Topographic maps

1-7 Maps that describe the location, type, and extent of geologic features such as rock formations and edges of earth movement, are called:

 a. Geologic maps
 b. Geographical maps
 c. Thematic maps
 d. Topographic maps

1-8 Maps designed to provide information about specific topics, or themes, such as the amount of vegetation on the surface of the earth, observing the effects of wildfires, and plotting human population patterns, are called:

 a. Geologic maps
 b. Geographical maps
 c. Thematic maps
 d. Topographic maps

1-9   Specific notes are also referred to as:

    a. Exact
    b. Detailed
    c. Local
    d. General

1-10   Notes that apply to an entire drawing are called:

    a. Specific notes
    b. General notes
    c. Delta notes
    d. Key notes

PROBLEMS

P1-1   Below each line in Figure P1–1, or on separate paper, as specified by your instructor, draw five more lines exactly the same, using your drafting pencil and a straightedge. Make your lines dark and crisp. Use a CADD system if recommended by your course objectives.

P1-2   Use your best freehand lettering skill or a CADD program, depending on your course objectives, to duplicate each sentence lettered in Figure P1–2. Make your own very light guide lines 1/8 in. apart to guide your manual lettering, if used. Try to make your lettering the same as the example unless otherwise indicated by your instructor. A soft 2H, H, or F pencil lead and a 0.5-mm automatic pencil are recommended for manual lettering. The Romans or similar font is recommended for CADD text.

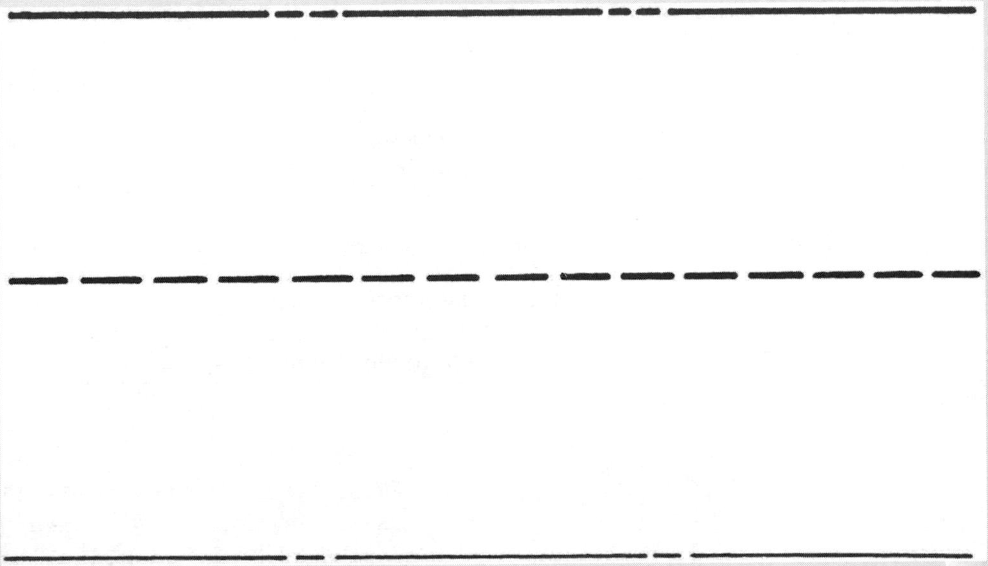

Figure P1–1.

THE LETTERING QUALITY GREATLY AFFECTS THE APPEARANCE OF THE ENTIRE DRAWING. DRAFTERS USING MANUAL TECHNIQUES CREATE VERY NEATLY DRAWN LETTERS WITH SINGLE STROKES. THIS PRACTICE IS REFERRED TO AS FREEHAND LETTERING. ALWAYS USE LIGHTLY DRAWN GUIDE LINES TO CONTROL THE HEIGHT OF FREEHAND LETTERING. WHEN LETTERING IS CREATED USING COMPUTER-AIDED DESIGN & DRAFTING (CADD), THE LETTERING IS CALLED TEXT. TEXT IS EASILY PLACED ON A DRAWING WHEN USING CADD. A VARIETY OF TEXT STYLES CAN BE CREATED WITH CADD, BUT TEXT ON CIVIL DRAWINGS GENERALLY LOOKS SIMILAR TO THE STYLE SHOWN IN THIS PARAGRAPH. CONFIRM THE PROPER STYLE TO USE WITH YOUR INSTRUCTOR OR COMPANY STANDARDS.

Figure P1–2.

SOME CIVIL ENGINEERING COMPANIES USE AN ARCHITECTURAL STYLE OF LETTERING ON DRAWINGS. THIS DEPENDS ON COMPANY STANDARDS AND SHOULD BE CONFIRMED BEFORE USE. FREEHAND ARCHITECTURAL LETTERING IS MORE ARTISTIC IN NATURE THAN TRADITIONAL LETTERING USED ON MOST DRAWINGS. TYPICAL ARCHITECTURAL LETTERING LOOKS SIMILAR TO THE EXAMPLE REPRESENTED IN THIS PARAGRAPH. WHEN USING CADD, LETTERING IS CALLED TEXT. A TEXT STYLE CAN BE SELECTED THAT CLOSELY REPRODUCES THE APPEARANCE OF FREEHAND ARCHITECTURAL LETTERING. THE TEXT STYLE USED IN THIS EXAMPLE IS NAMED STYLUS BT.

Figure P1–3.

P1–3   Practice an architectural lettering style by duplicating each sentence lettered in Figure P1–3. Use the StylusBT or similar font if CADD is used.

P1–4   Use mechanical lettering equipment, if available, or use CADD unless otherwise specified by your instructor, to duplicate each sentence lettered in Figure P1–4.

P1–5   Use a CADD system, if available, to duplicate each line shown in Figure 1–21. Use text styles similar to those in the example or substitute another text style if these are not available. Make a print or plot of your drawing, if available.

MECHANICAL LETTERING EQUIPMENT WITH TECHNICAL INK PENS WAS ONCE COMMONLY USED IN CIVIL DRAFTING TO PRODUCE QUALITY LETTERING. IF YOU ARE ASKED TO MAKE CHANGES ON ARCHIVE DRAWINGS WHERE MECHANICAL LETTERING WAS USED, YOU SHOULD READ THE MANUFACTURER INSTRUCTIONS AND PRACTICE BEFORE BEGINNING. MECHANICAL LETTERING HAS BEEN REPLACED BY THE USE OF CADD. CADD LETTERING IS CALLED TEXT AND IS EASY TO USE. CADD TEXT HAS A CONSISTENT AND EASY-TO-READ APPEARANCE THROUGHOUT THE ENTIRE DRAWING.

Figure P1–4.

Figure P1–5.
(Courtesy of the City of Portland, Oregon)

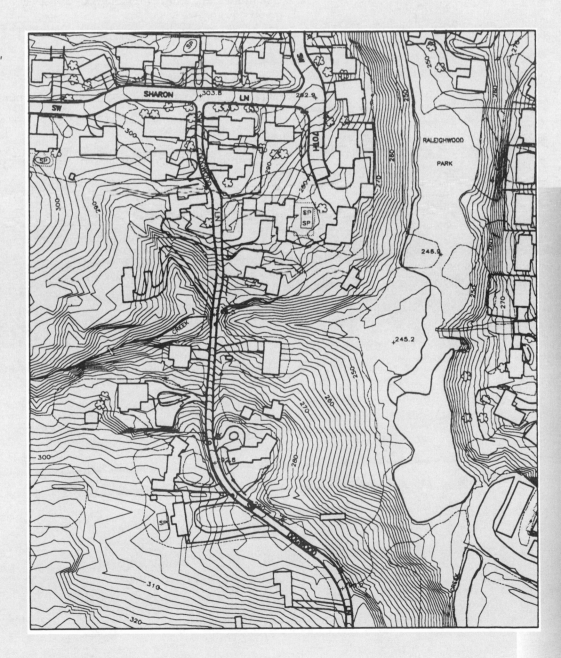

P1-6   Use a CADD system to create an architectural text style similar to the example in Figure P1–3 and create a mechanical text style similar to the example in Figure P1–2. Make the text 1/8 in. high. Use the architectural style with all uppercase letters to define civil drafting. Fit the text into a compressed space, not to exceed 5 in. Use the mechanical text style with all uppercase letters that are slanted 15° to the right to define civil engineering. Make a print or plot of your drawing, if available.

P1-7   Classify the type of map shown in Figure P1–5. Describe how you came to your conclusion.

P1-8   Use manual lettering or CADD text to display an example of at least two general notes.

P1-9   Continue from P1–8 to add a third delta note that is a specific note placed with the general notes, providing the number 3 inside a triangle.

P1-10   Use manual lettering or CADD text to give an example of at least one specific note.

Computer-Aided Design and Drafting (CADD)

Learning Objectives

After completing this chapter, you will be able to:

- Discuss the applications of one or more CADD software programs.
- Write about the U.S. National CAD Standard for architecture, engineering, and construction.
- Discuss layers and layer standards.
- Explain the use of drawing templates.
- Provide information about the importance and use of symbols and symbol libraries.
- Discuss the importance of reusing drawing content and give some examples.
- Explain file management.
- Discuss the importance of ergonomics related to the CADD environment.
- Use exercise, as needed, to relieve discomfort associated with computer use, if approved by your doctor.

Key Terms

CADD (computer-aided design and drafting)
CAD (computer-aided design or computer-aided drafting)
Uniform Drawing System
Drawing file organization
Line standards
Text styles and fonts
Drawing scales
Dimensions
Scale factor
Layers
Template
Symbol
Symbol library
Dynamic symbols
Drag-and-drop
Soft copy
Hard copy
Model
Sheet
Internet
World Wide Web (WWW)
Hypertext
Ergonomics

Introduction to Computer-Aided Drafting

You have already heard the term computer-aided design and drafting (CADD) used a number of times in this textbook. The term computer-aided design (CAD) is also commonly used. CAD is also often referred to as computer-aided drafting. No matter which acronym is used, the concept represents the entire spectrum of design and/or drafting with the aid of a computer. CADD has replaced traditional manual, or board, drafting in most situations. The *personal computer (PC)* has forever changed the way most daily activities are done in industry and at home. Today's PCs have the capability of storing, processing, and retrieving huge amounts of information very quickly. The PC's versatility and affordability have helped it, loaded with CADD software, to become the primary tool used for creating drawings and calculating engineering data.

CADD technology provides many powerful engineering tools for the creation and analysis of precision technical drawings. Many of these drawings can be used as a source of information for creating computer-generated models, such as digital elevation model maps used in civil engineering analysis.

The area of CADD that is associated with the creation and editing of technical drawings is known as computer-aided drafting (CAD). The use of computers—rather than pencils, scales, and templates—for drafting has many benefits. One of the main benefits is accuracy. Modern CADD software programs provide a virtually unlimited drawing area, in which most objects can be drawn actual size, regardless of how large or small they are. The drawing display can be changed quickly to show any area of the drawing. This means that, as with a camera lens, you can zoom in or out, allowing you to get very close to work with small features of your drawing or back off so you can see the entire drawing.

The greatest benefit to productivity within a drafting department comes from the fact that, with CADD, objects need only be drawn once, after which they can be used over and over again. A huge variety of civil engineering and mapping symbols can be drawn once and then copied to every location in the drawing where the symbols are needed. The symbols can also be saved permanently to a symbol library and used in other drawings. Companies using CADD benefit from these symbol libraries in their day-to-day drafting tasks.

Revisions to existing drawings can be done quickly and efficiently using CADD. After the required changes have been made, a new drawing can be produced within minutes, using modern printers and plotters.

CADD Software Products for Civil Design and Drafting

The following sections provide general information about a variety of CADD software manufacturer products. Much of the information is taken from the related Web sites. The information provided is intended as an introduction only. For more information, refer to the related Web sites referenced with each product. This discussion is not intended to promote or endorse any of the products represented. Other CADD software products are available. Do an Internet search using keywords such as computer-aided drafting, computer-aided design, computer-aided design and drafting, civil drafting, civil drafting software, CADD, or CADD software, to find additional products.

Autodesk, Inc.

Autodesk's core product is AutoCAD (see **www.autodesk.com**). AutoCAD is a 2D and 3D drafting and design software product. AutoCAD LT software is a 2D drafting product. Autodesk products are available for industries such as building, infrastructure, manufacturing, media and entertainment, and wireless data. Autodesk has a variety of CADD software programs created for specific disciplines such as architectural, civil, electrical, and mechanical engineering. The following provides a small example of some of the additional products from Autodesk, Inc., used for architecture, engineering, and construction.

AutoCAD Civil 3D software is used for civil engineering applications using a dynamic engineering model, which means that changes made in one place are reflected instantly throughout the entire project.

AutoCAD Land Desktop software provides a base level of land development functionality to streamline the completion of common land planning and analysis tasks.

AutoCAD Map 3D is an engineering geographic information systems (GIS) platform for creating and managing spatial data. You can streamline entire workflows and increase productivity with powerful AutoCAD tools.

Autodesk Survey automates field data collection, cost-effectively closing the gap between gathering data and incorporating data into drawings.

Autodesk Utility Design is a comprehensive facility design tool that helps you plan utility distribution networks from start to finish.

AutoCAD Architecture provides the efficiency of real-world building objects, design, and documentation productivity for architects and architectural designers.

Revit Architecture is used for building information modeling.

Carlson Software

Carlson Software, **www.carlsonsw.com**, provides a wide range of software solutions for the survey, civil engineering, construction, and mining industries. These applications can all use AutoCAD as the base drafting software if the user already owns AutoCAD, and they can now also run on included IntelliCAD. A new survey program now also runs on MicroStation, and new applications are in development based on using Environmental Systems Research Institute, Inc. (ESRI) and others.

Carlson SurvCE is data collection software that runs on a handheld data collector. This allows for highly efficient data collection and construction stakeout.

Carlson Survey addresses all the survey requirements on the office side, including the processing of raw survey data, traverse adjustment, field-to-finish, general Co-ordinate Geometry (COGO) commands, and legal description writing.

Carlson Civil provides advanced tools for roadway design, lot layout, and site grading.

Carlson Hydrology performs watershed delineation and analysis, pond design, and the design of pipe networks for storm drains and other utilities.

Carlson GIS brings sets of tools to link drawing objects to external databases, importing and exporting of ESRI shape files, and manipulation of geo-referenced images.

Carlson Takeoff is for construction estimating of earthwork quantities from drawing files. Carlson Mining programs provide tools for the specific needs of the mining industry.

Carlson Grade software uses a digital terrain model (DTM) to guide the heavy earth-moving equipment on the construction site in a process known as machine control.

Bentley Systems, Inc.

Bentley Systems, **www.bentley.com**, provides software for building, plant, and civil engineering as well as geospatial, architecture, engineering, construction, and operations. MicroStation is Bentley's key product for the design, construction, and operation applications. MicroStation is a CADD platform used by teams of architects, engineers, contractors, and GIS professionals to integrate work on buildings, civil engineering projects, power plants, and geospatial information.

Bentley also has a wide range of civil solutions that support each phase of the project life cycle, such as planning, design, engineering, construction, maintenance, and operation. Bentley GEOPAK is a family of integrated civil design and engineering software suited to civil engineering and transportation projects of all types. Developed and supported by practicing civil engineers and professional surveyors, GEOPAK applications offer a plan-production focus that allows engineers to concentrate on delivering high-quality projects in one continuous cycle, survey through construction. The GEOPAK software line represents a comprehensive, field-to-finish solution for transportation infrastructure, water resources, and land development.

Eagle Point Software Corporation

Eagle Point Software Corporation, **www.eaglepoint.com**, provides Eagle Point's Civil Design solutions with a complete line of Civil Design modules for easy design of a site, from building pads and surface models to roads and intersections.

Intersection Design helps automate the entire design process, from pavement, island, and median design; to curb, shoulder, and sidewalk layout; and finishing with analyzing the design and calculating intersection quantities.

The Profiles program assists in the computation, annotation, and drafting of tangents, vertical curves, structures, and pipe placement.

Use Profiles on its own or in conjunction with RoadCalc for subdivision, sewer, and road design.

Quantity Takeoff is a program that reduces the time spent counting and measuring items within a project, giving you more time to analyze projects and their costs.

Site Design is used to analyze and design every type of earthwork project, including landfills, parking lots, building pads, reservoirs, and drainage ditches, and to quickly assign elevations and slopes to various feature lines.

Surface Modeling is used to create contours and grids and ensures that your contours never cross and always agree with spot elevation labels. Flexible contour annotation lets you annotate the elevations where you want them and how you want them.

Graphisoft

Graphisoft, **www.graphisoft.com**, is the manufacturer of the ArchiCAD design/building series, a set of tools for builders and residential designers. Graphisoft packages are based on open standards, allowing you to create data without re-creation. A Graphisoft product called Virtual Building manages the full information cycle of buildings, from concept through occupancy. The program contains information about building materials and characteristics. Virtual Building is a 3D digital database that tracks all elements that make up a building, allowing the designer to use items such as surface area and volume, thermal properties, room descriptions, costs, product information, and window, door, and finish schedules.

SoftPlan Systems, Inc.

SoftPlan Architectural Design Software, **www.softplan.com**, is a residential and light commercial CADD software package. SoftPlan allows you to create floor plans, cross sections, elevations, framing plans, detail drawings, and site plans. Drawings are created with features such as walls, windows, doors, and beams.

SoftView takes a drawing created in SoftPlan and generates a three-dimensional rendering of the model. You can also create photo-realistic interior and exterior 3D renderings from any view.

The U.S. National CAD Standard

In 1995, a group of agencies including the CADD/GIS Technology Center (CGTC), the American Institute of Architects (AIA), the Construction Specifications Institute (CSI), the U.S. Coast Guard, the Sheet Metal and Air Conditioning Contractors National Association (SMACNA), and the National Institute of Building Sciences (NIBS) came together to develop a single CADD standard for the United States, now referred to as the U.S. National CAD Standard. Standards are very important in drafting. The purpose of the U.S. National CAD Standard is to allow consistent and streamlined communication among owners, architects and designers, and construction teams. Use of the standard can result in reducing costs for developing and maintaining office standards and greater efficiency in the transfer of building design information from design to construction. The standard is not intended to be applied with any specific CADD software program. However, because of their wide industry acceptance, AutoCAD and MicroStation were used to establish the fundamentals, styles, and applications found in the standard.

The Uniform Drawing System

The Construction Specifications Institute (CSI) created the Uniform Drawing System, an eight-module system for organizing and presenting building design information. The Uniform Drawing System was adopted by the U.S. National CAD Standard. The following provides the basic content found in each module, as provided in the CSI Web site:

- Module 1—Drawing Set Organization establishes set content and order, sheet identification, and file naming for a set of construction drawings.
- Module 2—Sheet Organization provides format for sheets. Includes drawing, title block, and production reference areas and their content. Also includes a coordinate-based location system and preferred sheet sizes. The U.S. National CAD Standard CD has ready-to-use sheet formats.
- Module 3—Schedules sets consistency in format, terminology, and content. Additional guidelines include how to create a project-specific schedule and an organizational system for identifying and filing schedules. The U.S. National CAD Standard CD has ready-to-use schedule formats.
- Module 4—Drafting Conventions addresses standard conventions used in drawings: drawing orientation, layout, symbols, material indications, line types, dimensions, drawing scale, diagrams, notation, and cross-referencing.
- Module 5—Terms and Abbreviations provides standard terms and standard abbreviations used in construction documents and specifications. It provides consistent spelling and terminology, standardizes abbreviations, and describes common notes usage.
- Module 6—Symbols addresses commonly used standard symbols, classifications, graphic representation, and organization in creating, understanding, and fulfilling the intent of construction documents. The CD includes a search index for selecting and viewing the symbols, with a copy function to bring the selected symbol into CADD applications. This is a product of a joint effort of the CADD/GIS Technology Center and CSI.
- Module 7—Notations provides guidelines for notation classification, format, components, and location; use of notes; terminology; and linking to specifications.
- Module 8—Code Conventions identifies types of general regulatory information that should appear on drawings, locates code-related information in a set of drawings, and provides standard

graphic conventions. Can be a tool to expedite code review by designers and plan review authorities.

The following text identifies and discusses specific elements of the U.S. National CAD Standard.

Drawing File Organization

Drawing file organization in the U.S. National CAD Standard covers drawing units, file naming, and sheet identification.

Drawing Units   CADD systems use real-world units for drafting with feet and inches, feet and tenths of feet, or meters and millimeters, as appropriate for a specific drawing.

CADD Files   There are two file types identified in the standard; model files and sheet files. A *model file* contains the individual elements that make up the final drawing, such as the property lines, buildings, utilities, dimensions, and various drawing features on their own layers, as shown in Figure 2–1. A *sheet file* brings the model files together to create the composite drawing and includes the border and title block. See Figure 2–2. CADD layers are covered in detail later in this chapter.

File names are established in a standard format that has four elements: the project code, the discipline designator, the model file

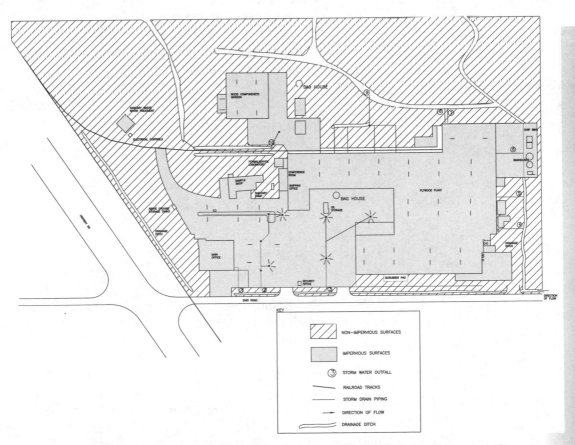

Figure 2–1.   **Model files contain the individual elements that make up the final drawing, such as the property lines, buildings, utilities, dimensions, and various drawing features on their own layers.**

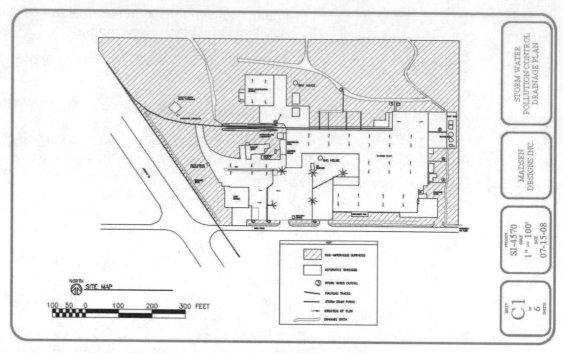

Figure 2–2. A sheet file brings the model files together to create the composite drawing, and it includes the border and title block.

type, and the user definable code. The *project code* is optional and is established for each specific project, as determined by the designer or architect. The project code can have up to 20 characters. The *discipline designator* has two characters, with the second character being a hyphen (-). The first character of the discipline designator is one of the following:

Discipline	Designator
General	G
Hazardous materials	H
Survey/mapping	V
Geotechnical	B
Civil works	W
Civil	C
Landscape	L
Structural	S
Architectural	A
Interiors	I
Equipment	Q
Fire protection	F
Plumbing	P
Process	D
Mechanical	M
Electrical	E
Telecommunications	T
Resources	R
Other disciplines	X
Contractor/shop drawings	Z
Operations	O

The *model file type* characterizes the type of drawing. There is a long list of possible model file types. The following are specifically related to the general and civil discipline designators:

Discipline	Code	Definition	
General (G)			
	BS	Border sheet	
	KP	Keyplan	
Civil (C)			
	D	Civil demolition	Structure removal and site clearing
	G	Civil grading	Excavation, grading, drainage, and retention ponds
	I	Civil improvements	Pavers, flagstone, exterior title, furnishings, retaining walls, and water features, permanent signing, striping, and bumpers
	J	User defined	
	K	User defined	
	P	Civil paving	Roads, bridges, drives, and parking lots
	S	Civil survey (site)	Plats, topographic, dimension control, and layouts
	T	Civil transportation	Waterway construction, wharves, docks, trams, railway systems, and people movers
	U	Civil utilities	See discipline civil works exterior utilities (W) for exterior utilities

The last four characters are user definable, such as G1 for civil grading 1. If all four characters are not used, the remaining spaces are filled with "X"—for example, G1XX.

A complete file name might be PR2003C-GIXX.dwg, where:

- PR2008 is the project code.
- C- is the discipline designator.
- G is the model file type.
- G1XX is the user-definable characters.
- The ending .dwg is the AutoCAD file extension. The ending .dgn is a MicroStation file extension.

Organizing Drawing Files   Drawing files must be organized, so you or anybody else in the office can easily find a drawing when needed. When organizing files, create a project folder that contains subfolders for each of the projects. The subfolders can be named for the project, client, or job number. The files in each project subfolder can include drawing files, word processing documents, and spreadsheets, as needed. This helps keep the entire project together, making it easier to manage. Figure 2–3 shows a file structure for organizing drawing files.

Sheet Name Standard   Sheet names are similar to file names, with the first characters being the project code, and the next two characters the discipline designator, with a level 2 designator, which adds one more character to the discipline for specific applications, such as CD for civil demolition. This is followed by a sheet type designator followed by a two-character sheet sequence number, for example 02-12. Three more characters can be added for user-definable content. The sheet type designators are:

Figure 2–3.   A file structure for organizing drawing files.

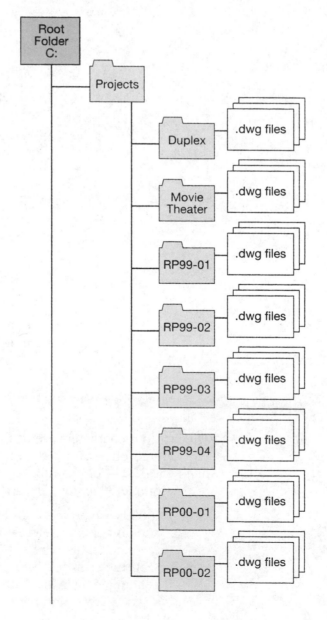

Discipline	Code	Definition
Civil (C)		
	D	Civil demolition
	G	Civil grading
	I	Civil improvements
	J	User defined
	K	User defined
	P	Civil paving
	S	Civil survey (site)
	T	Civil transportation
	U	Civil utilities

Sheet Type	Designator
General	0
Plans	1
Profiles	2
Sections	3
Large-scale views	4
Details	5
Schedules and diagrams	6
User defined	7 and 8
3D	9

A sample sheet name might be PR2008CD102XXX.dwg, where:

- PR2008 is the project code.
- CD is the discipline designator with level 2, civil demolition.
- 1 is the sheet type.
- 02XXX is the sheet sequence number and user-definable characters.
- The ending .dwg is the AutoCAD file extension. The ending .dgn is a MicroStation file extension.

Sheet Identifier   The sheet identifier is located in the title block and in any reference to the sheet on a drawing. Coordination between the sheet name and the sheet identifier is the discipline designator, sheet type designator, and the sheet sequence number. For example, the sheet reference number C-124 means:

- C- is the civil discipline.
- 124 means that 12 is the total number of sheets, and 4 is the specific sheet. Another way of entering this is sheet 4 of 12.

CADD Graphics

Civil drafting is a graphic language made up of features such as lines, symbols, and text. This part of the U.S. National CAD standard deals with these elements of the drawing. Line standards include designations of line weights and line colors, discussed in the following sections.

Line Weights

Typical civil drawing lines were introduced in Chapter 1. The following relates the same and similar lines to the U.S. National CAD Standard. A variety of line weights help to improve drawing clarity. Line weights are also referred to as line thicknesses. Certain features are drawn thick in order for them to stand out from thin features. *Line thickness* and *line weight* are terms used interchangeably in CADD. While a large variety of line weights are possible, the standard acknowledges the following:

Line Thickness	in.	mm	Use
Fine	.007	0.18	Use sparingly for features such as patterns
Thin	.010	0.25	Dimensioning features, phantom lines, hidden lines, centerlines, long break lines, schedule grid lines, and background objects
Medium	.014	0.35	Minor object lines, dimension text, and text for notes and in schedules
Wide	.020	0.50	Major object lines, cutting plane lines, short break lines, and title text
Extra wide	.028	0.70	Minor title underlines, schedule outlines, large titles, special emphasis object lines, and elevation and section grade lines

Line Thickness	in.	mm	Use
Option 1	.040	1.00	Major title underlines and separating portions of a drawing
Option 2	.055	1.40	Border lines, cover sheet lines, and art work
Option 3	.079	2.00	Same as Option 2

Line Types

A variety of line types are included in the standard, as shown in Figure 2–4. The commonly used line types are introduced and displayed throughout this book, with examples of their applications.

Figure 2–4. A variety of line types are included in the U.S. National CAD Standard.

LINE	LINE TYPE
————————————	CONTINUOUS
· · · · · · · · · · · · · · · · · · ·	DOTTED
– – – – – – – –	DASHED
— — — —	DASHED SPACED
– · – · – · – · –	DASHED DOTTED
— ·· — ·· —	DASHED DOUBLE–DOTTED
— ··· — ··· —	DASHED TRIPPLE–DOTTED
— – — – —	CHAIN
— – – — – – —	CHAIN DOUBLE–DASHED

Line Color

The use of color in a CADD drawing and a plotted drawing aid in clarity and visualization. While most CADD systems can display up to 256 colors, the standard recommends white (black), red, green, blue, gray, yellow, magenta, and cyan. Colors such as yellow, magenta, and cyan can be difficult to see and should be avoided.

Text Styles and Fonts

Text styles and fonts were introduced and discussed in Chapter 1. The text fonts recommended by the standard are the basic monotext font and a variety of forms of the Romans font. These fonts are selected because of their clarity and ease of reading. Monotext font was used in early CADD applications because of its ease in regeneration and plotting. However, monotext font should no longer be used because of advancement in computer technology. Preferred fonts are proportional and slanted fonts. CADD programs typically have proportional and slanted fonts with names such as Romans, Romand, and Arial that look good, are easy to read, and meet national standards. Confirm the specific font style used at your school or company. See Figure 2–5. While these fonts are recommended by the standard, they do not allow for the creativity often desired in an architectural drawing. Architectural-style fonts are not commonly used in civil drafting, but some companies prefer their appearance. This is especially true when the company creates civil drawings along with primary architectural drawings. Fonts used in architectural applications are generally more stylish than those recommended by the standard. Two common architectural fonts are StylusBT and CityBlueprint.

Terms and Abbreviations

The standard provides a complete listing of terms and abbreviations used in the construction industry. The proper terms and abbreviations are provided throughout this text where they apply to specific content. Abbreviations should be used to save time and drawing space.

Drawing Notes

Drawing notes were introduced in Chapter 1. The types of notes recommended by the standard are:

- General notes that relate to the entire drawing
- General discipline notes that reflect information about specific disciplines, such as sewer, water, or other utilities

Figure 2–5. The text fonts recommended by the standard are the basic monotext font and a variety of forms of the Romans font.

ABCDE	12345	MONOTEXT FONT
ABCDE	12345	PROPORTIONAL FONT
ABCDE	*12345*	*SLANTED FONT*
ABCDE	**12345**	**FILLED FONT**
ABCDE	12345	OUTLINE FONT

- General sheet notes, which provide information about the sheet or sheets in a set of drawings
- Key notes that are specific notes placed with general notes and keyed to specific features on the drawing

CADD Symbols

CADD symbols were introduced earlier in this chapter and are discussed and shown where they apply to specific content throughout this book. Civil drafting and mapping symbols are covered in detail in Chapter 3. The standard provides a complete range of recommended symbols for all disciplines. The following is a list of the classification of symbols by type:

- Reference symbols
- Line symbols
- Identity symbols
- Object symbols
- Material symbols
- Text symbols

Sheet Sizes, Borders, and Title Blocks

Sheet sizes, borders, and title blocks were discussed and shown in Chapter 1. The standard recommends that title blocks be placed vertically along the right side of the sheet and contain the following compartments:

- *Designer identification block*—The logo or name of the agency or company
- *Issue block*—Revision area or addenda
- *Management block*—Information about the designer, checker, and drafter
- *Project identification block*—Project name and location
- *Sheet identification block*—The sheet identifier

Sheet Sizes

The American National Standards Institute (ANSI) and the American Society of Mechanical Engineers (ASME) standard sheet sizes are generally used for inch drawings and are provided in the *Decimal Inch Drawing Sheet Size and Format* document ASME Y14.1. The International Organization for Standardization (ISO) sheet sizes are used for metric drawings and are referenced in the *Metric Drawing Sheet Size and Format* document ASME Y14.1M. ANSI Y14.1 specifies sheet size specifications in inches as follows:

Size Designations	Size in Inches	
	Vertical	Horizontal
A	81/2	11 (horizontal format)
	11	81/2 (vertical format)
B	11	17
C	17	22
D	22	34
E	34	44
F	28	40

There are four additional size designations—G, H, J, and K—that apply to roll sizes.

The M in the title of ASME Y14.1M means all specifications are given in metric. Standard metric drawing sheet sizes are designated as follows:

Size Designations	Size in Millimeters	
	Vertical	Horizontal
A0	841	1189
A1	594	841
A2	420	594
A3	297	420
A4	210	297

Longer lengths are referred to as elongated and extra-elongated drawing sheet sizes.

Standard inch sheet sizes are shown in Figure 2–6a, and metric sheet sizes are shown in Figure 2–6b. While the CAD standard does not recommend specific sheet sizes, U.S. government agencies often require ANSI sheet sizes. Refer to the ANSI/ASME standards and the textbook *Engineering Drawing and Design*, by David A. Madsen.

Drawing Scales

Drawing scales give the relative size of the object compared to the sheet size. Drawings are scaled so the object represented can be illustrated clearly on standard sheet sizes. Civil drawings are generally scaled in increments of several feet to 1 inch, such as 1 inch equals 100 feet. This is stated as 1″ = 100′. Sometimes civil drawings are scaled using architectural applications, where a fraction of 1 inch equals 1 foot. For example, an architectural scale is represented as 1/4″ = 1′-0″. This means that every 1/4″ on the drawing represents 1 ft. Metric scales are designated by the amount by which they reduce or enlarge the original object. For example, a metric scale shown as 1:5 is a 1/5 scale. This means that the object is reduced to 1/5 of its original size. A typical civil drawing might be 1:200, meaning a 1/200 scale reduction. Recommended drawing scales are also discussed in chapters where they apply to the content, and they may differ from the recommended standard. The scale you select is based on a variety of factors, such as the area size

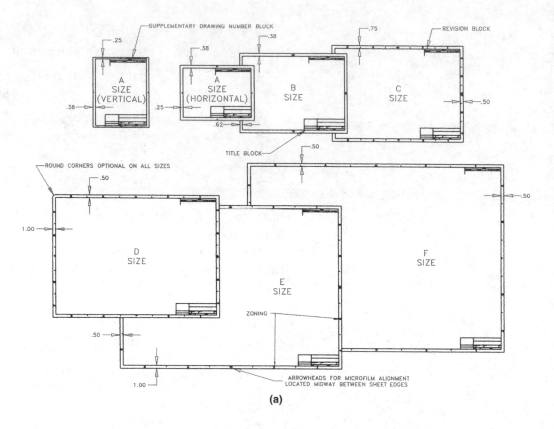

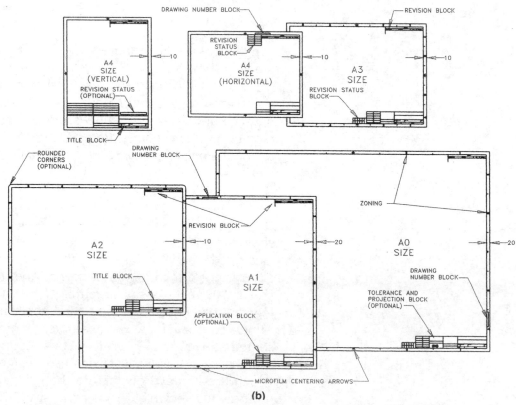

Figure 2-6.   a) Standard drawing sheet sizes (ASME Y 14.1). b) Standard metric drawing sheet sizes (ASME Y 14.1M).

represented in the drawing, the amount of detail shown, and the sheet size used. The standard specifies a variety of general scales. Additional discussion and examples are provided related to specific applications throughout this textbook. The following combines the standard recommended scales for a variety of civil drawing types in inches and metric:

Drawing Type	Inch	Metric
Site plans	1″ = 10′	1:100
	1″ = 20′	1:200
	1″ = 30′	1:400
	1″ = 40′	1:500
	1″ = 50′	1:600
	1″ = 60′	1:700
	1″ = 100′	1:1000
	1″ = 200′	1:2000
	1″ = 400′	1:5000
	1″ = 500′	1:6000
	1″ = 1000′	1:10000
	1″ = 2000′	1:20000
Profiles		
Horizontal scale	1″ = 50′	1:600
	1″ = 100′	1:1000
Vertical scale	1″ = 50′	1:600
	1″ = 100′	1:1000

Drawing Type	Inch	Metric
Road layout	1″ = 50′	1:600
	1″ = 100′	1:1000
Cut and fill	1″ = 50′	1:600
	1″ = 100′	1:1000
Details	1/4″ = 1′-0″	1:50
	1/2″ = 1′-0″	1:20′
	3/4″ = 1′-0″	1:10
	1″ = 1′-0″	1:10
	1 1/2″ = 1′-0″	1:5
	3″ = 1′-0″	1:5

Dimensioning

Dimensions provide the size and location of features on a drawing. Civil drawings are generally dimensioned in feet (′) and inches (″), such as 25′-6″, or in decimal feet, such as 25.5′. Metric drawings are typically dimensioned in millimeters (mm) or meters (m). Both feet and inches, and metric practices, are covered and relate to this standard.

Additional CADD Fundamentals

The previous content provided an introduction to CADD and discussed the U.S. National CAD Standard. The following gives you additional information about CADD applications, including scale factors, CADD layers, managing CADD files, exchanging drawing files, reusing drawing content, Internet use, and ergonomics.

Scaling and Scale Factors

Drawings created with CADD are drawn full scale and plotted to a specific scale. A scale factor is a numerical value used in the proper scaling of text and other drawing elements. Civil drawings typically use the architectural and civil scales introduced earlier. Architectural drawings are representations of buildings and use scales such as $1/4' = 1'-0''$ and $1/8'' = 1'-0'$. Some of the smallest-scale drawings are in the civil engineering field. A *small-scale drawing* shows a large area, while a *large-scale drawing* shows a small area. Large-scale drawings represent areas of land measured in feet or miles, and some of the scales used are $1'' = 10'$, $1'' = 20'$, $1'' = 50'$, and $1'' = 100'$.

The most important point to remember when using CADD is that you always draw full size and print or plot at the proper scale to fit the desired sheet. This also means you must plan ahead and know the scale of the final plotted drawing. Drawing in CADD at full scale means that if a property line measures $100'-0''$ long, you draw it $100'-0''$ long. Even if the final drawing will be plotted on a sheet of paper at $1'' = 20'$, it is still drawn at full size in CADD. It is critically important to plan your work carefully so you set up the correct drawing limits within which to work. Establishing the correct drawing limits allows you to draw anything full size within the limits. The term *limits* refers to the actual space required for your drawing to fit.

The planning that should occur prior to beginning the drawing involves, but is not limited to, the following items related to scaling:

- Size of paper for the final plot or print
- Size of the object to be drawn
- Height of plotted text
- Type of dimensioning to be used

Planning the scale at which a drawing is to be plotted is important because the plotted scale dramatically affects the size of drawing objects, such as text and dimensions. To start this planning, first determine what you have to draw and what size of paper it will be plotted on. Next, determine the scale at which the drawing should be plotted.

Text height and dimension text heights are directly affected by the plotting scale and must be considered early in the planning of your drawing. Use the following procedure to create a text style and dimension style that work together to create properly sized dimension text heights:

1. Create a new text style using the font of your choice, such as Romans or StylusBT.

2. Create a new dimension style and give it a name that reflects the type of dimensioning to be used—for example, Civil.

3. Choose the text style you created in step 1.

4. Select the proper text height; for example, .12 in. (3 mm) is a common text height on civil drawings. A text height of .25 in. (6 mm) is typically used for drawing titles, as described in Chapter 1.

5. Set all values for dimension line, extension line, and arrowhead sizes and offsets.

6. Set the scale factor according to the drawing scale factor. As explained in detail below, this is the number of times smaller or larger the drawing display is from the original.

7. Save the dimension style and set it current so it can be used. Whenever you begin a new drawing, always remember to set the appropriate dimension style current.

Civil drawing scales typically contain units, such as 1/4″ = 1′-0″ or 1″ = 200′. For these applications, you must first convert both numbers to the same unit format. Once you make the conversion, you can identify the scale factor. For example:

Civil

Large Scale

$$1/4″ = 1′-0″$$
$$\downarrow$$
$$1/4″ = 12″$$
$$\downarrow$$
$$.25″ = 12″$$
$$\downarrow$$
$$12/.25 = 48$$

The scale factor for a drawing scale of 1/4″ = 1′-0″ is 48.

Civil

Small scale

$$1″ = 200′$$
$$\downarrow$$
$$1″ = 2400″$$
$$\downarrow$$
$$2400/1 = 2400$$

The scale factor for a drawing scale of 1″ = 200′ is 2400.

The second important aspect of using the scale factor of the drawing is the text height. Always multiply the intended plotted text height by the scale factor to find the CADD text height. For example, if you want to have text displayed .125″ high on a drawing with a scale of 1/4″ = 1′-0″, first multiply the desired text height by the scale factor, in this case 48:

$$.125 \times 48 = 6$$

The value 6 is the text height. Therefore, you should set your text height to 6 when drawing in CADD. The text appears correct on the screen. When you plot the drawing at the scale of $1/4'' = 1'-0''$, the text height is multiplied by the scale to produce the plotted text height.

The same technique is used for any other scaled drawings. Calculations for a .125" text height for the civil scale previously shown are:

$$.125 \times 2400 = 300$$

Therefore, civil CADD text height of 6 in. produces .125" text when the civil drawing is plotted correctly. Likewise, a text height of 300 in. in the civil drawing produces the proper .125" text height when the drawing is plotted.

As you can see, planning your drawing with scales and scale factors is a critically important task and one that should become a fundamental part of your drawing habits.

Using CADD Layers

Layers allow for details of a design or different drafting information to be separated. Layers are generally of different colors and have their own names. Layers can be kept together, or individual layers can be turned on or off as needed.

A layer is a logical grouping of data, like transparent overlays of drawing information. Try to envision these overlays as clear sheets together. You can see through each sheet to the drawings on the sheets below. You can view the overlays or layers individually, in any combination, or all together. You can consider layers as a series of drawing overlays. In civil drafting, layers can be made up of several overlays, including border and title block, property lines, contours and elevations, structures, roads, parking areas, utilities, dimensions, and notes. Layers can be established with their own linetype and color. The linetype matches the civil drafting standard for the specific line and can be created to a desired thickness for display on the screen and for plotting. The color can be assigned as desired to make the line stand out on the computer screen and in the plot. Layers can be displayed and plotted individually, in any combination, or all together in black and white or in colors. Figure 2–7 provides a pictorial example of how layers work.

A good layer management system and record keeping are very important. Layers can be managed by name or number, by the project, or based on company or national standards. Layer names should be recorded in a procedures manual or drawing log, with information about the content. The manual should provide the layer name, color, linetype, and specific information about the layer content and use. A good example of a layer management system is published in *CAD Layer Guidelines*, by the American Institute of Architects (AIA) Press, 1735 New York Avenue, N.W., Washington, D.C. 20006. Information regarding the *CAD Layer Guidelines* can also be found at the AIA Online Network Web site, at **www.aia.org**. In this format, layer names are based on abbreviations that are easy to recognize. Layer names are organized in a logical grouping of objects in the drawing, such as C-TOPO for contour lines and elevations. AutoCAD, for example, lists layers alphabetically by name for ease of location.

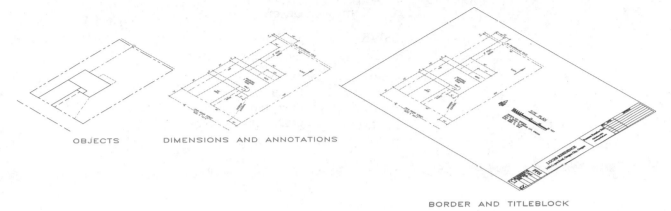

OBJECTS DIMENSIONS AND ANNOTATIONS

BORDER AND TITLEBLOCK

Figure 2–7. A simplifies pictorial representation of a CADD layering system, showing how information is shared among drawing components. Typically, each group of items is drawn on its own layer.

Use of a common prefix for all similar layers helps when you are trying to locate, sort, or manage layers. The AIA has established the following eight major groups of layer prefixes:

A	Architectural, interiors, and facility management
S	Structural
M	Mechanical
P	Plumbing
F	Fire protection
E	Electrical
C	Civil engineering and site work
L	Landscape architecture

You should determine whether company, school, or national standards are available and, if so, follow them when designing your layer names and content. If not, set up your layer naming system based on information found in the drawing.

The AIA *CAD Layer Guidelines* has established the heading Civil Engineering and Site Work as the major group for CADD layers related to civil drafting, as previously indicated. The following are some of the key recommended CADD layer names for civil drafting site plan applications:

Layer Name	Description
C-PROP	Property lines and survey bench marks
C-TOPO	Contour lines and elevations
C-BLDG	Proposed building footprint; the term *footprint* is often used to describe the area directly below a structure
C-PKNG	Parking lots
C-STRM	Storm drainage, catch basins, and manholes
C-COMM	Site communication system, such as telephone
C-WATR	Domestic water installations
C-FIRE	Fire protection hydrants and connections
C-NGAS	Natural gas systems

Layer Name	Description
C-SSWR	Sanitary sewer systems
C-ELEV	Elevations
C-SECT	Sections
C-DETL	Details
C-PSIT	Site plan
C-PELC	Site electrical systems plan
C-PUTL	Site plan utility
C-PPAV	Paving plan

Managing CADD Files

In a CADD environment, computer files are at the very heart of everything you do. The programs you use rely on information stored in files that the computer evaluates and executes. A program such as AutoCAD has features such as linetype and hatch pattern definitions that are stored in files. Most importantly, the drawings you create are stored in drawing files. Understanding proper file management techniques allows you to maximize the potential of your workstation and saves you time when working in CADD.

The size of the drawing you are working in can affect the speed of your workstation. Used in this sense, the term *size* does not refer to the area displayed within the drawing; rather, it reflects the amount of information contained in the drawing. A single line on the drawing, for example, stores a record of its coordinate location, layer, color, linetype, elevation, thickness, linetype scale, and more. Therefore, a simple line can occupy a good bit of storage space within a drawing. Considering the number of lines, arcs, circles, and other objects in a typical drawing, it is easy to see how files can become large in a short time.

In addition to the objects on the screen that you can see, other types of information within drawings can add to the overall file size. For example, symbol block definitions are not visible on your drawing but exist within the drawing. A *block* is a named object that is defined from one or more other objects, handled as a single object such as a symbol. These can consume valuable space for no reason. Some drafters will load all the linetype definitions for convenience when working. When the drawing is complete, the unused linetype definitions are also unnecessary. All the unnecessary information in a drawing makes the file larger than it needs to be. For this reason, using blocks and external references can help keep the drawing size at a minimum. Another technique for maintaining efficient drawing sizes is to purge unnecessary data from the drawing. AutoCAD, for example, provides an easy dialog interface for purging unreferenced drawing data. The term *unreferenced* indicates data that defines something that is not used within the drawing. For example, a layer that contains no objects is an example of unreferenced data. AutoCAD provides the PURGE command for removing unreferenced data from the drawing. This should be used at the end of each project to help minimize the file size.

Exchanging Drawing Files

Drawing files can be imported and exported between CADD software programs and other software programs. Several file formats are supported, including vector and raster. *Vector* information is composed of actual objects, such as lines and text. A *raster format* file is a record of pixels, with each pixel separate from all others. The term *pixel* is an acronym for picture elements. Display quality is measured by the total number of pixels that can be displayed on the screen and the number of colors that can be used. The type of file used depends on the type of application. CADD-based applications usually create vector files, and paint programs usually create raster files.

An example is the drawing interchange format (.dxf extension) that is a proprietary file format created by Autodesk, Inc., for exchanging drawing file information between applications. Many applications can read DXF files and convert them to their own format. Most applications that can read a DXF file can also create a DXF file.

A process known as referencing an external drawing allows you to reference a source file for information rather than storing it in the current drawing. This helps minimize file size and provides other values. An *external drawing* is a drawing database that is stored outside the current drawing. The term *referencing* means that the CAD program refers to the source file for information rather than storing it in the current drawing. Therefore, an *external reference* is a source drawing outside the current drawing that CADD refers to for information displayed in the current drawing.

Using external references has many advantages over inserting other drawings into the current drawing. One advantage is that the information is not permanently added to the current drawing, keeping the drawing file size from getting unnecessarily large. Another advantage of external references is that any number of drawings can reference a specific drawing file. A big advantage is that the CADD software reads the source drawing file for each external reference every time you open a drawing that uses external references. So, all the drawings that reference external drawings automatically reflect the latest state of the referenced drawing file. In AutoCAD, the primary command used for working with externally referenced drawing files is the XREF command. In fact, an external reference is most commonly called an *xref*.

File Management Guidelines

Your use of CADD files can be as easy as opening a drawing file, working on it, and saving it in the same location. You might also be responsible for creating new folders and subfolders for new projects and managing files for the company. An important objective is to become familiar with file management and maintenance. Project file management should include these elements:

- Save all working files on a regular basis. Save files to at least two different media, such as the hard drive, a separate external hard drive, an optical disc, and a USB (Universal Serial Bus) flash drive, also known as a thumb drive. Establish safeguards for saving work on a regular basis. For example, set your CADD automatic save option to save your work every 10 to 15 minutes.

- Create storage media directories and folders for all files.
- Never save your working files in folders that contain program files.
- Create a separate folder for each project and subfolders for different types of files in the project.
- Store template files in a protected location that allows only selected individuals to edit and save these files.
- Keep drawing files separate from files such as text documents, spreadsheets, and database files.
- Maintain off-site locations for file storage and archiving.
- Establish a regular schedule for deleting all backup and temporary files from your storage media.
- Use hard disk management software to rearrange software and data on the hard disk to reclaim space occupied by deleted files.
- Install only licensed software on your computer system. It is illegal to use unlicensed software.
- Never install software without approval from your supervisor or instructor.

Using Template Drawings

A template is a pattern of a standard or commonly used feature or features that is created once and then used on following drawings. A collection of symbols in a symbol library could be called a template. If you create a base drawing that contains standard components, values, settings, and borders and title blocks, it is referred to as a *template drawing*. Most schools and companies use template drawings. Template drawings save time and help produce consistency in the drawing process.

Template Drawing Contents Template drawings should be stored in a common location that is accessible to everyone who needs them. This is often on a network computer. If you maintain your own templates, be sure they are stored in at least two different locations for safekeeping. Template drawings can and should be updated and added to; therefore, it is important that you replace all old copies with the updated versions. Keep on file a variety of template drawings that contain settings for different drawing disciplines, drawing applications, and scales. Template drawings can contain, but are not limited to, the following items:

- Border and title block with standard title block text information completed if desired
- Several named text styles with heights to match different scale drawings
- Named dimension styles with values and settings for specific drawing scales
- Named layers containing colors, linetypes, and line weights
- Display settings for point styles, line styles, and line weights

- User profiles containing display screen menu layouts, colors, fonts, and configuration
- Drafting settings, such as object snaps, grid, snap, units, and limits
- Section patterns (hatch) and scales
- Plot styles and settings

Using Template Drawings   Template drawings help you create new drawings by referencing a base drawing that contains many of the standard items required for multiple drawing projects. Using template drawings is an easy process, and if a standard procedure is followed, creates a productive drawing session and ensures consistency in your drawings. Template drawings function and are used differently, depending on the CADD program. Many programs provide convenient tools for referencing stored drawing templates. This automates the traditional method of opening a template file and then saving a copy of the template file using the name of the new drawing.

For example, AutoCAD software makes use of drawing template (DWT) files. Other CADD programs have different but similar applications. Once you create a DWT file containing standard drawing settings and objects, save the file in an easily accessible location and create backup copies. When you are ready to prepare a new drawing (DWG) file, use the New command to reference an existing DWT file. A new drawing file appears, with all the template file settings and contents. Use the Save command immediately to save the drawing in the appropriate location and with the desired name. The new drawing name is probably related to the drawing type or project; confirm this with your school or company standards. You are now ready to begin work on the new drawing project.

As you work, you may discover additional items that should be included in your template drawings. When using AutoCAD, for example, use the Open command to open a DWT file. Then add content to the file as needed. Once you resave the file, the modified template is ready to use. This leads to greater productivity in future work. Sample templates are available for your use on the Web site.

Creating and Using Symbols

A symbol is a graphic representation of a feature or an object. One of the great time-saving features of CADD technology is the ability to draw a feature once, save it, and then use it over and over without ever having to draw it again. That is why one of the first things a company does with a CADD system is begin developing symbol libraries. A symbol library is a file of symbols that can be accessed for use on a drawing.

Drawing a Symbol   The process of creating a symbol is easy. To create a symbol, begin a drawing with the name of the symbol as the file name. When you start drawing the symbol, begin by placing the origin of your coordinate system at a spot on the symbol that is convenient to use as a point of reference or location on a drawing. Look at the symbols in Figure 2–8. These symbols have a small crosshairs at the location point. This is the spot you point to on your drawing to locate the symbol. This point is called the *insertion point*.

Figure 2–8. **The location of the insertion points on mapping symbols.**

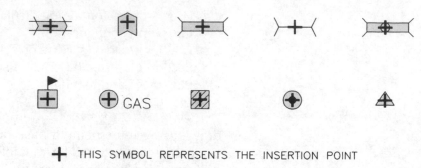

+ THIS SYMBOL REPRESENTS THE INSERTION POINT

When the symbol has been drawn, it must then be stored, but in a slightly different manner from a regular drawing. It is stored as a symbol. CADD programs have commands that let you save an object as a symbol in the current drawing or for use in any drawing. This allows you to use the symbol multiple times by inserting it when needed. Confirm the command names and applications with your CADD program Help files or related textbook.

Creating a Symbol Library   After all the required symbols are drawn, they can be used in a variety of ways. It is important that all the symbols or blocks be located in a common area, such as a directory on the hard drive, or a drive or folder on the network server. If you have the ability to customize the software's menus, the symbols can be added to pull-down menus, toolbars, or tool palettes for easy access. These methods of locating the symbols in menus allow them to be picked and then placed in the drawing, thus eliminating the need to type file names.

Using Symbols   Most of the editing features for revising drawings can be used to edit symbols. In addition, there are several commands that allow you to work with the symbols. Symbols are fluid, just like the rest of the drawing, and can be changed, moved, renamed, and copied. Commands such as ROTATE, COPY, MIRROR, and MOVE can all be used to work with symbols.

Dynamic Symbols   **Symbol libraries** can contain hundreds or even thousands of **symbols**. The more symbols you have, the more time it takes to manage and work with them. When a new symbol needs to be created, additional symbols may also need to be created that resemble the first symbol, with slight variances. For example, you may need to create a symbol of a bridge that is 100′ long. If the same style of bridge is also available in three other lengths, then three additional symbols need to be created, or one symbol with dynamic properties can be created.

CADD software programs allow you to create symbols for multiple use and allow you to insert symbols with the dynamic properties previously described. A **dynamic symbol** is a normal symbol that has *parameters* and *actions* assigned to objects within the symbol. A *parameter* is a value, a name, an option, or a characteristic that is part of a command or CADD application that can be edited to automatically change the object to match the edit. This allows special modifications to be performed on a single symbol while it is in the drawing, without affecting other instances of the same symbol. Using the previous bridge example, the bridge symbol can be assigned a *linear parameter* with a *stretch action*, which allows the bridge to be stretched to different lengths. Various types of parameters and actions can be used on blocks. Sample symbols are available for your use on the Web site.

Reusing Drawing Content

In virtually every drafting discipline, individual drawings created as part of a given project are likely to share a number of common elements. All the drawings within a specific drafting project generally hold the same set of governing standards. Drawing features such as the text size and style used for text, line types, standardized dimensioning methods and appearances, layer names and properties, drafting symbols, drawing layouts, and even typical drawing details are often duplicated in many different drawings. These and other components of CADD drawings are referred to as *drawing content*. One of the most fundamental advantages of computer-aided drafting systems is the ease with which content can be shared between drawings. Once a frequently used drawing feature has been defined, it can be used again as needed, in any number of drawing applications.

Using drawing templates represents one way to reuse drawing content that has already been explained. Creating your own customized drawing template files provides an effective way to start each new drawing using standard settings. However, drawing templates provide only a starting point. During the course of a drawing project, you often need to add content to the current drawing that has been defined previously in another drawing. Some drawing projects require you to revise an existing drawing rather than start a completely new drawing. For other projects, you may need to duplicate the standards used in a drawing supplied by a client.

CADD software programs allow you to share content between drawings in different but similar ways. Generally, content that has already been defined in previous drawings can be copied and reused in other drawings with a simple drag-and-drop operation.

Drag-and-drop is a feature that allows you to perform tasks by moving your cursor over the top of an icon in a folder or menu source. The icon represents a document, a drawing, a folder, or another application. Next, you press and hold the button on your pointing device, and then you drag the cursor to the desired folder or drawing and release the button. The selected content is added to your current drawing or chosen file.

Techniques for reusing drawing content differ between CADD programs. Refer to your CADD program Help files or related textbook for specific commands and applications.

CADD Plotting Guidelines

A drawing created in CADD exists in two forms: one form is a soft copy and the other is a hard copy. Soft copy is the computer software version of the drawing that you see on the computer screen, or the actual data file. **Hard copy** is a physical drawing produced on paper or some other media by a printer or plotter.

A Review of Scale Factors   Scale factors were introduced earlier. Additional information related to plotting is provided for your review. For a review, a scale factor is a numerical value used in the proper scaling of text; dimension objects, such as dimension text and arrowheads or slashes; and the size of the model limits. When drawing in CADD, objects are always drawn at full scale. For example, a 50'-0" × 30'-0" (15,240 × 9,244 mm) building is drawn 50' × 30'. After the building is drawn, the notes and other text are added. If you use standard text height, the text needs to be plotted 1/8" (3 mm) high on the drawing. If 1/8" text is placed into the 50' × 30' building, the text on the computer screen and on the plot will be too small to read. This is where the scale factor becomes important. The scale factor of a drawing is something you need to plan in advance and is part of your CADD template. As discussed earlier, a template is a file containing standard settings such as layer names, dimension and text styles, and line types, applied to the drawing. To make the text readable on the plotted paper, the desired plotted text height of 1/8" is multiplied by the scale factor to determine the height of the text when in the drawing. The scale factor is also used to scale dimension features.

The scale factor can be determined by first deciding the drawing scale for the plotted drawing. The scale factor is then determined by dividing the plotted units into the drawing units. The following formula demonstrates this concept:

$$Plotted\ units = Drawing\ units$$
$$Plotted\ units\ (drawing\ units) = Scale\ factor$$

A civil drawing to be plotted at 1/8" = 1'-0", for example, has a scale factor calculated like this:

$$1/8" = 1'\text{-}0"$$
$$.125" = 12"$$
$$12/.125 = 96$$

The scale factor is 96.

Once the scale factor has been determined, calculate the actual text height to be used in the CADD program. If the desired text height is 1/80", multiply the plotted text height by the scale factor. So, for the 1/8" = 1'-0" scale drawing, the text height is:

$$1/8" \times 96 = 12"$$

Therefore, 1/8" high text on the plotted drawing is created at 12" high on the drawing.

Another example of a scale factor used on a civil engineering drawing with a scale of 1" = 60' is:

$$1" = 60'$$
$$1" = 60 \times 12 = 720$$

The scale factor is 720.

When using the $1'' = 60'$ scale, text drawn at 1/8″ high appears as a dot. The $1'' = 60'$ scale means that the full-size civil engineering drawing is 720 times larger than it will be when plotted at the chosen scale. This means that you must multiply the desired text height of 1/8″ by 720 in order to get text that appears in correct proportion in your drawing on the screen. For this scale, calculate 1/8″ text height as follows:

$$1/8'' \times 720 = 90$$

The proper text height for this drawing is 90.

Plotting the Model and Sheet   While terminology can vary with programs, CADD files are generally created as models and sheets. The place where drawing objects are created is referred to as the **model**, and the **sheet** is often called the layout. The *layout space* is an area used to lay out the sheet of paper to be plotted. As previously mentioned, everything you draw in the CADD model is drawn full scale. When you enter the layout space, a real-size imaginary sheet of paper is placed over the top of the model drawing. Border line, title blocks, and notes are also found on the layout. The model drawings and the layout sheet are put together for plotting. In Figure 2–9, the drawing model is combined with the layout sheet. When setting up the drawing to be plotted, multiple models can be arranged on the layout sheet. For example, a site plan sheet can have the site plan at one scale and separate details at another scale.

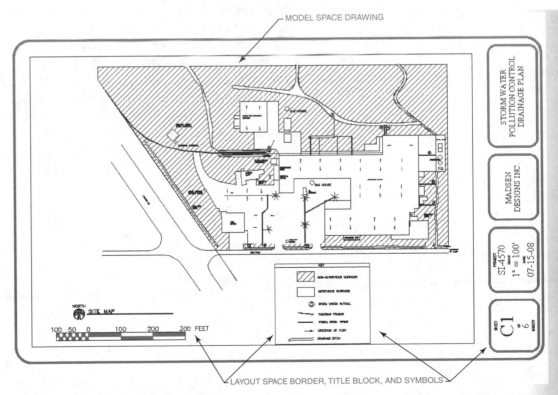

Figure 2–9.   When you enter sheet layout, a real-size sheet of paper is placed over the top of the model drawing. Border line, title blocks, and notes are also found on the real-size paper layout. The model drawings and the layout sheet are put together for plotting.

Getting Ready to Plot

When the layout is prepared as desired, the sheet can be set up for plotting. During this process, you can select plotter settings, pen settings, and paper size. Each layout can have a unique sheet setup. For example, you can create two layouts for a site plan. One layout can be assigned a 36″ × 24″ sheet size, and another can be assigned a 14″ × 8 1/2″ sheet size. This allows you to maximize the plotting possibilities with the same drawing. Your CADD program has a sheet or page setup dialog box where plotter configurations can be selected. If you use the Windows operating system where printers and plotters are configured, they also show up on the list.

After the plotter is selected, you can specify the desired pen settings. To do this, you can assign a plot style table to the layout. A *plot style table* is a pen configuration that allows you to have control over how your drawing appears when plotted. Two common plot style tables are the color table and the style table. *Color tables* assign different pen values to the colors in the CADD program. For example, if the color red is assigned a heavy-weight pen that plots with black color, then any objects with a red color are plotted with heavy black lines. *Style tables* are names with pen settings that can be assigned to layers or objects. For example, a style table can include a named style called property lines, which has been assigned a heavy dash–double dash red line. The property line style can then be assigned to the property line layer in the drawing. Anything that is drawn on the property line layer then plots as a heavy dash–double dash red line. After the desired plot style table is set up, you are ready to send the drawing to the plotter. Standard applications of line weights and linetypes were discussed earlier in this chapter. Additionally, line weights are covered throughout this book where they apply to specific drawing applications. There are likely more settings required for your specific CADD program, such as AutoCAD or MicroStation. Carefully review the Help files or an in-depth textbook for your CADD software for detailed information. For AutoCAD reference, see *AutoCAD and Its Applications*, by Terence M. Shumaker and David A. Madsen.

Plotting to a File

It is possible to plot your drawing to an electronic file. This is often done to allow your drawing to be published to the Internet and viewed using a Web browser. One advantage of plotting to files is that the drawings can be shared by another person without that person physically having the CADD program to view the drawings. For others to view your CADD drawings in this manner, they need a viewer program. Another advantage of this option is that drawings cannot be edited. Plotting to files also provides a great means for archiving projects because the actual drawing files do not have to be opened and viewed from the CADD program. These files are also considerably smaller in size than the originals and can be easily sent through e-mail.

CADD and the Internet

New technologies are rapidly changing the way things are done in industry. One of the most influential technologies in today's design and drafting industry is the Internet. The Internet is a worldwide network of computers connected to one another through telecommunication lines or satellites. One of the most popular uses of the Internet is for fast and convenient communications through e-mail. *E-mail*, or electronic mail, uses the Internet to transmit messages and computer files anywhere in the world in a matter of minutes.

The World Wide Web is probably the most widely known application of Internet technology. The World Wide Web (Web or WWW) provides an easy-to-understand interface for the Internet. This powerful medium uses Hypertext Markup Language (HTML) files to present information. When viewed with a piece of software known as a Web browser, HTML files provide a *graphical user interface (GUI)* to the Internet, similar to the way the Windows operating system simplifies complex computer processes using buttons, icons, and menus. The term hypertext describes text items that are linked to other resources, but links are often attached to images, icons, and menus as well. Items in HTML documents that are linked to other Web resources are called *hyperlinks*.

Web technologies are now widely used in the design and drafting industry. This industry is driven by information, so the Web is a perfect medium for presenting and accessing information quickly and easily. CADD programs generally provide powerful tools for incorporating Web-based technologies into the design process. Using these tools, you can share your drawings with anyone, anywhere in the world. You can plot drawing files electronically so they can be viewed using a Web browser. This means that coworkers and clients can view the CADD drawings in an electronic format even if they do not have the CADD software. For comprehensive coverage of these and other CADD-related applications, refer to *AutoCAD and Its Applications*. For complete coverage of related disciplines, refer to *Engineering Drawing and Design*.

Ergonomics

Ergonomics is the study of a worker's relationship to physical and psychological environments. There is concern about the effect of the CADD working environment on individual workers. Some studies have found that people should not work at a computer workstation for longer than about four hours without a break. Physical problems can develop when someone is working at a poorly designed CADD workstation; these problems can range from injury to eyestrain. The most common type of injury is referred to as *repetitive strain injury (RSI)*, but it also has other names, including *repetitive movement injury (RMI)*, *cumulative trauma disorder (CTD)*, and *occupational overuse syndrome (OOS)*. One of the most common effects is *carpal tunnel syndrome* (*CTS*), which develops when inflamed muscles trap the nerves that run through the wrist. Symptoms of CTS include tingling, numbness, and possibly loss of sensation. An RSI usually develops slowly and can affect many parts of the body. You should be concerned if you experience different degrees and types of discomfort that seem to be aggravated by computer usage. Many factors can help reduce the possibility of RSI.

Ergonomic Workstations

An ergonomically designed workstation is shown in Figure 2–10. In general, a workstation should be designed so you sit with your feet flat on the floor, with your calves perpendicular to the floor and your thighs parallel to the floor. Your back should be straight, your forearms should be parallel to the floor, and your wrists should be straight. For some people, the keyboard should be either adjustable or separate from the computer to provide more flexibility. The keyboard should be positioned, and arm or wrist supports should be used, to reduce elbow and wrist tension. Also, when the keys are pressed, a slight sound should be heard to assure the key has made contact. Ergonomically designed keyboards are available.

The monitor location and position is a concern. The monitor should be 18″ to 28″, or approximately one arm's length, away from your head. The screen should be adjusted to 15° to 30° below your horizontal line of sight. Eyestrain and headache can be a problem with extended use. If the position of the monitor is adjustable, you can tilt or turn the screen to reduce glare from overhead or adjacent

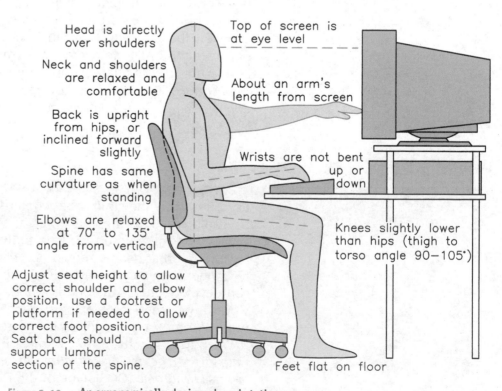

Figure 2–10. An ergonomically designed workstation.

lighting. Some users have found that a small amount of background light is helpful. Monitor manufacturers offer large nonglare screens that help reduce eyestrain. Some CADD users have suggested changing screen background and text colors weekly to give variety and reduce eyestrain.

The chair should be designed for easy adjustments, to give optimum comfort. It should be comfortably padded. Your back should be straight or up to 10° back, your feet should be flat on the floor, and your elbow-to-hand movement should be horizontal when you are using the keyboard, mouse, or digitizer. The mouse should be close to the monitor so movement is not strained and equipment use is flexible. You should not have to move a great deal to look directly over the cursor to activate commands.

Positive Work Habits

In addition to an ergonomically designed workstation, your own personal work habits can contribute to a healthy environment. Try to concentrate on good posture until it becomes second nature. Keeping your feet flat on the floor helps improve posture. Try to keep your stress level low because increased stress can contribute to tension, which can aggravate physical problems. Take breaks periodically to help reduce muscle fatigue and tension. You should consult with your doctor for further advice and recommendations.

Exercise

If you feel the pain and discomfort that can be associated with computer use, some stretching exercises can help. Figure 2–11 shows some exercises that can help reduce workstation-related problems. Some people have also had success with yoga, biofeedback, and massage. Again, you should consult with your doctor for further advice and recommendations before using any of these practices.

Sitting at a computer workstation for several hours in a day can produce a great deal of muscle tension and physical discomfort. You should do these stretches throughout the day, whenever you are feeling tension (mental or physical).

As you stretch, you should breathe easily—inhale through your nose, exhale through your mouth. Do not force any stretch, do not bounce, and stop if the stretch becomes painful. The most benefit is realized if you relax, stretch slowly, and *feel* the stretch. The stretches shown here take about $2\frac{1}{2}$ minutes to complete.

1. 5 seconds, 3 times:	7. 5 seconds:
2. 5 seconds, 3 times:	8. 10 seconds, each arm:
3. 5 seconds, 2 times:	9. 10 seconds
4. 5 seconds, 2 times:	10. 10 seconds:
5. 5 seconds, each side:	11. 10 seconds each side:
6. 5 seconds, each side:	12. 10 seconds:

Figure 2–11. Exercises that can help reduce workstation-related problems. You should consult with your doctor for further advice and recommendations before using any of these practices.

TEST

Define or describe the following. Use your best hand lettering or access this test on the Student Web site and follow the instructions to respond electronically.

2–1 Layer

2–2 Model files

2–3 Sheet file

2–4 Drawing scale

2–5 Dimensions

2–6 Limits

2–7 External drawing

2–8 External reference

2–9 Template

2–10 Template drawing

2–11 Symbol library

2–12 Drawing content

2–13 Parameter

2-14   Dynamic block

2-15   Scale factor

2-16   Model space

2-17   Layout space

2-18   Internet

2-19   Hypertext

2-20   Ergonomics

PROBLEMS

P2-1   This problem involves a written report. Chose one or more of the following topics and write an approximately 250-word report on the subject or subjects. Include graphics as needed to illustrate the content. Research for the content of your report can be done using this textbook, on the Internet, at local suppliers, trade magazines, journals, brochures, advertisements, news reports, instruction manuals, telephone or personal visitation interviews, workshops, conferences, conventions, or other sources. Additional detailed information can be found in one or both of the following textbooks:

AutoCAD and Its Applications, by Shumaker, Madsen, and Madsen.

Engineering Drawing and Design, by Madsen.

Be specific, especially if a manufacturer makes more than one model of CADD system. Check with your instructor about any specific requirements related to the report.

- 2D and 3D coordinate systems
- Layers and layer management
- The U.S. National CAD Standard
- File management
- Drawing templates
- Reuse of drawing content
- Symbols and symbol libraries
- Ergonomics
- CADD software manufacturer with civil design and drafting programs

- CADD system and workstation
- Input devices
- Output devices, such as printers and plotters used for CADD applications
- Storage devices and storage media
- Drafting media

P2–2   Write a short, approximately 150-word, report that discusses the differences among pen plotters, inkjet plotters, and laser printers. You can use any sources that provide the needed information, such as those suggested in problem P2–1. Include the following points in your report:

- Type of media required, such as paper and pens
- Media size
- Purchase and operational cost
- Quality of final print or plot
- Usefulness in your application
- Warranties and service contracts
- Durability
- Reputation
- Length of time on the market

P2–3   Create a specification sheet for the purchase of a single CADD workstation, operating system software, word processing software, spreadsheet software, and civil design and drafting software for use on the computer. You can do this as a report, form, or list. Computer speed and capabilities change rapidly, so look for the most current specifications. Itemize the cost of each component and establish a total price. Obtain at least two competitive quotes.

The assignment should include the following elements in addition to information found in your research:

- Computer memory
- Processor speed
- Hard drive capacity
- Portable or built-in storage media
- Graphics card
- Ports
- Monitor
- Input device
- Printer or plotter
- Operating system
- Civil CADD software
- Word processing software
- Spreadsheet software

P2–4   Using existing computer equipment, vendor catalogs, or other research, measure the equipment or get needed measurements to design a CADD workstation, including but not limited to computer, monitor, keyboard, and pointing device.

After designing and drawing the table with equipment displayed, create and draw a computer lab arrangement with 12 workstations, unless otherwise specified by your instructor. Use symbols to your best advantage, as discussed in this chapter. Consider the following when designing the lab:

- Marker board
- Aisles and access
- Glare from windows
- Power connections
- Location of printers and plotters
- Supply storage
- Instructor or supervisor desk or podium
- Projection system and instructor or supervisor workstation

P2–5   Create template drawings for civil drafting projects to be created throughout this textbook. These template files will have basic content now, and additional content can be included later as your drawing needs develop. Create at least one template for each drawing size, as needed, for future drawings. Research proper industry drawing sheet size and format standards and create your templates based on these sheet sizes:

Inch		*Metric (mm)*	
Size	**Dimensions**	**Size**	**Dimensions**
A	11 × 8.5	A3	297 × 210
B	17 × 11	A2	594 × 420
C	22 × 17	A1	841 × 594
D	34 × 22	A0	1189 × 841

Note: Dimensions are given with the horizontal value followed by the vertical size (H × V).

The following items should be included in your initial template drawings:

- Border and title block
- Title block text, with school, personal, or company logo and information
- Standard civil layers
- Text styles
- Dimension styles

Map Scales

Learning Objectives

After completing this chapter, you will be able to:

- Define map scale and scale factor.
- Create graphic scales.
- Convert representative fractions to graphic scales.
- Convert graphic scales to representative fractions.
- Convert verbal scales to representative fractions.
- Draw plot plans from engineering sketches and given information.

Key Terms

Map scale
Map
Numerical scale
Representative fraction (RF)
Graphic scale
Verbal scale
Civil engineer's scale
Metric scale
Scale factor

This chapter explains the purpose and types of map scales. Illustrations are provided to show how scales affect the map that is being represented.

The topics covered include:

- CADD scales
- Numerical scale
- Graphic scale
- Verbal scale
- Scale conversion
- Use of the civil engineer's scale
- Metric scales

Map scales vary as to purpose, size, and desired detail. For example, if a map of the State of New York were to be painted to scale on a large, blank wall of a building, the scale would be different than if the New York map were drawn to scale on an 11- by 17-in. sheet of paper. Also, a map scale varies according to the area of the earth's surface covered. A map of your school drawn on this page will have a different scale than if it were a map of the United States.

A simple definition of map is a representation of a portion of the earth's surface reduced to a small size. A map's scale aids you in estimating distances and gives you an idea of what to expect in the way of detail. The map scale shows the relationship between the measurements of the features shown on the map compared to the actual features on the earth's surface.

Maps are commonly drawn using a scale that is established in multiples of 10 feet (ft) to 1 inch (in.). For example, 1 in. = 10 ft, 1 in. = 100 ft, 1 in. = 1000 ft, and 1 in. = 10,000 ft. Selecting the appropriate scale depends on the size of the geographical area, the amount of required detail, and the size of the sheet on which the map is drawn.

There are three methods of expressing scale:

1. Numerical scale or representative fraction

2. Graphic scale

3. Verbal scale

Numerical Scale

The numerical scale gives the proportion between the length of a line on a map and the corresponding length on the earth's surface. This proportion is known as the representative fraction (RF). The first number is a single unit of measure equal to the distance on the map = 1. The second number is the same distance on the earth, using the same units of measure. It can be written in two ways: 1/150,000 or 1:150,000.

RF (representative fraction) = Distance on map/Distance on earth

It is very important to note that this map scale must always refer to map and ground distances in the same unit of measure. The unit of measure most commonly used in the representative fraction is the inch. For instance, a scale of 1 in. on your map representing 1 mile (mi) on the earth's surface is expressed as follows: RF = 1/63,360 or 1:63,360 because 1 mile equals 63,360 in.

Remember that the numerator is always 1 and represents the map. The denominator is always greater because it represents the ground. The *numerator* is the number above the fraction bar. For example, 1 is the numerator in the fraction 1/10. The *denominator* is the number below the fraction bar. For example, 10 is the denominator in the fraction 1/10. So, the larger the denominator, the smaller the scale. A map with a small scale and large RF denominator, drawn on a specific size of paper, shows more of the earth's surface than a map with a large scale and small RF denominator, drawn on the same size of paper.

To calculate the distance between two points on a map, you must multiply the measured distance in inches by the denominator of the RF. For example, if you measured 2 1/4 in. between points *A* and *B* on a map drawn to a scale of 1/100,000, the real distance between points *A* and *B* is Distance = 2 1/4 × 100,000 = 225,000 in. You can convert this to feet or miles if you desire. If the map is calibrated in metric, 1:100,000 means 1 cm = 100,000 cm = 1 km.

Small-Scale and Special Maps

Information compiled by the U.S. Department of Interior, Geological Survey, indicates that several series of small-scale and special maps are published to meet modern requirements. These include, but are not limited to:

1. *1:250,000 scale (1 in. on the map represents about 4 mi on the ground)*—For regional planning and as topographic bases for other types of maps

2. *State maps, at 1:500,000 scale (1 in. represents 8 mi)*—For use as wall maps and for statewide planning

3. *Shaded-relief maps, at various scales*—For park management and development and as tourist guides

4. *Antarctic topographic maps, at various scales*—For scientific research

5. *International map of the world (IMW), at 1:1,000,000 scale*—For broad geographic studies

Figure 3–1 provides a graphic example of maps at different scales.

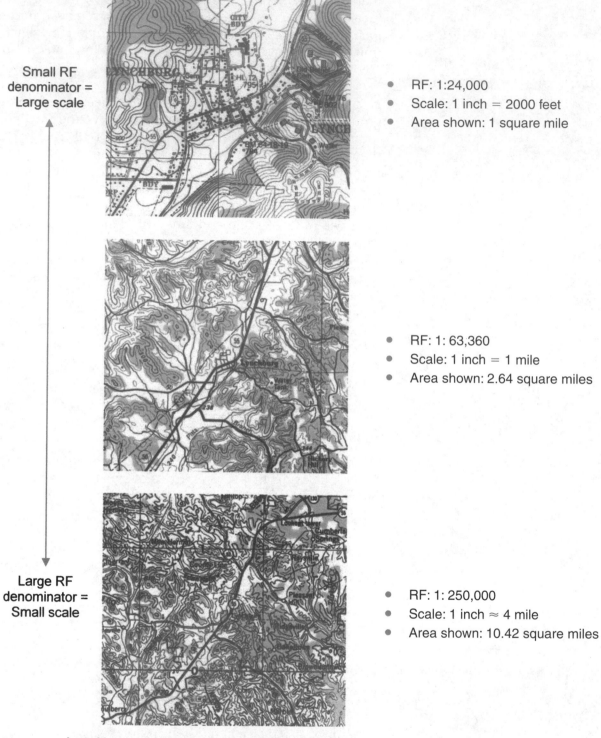

Small RF
denominator =
Large scale

- RF: 1:24,000
- Scale: 1 inch = 2000 feet
- Area shown: 1 square mile

- RF: 1: 63,360
- Scale: 1 inch = 1 mile
- Area shown: 2.64 square miles

Large RF
denominator =
Small scale

- RF: 1: 250,000
- Scale: 1 inch ≈ 4 mile
- Area shown: 10.42 square miles

Figure 3-1.   A graphic example of maps created at different scales.
(Courtesy U.S. Geological Survey, www.usgs.gov)

Graphic Scale

A graphic scale is like a small ruler in the legend or margin of a map. The divisions on the graphic scale represent increments of measure easily applied to the map.

There are no standards that specify exactly what a graphic scale should or should not include or what it should look like. A graphic scale can be as simple or as elaborate as the drafter or civil engineering company desires. Typically, graphic scales consist of two or three segments that correspond to specific increments of measure. Above or below the segment edges are numbers that define the increments of measure, and usually one or more of the numbers identify the unit of measure.

Ordinarily, graphic scales begin at zero, but many have an extension to the left of the zero that allows you to determine distances less than the major unit of the scale. A graphic scale uses relatively even units of measure, such as 500 or 1000. Figure 3–2 illustrates three graphic scales, each calibrated differently.

There are a number of techniques for using graphic scales. You can use a graphic scale as a quick reference by visually comparing the graphic scale information to features on the map, or you can approximate a distance on the map using your fingers to transfer map measurements to the graphic scale. To use your fingers, create a space between your thumb and forefinger that matches a desired distance on the map. Keeping the space between your thumb and forefinger constant, move your fingers to the graphic scale and read the measurement of the same distance on the graphic scale. However, if you need a more accurate measurement, you can use a pair of mechanical dividers to associate distances on the graphic scale to map features, or you can use a piece of paper to reference distances on the map. A *mechanical divider*, also referred to as a *divider*, is a drafting instrument consisting of two pointed legs, pivoted together at one end and used for transferring distances. For example, suppose you want to measure the distance on a road between points *A* and *B* on the simple map shown in Figure 3–3. To do this, apply a straight-edged strip of plain paper on the map along the distance between the two points and make marks on the paper strip where the edge touches *A* and *B*. Then move the strip of paper to the graphic scale and measure. Point *A* is

Figure 3–2. **Sample graphic scales.**

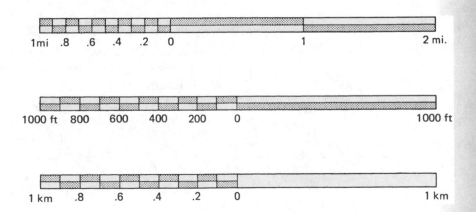

Figure 3–3.   **Measuring with a graphic scale.**

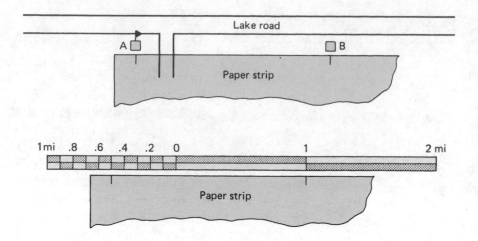

found to be 1.5 miles down the road from point *B*. Figure 3–3 also illustrates how the piece of paper is used to mark the distance on the map and then determine the distance measured.

Verbal Scale

Verbal scale is usually expressed in the number of inches to the mile. Usually, the mileage is rounded. For example, 1 in. on an RF scale of 1:1,000,000 equals 15.78 mi. This distance expressed in verbal scale rounds off the 15.78 to 16. So, the verbal scale is 1 in. = 16 mi. This is a close approximation for discussion purposes. The verbal scale is not meant to be accurate, only a rough estimate. Use the RF scale for accurate measurements.

Scale Conversion

In map drafting or map reading, it is often necessary to convert from one scale to another. You may have to convert an RF scale to a graphic scale for display on a map.

Converting a Representative Fraction to a Graphic Scale

The following is an example of how to convert a representative fraction to a graphic scale. You must identify components of the conversion equation based on the representative fraction, the size of the geographic area, the amount of detail required, and the size of the sheet on which the map is drawn. Use the following example to understand the conversion process and as a model for converting other representative fractions to graphic scales.

Example: Given a representative scale of 1:300,000, find the graphic equivalent. Remember that the 1 equals 1 in. on the map, and the 300,000 equals 300,000 in. on the earth's surface. You must first determine the number of miles that are represented by the 300,000 in. There are 63,360 in. in a mile, so

$$\frac{300,000 \text{ in. on earth}}{1} \times \frac{1 \text{ mile on earth}}{63,360 \text{ in. on earth}} = 4.73 \text{ miles on earth}$$

Therefore, 1 in. on the graphic scale = 4.73 miles on the earth's surface.

This scale is not practical because it is difficult to imagine odd measurements such as 4.73 miles, as shown in Figure 3–4. Instead, graphic scales are drawn using units like 0–1–2–3–4 or 0–2–4–6 or 0–5–10–15–20. It is necessary to find out how many inches are used to show any even number larger than the 4.73 miles previously determined. For example, use 10 mi. This would be set up in a ratio:

$$\times \quad \frac{4.73 \text{ miles}}{1 \text{ in.}} = \frac{10 \text{ miles}}{\text{(unknown no. of inches)}}$$
$$4.73x = 10$$
$$x = 2.11 \text{ in.}$$

The solution to this formula means there are 2.11 in. in 10 miles. Once you generate this information, you can create a graphic scale by drawing 2.11 in. segments. Then, divide the left segment into 10 equal parts to provide distances less than the major unit of scale; in this case, each division equals 1 mile. Remember, in this example, each 2.11 in. segment represents 10 miles on the map. Figure 3–5 shows a typical graphic scale created based on the previous example. This graphic scale consists of three 2.11 in. segments, with the left segment divided into 10 equal parts. Additional lines, fills, and text have also been added. The dimensions are for reference only and should not be added.

Converting a Graphic Scale to a Representative Fraction

Example: Given that 1 in. on the graphic scale of a map equals 5 miles, determine the representative scale. This can be done by applying as a conversion factor the fact that 1 mile equals 63,360 in.:

$$\frac{5 \text{ miles on earth}}{1} \times \frac{63,360 \text{ in. on earth}}{1 \text{ mile on earth}}$$
$$= 316,800 \text{ in. on the earth's surface}$$
$$RF = 1{:}316{,}800.$$

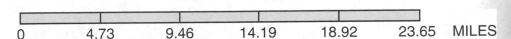

| 0 | 4.73 | 9.46 | 14.19 | 18.92 | 23.65 | MILES |

Figure 3–4. This graphic scale is not practical because it is difficult to imagine the odd measurements shown.

10 8 6 4 2 0   10   20 MILES

|← 2.11 in. →|

Figure 3–5. Correct graphic scale with one segment divided into 10 equal spaces.

Example: Determine the representative fraction for a map with no scale. The representative fraction can be determined by measuring the length of 1° of latitude along a meridian of the map. An angle of 1° of latitude is about 69 statute miles. Now convert that distance to inches:

$$\frac{69 \text{ miles on earth}}{1} \times \frac{63,360 \text{ in. on earth}}{1 \text{ mile on earth}}$$
$$= 4,371,840 \text{ in. on the earth's surface}$$

Suppose the length of 1° of latitude on the map is 2.3 in. Then, because the representative fraction is the ratio of 1 in. on the map to the number of inches on the earth's surface, use this calculation:

$$\text{RF} = \frac{\text{in. on map}}{\text{in. on earth}} = \frac{2.3}{4,371,840}$$

Reducing this ratio by dividing the numerator and denominator by 2.3:

$$2.3 \div 2.3 = 1$$
$$4,371,840 \div 2.3 = 1,900,800$$
$$\text{RF} = 1:1,900,800$$

Civil Engineer's Scale

A **civil engineer's scale** was once the principal tool for drawing maps and plans to scale. Today, a civil engineer's scale continues to be a very useful instrument, though with the advent of CADD, it is rarely used to manually draw maps to a specific scale. Figure 3–6 shows examples of typical triangular and flat engineer's scales. The following are primary uses of the civil engineer's scale:

- Read, measure, and understand existing maps and plans that are drawn to scale.
- Check the scale accuracy of a CADD plot.
- Prepare sketches and archival drawings to scale.

There are six scales found on a triangular *civil engineer's scale*. Each scale is a multiple of 10 and can be used to calibrate a drawing in any units, such as feet, meters, miles, or tenths of any typical unit.

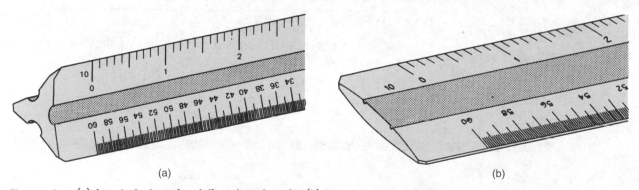

(a)   (b)

Figure 3–6.   (a) A typical triangular civil engineer's scale. (b) Flat civil engineer's scale.

This list shows the six possible scales found on the triangular civil engineer's scale:

10 scale: 1 in. = 1.0 ft; 1 in. = 10.0 ft; 1 in. = 100.0 ft; etc.
20 scale: 1 in. = 2.0 ft; 1 in. = 20.0 ft; 1 in. = 200.0 ft; etc.
30 scale: 1 in. = 3.0 ft; 1 in. = 30.0 ft; 1 in. = 300.0 ft; etc.
40 scale: 1 in. = 4.0 ft; 1 in. = 40.0 ft; 1 in. = 400.0 ft; etc.
50 scale: 1 in. = 5.0 ft; 1 in. = 50.0 ft; 1 in. = 500.0 ft; etc.
60 scale: 1 in. = 6.0 ft; 1 in. = 60.0 ft; 1 in. = 600.0 ft; etc.

Along the margin of the civil engineer's scale, in Figure 3–6, you see a 10 on one edge. The 10 represents the 10 scale. Another edge has a 20 in the margin representing the 20 scale. The edges have the 30, 40, 50, and 60 scales. Figure 3–7 is a close-up of the margin on an engineer's scale.

Measurements are easy to multiply and divide because they are given in decimals rather than in feet and inches. Figure 3–8 provides illustrations of how the civil engineer's scale is used to measure distances.

Figure 3–7. **Margin of triangular civil engineer's scale.**

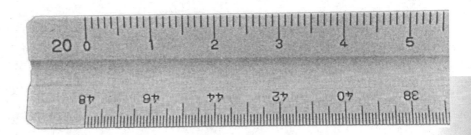

Figure 3–8. **Three examples of margins and scales on a civil engineer's scale.**

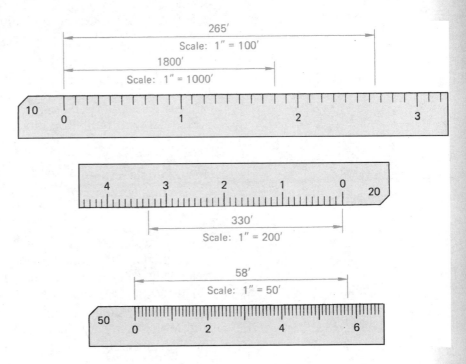

Metric Scales

The unit of measure commonly used in **metric scales** is the millimeter, which is based on the International System of Units (SI). Metric units are abbreviated as follows:

Unit	Abbreviation
millimeter	mm
centimeter	cm
decimeter	dm
meter	m
dekameter	dam
hectometer	hm
kilometer	km

Metric scales are convenient to work with because they are calibrated in units of 10, which makes metric-to-metric conversions easy, as follows:

$$10 \text{ mm} = 1 \text{ cm}$$
$$10 \text{ cm} = 1 \text{ dm}$$
$$10 \text{ dm} = 1 \text{ m}$$
$$10 \text{ m} = 1 \text{ dam}$$
$$10 \text{ dam} = 1 \text{ hm}$$
$$10 \text{ hm} = 1 \text{ km}$$

Common metric-to-U.S. equivalents are as follows:

$$1 \text{ mm} = 0.03937 \text{ in.}$$
$$1 \text{ cm} = 0.3937 \text{ in.}$$
$$1 \text{ m} = 39.37 \text{ in.}$$
$$1 \text{ km} = 0.624 \text{ mi}$$

Common U.S.-to-metric equivalents are as follows:

$$1 \text{ mi} = 1.6093 \text{ km} = 1609.3 \text{ m}$$
$$1 \text{ yd} = 0.9144 \text{ m} = 914.4 \text{ mm}$$
$$1 \text{ ft} = 0.3048 \text{ m} = 304.8 \text{ mm}$$
$$1 \text{ in.} = 0.0254 \text{ m} = 25.4 \text{ mm}$$

The most commonly used inch-to-metric conversion formula is:

$$\text{inches} \times 25.4 = \text{mm}$$

For example, 6.5 in. $\times$ 25.4 = 165.1 mm.

When converting millimeters to inches, use the formula:

$$\text{mm}/25.4 = \text{inches}$$

For example, 50 mm/25.4 = 1.97 in.

When placing metric dimensions on a drawing, the metric abbreviation is usually omitted. A general note specifying METRIC, or UNLESS OTHERWISE SPECIFIED, ALL DIMENSIONS ARE IN MILLIMETERS is placed on the drawing.

Metric scales may be enlarged or reduced as needed for the desired drawing scale because any scale is a multiple of 10. For

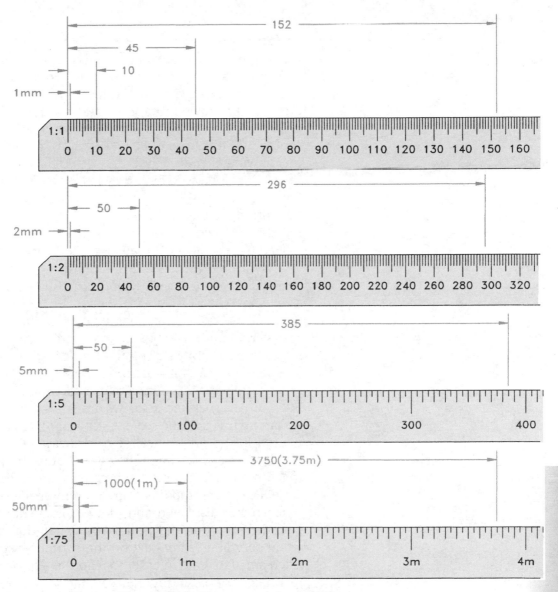

Figure 3–9. Metric scales examples, with common scale applications.

example, enlarging a scale such as the 1:5 scale in multiples of 10 makes the 100 division equal to 1000, creating a 1:50 scale. Common metric scales are shown in Figure 3–9.

The following displays common map scales and their U.S. custom and metric equivalents:

Map Scale	U.S. Custom	Metric
1:10,000	.158 mile (mi)	0.1 km
1:25,000	.395 mi	0.25 km
1:50,000	.789 mi	0.5 km
1:75,000	1.18 mi	0.75 km
1:100,000	1.58 mi	1 km
1:250,000	3.95 mi	2.5 km
1:500,000	7.89 mi	5 km
1:1,000,000	15.78 mi	10 km

CADD Scales

CADD greatly affects the ability to create maps and plans to scale. Drawings can be displayed and plotted according to any scale, on many different-sized sheets, with very minimal effort. CADD drawings are typically drawn using *real-world coordinates*. This means that if a property lot line is 100 ft long, the line is actually drawn in CADD at exactly 100 ft instead of being drawn at a reduced scale. The scale in the drawing environment is 1:1, or FULL. Usually, scaling of a CADD drawing is done when the drawing is ready to be plotted or printed. For example, if a drawing is to be plotted at a scale of 1 in. = 50 ft, that information is given to the CADD system, which scales the drawing display down to 1 in. = 50 ft. The final result is a properly scaled plotted hard copy of the map or civil engineering plan.

Creating drawings at full scale using CADD offers tremendous benefits. Drawings can be plotted at any scale, on many different-sized sheets, and accurate overlays, or layers, can also be applied. For example, a digital topographic map that has been drawn using real-world coordinates can be layered over any other plan or map that has been drawn using real-world coordinates, to provide accurate topographic information of a site. CADD scale factors, layers, and plotting applications were discussed in detail in Chapter 2.

A CADD scale factor allows drawings to be displayed and plotted according to a specific scale. A scale factor is a numerical value that is used in the proper scaling of drawing objects, text, and dimensions. Typically, scaling a drawing is done by providing scale information to the CADD system before the drawing is plotted. However, scale factors are important any time information, such as text, must be correctly displayed and plotted. For example, if 1/8 in. text is placed onto a drawing with a 100 ft long lot line drawn using real-world coordinates, the text on the computer screen and on the plot is too small to read. In order to read the text on the plot, multiply the text height of 1/8 in. by the scale factor. The resulting text height is 1/8 in. tall on the plot, though the text height in the drawing environment is much larger. To determine the scale factor, you must first identify the desired drawing scale, such as 1 in. = 50 ft. Next, convert the drawing units into the same unit of measurement as the plotted units and divide the plotted units into the drawing units. The following is an example:

Step 1: 1 in. = 50 ft
50 ft. × 12 = 600 in.
Step 2: 1 in. = 600 in.
Step 3: 600 in./1 in. = 600
The scale factor is 600.

Once the scale factor is identified, calculate the actual text height to be used in the CADD system. If the desired plotted text height is 1/8 in., multiply 1/8 in. by the scale factor. So, for the 1 in. = 50 ft scale drawing, multiply 1/8 in. by 600 to get 75 in. This means that 1/8 in. tall text on the plotted drawing is actually drawn 75 in. high in the drawing environment.

The following chart provides a variety of civil drawing scales, scale factors, and drawing sheet size limits:

Drawing Scale	Scale Factor	Sheet Size Limits
1″ = 10′	120	"A" (11 × 8.5) 110′ × 83′ "B" (17 × 11) 170′ × 110′ "C" (22 × 17) 220′ × 170′ "D" (34 × 22) 340′ × 220′ "E" (44 × 34) 440′ × 340′
1″ = 20′	240	"A" 220′ × 170′ "B" 340′ × 220′ "C" 440′ × 340′ "D" 680′ × 440′ "E" 880′ × 680′
1″ = 30′	360	"A" 330′ × 255′ "B" 510′ × 330′ "C" 660′ × 510′ "D" 1020′ × 660′ "E" 1320′ × 1020′
1″ = 40′	480	"A" 440′ × 340′ "B" 680′ × 440′ "C" 880′ × 680′ "D" 1360′ × 880′ "E" 1760′ × 1360′
1″ = 50′	600	"A" 550′ × 425′ "B" 850′ × 550′ "C" 1100′ × 850′ "D" 1700′ × 1100′ "E" 2200′ × 1700′
1″ = 60′	720	"A" 660′ × 510′ "B" 1020′ × 660′ "C" 1320′ × 1020′ "D" 2040′ × 1320′ "E" 2640′ × 2040′

TEST

Part I

Fill in the blanks below with the responses necessary to complete each statement. Use your best freehand lettering. Alternatively, access this test on the Student Web site and follow the instructions to respond electronically.

3-1 A _____ is a representation of a portion of the earth's surface reduced to a small size.

3-2 The proportion between the length of a line on a map and the corresponding length on the earth's surface is called the _____ _____.

3-3 A scale used to approximate distances on a map, which usually looks like a small ruler found near the legend or title block, is called the _____ _____.

3-4 Representative fraction = RF = _____ / _____.

3-5 A scale that is often used for rough estimates of distances on a map is called the _____ _____.

Part II

Make the following scale conversions. Be neat and accurate. Show your calculations in the space provided or access the Student Web site and follow the instructions to respond electronically.

3-1 Convert RF = 1:100,000 to a graphic scale.

3-2 Convert RF = 1:2000 to a graphic scale.

3-3 Convert a verbal scale of 1 in. = 1 mi to a representative fraction.

3-4 Convert a verbal scale of 1 in. = 100 mi to a representative fraction.

3-5   If the number of inches between 1° of latitude on a map is measured to be 4.75 in., what is the RF of the map?

Part III

Use a civil engineer's scale to measure each line shown below. The scale calibration is identified to the left of each line. Place your answer to the right or access the Student Web site and follow the instructions to respond electronically.

		Scale	Answer
3-1	1 in. = 10 ft	_____	_____
3-2	1 in. = 20 ft	_____	_____
3-3	1 in. = 30 ft	_____	_____
3-4	1 in. = 40 ft	_____	_____
3-5	1 in. = 50 ft	_____	_____
3-6	1 in. = 60 ft	_____	_____
3-7	1 in. = 2 ft	_____	_____
3-8	1 in. = 100 ft	_____	_____

Part IV

Use your best hand lettering with short, complete statements to answer the following questions related to CADD applications or access the Student Web site and follow the instructions to respond electronically.

3-1   Give an example of what it means to create CAD drawings using real-world coordinates.

3-2   Usually, scaling of a CAD drawing is done when the drawing is ready to be plotted or printed. Discuss and give an example of this application.

3-3   Identify at least two benefits of creating drawings at full scale using CAD, and give an example.

3-4   Show the formula and calculate the scale factor for a civil engineering scale of 1 in. = 50 ft.

3-5   Calculate the actual text height to be used in a CAD system if the desired plotted text height is 1/8 in. and the scale is 1 in. = 50 ft.

3–6 Given a 1 in. = 10 ft civil engineering scale, identify the scale factor and drawing limits for a C size (22 × 17 in.) sheet.

PROBLEM

P3–1 Convert the engineer's sketch in Figure P3–1 to a formal drawing. Remember, the sketch is not accurate, so you will have to lay out all bearings and distances. Use manual drafting or CADD, based on your course objectives. Use the following unless otherwise specified by your instructor:

1. Use a C-size 17 × 22 in. sheet.

2. Include:

   a. Title

   b. Scale 1 in. = 10 ft or 1 in. = 20 ft

   c. Graphic scale

   d. North arrow

   e. Your name and date

3. Make a print for instructor evaluation unless otherwise specified.

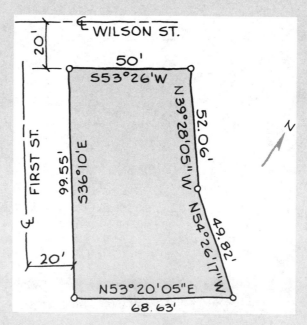

Figure P3–1.

Map Symbols

Learning Objectives

After completing this chapter, you will be able to:

- Define specific map symbols.
- Sketch map symbols.
- Use shading techniques to sketch examples of different types of terrain.
- Create CADD map symbols.
- Use map symbols to draw a map from given information.

Key Terms

Culture symbol
Relief
Contour lines
Water features
Vegetation features
Topographic features
CADD symbol

This chapter discusses and shows examples of some of the symbols commonly used in civil drafting. These are only a few of the symbols that are available for use. The purpose of a map dictates the required symbols to be used. Special symbols sometimes have to be designed for a specific purpose. The symbols shown may change slightly, depending on company, school, or map standards. Symbols can include colors or can be plotted in black and white.

The topics covered include:

- Types of map symbols
- Symbol colors, when used
- Special-effect symbols

Standard symbols are used in civil drafting, as they are in any other field of drafting. When you look at a road map, for example, you generally take it for granted that symbols on the map help you get where you want to go. However, without these symbols, the map would be useless. Each type of map may have certain symbols that are special to the intent of the map. Specific symbols are also used to help keep information on a map to a minimum so the map remains as uncluttered as possible. Symbols are as condensed and to the point as possible to describe the objective.

Types of Map Symbols

The various symbols used in map drawings can be grouped under four types: culture, relief, water, and vegetation.

Culture

Culture symbols represent works of people. When maps are printed in color, these symbols are usually black. Text on maps that identify cultural representation is usually in using vertical uppercase letters. However, variations of text style are found in CADD standards. The topographic map symbols shown in Figure 4–1 show several different cultural symbols.

Relief

Relief symbols are used to show characteristics of land. Mountains, canyons, and other land features are shown with relief. The relief may be shown by contour lines or by more descriptive means, such as color and/or technical shading methods. Contour lines are lines on a map representing points of the same elevation. Contour lines are usually thin lines, with every fifth line drawn thicker and broken, somewhere to insert the elevation number. This number represents the elevation of the line in feet above sea level. Text on a map in conjunction with relief is usually in vertical uppercase letters. Contour lines and other relief symbols are usually brown when the map is in color. Contour lines are discussed in Chapter 9.

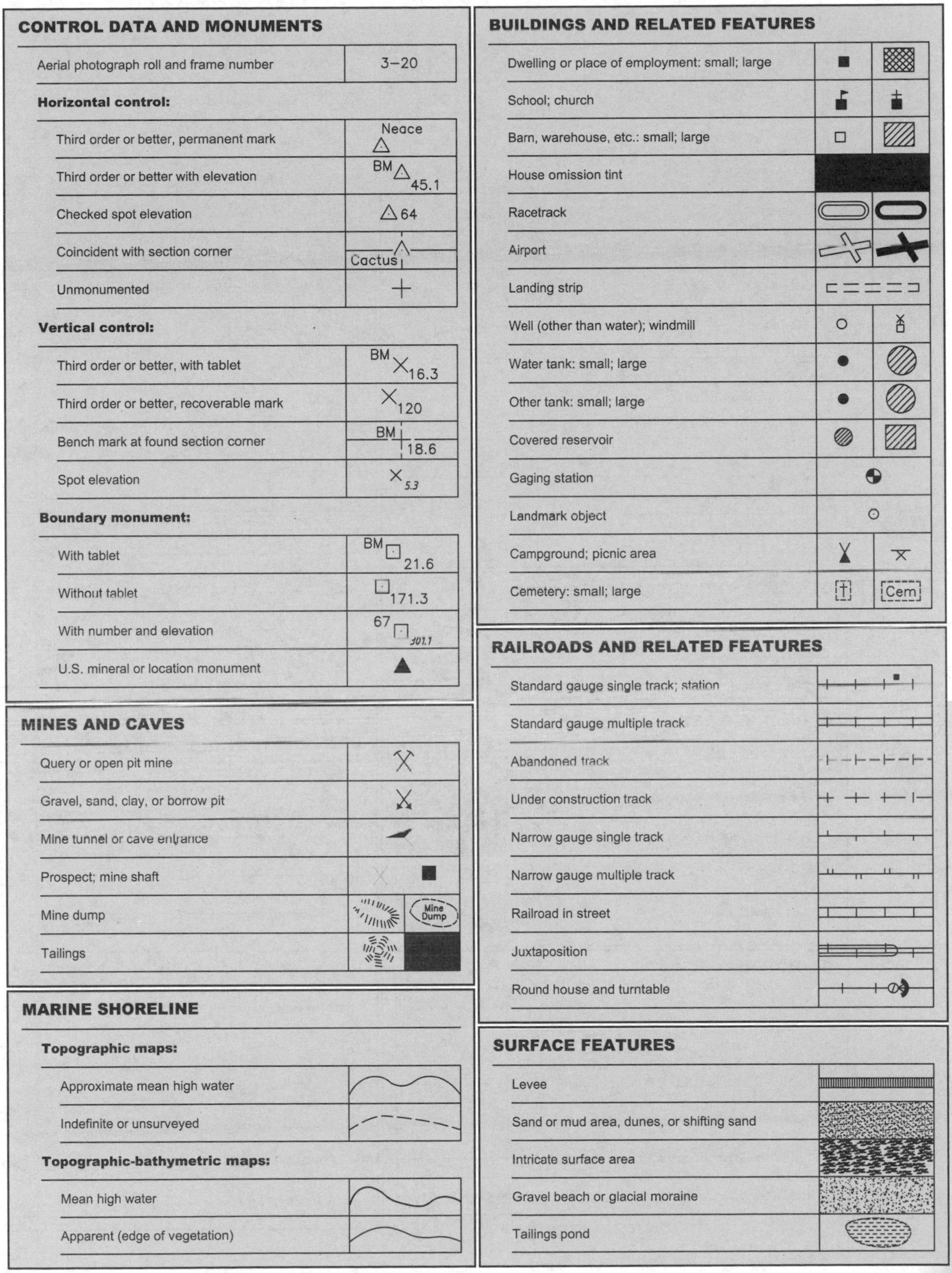

CONTROL DATA AND MONUMENTS

Aerial photograph roll and frame number	3—20

Horizontal control:

Third order or better, permanent mark	Neace △
Third order or better with elevation	BM △ 45.1
Checked spot elevation	△ 64
Coincident with section corner	△ Cactus
Unmonumented	+

Vertical control:

Third order or better, with tablet	BM ✕ 16.3
Third order or better, recoverable mark	✕ 120
Bench mark at found section corner	BM ✕ 18.6
Spot elevation	✕ 5.3

Boundary monument:

With tablet	BM □ 21.6
Without tablet	□ 171.3
With number and elevation	67 □ 301.1
U.S. mineral or location monument	▲

MINES AND CAVES

Query or open pit mine	⚒
Gravel, sand, clay, or borrow pit	⚒
Mine tunnel or cave entrance	➤
Prospect; mine shaft	✕ ■
Mine dump	Mine Dump
Tailings	

MARINE SHORELINE

Topographic maps:

Approximate mean high water	
Indefinite or unsurveyed	

Topographic-bathymetric maps:

Mean high water	
Apparent (edge of vegetation)	

BUILDINGS AND RELATED FEATURES

Dwelling or place of employment: small; large	■	▦
School; church	♪	✝
Barn, warehouse, etc.: small; large	□	▨
House omission tint		■
Racetrack	⬭	⬭
Airport	✕	✕
Landing strip	⊏ = = ⊐	
Well (other than water); windmill	○	☓
Water tank: small; large	●	⬮
Other tank: small; large	●	⬮
Covered reservoir	⬮	▨
Gaging station	◕	
Landmark object	◎	
Campground; picnic area	⋏	⊼
Cemetery: small; large	[✝]	[Cem]

RAILROADS AND RELATED FEATURES

Standard gauge single track; station	
Standard gauge multiple track	
Abandoned track	
Under construction track	
Narrow gauge single track	
Narrow gauge multiple track	
Railroad in street	
Juxtaposition	
Round house and turntable	

SURFACE FEATURES

Levee	
Sand or mud area, dunes, or shifting sand	
Intricate surface area	
Gravel beach or glacial moraine	
Tailings pond	

Figure 4–1. Standard topographic map symbols.
(Based on U.S. Geological Survey symbols, www.usgs.gov)

COASTAL FEATURES

Foreshore flat	
Rock or coral reef	
Rock bare or awash	
Group of rocks bare or awash	
Exposed wreck	
Depth curve; sounding	
Breakwater, pier, jetty, or wharf	
Seawall	

BATHYMETRIC FEATURES

Area exposed at mean low tide; sounding datum	
Channel	
Offshore oil or gas: well; platform	
Sunken rock	

GLACIERS AND PERMANENT SNOWFIELDS

Contours and limits	
Form lines	

SUBMERGED AREAS AND BOGS

Marsh or swamp	
Wooded marsh or swamp	
Submerged wooded marsh or swamp	
Rice field	
Land subject to inundation	

BOUNDARIES

National	
State or territorial	
County or equivalent	
Civil township or equivalent	
Incorporated city or equivalent	
Park, reservation, or monument	
Small park	

LAND SURVEY SYSTEMS

U.S. Public Land Survey System:

Township or range line	
Location doubtful	
Section line	
Location doubtful	
Found section corner; found closing corner	
Witness corner; meander corner	WC / MC

Other land surveys:

Township or range line	
Section line	
Land grant or mining claim; monument	
Fence line	

TRANSMISSION LINES AND PIPELINES

Power transmission line: pole; tower	
Telephone or telegraph line	Telephone
Above ground oil or gas pipeline	
Underground oil or gas pipeline	Pipeline

CONTOURS

Topographic:

Intermediate	
Index	
Supplementary	
Depression	
Cut; fill	

Bathymetric:

Intermediate	
Index	
Primary	
Index primary	
Supplementary	

Figure 4–1. (*Continued*)

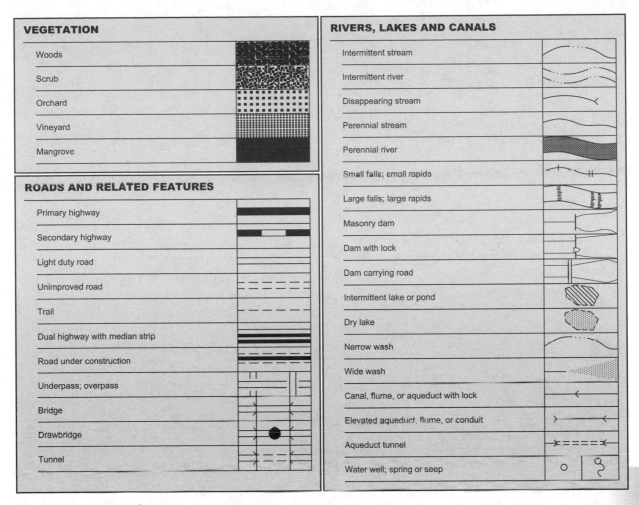

Figure 4-1. *(Continued)*

Water

Water features represent lakes, rivers, streams, and even intermittent waters. Water features are colored blue when the map is in color. A unique aspect of water features is that they are labeled on a map using inclined uppercase letters. For example:

MISSISSIPPI RIVER

Vegetation

Vegetation features include forests, orchards, croplands, and other types of plant life. When a map is drawn in color, these features are usually green. Look at Figure 4-1. If vegetation is planted by people, such as a field of corn, some maps classify this as culture.

Symbols have been made by various governmental agencies for their particular maps. Also, agencies of private industry may have their own mapping symbols. Some examples are:

Governmental

- U.S. Office of Management and Budget
- National Oceanic and Atmospheric Administration

■ U.S. Geological Survey
■ U.S. Forest Service
■ Army Map Service
■ Federal Aviation Administration

Private Industry

■ American Railway Engineering and Maintenance of Way Association
■ American Council of Engineering Companies

Special Map Techniques

Special methods are often used to show symbols or to represent specific concepts on a map. For example, it was discussed earlier that relief is sometimes shown using graphic techniques. This is done to achieve special effects, such as a three-dimensional appearance. Graphic techniques for drawing topographic features are shown in Figure 4–2.

You may even draw a representation of water features with rapids and whirlpools, depending on the purpose of your map, as shown in Figure 4–3.

Maps can show specific crops grown in an area or information about how land is being used. Optional vegetation symbols are shown in Figure 4–4.

There are probably as many symbols as there are purposes for maps. You have seen many of standard symbols. There are many more that can be found on maps, and there also can be some minor differences from one map preparer to the next. Figure 4–5 displays some additional map symbols.

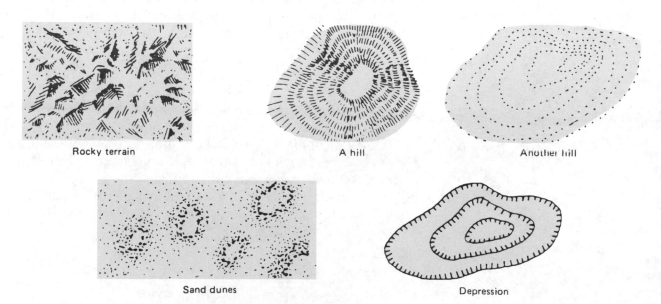

Rocky terrain   A hill   Another hill

Sand dunes   Depression

Figure 4–2. **Graphic techniques for drawing topographic features.**

Figure 4–3. **Representation of water features with rapids and whirlpools.**

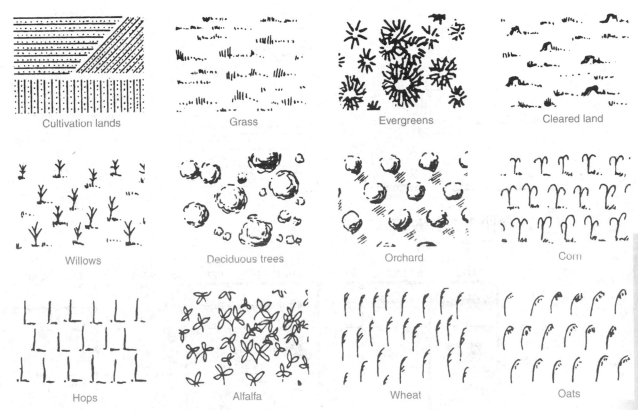

Cultivation lands	Grass	Evergreens	Cleared land
Willows	Deciduous trees	Orchard	Corn
Hops	Alfalfa	Wheat	Oats

Figure 4–4. **Optional vegetation symbols.**

Drawing Map Symbols with CADD

Computer-aided drafting symbols are available and can be made for a variety of drafting applications. Most CADD programs contain or allow you to create mapping symbols and then store the symbols in a separate file, known as a *symbol library*. CADD systems can be customized or come available with tools that allow you to use existing symbol libraries designed by someone else, or you can generate your own symbol libraries. Additionally, many government and private organizations publish symbols and symbol libraries in a variety of formats for use in developing maps and plans. CADD symbols can be added to drawings using a number of techniques, based on the

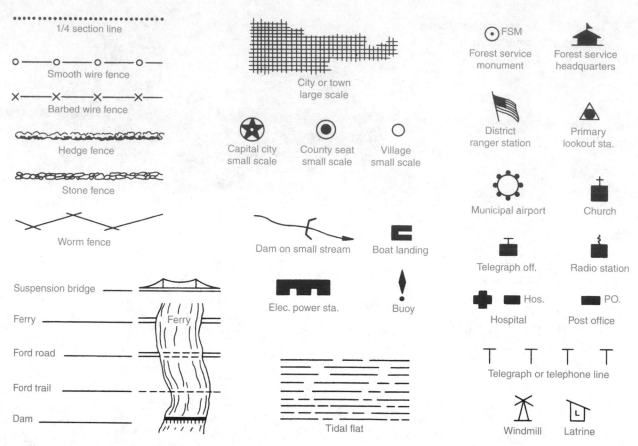

Figure 4-5. Additional optional map symbols.

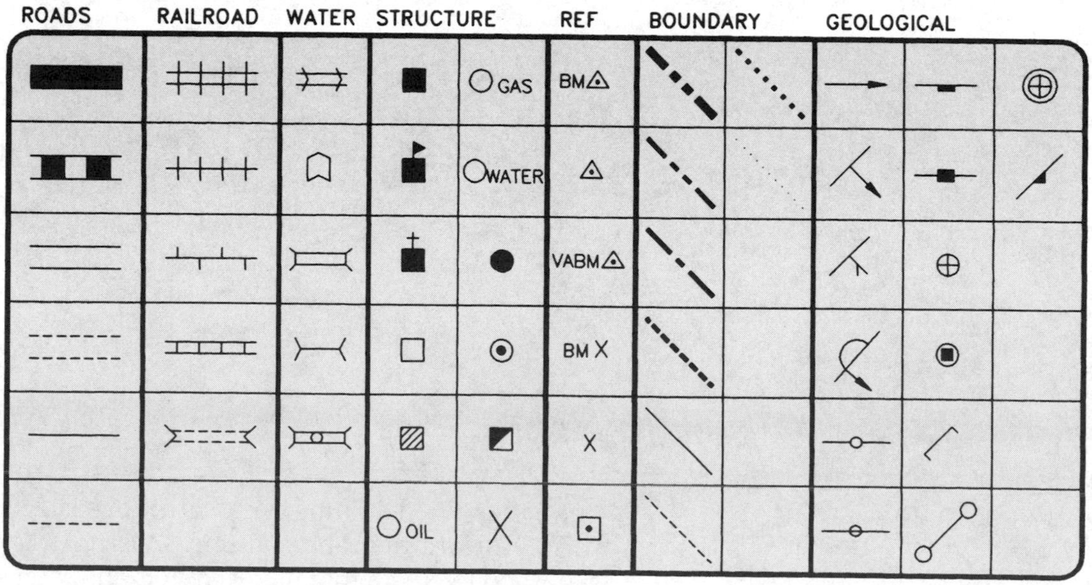

Figure 4-6. A customized map symbol library for CADD.

particular CADD system. On-screen menus, toolbars, and dialog boxes are the most common symbol access tools. Figure 4-6 shows an example of a CADD symbol library. This library allows you to insert a number of commonly used mapping symbols, such as building and bridge symbols, and quickly reference feature properties, such as the line style used to draw a property boundary.

Creating Your Own CADD Map Symbols

One of the greatest time-saving features of CADD is the ability to draw a symbol, save it, and then use it any time the symbol is needed. CADD systems refer to these stored symbols as *blocks*, or *cells*. AutoCAD, for example, uses the BLOCK and WBLOCK commands to create and store drawing symbols for later use. With this system, a symbol can be inserted as many times as needed, and the symbol can be scaled and rotated to fit the drawing requirements when inserted in a drawing.

Follow these guidelines when creating a symbol for future use:

- Establish an insertion point. The insertion point is a point or location on the symbol that targets where the symbol is placed on the drawing. Though symbols can be moved, copied, and otherwise manipulated once inserted, an effectively defined insertion point can help save time and assist in accurately placing the symbol. Figure 4–7 shows common mapping symbols and their insertion points for placement on drawings.
- When you create a symbol, use the desired color, line type, text style, layer, and any other characteristics, so every time the symbol is used, these properties are already defined.
- Give the symbol a name and record a copy of the symbol, its name, and the insertion point in a symbol library for future reference.
- When designing a symbol, make it one unit wide by one unit high. This allows the symbol to be inserted in relationship to the drawing units, whether they are feet or meters. This also gives you the flexibility to easily scale the symbol to fit the requirements of any drawing when it is inserted.

Figure 4–8 shows the steps in creating a symbol for future use.

Additional CADD Map Symbol Techniques

In addition to using and creating CADD symbols, as previously discussed, several other CADD mapping symbol techniques are available, depending on the specific CADD software program. Refer to Figure 4–1 for a moment. Many of the symbols displayed in Figure 4–1 can

Figure 4–7.   Insertion points for several map CADD symbols.

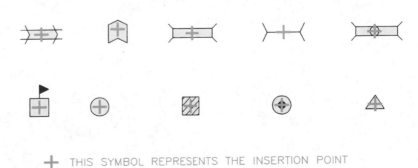

THIS SYMBOL REPRESENTS THE INSERTION POINT

Figure 4-8. **Creating a custom CADD mapping symbol.**

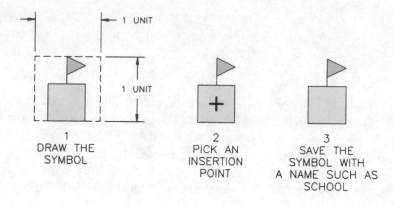

1
DRAW THE
SYMBOL

2
PICK AN
INSERTION
POINT

3
SAVE THE
SYMBOL WITH
A NAME SUCH AS
SCHOOL

+ THIS SYMBOL REPRESENTS THE INSERTION POINT

be created using a variety of tools and commands. For example, each boundary or contour line style can be drawn using customized line types and object tools. You can also create a dashed line, for example, that automatically places the letter T, representing Telephone, along the line to easily add a telephone line symbol to a map.

As you become familiar with CADD, you will discover many options that enhance your ability to quickly and accurately place mapping symbols. Another mapping symbol technique involves the use of graphic pattern tools such as AutoCAD's Hatch command. With this system, multiple copies of a certain symbol can be applied to a specific area, creating a pattern. Figure 1–5 shows an example of an engineering map on which areas of symbols have been placed using a graphic pattern tool. Notice how paved areas, such as walkways, are represented using diagonal lines, building rooftops are shown using horizontal dashed lines, and grassy areas are represented by grass symbols. Each of these areas, or pattern boundaries, was created with one step using a graphic pattern tool.

TEST

Part I

Define each of the following types of map symbols. Use your best freehand lettering or access the Student Web site and follow the instructions to respond electronically.

4-1   Culture

4-2   Relief

4-3   Water

4-4   Vegetation

Part II

In the space provided, carefully sketch an example of each of the following map symbols.

4-1   Primary highway

4-2   Light-duty road

4-3   Railroad, single track

4-4   Bridge and road

4–5   Building (dwelling)

4–6   Power transmission line

4–7   Perennial stream

4–8   Intermittent stream

4–9   Marsh

4–10   Orchard

Part III

Using shading techniques, sketch examples of each of the following features.

4–1   Rocky terrain

4–2   Hill

4–3   Depression

4–4   Sand dune

4–5   River

PROBLEMS

P4–1   Use manual drafting or CADD, based on your course objectives. For a CADD solution, use AutoCAD to open the file (P4–1) on the Student Web site. Use the following instructions to draw the map:

1. Use standard topographic symbols.

2. Use appropriate mapping colors, unless otherwise instructed.

3. North is toward the top of the page.

4. The scale is 1 in. = 200 ft.

5. Draw a hard-surface medium-duty road from point *A* to point *F*.

6. Beginning 975 ft from point *A*, draw a bridge over a 40-ft-wide river.

7. The center of the river runs through points *B, C, D,* and *E*.

8. At 420 ft from point *A* along the hard-surface road, draw an improved light-duty road to point *G*.

9. A small creek enters the river at point *C*. The creek is straight and runs for 385 ft at a 45° angle, then turns, with a radius of 200 ft, approximately due north.

10. North of the medium-duty road and southwest of the river, the entire area is orchard to within 200 ft of the river.

11. The area south of the medium-duty road and west of the light-duty road is a corn crop.

12. On both sides of the small creek is a grove of deciduous trees 100 ft wide.

13. All other areas are grasslands.

14. At 200 ft northeast of the bridge and on the north side of the medium-duty road is a forest service headquarters.

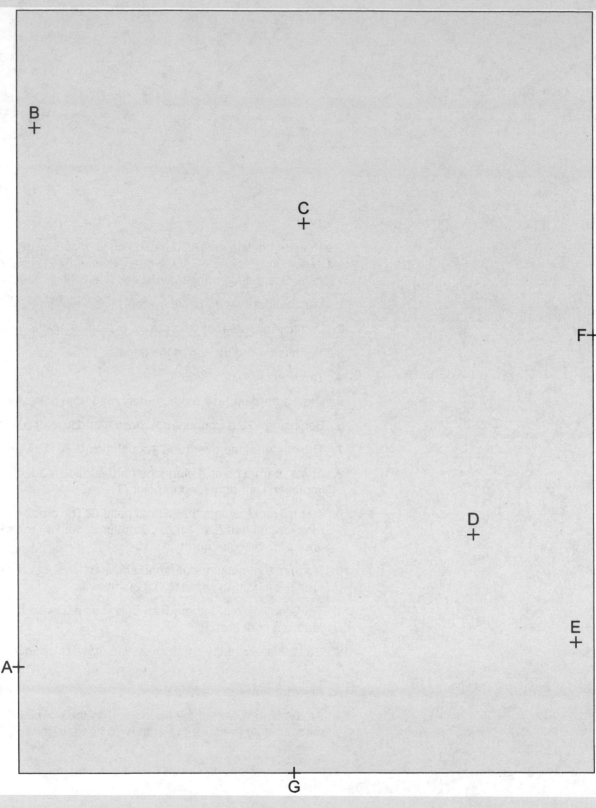

Figure P4–1.

Measuring Distance and Elevation

Key Terms

Electronic distance meter (EDM)
Cube corner prism
Total station
Differential leveling
Backsight
Foresight
Bench mark (BM)

Learning Objectives

After completing this chapter, you will be able to:

- Describe methods of distance measurement.
- Identify instruments used for distance measurement.
- Identify and describe instruments used for elevation measurement.
- Identify and read the markings of a level rod.
- Calculate leveling field notes to determine instrument heights and unknown elevations.
- Describe the function of a rotating-beam laser level.

Land measurement has three components: distance, elevation, and angles between points. The ancient Egyptians employed people called *rope stretchers*, who used ropes knotted at intervals to measure and lay out plots and farmland. Today we use satellites and sophisticated electronic surveying instruments to locate points, determine elevation, and measure distances. This chapter provides an introduction to distance and elevation measurement. Angle measurement is discussed in Chapters 6 and 7.

This chapter covers the following topics:

- Mcasuring distance
- Measuring elevation
- Recording measurements

Measuring Distance

Traditional Distance Measurement

The advent and refinement of *electronic distance measurement* over the past several decades has rendered traditional manual methods of distance measurement obsolete. These methods include "chaining" or "taping" and distance by stadia. Although little used today, these methods have historical significance. Refer to Appendix A for information on these procedures.

Electronic Distance Measurement

Electronic signals can be transmitted from an instrument on a tripod to a reflector on a distant tripod, which beams the signal back to the transmitting instrument. The time required for the signal to return is measured and translated into a distance. Signals such as radio waves (electromagnetic or microwave) and light waves (infrared and laser) have been used in electronic distance measurement.

Current electronic distance meters (EDMs) utilize infrared and laser technology. Lasers can be used to record distances between the surveying instrument and a prism or prism array mounted on a tripod. Greater distances may require larger prism arrays. A single reflector uses what is called a cube corner prism, which is a corner cut off a cube of glass. This type of prism can be slightly out of alignment with the EDM and still provide an accurate measurement. See Figure 5–1.

Distances are automatically recorded and stored in an EDM. Distances can be measured on a level line of sight or on a slope. Horizontal and vertical angles between the instrument and the measured points, when combined with a distance measurement, can provide location and elevation (X, Y, and Z) data for any point. The instrument that combines EDM and angle measurement is called a total station.

Laser EDMs are also available in "reflectorless" mode, in which a prism is not required to measure the distance. The laser beam can be aimed at any object, such as a well, curb, or street intersection, and

Figure 5–1. A single reflector uses a cube corner prism, which is a corner cut off a cube of glass.

the distance is calculated. This technology is not accurate over great distances (more than 4000 m, or approximately 2.5 mi).

A total station contains all the data gathering components in a single unit. See Chapter 6 for a discussion and illustration of a total station.

Measuring Elevation

Elevation

The term *elevation* refers to the vertical measurement of a point either below or above a reference. The reference datum that is used for a survey may be any solid object whose elevation is known, such as a U.S. Geological Survey bench mark (explained later) or a temporary control point established by a surveyor. The principal reference datum for all surveys is *mean sea level* (MSL). This is the elevation of 0.00 ft/m established by the National Geodetic Survey. It is based on the National Geodetic Vertical Datum of 1929 and adjusted by the North American Vertical Datum of 1988.

Electronic Elevation Measurement

A variety of methods are used to determine elevations. The method used is governed by the nature of the project or survey. Elevations measured by a global positioning system (GPS) may achieve

Figure 5-2.   A single surveyor can use a robotic total station to record the location and elevation for thousands of points.

accuracies to plus or minus 10 m, depending on the location. More accurate elevations can be calculated using a total station and existing reference points having known elevations. This method is often used to locate *X, Y,* and *Z* values of thousands of points in a project such as a new subdivision. A single surveyor can use a robotic total station for such a project. See Figure 5-2.

Elevation by Level and Rod

When the difference in elevation between points is required, the process of differential leveling is used. This type of leveling begins at a point of known elevation and works toward points whose elevation is unknown. It is normally performed using a *level*, a tripod, and a level *rod*. The digital level shown in Figure 5-3a provides vertical accuracy of .3 mm over a distance of 1 km. Unlike the standard automatic level shown in Figure 5-3b, the digital level's graphical display provides a clear readout of elevations. Field measurements can be stored in the digital level's internal memory or transferred to a USB storage device. The data files can in turn be transferred from the USB device to an office computer. The levels are mounted on a tripod (see Figure 5-4).

Field work and preliminary site work often require approximations before accurate leveling or surveying can begin. This can be accomplished with the use of a hand level (see Figure 5-5).

Several different types of level rods can be used with the level for measuring elevations. See Figure 5-6. The rod is placed on the known elevation, and the instrument is set up approximately halfway to the unknown point. Long distances may require several

Figure 5–3a. The digital level measures elevation along a horizontal line of sight and provides vertical accuracy of .3 mm over a distance of 1 km.
(Courtesy of Trimble Navigation)

Figure 5–3b. The automatic level maintains a horizontal line of sight once the instrument is leveled.
(Courtesy of Topcon Positioning Systems, Inc.)

setups. The tripod is anchored firmly in the ground, and the instrument is attached to the tripod. The instrument is leveled with three leveling screws on its base. A spirit bubble indicates when the instrument is level. A reading is then taken on the backsight (rod location). This is added to the elevation of the known point to give the *height of the instrument* (H.I.). The rod is then placed on the unknown elevation (foresight), and a reading is taken. This reading is subtracted from the height of the instrument to give the unknown elevation (see Figure 5–6).

Figure 5–4. The tripod is used to mount levels and other surveying instruments.
(Courtesy of Sokkia)

Figure 5–5. Hand levels are used to obtain approximate elevations.
(Courtesy of Sokkia)

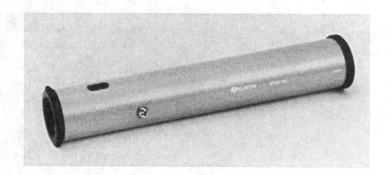

Figure 5–6. Finding an elevation with level and rod (leveling).

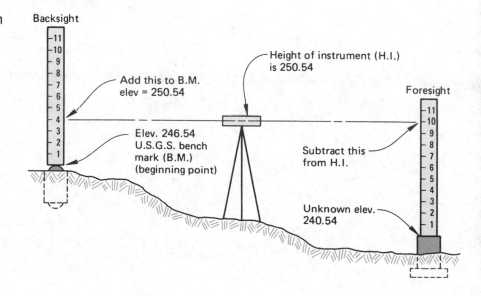

Backsight

Add this to B.M.
elev = 250.54

Height of instrument (H.I.)
is 250.54

Foresight

Elev. 246.54
U.S.G.S. bench
mark (B.M.)
(beginning point)

Subtract this
from H.I.

Unknown elev.
240.54

Accurate recording of elevations must begin at known elevation points. The most accurate points, established by the U.S. Geological Survey (USGS) are called bench marks. A **bench mark (BM)** is a permanent marker, most often a brass cap mounted in concrete, that provides longitude, latitude, and elevation above sea level. The BM displays an identification number that must be used when contacting the USGS in order to get the current values for the BM. When running levels, it is best to begin and end on BMs because these markers provide excellent checks for the accuracy of the leveling.

Surveyors will often need to establish semipermanent points, referred to generically as *local control*. Because these points are temporary but serve the same purpose as a bench mark, they are called *temporary bench marks (TBMs)*. The most temporary TBM is known as a *turning point*, and it is used when level measurements must be made over long distances. A turning point can be a large rock, a fire hydrant, a concrete curb or foundation, a wooden stake, or even a long screwdriver driven into the ground.

A *footplate* used with some level rods provides a stable, well-defined foundation for the rod. This is a cone-shaped device that is anchored in the ground and has pointed feet.

The turning point is just a pivot for the rod, which is used as a backsight and a foresight. The instrument reading as a foresight is subtracted from the H.I. to find the level of the TBM, and then the instrument and tripod are physically moved ahead of the rod and reset. The next reading is a backsight, which is added to the TBM elevation to become the H.I. Now the rod can be moved to the next foresight position. Figure 5–7 illustrates leveling with several turning points. For a clearer understanding of the leveling calculation process, take a few moments to work through this example.

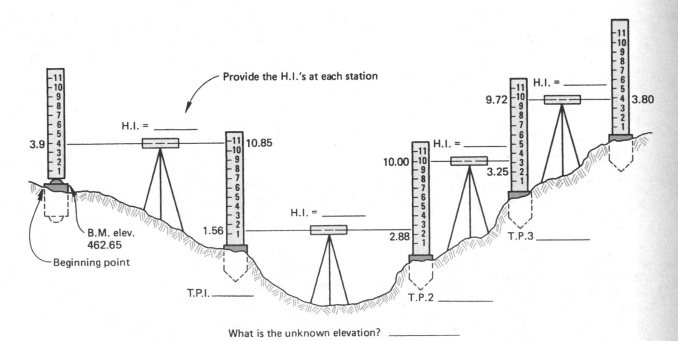

Figure 5–7. Using turning points to find an unknown elevation.

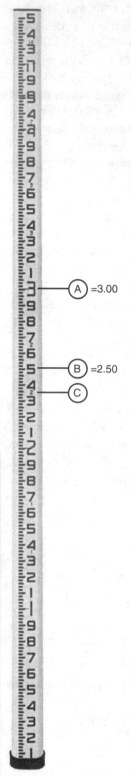

Before beginning this exercise, remember the basic rule for calculating elevation when running levels: Add the backsight and subtract the foresight. In this example, the beginning point elevation of the BM is 462.65 ft. The level rod is placed on this point. The level instrument is set up an appropriate distance away, in the direction of the unknown elevation. The rod reading of 3.9 is taken. This is the backsight, so it is added to the BM elevation of 462.65 to get the H.I., which is 466.55:

$$
\begin{array}{lr}
\text{BM} = & 462.65 \\
\text{Backsight} & +3.90 \\
\hline
\text{H.I.} = & \mathbf{466.55}
\end{array}
$$

Now that the elevation of the instrument is known, the rod can be moved ahead to the next location, which is determined by terrain and distance. This rod location becomes turning point 1 (T.P. 1). The rod is physically placed on a stable object and is not moved again until both foresight and backsight readings are made. The instrument reading is taken on the foresight. In this case the level rod reading is 10.85. This is subtracted from the H.I. of 466.55 to get 455.70. This is now the elevation of T.P. 1:

$$
\begin{array}{lr}
\text{H.I.} = & 466.55 \\
\text{Foresight} & -10.85 \\
\hline
\text{T.P. 1} = & \mathbf{455.70}
\end{array}
$$

The instrument can now be safely moved to the next location, and the process is repeated. Notice in Figure 5–7 that the second position of the instrument in the valley is the exact situation as the first instrument setup. Therefore, the next reading to be taken, the backsight, is read and calculated exactly the same as the first in this exercise. Set up your calculations as follows:

$$
\begin{array}{lr}
\text{T.P. 1} = & 455.70 \\
\text{Backsight} & +1.56 \\
\hline
\text{H.I.} = & \mathbf{457.26}
\end{array}
$$

The rod is moved ahead to T.P. 2, and the foresight reading of 2.88 is taken. This is subtracted from the H.I. of 457.26. Complete this exercise as described above to determine the unknown elevation. The answer is provided at the end of the chapter.

Reading a Level Rod

A typical level rod, such as the telescoping rod shown in Figure 5–8, is divided into whole feet, tenths, and one-hundredths of a foot. Rods are also available in metric values. The whole foot values on the level rod are shown in large red numerals (A). The large black numerals (B) indicate tenths of a foot and are located at a pointed black band on the rod. Each black band is one-hundredth of a foot wide. Notice the small numbers (C) located every three-tenths of a foot on the rod face. These red numbers indicate the whole foot value and are references in case the view through the instrument shows only a small portion of the rod, and no large red number is visible.

Figure 5–8. This telescoping rod is divided into whole feet and one-hundredths of a foot. The rod shown here is not extended to its full length.
(Courtesy of Topcon)

Figure 5-9. **The vernier on the level rod target reads to 0.001 ft.** (Courtesy of Sokkia)

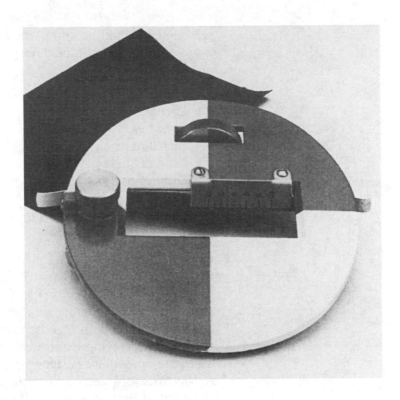

Level Rod Targets

Rods that can be read by the person operating the instrument are called *self-reading rods*. But if elevation readings must be measured over distances longer than 200 or 300 ft, a *target* is often used. See Figure 5–9. The target is moved by the rodperson as directed by the person running the instrument. When the target is located precisely, the rodperson can then read the graduations on the rod and target vernier and record the elevation. The vernier on the target allows measurements of 0.001 ft.

Recording Measurements

For most practical surveying purposes, the age of hand-recorded data in field books is past. Because many digital surveying instruments can store data as text files, log books may not be required for many jobs. Therefore, although the leveling techniques are the same, many of the log book items listed in the next section can be entered digitally into a data collector and saved as a file.

Leveling Log Books and Field Notes

Surveyors used to record their measurements, instrument readings, and calculations for every project in a *field notebook*. This notebook may become an important document for future reference or as legal evidence. In addition, persons working in the office may have to interpret field notes in order to construct maps or drawings. Therefore, field notes should be complete, neat, and uncrowded. The following items are important in field notes:

- Title of the survey
- Members of the survey crew
- Location
- Sketches
- Instrument numbers
- Date of survey
- Duty of each crew member
- Weather
- Mistakes crossed out, not erased

The type of survey determines the content of the field notes. For example, field notes for a traverse may contain deflection angles (see Chapter 6), bearings, distance on slope, vertical angles, and horizontal distances. This information can then be used by a computer program to automatically generate a database and a drawing, or it can be used by a drafter to construct a drawing.

When surveying instruments such as electronic total stations are used, the notebook and field notes are stored within the instrument. A data collector receives transmissions from the total station and stores all field data for later download to a computer. (See Figure 5–10.)

Figure 5–10. **A data collector transmits to the total station and stores all field data for later download to a computer.**

Station	Backsight (+)	H.I.	I.F.S. (−)	Foresight (−)	Elev.
BM E635	4.62	740.24			735.62
TP #1	6.81	743.27		3.78	736.46
TP #2	1.04	732.95		11.36	731.91
T.O. Hydrant			6.77		726.18
T.O. Curb				10.19	722.76
					735.62 −722.76 **12.86**
Level check	BS total = **12.47**	FS 25.33 − BS 12.47 **12.86**		FS total = **25.33**	

Figure 5–11. **Field notes based on leveling contain only location and elevation information.**

The following are some abbreviations that may be found in a field book:

BM—Bench mark
MON—Monument
FS—Foresight
BS—Backsight
IFS—Intermediate foresight
TP—Turning point
Elev—Elevation
T.O.—Top of (e.g., T.O. curb)

Field notes based on leveling contain only location and elevation information. Look at the field notes in Figure 5–11. The left column contains the location of the rod. *BM* indicates a benchmark, or permanent marker. *TP* represents a turning point. This is a temporary point on which the rod is rested in order for the instrument to get a reading. It is called a turning point because once an elevation has been determined for the T.P., the instrument is physically moved to the next station point. The rod is then physically turned to face the instrument. The backsight reading is taken looking back toward the point of beginning. *H.I.* is the height of instrument and is calculated by adding the reading taken from the backsight. After the backsight reading is taken, the rod is physically moved forward and set up on the next T.P. The next reading, called the foresight (FS), is taken and subtracted from the H.I. to give the elevation (Elev.) of the new T.P., which is listed in the last column. The leveling process continues until the final elevation is determined.

The difference between the totals of the backsights and the totals of the foresights equals the difference in elevation between the benchmark and the final elevation. This value can be used to check for error in the intermediate calculations. See Figure 5–11.

Notice at the bottom of the right column that the difference between the bench mark and final elevation is calculated to be 12.86. The last row of the field notes, labeled "Level check," shows the totals of the backsight and foresight columns. The difference between these two is also 12.86, which means there have been no errors in the intermediate calculations.

An *intermediate foresight* (IFS) is a separate elevation taken in addition to the run of levels for information purposes. Its accuracy cannot be readily checked.

Precision Leveling Techniques

A *digital level* can be used to process elevations and distances electronically when used with a special rod. The face of the rod is graduated with a bar code. The reverse side of the digital rod contains standard numerical increments. See Figure 5–12. The level captures the image of the bar code and compares it with the programmed image of the entire rod, which is stored in memory. The comparison of the captured image and the programmed image enables the height and distance to be calculated. These readings can be stored in memory or transferred to another location for processing.

An *optical-micrometer level* employs a special lens that can be rotated to vertically deflect the incoming light ray from the line of sight. The level instrument can then subdivide the level rod graduations to achieve an accuracy of ± 0.02 of the level rod graduation. The highest order of leveling and surveying is called *first order*, and this kind of accuracy can be achieved with optical-micrometer levels.

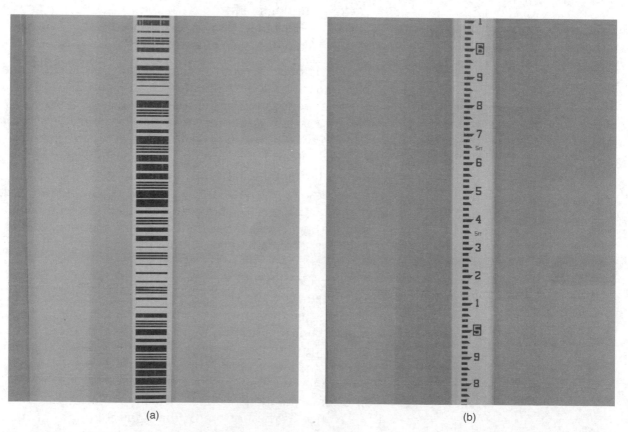

(a)   (b)

Figure 5–12.   (a) The face of the digital level rod is graduated with a bar code. (b) The reverse side of the digital rod contains standard numerical increments.

Figure 5–13. **A laser level projects a rotating beam as a plane of reference.** (Courtesy of Topcon Positioning Systems, Inc.)

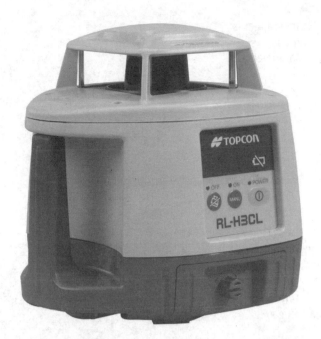

Construction Leveling and Grading by Laser

Construction work usually requires the use of leveling to set elevation grade stakes for road, parking lot, and driveway grades, as well as elevations for excavations, fills, concrete work, plumbing, and floor level verification. The electronic, or laser, level is used for these purposes. The *rotating beam* laser is commonly used because it projects a plane of reference as the beam rotates 360°. The laser beam can be picked up on special *beam detectors* fitted to rods or telescoping detector poles. Figure 5–13 shows an electronic level.

The laser can be set either to provide a level plane or to provide a single beam for use in pipelines and tunnels. The beam or plane can also be tilted to provide a slope for establishing parking lot and road grades. Laser beams can be effective to a radius of more than 600 ft.

Laser Scanning

Survey instruments are now available that use a method of scanning a site with a laser to produce a mass of 3D point data, known as a "point cloud," that can be processed with software to produce a digital terrain model (DTM). While laser scanning does not replace traditional optical survey instruments, or GPS, this is a new method that can be utilized in many situations, such as producing a model of existing structures (e.g., buildings, bridges, tunnels, topographic features). The 3D laser scanner shown in Figure 5–14a is used for fast, accurate work in industrial and outdoor environments. The instrument illustrated in Figure 5–14b is a high-resolution 3D spatial imaging scanner designed for capturing photorealistic detail required in worksite evolution, historic restorations, and crime scene and accident forensics.

The laser scanner is set up on a tripod, just like a traditional survey instrument, and pointed toward the area to be scanned. The scan covers a specific field of view (in degrees) horizontally and

Figure 5–14a.   This 3D laser scanner is
used for fast, accurate work in
industrial and outdoor environments.
(Courtesy of Trimble Navigation)

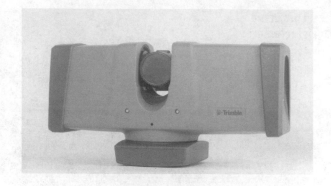

Figure 5–14b.   This high-resolution 3D
spatial imaging scanner is designed for
capturing photorealistic detail required
in worksite evolution, historic
restorations, and crime scene and
accident forensics.
(Courtesy of Trimble Navigation)

Figure 5–15.   A 3D laser scanner in use
at a job site to capture spatial imaging
of buildings.
(Courtesy of Trimble Navigation)

vertically. If a larger area is required than can be covered in a single
scan, the instrument is repositioned and another scan is taken.
These multiple scans can be "stitched" together with software to produce a single cloud and subsequent 3D model. Figure 5–15 shows a
3D laser scanner in use at a job site.

TEST

5-1   What is an EDM?

5-2   What is a total station?

5-3   In "reflectorless" mode, laser EDMs are not accurate beyond what approximate distance?

5-4   What is an elevation?

5-5   What is differential leveling?

5-6   Name the two principal instruments used in leveling.

5-7   Identify the following abbreviations:

BS   IFS
FS   H.I.
BM   T.P.

5-8   What is the basic rule for calculating elevations when running levels?

5-9   What is the smallest increment marking on a level rod?

5-10   What do the small red numbers on a level rod represent?

5-11   How accurate can level rod measurements be when a rod target is used?

5-12   Describe the process for checking the values determined in the leveling process.

5-13   What two types of levels can be used for precision leveling?

5-14   What type of instrument is used for construction grading?

5-15   What type of projects can a high-resolution 3D scanner be used for?

PROBLEMS

P5-1   Give the elevations indicated by the rod reading in Figure P5-1.

P5-2   Calculate the unknown elevations in Figure P5–2a and Figure P5–2b.

P5-3   Calculate the unknown elevations from the field notes provided in Figure P5–3.

(Note that the foresight to T.P. 1 from the first instrument setup is shown on the second line of the notes, on the same line as the label T.P. 1.)

Problems 5–4 to 5–6 are incomplete level field notes. Complete the field notes, adding all missing H.I.s and elevations. Check your final answer mathematically, as discussed in the chapter.

Figure P5–1.

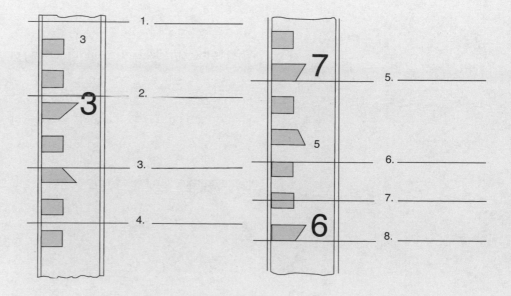

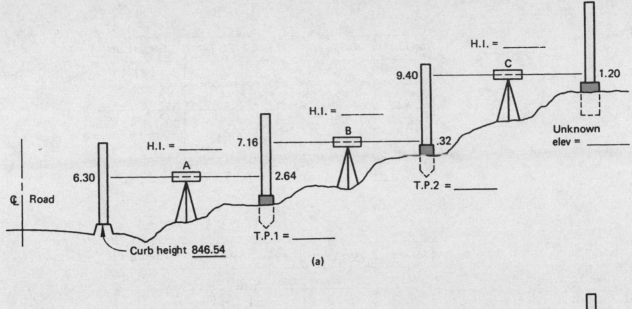

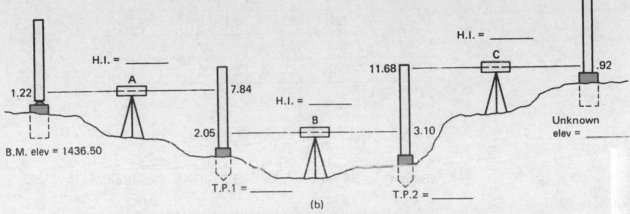

Figure P5-2.

Figure P5-3.

Station	Backsight (+)	H.I.	Foresight (−)	Elevation
US.GS.B.M.I	6.21			422.34
T.P.1	8.90		3.46	
T.P.2	7.82		4.63	
T.P.3	5.60		2.45	
B.M.2	12.04		3.86	
T.P.4	4.62		7.70	
T.P.5	7.31		4.06	
B.M.3			3.64	

P5–4

Station	BS (+)	H.I.	FS (−)	Elevation
BM-1	3.63			247.4
TP-1	6.24		5.29	
TP-2	8.65		6.04	
TP-3	2.51		10.16	
BM-2			7.55	

P5–5

Station	BS (+)	H.I.	FS (−)	Elevation
BM-1	8.21			946.85
TP-1	5.36		4.89	
TP-2	7.81		10.63	
TP-3	9.07		6.32	
TP-4	5.11		4.99	
BM-2			7.25	

P5–6

Station	BS (+)	H.I.	FS (−)	Elevation
BM-1	6.992			946.85
TP-1	7.964		9.376	
TP-2	3.560		4.096	
TP-3	7.455		3.675	
TP-4	3.442		7.521	
TP-5	8.459		12.680	
TP-6	9.456		3.442	
TP-7	6.087		4.358	
BM-2			2.961	

Problems 5–7 and 5–8 are illustrations of leveling. Using the information given, set up appropriate field notes and provide all necessary information. Solve the problems for all H.I.s, elevations, and final BM 2 elevations. Provide a mathematical check of your work in the field notes.

P5-7

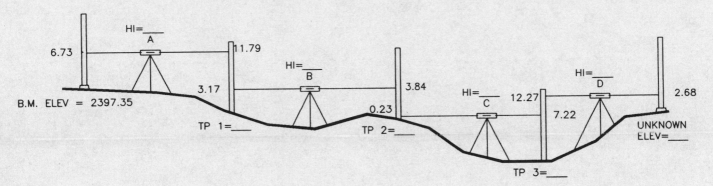

Figure P5-4.

P5-8

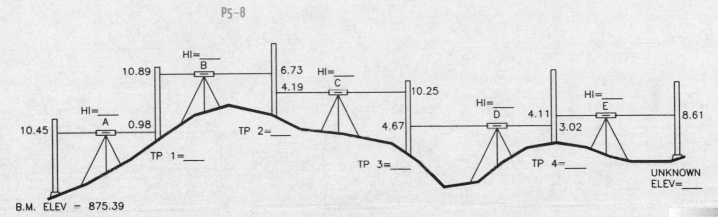

Figure P5-5.

Problems 5–9 and 5–10 are illustrations of plan views of two differential leveling operations. Prepare appropriate field notes, including all elevations and a math check for each problem. The small circles along the level line indicate instrument setups, and the numbers are foresight and backsight readings from the instrument.

P5-9

Figure P5-6.

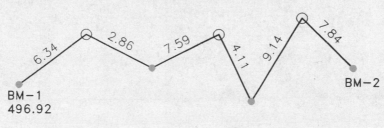

Figure P5-7.

Figure 5-7 exercise answer: 467.05

P5-10

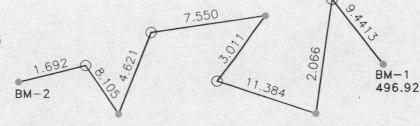

Surveying Fundamentals

Learning Objectives

After completing this chapter, you will be able to:

- Identify different types of surveys and the maps created by them.
- Identify a variety of surveying equipment.
- Identify and describe different types of land traverses.
- Describe the important difference between open and closed traverses.
- Define the numerical components of an angular measurement.
- Calculate bearings of property lines when given azimuths.
- Use mathematical formulae to calculate and check the total angles of a property plat.
- Describe global navigation satellite system (GNSS) and global positioning system (GPS) technology.

Key Terms

Plane survey
Chord
Closed traverse
Geodetic survey
Triangulation
Aerotriangulation
Stereoscope
Stereo pair
Construction survey
Azimuth
Quadrant
Traverse
Global navigation satellite system (GNSS)
Global positioning system (GPS)

Accurate maps are created using information obtained from a variety of surveying methods. *Surveying* is the process used to obtain information about natural and human-made features. This information is most often the location and elevation of a single point on the ground and the angular and height relationships between points. The horizontal location of a point on the earth's surface is its longitude and latitude. The elevation of a point is its height above mean sea level (MSL), which is the average of high and low tides taken over an extended period of time.

For mathematical and CADD applications, the longitude, latitude, and elevation of a point is also referred to as the *XYZ* location of a point. Detailed coverage of this is found in Chapter 7.

This chapter examines some of the methods and instruments used in gathering information from which maps are made.

Specifically, topics covered include:

- Types of surveys
- Traversing methods
- Electronic traversing
- Global positioning systems

The Shape and Size of the Earth

The earth is referred to as a sphere, but it is technically an *oblate spheroid*, or a sphere flattened at the ends (poles). The approximate measurements of the earth are:

Equatorial diameter	7928 mi (12,756 km)
Equatorial circumference	24,907 mi (40,075 km)
Length of 1 degree of longitude at equator	69.186 mi
Polar diameter	7901 mi (12,713 km)
Polar circumference	24,822 mi (39,938 km)
Length of 1 degree of latitude	68.95 mi (approx.)

The diameter of the earth measured through the poles is approximately 27 miles less than the diameter measured at the *equator*. See Figure 6–1. The rotation of the earth creates the 27-mile bulge at the equator. This causes a variation in the length of a degree of latitude near the poles. See Chapter 7 for a discussion of longitude and latitude.

Figure 6–1. The diameter of the earth measured through the poles is approximately 27 miles less than the diameter measured at the equator.

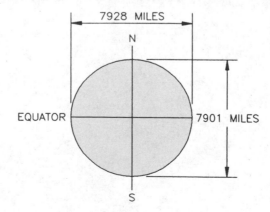

Types of Surveys

Plane Surveys

A *plane* is a flat surface, and a plane survey is conducted as if the earth were flat. Because the curvature of the earth has such a minimal effect over short distances, it is not a factor in plane surveys. This means that mathematical calculations in plane trigonometry and plane geometry can be used. For example, the length of an arc along the curved surface of the earth is only approximately 0.66 ft (20.12 cm) longer across the 36-mile width of a section of land than the length of a straight line, or chord, between the arc's end points. See Figure 6–2. Because most surveys cover far smaller areas of ground, the plane survey serves well.

Another example of the offset of a plane in relation to the earth's surface is shown in Figure 6–3. In this case, at the end of a 1-mile arc, a horizontal plane is only 0.66 ft above the earth's surface.

Land or Boundary Surveys

Most of us are familiar with land surveys. If you own land, a property plat of the plot is on file at your county courthouse. This type of plane survey locates property corners and boundary lines. It is normally a

Figure 6–2. The lengths of a 36-mile arc and a chord connecting the arc's ends vary by only 0.66 ft.

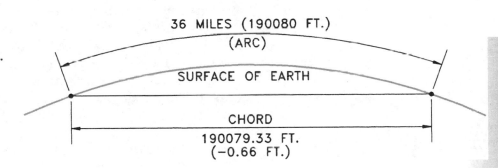

Figure 6–3. A horizontal plane is only 0.66 ft above the earth's surface at the end of a 1-mile arc.

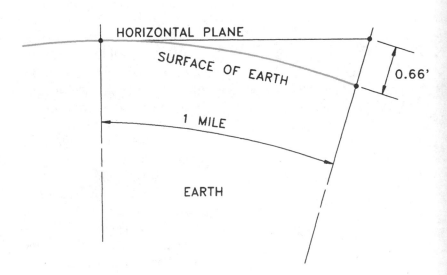

closed traverse because the survey always returns to the *point of beginning* (POB) or another control point. An example of a land survey is shown in Figure 6–4.

Topographic Survey

Anyone who has ever worked with a contour map has seen the results of a *topographic survey*. The principal function of this survey is to locate elevations and features on the land, both natural or artificial (see Figure 6–5).

Geodetic Survey

The geodetic survey is a grand survey, often spanning nations, in which the curvature of the earth is a factor. Large areas are mapped using a process called triangulation. A series of intersecting triangles is established as a net. Some sides of these triangles may be hundreds of miles long, stretching from one mountain peak to another. The control established by geodetic surveys is often used as references for other surveys. Figure 6–6 illustrates the size of a typical geodetic survey.

Photogrammetric Survey

Most topographic maps are made using aerial photographs. Photographs taken at various altitudes constitute the *field notes* of a *photogrammetric survey*. Measurements are taken on the photos of known distances on the ground (often established by a land survey or open traverse) to check for accuracy. Maps are then compiled using the information contained in the photograph. Many overlapping flights are flown before an accurate map can be created.

Advances in global positioning system (GPS) technology have changed the relationship of aerial photography and ground surveying. Aerial photography and GPS technology are now combined in a process called aerotriangulation. This procedure incorporates a GPS antenna mounted and locked over the camera on the fuselage of the airplane. The aerial photos are linked to accurate location data, using camera-mounted and ground-based GPS receivers. Each time the camera shoots an exposure, a pulse is sent to the onboard GPS receiver. Satellite readings of GPS position and time data are recorded for each camera exposure. GPS receivers on the camera and ground ensure accurate recording of data. Sophisticated software handles mathematical interpolation for the lack of time synchronization between camera exposure and GPS signal recording. In addition, software routines for 3D earth curvature help to reduce errors.

Aerotriangulation still requires that ground surveys establish control points for accuracy. But the number of ground control points is greatly reduced because of the accuracy of the GPS data and procedures.

Aerial photographs are used for a wide variety of applications and for different stages of a project. Photos are taken at various altitudes to

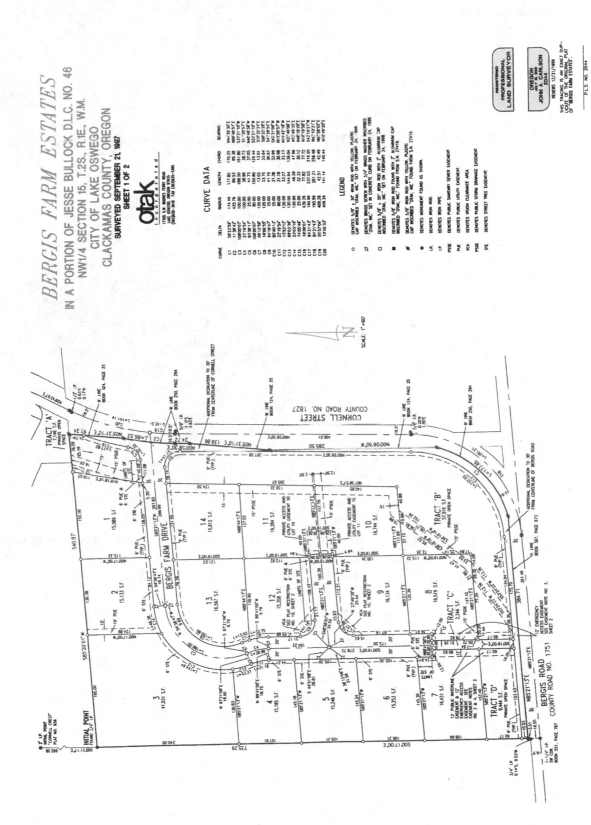

Figure 6-4. Typical land survey of a subdivision.
(Courtesy of Otak, Inc.)

Figure 6-5.   A topographic survey is used to compile the information needed to create this topographic map. (Reproduced by permission of the U.S. Geological Survey)

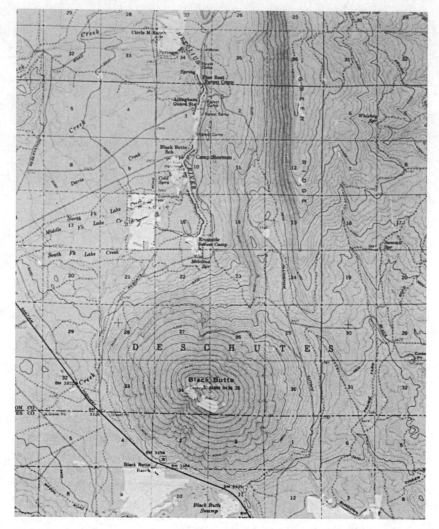

create images at different scales. For example, look at the three photos shown in Figure 6–7a–c. Small-scale photos show a larger area, and large-scale photos show a smaller area. Figure 6–7a has a small scale of 1″ = 1700′. This type of photo has less accuracy and would be used for project plan overview and preliminary studies. A larger-scale photo of the same area shown in Figure 6–7b has a scale of 1″ = 850′ and is used for preliminary studies, map design, and geographic information systems (GIS) applications. The largest-scale photo, shown in Figure 6–7c, is 1″ = 170′, has greater accuracy, and is used for engineering and design work.

Aerial photography in the 1″ = 1000′ to 1″ = 2000′ range provides accuracy suitable for mapping at 1″ = 200′ to 1″ = 400′, with a contour interval supported to 5′. Maps created from these photos are large-area views and have limited accuracy. They are suitable for preliminary planning, forestry applications, and county-wide mapping.

Aerial photographs taken at a scale of 1″ = 400′ to 1″ = 700′ provide accuracy suitable for mapping at 1″ = 100′, with 2′ contours. In the engineering world, this aerial photography accuracy is used for the preliminary planning level. Environmental studies, large area developments, and drainage studies/plans fall under this scale. It is also currently (as of this printing) the scale of choice for GIS base mapping by

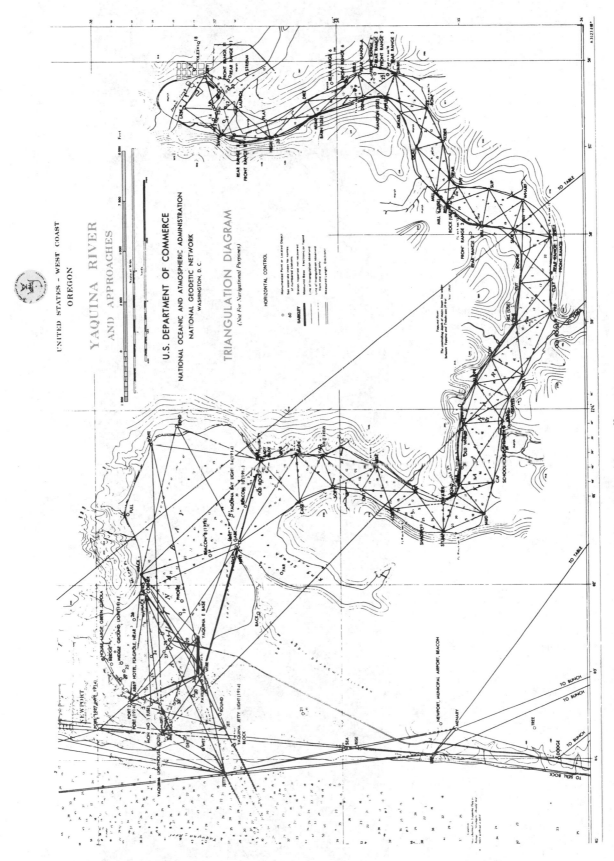

Figure 6–6.   A geodetic survey defines major control points that can be used for smaller surveys.
(Courtesy of National Geodetic Survey)

Figure 6-7a. This type of aerial photograph has a small scale of $1'' = 1700'$ and would be used for project plan overview and preliminary studies.
(Courtesy of Spencer B. Gross, Inc., Portland, Oregon)

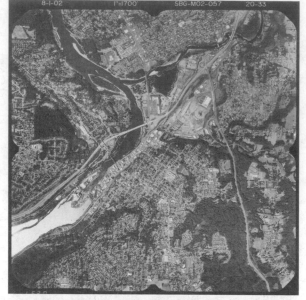

Figure 6-7b. This photo has a larger scale of $1'' = 850'$ and would be used for preliminary studies, map design, and GIS applications.
(Courtesy of Spencer B. Gross, Inc., Portland, Oregon)

Figure 6-7c. This type of $1'' = 170'$ large-scale photo would be used for engineering and design work.
(Courtesy of Spencer B. Gross, Inc., Portland, Oregon)

most municipalities. This trend is shifting, however, toward a more accurate mapping scale of 1″ = 50′, with 1′ contour interval.

Large-scale aerial photographs of 1″ = 170′ to 1″ = 300′ provide accuracy suitable for mapping at 1″ = 20′ to 1″ = 50′, with 1′ contours. If the ground control is very precise, 0.5′ contours are possible from 1″ = 170′ photos. This is design-level accuracy, approaching accuracies that can be observed using terrestrial surveying. Applications would be highway and airfield design.

Aerial photographs containing *XYZ* data become vital documents in creating civil engineering design and construction drawings. Civil engineering detail drawings are discussed in Chapter 14. Aerial photographs are also used to compile digital maps that can then be used with a CADD system. The known distances on the ground also have known elevations. With the use of a 3D stereoscopic mapping workstation, such as the one shown in Figure 6–8, a photogrammetrist can see and plot data such as buildings, streets, and water edges, as well as data that is dependent on elevations, such as contours, spot elevations, and depressions (see Chapter 9). The CADD operator can then access this data in digital form by requesting information about specific lines and by reading the coordinates.

An individual aerial photo can be viewed in 3D with the aid of a stereoscope. This instrument is composed of eyepieces similar to binoculars and sits above the photos on collapsible legs. See Figure 6–9. Aerial photos that have overlapping images are referred to as a stereo pair and are placed under the stereoscope for viewing.

Route Survey

An *open traverse* is a traverse that does not close on itself. An open traverse is conducted when mapping linear features such as highways, pipelines, or power lines. These are termed *route surveys*. They can begin at a control point such as a bench mark and consist of straight lines and angles. These surveys do not close. An example of a route survey is shown in Figure 6–10.

Figure 6–8. Specialized 3D stereoscopic mapping workstations and eyewear enable the CAD operator to work in a 3D environment.

Figure 6-9. A stereoscope is used to analyze stereo photos.

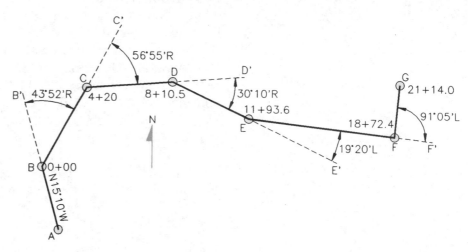

Figure 6-10. A route survey or an open traverse does not close on itself.

Construction Survey

As the name implies, a **construction survey** is performed at construction sites. Building lines and elevations of excavations, fills, foundations, and floors are established by this localized type of survey (see Figure 6-11).

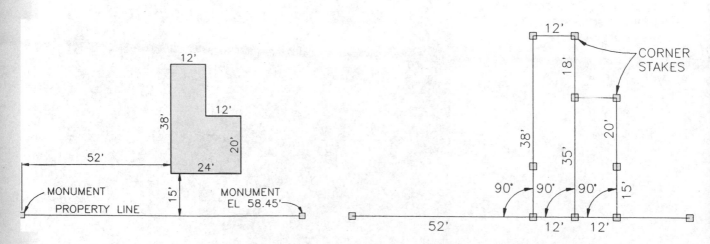

Figure 6-11. Construction survey showing locations of corners and staking out of house with angles and distances.

Angular Measurements

The basis of all surveys is the angular measurement. A detailed discussion of angular bearings and azimuths is provided in Chapter 7, but a brief introduction is provided here.

Angular measurements taken by surveyors are normally taken from north or south and then measured to the east or west. Angles measured in a full circle can have a value from 0° to 360° and are called azimuths. Azimuths are most often measured from north in a clockwise direction but can be measured from south. Angles can also be measured in 90° quadrants. This type of angular measurement is a *bearing*. It is measured from north or south to the east or west and has a value of 0° to 90°.

The basic unit of an angle is the *degree*. A degree can be divided into 60 *minutes* (60′), and 1 minute can be divided into 60 *seconds* (60″). Therefore, a bearing written as N55°25′36″ E means the angle was measured from north toward the east and is located in the northeast quadrant of the compass. An angle written as N245°14′22″ is an azimuth measured clockwise from north. If each compass quadrant is 90°, in which compass quadrant does this azimuth lie? The southwest (SW) quadrant.

Azimuths can be converted into bearings and vice versa. For example, the previous azimuth of N245°14′22″ is in the SW quadrant, which means if it is to be written as a bearing, it must have a value measured from south to west. A measurement from north clockwise to south is half a circle, or 180°. Therefore, you must subtract 180° from 245°14′22″ to find the bearing. The bearing is S65°14′22″W.

Traversing

A traverse is a series of continuous lines connecting points called *traverse stations*, or *station points*. The lengths of the lines connecting the points are measured, as are the angles between the lines. Several traverse types are currently in use.

Open Traverses

An open traverse, as seen in Figure 6–12 and mentioned previously, consists of a series of lines that do not return to a POB and do not necessarily have to begin or end on a control point. Exploratory surveys employ this type of traverse, where accuracy is not critical and estimates will satisfy the project requirements. The open traverse cannot easily be checked and is not suitable for work other than route surveys.

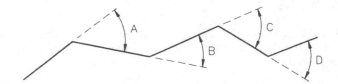

Figure 6–12. **An open traverse does not begin or end at a control point and cannot be easily checked.**

Figure 6–13.   A connecting traverse is one in which the beginning and end points are known.

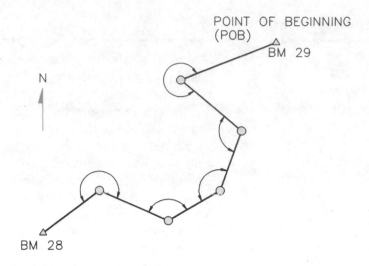

Figure 6–14.   A loop traverse closes on itself and can be checked easily.

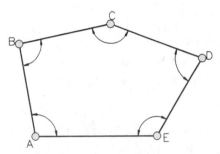

Connecting Traverses

A *connecting traverse* begins and ends at known points. This type of traverse can result in an accurate survey because both angular and linear measurements can be checked to determine location. The traverse in Figure 6–13 appears to be an open traverse, but is technically a closed traverse because it connects known points (bench marks), and is easy to check.

Closed Traverses

In a closed traverse, the lines close on the point of beginning, as in a *loop traverse*, or close on a different known control point, as in the *connecting traverse*. A closed traverse can be checked for accuracy and is thus used exclusively for *land surveys* and construction surveys. Figure 6–14 shows an example of a loop traverse.

Compass Bearing Traverses

Bearings are angular measurements of 0° to 90° taken from a north or south line and are oriented either east or west. The surveyor's compass was originally used when laying out a traverse, and the bearings were read directly from the compass. In a present-day compass bearing traverse, bearings are calculated using an instrument such as the total station (see Figure 6–15a). The robotic total station is a complete instrument that measures horizontal and vertical angles and contains a built-in electronic distance meter (EDM) that measures distance using infrared and laser signals. A surveyor utilizes a control unit attached to the total station to input and manipulate survey data. See Figure 6–15b. This robotic total station is used in conjunction with a tracking target and control unit, as shown in Figure 6–15c. A single surveyor can detach the control unit from the total station, mount it to a rod with a tracking target, and, using the robotic total station, survey an entire job site without assistance. A GPS receiver can be employed with the tracking target to provide accurate GPS data in addition to the measurements previously mentioned. See Figure 6–15c.

Figure 6–15a.   The robotic total station combines vertical and horizontal angle measurements with an EDM.
(Courtesy of Trimble Navigation)

Figure 6–15b. **A surveyor uses a control unit to operate the total station.** (Courtesy of Trimble Navigation)

Figure 6–15c. **A GPS receiver is mounted on top of a tracking target to provide accurate GPS data in addition to the measurements taken by the total station.** (Courtesy of Trimble Navigation)

Data recorded in an electronic total station can be saved in an electronic data collector or field computer (see Figure 6–15d). Data can then be downloaded at the office into a computer or transmitted directly from the site to the office. Bearings measured with these instruments are more accurate and can be used with great precision in calculations for mapping. The bearing of the backsight is known, and the angle is then measured to the foresight. This angle is applied to the backsight bearing to determine the foresight bearing. This method is often used in connecting traverses, as shown in Figure 6–13.

Direct or Interior-Angle Traverses

Closed traverses are principally measured using direct or interior angle traverses. The traverse proceeds either clockwise or counterclockwise around the plot and measures the *interior angles*. The closed traverse shown in Figure 6–14 is plotted using the direct angle method. Bearings can later be applied to the direct angles if required.

An interior-angle traverse can be run clockwise or counterclockwise. Regardless of the direction of the survey, the sum of the interior angles should always equal $(n-2)180°$, where n is the number of sides in the polygon.

Deflection-Angle Traverses

A *deflection angle* is an angle that veers to the right or left of a straight line (see Figure 6–16). This method of angle measurement is commonly used in route surveys. An angle to the right or left of the backsight is measured and is always 180° or less. The letter R or L must always be given with the angle.

When the preceding line of a survey is extended beyond the current station point, it is said to be a *prolongation* of that line. The deflection angle is measured from the prolongation of the succeeding line. But the surveyor does not just measure a 180° horizontal angle from the preceding line because improper instrument adjustment may lead to error. Instead, the instrument is aimed at the backsight and then flipped on its transverse, or horizontal axis, to achieve the prolongation. Then the deflection angle is measured to the foresight (next station point). When an instrument is flipped, or turned over on its transverse axis, it is said to be *plunged*. A deflection angle

Figure 6–15d. **Data recorded in an electronic total station can be saved in an electronic data collector.**
(Courtesy of Topcon Positioning Systems, Inc.)

Figure 6–16. **Deflection-angle traverse.**

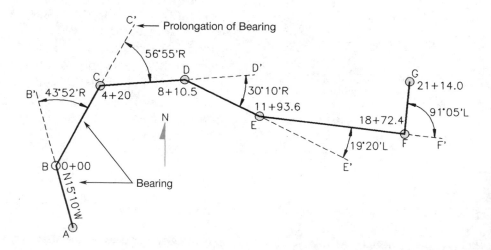

will close when the difference between the angles to the right and the angles to the left equals 360°.

Angles-to-the-Right Traverses

A survey using angles to the right always measures the foresight by turning the instrument clockwise from the backsight. Closed properties are normally surveyed counterclockwise in order to create interior angles. A traverse route that is counterclockwise creates interior angles inside the polygon. The sum of these angles should total $(n-2)\,180°$.

Exterior angles measured clockwise are used to check the accuracy of the interior angles.

When the traverse route is clockwise, the angles to the right are exterior angles, or outside the polygon. The sum of these angles should total $(n + 2)180°$, where n is the number of sides in the surveyed property. Figure 6–17 shows the appearance of these two types of angle-to-the-right traverses.

Azimuth Traverses

Azimuth means horizontal direction. It is derived from the Arabic word "al-samt," which means "the way." In mapping, the term is used to refer to a direction that is measured from a north or south line. Unlike bearings, which measure only 90° quadrants, an azimuth is a measurement that encompasses the entire 360° of a circle. An azimuth traverse requires only one reference line that is most often a north–south line. This reference line can be either *true* or magnetic. In Figure 6–18, the azimuths are measured clockwise from the north line.

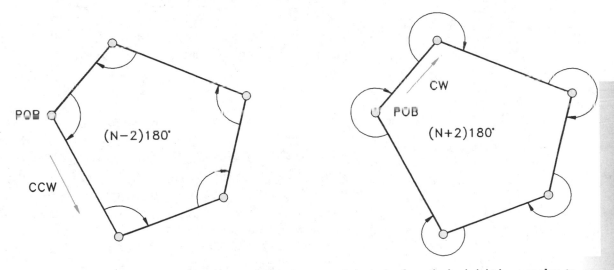

Figure 6–17. The foresight is measured by turning the instrument clockwise from the backsight in an angles-to-the-right survey.

Figure 6–18. An azimuth traverse measures each angle clockwise from north or south.

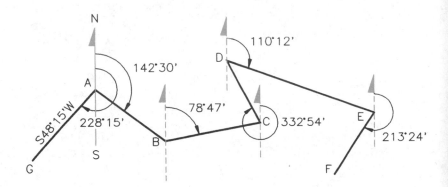

At each point in Figure 6–18 from *A* to *E*, an angular azimuth value is given. For example, the azimuth of line *AB* is measured from north with the instrument located at point *A*. This angle is 142°30′. Notice that line *AG* has also been measured, and the azimuth angle is 228°15′. In addition, the bearing of line *AG* is given as S48°15′W. The bearing angle is always measured from north or south to east or west. Therefore, the bearing angle is never greater than 90°. When you are given an azimuth you can easily convert it to a bearing by using simple math. We know that the angle measured from north to south is 180°, or a straight line. The azimuth of line *AG* is 228°15′, and the bearing will be the angle from south to line *AG*. Therefore, you just subtract to find the bearing:

$$\begin{array}{r} 228°15′ \\ -180° \\ \hline 48°15′ \end{array}$$

Because this bearing is measured from the south to the west, it is written S48°15′W.

The azimuth of line *BC* is measured with the instrument located at point *B*, and the angle is 78°47′. If the azimuth is measured from north, any angle in the northeast quadrant (quarter of the compass) will have the same azimuth and bearing value. The only difference is the way the angles are written. Therefore, the azimuth of line *BC* is N78°47′, and the bearing of line *BC* is N78°47′E. A detailed discussion of bearings and azimuths is found in Chapter 7.

Electronic Traversing

Measuring distances and elevations, as well as plotting traverses, is not usually accomplished in an isolated setting. In other words, surveys are begun by initially tying them either to previous surveys or to an organized reference grid or coordinate system. Many survey points have been established across the globe, allowing for a precise network of measurements. Grids of this kind enable us to accurately reflect curved land masses.

In the United States, two grid systems are used: the Lambert Conformal Projection and the Transverse Mercator Projection. These two systems are known as *State Plane Coordinate (SPC) systems*. An example of grid systems is shown on the edge of the Mount Hood North Quadrangle map in Figure 6–19.

Surveys of this nature are important in CADD work. With both aerial topographic maps and surveys being produced with the same SPC reference, the CADD operator is able to overlay the aerials and surveys with a high degree of accuracy, using the SPC coordinates for both types of maps. Refer to Chapter 7 for a more in-depth look at grid systems.

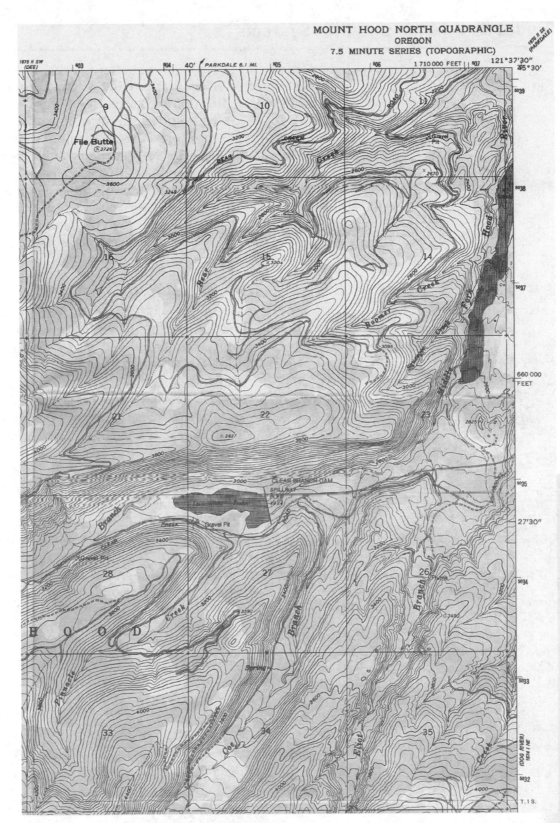

Figure 6-19. A topographic map showing State Plane coordinates and UTM rectangular coordinates. (Reproduced by permission of the U.S. Geological Survey)

Global Navigation Satellite Systems

Global navigation satellite system (GNSS) is a generic term for any system of satellites that provide global coverage for geographical positioning. The United States maintains its Global Positioning System (GPS), which utilizes a network of satellites in combination with earth-based receivers to determine locations on the earth. A wide variety of GNSS/GPS receivers are available today, varying greatly in accuracy and cost. Inexpensive handheld receivers can locate you within several feet on a map if you are out hiking in the woods, but for survey-grade accuracy, also known as sub-centimeter accuracy, much more sophisticated equipment is required.

In the early 1970s, the U.S. military established an orbital network of 21 *geosynchronous* satellites, each transmitting radio signals to the earth. A geosynchronous, or *geostationary*, orbit refers to a satellite traveling in an orbit 22,300 miles (35,900 km) above the earth's equator. At this altitude, the satellite rotates around the earth in 24 hours, thus matching the earth's rotation. Therefore, the satellite always remains in the same spot over the earth. This network of satellites, called NAVSTAR (NAVigation Signal Timing and Ranging GPS), was constructed so that four satellites would be in view from any position on the earth. A surveyor on earth, using a GNSS/GPS receiver (Figure 6–20), could determine longitude and latitude by using the signals from three satellites. The elevation of a point could be determined using a fourth satellite.

Since NAVSTAR's inception, more satellites have been added to the system, known as a constellation. Currently, the U.S. Air Force maintains the 24 operational satellites, and 5 satellites are available as spares. As satellites are retired, new ones are launched as replacements. Other nations have placed satellite constellations in orbit. GNSSs such as the GLONASS system built by Russia and the Galileo system by the European Union are in restoration and development stages. India is currently developing the Indian Regional Navigational Satellite System (IRNSS), and China's regional Beidou navigation system may be expanded into a global system.

Prior to May 1, 2000, the military degraded the signal used for civil purposes by using selective availability (SA) to achieve the

Figure 6–20. **This surveyor is using a GNSS receiver and a handheld controller to record and annotate global positioning system data.** (Courtesy of Trimble Navigation)

standard positioning services (SPS), creating an error factor of approximately 100 m. This degradation has now been removed, making more accurate measurements available to the public.

While a very coarse level of accuracy is acceptable for applications such as navigation devices for cars or boats, higher levels of accuracy are required for surveying applications. These higher accuracies can be calculated by using a technique called *differential GPS*. Using this system, GPS receivers are placed on known points, known as base stations. GPS positions are measured, and the differences between the known points and the GPS values are used to calculate the amount of error (differential) that can be used in subsequent GPS measurements. Recently, networks of base stations have been established by the public and private sectors, allowing the collection of survey-grade data with just a GPS receiver, thereby eliminating the need for each person collecting GPS data to invest in an expensive base station.

The uses of GPS extend not only to surveying but to a wide range of civil and private applications. GPS is used in motor vehicles, ships, aircraft, and pleasure boats for locating position. It can also be used for accurate measurement of elevations, as well as volcanic and seismic activity. As the system has improved, it has become a vital part of our overall measurement and data collection system, and its applications may be endless.

Raw Data and Coordinate Data: From Surveys to Drawings

As field data is collected, a file is created in the survey instrument that contains all the measurements and calculations. These steps taken in the field, known as "observations," were once meticulously recorded by hand in a paper field book, but they are now recorded electronically into what is known as a *raw data file*. Each survey instrument manufacturer maintains its own proprietary format for this data, but the end result is the same: a precise record of every step taken in the collection of the survey. These files are then downloaded to an office computer system and processed to produce coordinates for each point that was surveyed, or "shot," in the field. Figure 6–21 shows an example of raw data in the Carlson Survey raw data editor. The data can be edited here, if necessary, and then processed to produce coordinates. The survey can also be adjusted here; in this process, errors in field measurement are mathematically corrected using a variety of methods that have been accepted by the survey profession as a whole.

The calculated points are then stored in a coordinated file. Each software manufacturer has its own proprietary format for these files, but a universal method of storing this data is to use a simple text file that contains the point number, northing, easting, elevation, and description of each point. An example of a text file containing point data is shown in Figure 6–22.

Thousands of points can be stored in the data collector and then exported to a computer as a text file (with a .txt file extension). Text files can be created and saved in a wide variety of formats, and the surveyor determines this based on the type and amount of data gathered.

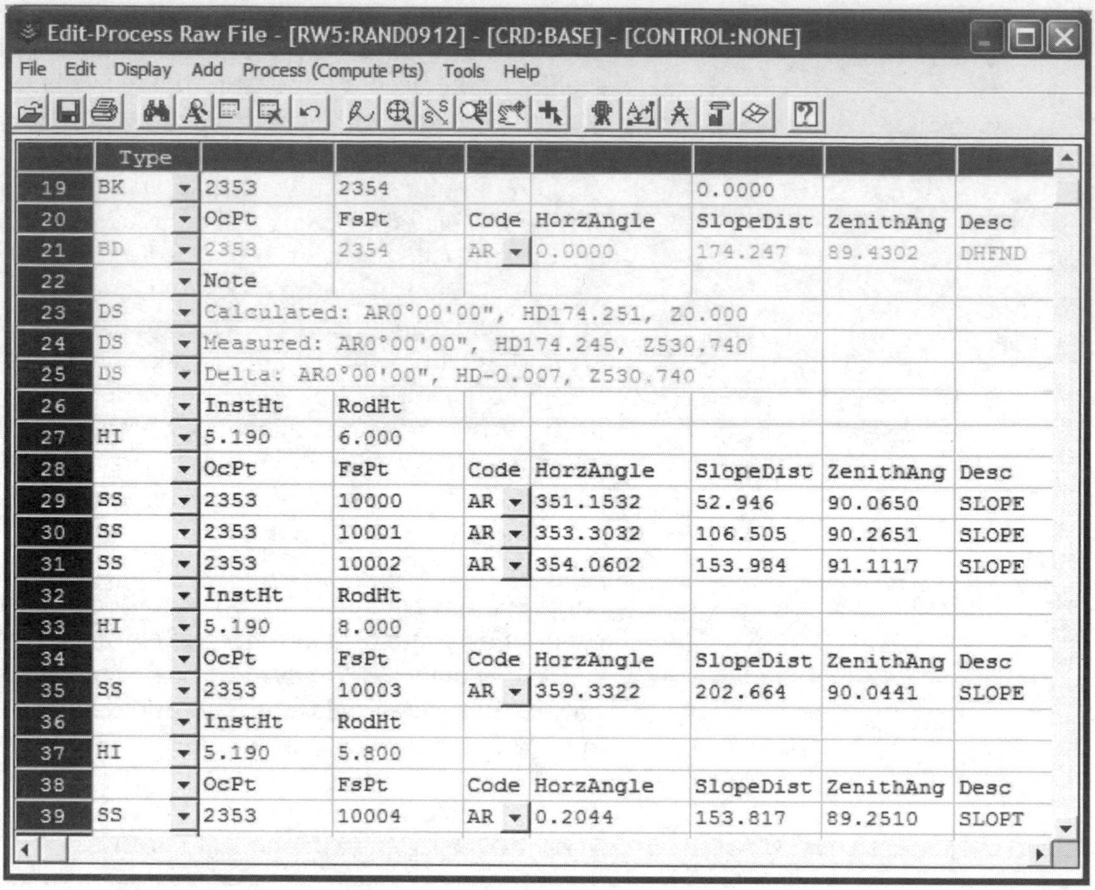

Figure 6-21. An example of a raw data file displayed in the Carlson Survey Edit/Process program.
(Courtesy Carlson Software)

A common text file format is *comma delimited*. Each piece of data is separated by a comma, and all data for an individual point appears on a single line. This is the format shown in Figure 6–22.

The text file can then be imported into a civil engineering software package, such as AutoCAD civil 3D, where it then is converted to a digital terrain model (DTM). Designers and engineers can then begin design work for the project and, together with civil drafters, can generate a wide variety of drawings, views, and shaded renderings. These procedures are discussed in greater detail in later chapters.

When a design element, such as a light rail route alignment, is created by engineers and applied to the DTM, a new text point file can be generated by the software. Point files can be created for any selected points, alignment, or area. This file is then given to surveyors, who go out into the field and lay out the new points, using the total station and data collector. This job can progress quickly when a robotics total station is used, such as the one shown in Figure 6–23.

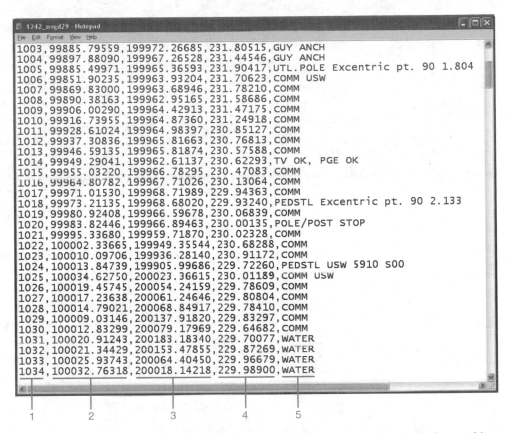

```
1242_nvgd29 - Notepad
File  Edit  Format  View  Help
1003,99885.79559,199972.26685,231.80515,GUY ANCH
1004,99897.88090,199967.26528,231.44546,GUY ANCH
1005,99885.49971,199965.36593,231.90417,UTL.POLE Excentric pt. 90 1.804
1006,99851.90235,199963.93204,231.70623,COMM USW
1007,99869.83000,199963.68946,231.78210,COMM
1008,99890.38163,199962.95165,231.58686,COMM
1009,99906.00290,199964.42913,231.47175,COMM
1010,99916.73955,199964.87360,231.24918,COMM
1011,99928.61024,199964.98397,230.85127,COMM
1012,99937.30836,199965.81663,230.76813,COMM
1013,99946.59135,199965.81874,230.57588,COMM
1014,99949.29041,199962.61137,230.62293,TV OK, PGE OK
1015,99955.03220,199966.78295,230.47083,COMM
1016,99964.80782,199967.71026,230.13064,COMM
1017,99971.01530,199968.71989,229.94363,COMM
1018,99973.21135,199968.68020,229.93240,PEDSTL Excentric pt. 90 2.133
1019,99980.92408,199966.59678,230.06839,COMM
1020,99983.82446,199966.89463,230.00135,POLE/POST STOP
1021,99995.33680,199959.71870,230.02328,COMM
1022,100002.33665,199949.35544,230.68288,COMM
1023,100010.09706,199936.28140,230.91172,COMM
1024,100013.84739,199905.99686,229.72260,PEDSTL USW 5910 S00
1025,100034.62750,200023.36615,230.01189,COMM USW
1026,100019.45745,200054.24159,229.78609,COMM
1027,100017.23638,200061.24646,229.80804,COMM
1028,100014.79021,200068.84917,229.78410,COMM
1029,100009.03146,200137.91820,229.83297,COMM
1030,100012.83299,200079.17969,229.64682,COMM
1031,100020.91243,200183.18340,229.70077,WATER
1032,100021.34429,200153.47855,229.87269,WATER
1033,100025.93743,200064.40450,229.96679,WATER
1034,100032.76318,200018.14218,229.98900,WATER
```

1   2   3   4   5

Figure 6-22. Surveyors can collect at least five pieces of data for a single point and store this as a text point file in the total station data collector. The text file is then used to generate a digital terrain model.

Figure 6-23. Point files of project features, such as water line connections in a subdivision, can be quickly laid out in the field by surveyors with an electronic robotic total station.

TEST

6-1   What is aerotriangulation?

6-2   What is a topographic survey?

6-3   In what type of survey is triangulation used?

6-4   A route survey is often termed an open traverse. Why?

6-5   What type of survey would be used to lay out a new highway?

6-6   Can the type of survey in question 6–5 be easily checked?

6-7   What is a station point?

6-8   What type of instrument is used to measure bearings?

6-9   What is the term for an angle to the right or left of the backsight?

6-10 Compare and contrast bearings and azimuths.

6-11 What is the difference, in miles, between the equatorial and polar diameters of the earth?

6-12 What type of mathematical calculations are used in a plane survey?

6-13 What is EDM?

6-14 What is the formula for calculating the sum of the angles of an interior-angle traverse?

6-15 What is the name of the system that uses satellites to locate points on the earth's surface?

6-16 Identify the types of traverses in Figure T6–1.

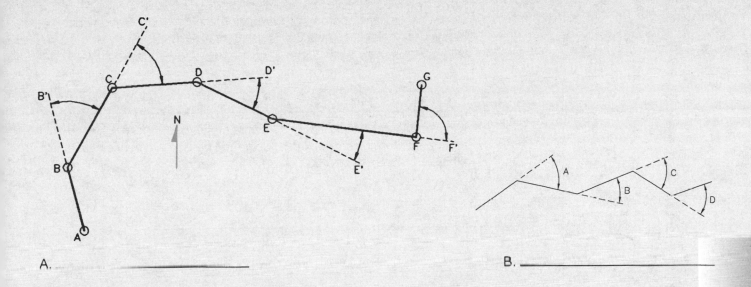

A. _____

B. _____

C. _____

D. _____

Figure T6–1.

6–17   Name at least four pieces of data about a point that can be recorded by a total station and stored in a data collector.

6–18   What type of map is shown in Figure 6–19?

PROBLEMS

P6–1   The two property plat surveys shown in Figure P6–1 were surveyed using angles to the right, and they are both composed of 90° angles. Property A was surveyed counterclockwise, and B was surveyed clockwise. Use the appropriate formulae given in the book and verify that your calculations equal 360° for each property.

P6–2   The two property plat surveys shown in Figure P6–2 were surveyed using angles to the right and are both odd-angled plots. Property A was surveyed counterclockwise, and B was surveyed clockwise. Use the appropriate formulae given in the book and verify that your calculations equal 360° for each property.

Figure P6–1. **Angles-to-the-right calculations.**

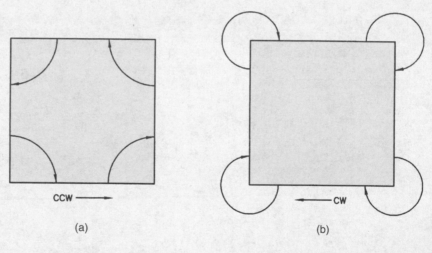

(a)   (b)

Figure P6–2. **Angles-to-the-right calculations.**

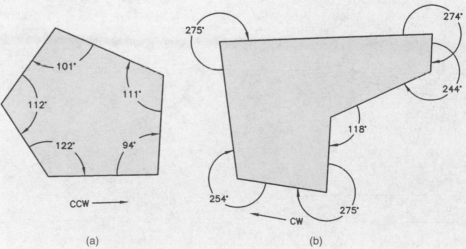

(a)   (b)

P6-3 Refer to Figure 6–18 to complete this problem. Convert the azimuths given in Figure 6–18 to bearings. Write your answers in the spaces provided below.

Line	Bearing
AB	_____
BC	_____
CD	_____
DE	_____
EF	_____

P6-4 Refer to Figure 6–16 to complete this problem. Convert the deflection angles given in Figure 6–16 to azimuths and bearings. Write your answers in the spaces provided below.

Line	Azimuth	Bearing
AB	_____	_____
BC	_____	_____
CD	_____	_____
DE	_____	_____
EF	_____	_____
FG	_____	_____

Location and Direction

Learning Objectives

After completing this chapter, you will be able to:

- Determine the azimuths of given lines.
- Calculate the distance on the earth's surface from given latitude and longitude points.
- Calculate the azimuth from given information.
- Use a protractor to determine the azimuth of given lines.
- Establish the bearing, distance, cosine, sine, latitude, and departure from a given traverse.
- Draw a traverse from given information.
- Determine the length and bearing of property lines from given northing and easting information and then draw the traverse.
- Draw an approximate magnetic declination line from given data.

Key Terms

Longitude
Latitude
Meridians
Prime meridian
International data line
Statute mile
Direction
Degrees
Minutes
Seconds
Surveyor's compass
Azimuth
True north (geographic north)
True azimuth (TA)
Magnetic north (MN)
Magnetic azimuth
Grid system
Grid north (GN)
Grid azimuth
Bearing
Magnetic declination
Local attraction
Quadrangle map
Traverse
Polygon
Coordinate geometry (COGO)
Error of closure
Departure

Identifying location and direction are two of the main purposes of map-making and use. This chapter explains the division of the earth into parts and how this system can be used to locate features. Also discussed are basic map geometry and construction of plats.

The topics covered include:

- Longitude
- Latitude
- Location on a map
- Direction
- Azimuth
- Bearing
- Map geometry
- Traverse

Location

The earth is gridded by imaginary lines, called lines of longitude and latitude. These lines were established to aid location of features on a map.

If the earth were square in shape, locations could easily be identified using a square gird system consisting of areas of equal-sized squares. However, the earth is spherical, which does not allow for location to be defined using a square grid system. As a result, specific points have been established on the earth from which measurements can be accurately made. These points are the north and south poles and the center of the earth. From these three points, a grid system has been established, using the degrees of a circle as reference. The grid lines are referred to as lines of longitude that circle the earth vertically and lines of latitude that circle the earth horizontally.

Longitude

Lines of *longitude* are imaginary lines that connect the north and south poles. These lines are also referred to as meridians. The imaginary line connecting the north and south poles, and passing through Greenwich, England, is called the prime meridian. The prime meridian represents 0° longitude, as shown in Figure 7–1. There are 180° west and 180° east of the prime meridian, forming the full circle of 360° around the earth. Meridians east of the prime meridian are referred to as *east longitude*. Meridians west of the prime meridian are called *west longitude*. The 180° meridian coincides roughly with the international date line. The date is one day earlier east of the international date line.

Length of a degree of longitude. A degree of longitude varies in length at different parallels of latitude, becoming shorter as the parallels approach the north and south poles. That is a little confusing but think about it for a bit and refer back to Figure 7–1, which shows how degrees of longitude get closer together as they near the north

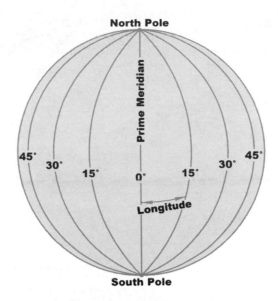

Figure 7–1. **Measuring longitude.**

Table 7-1. **Length of a degree of longitude**

Latitude	Statute Miles	Latitude	Statute Miles
0°	69.186	50°	44.552
10°	69.128	60°	34.674
20°	65.025	70°	23.729
30°	59.956	80°	12.051
40°	53.063	90°	0.000

and south poles. Table 7–1 shows the length of a degree of longitude at certain latitudes.

The length of a degree of longitude can be calculated using this formula:

$$\begin{array}{ccc} \text{Length of} & & \text{Length of} \quad \text{Cosine} \\ \text{a degree} & = & \text{a degree} \quad \times \quad \text{latitude} \\ \text{of longitude} & & \text{of latitude} \end{array}$$

The length of a degree of latitude is approximately 69 statute miles. Calculate the length of a degree of longitude at 45° latitude, for example, in the following manner:

$$\begin{aligned} \text{Length of a degree of longitude} &= \text{69 statue miles} \times \text{cosine 45°} \\ &= 69 \times 0.70711 \\ &= 48.791 \text{ statute miles} \end{aligned}$$

Latitude

Latitude is measured as an angular distance from the point at the center of the earth, as shown in Figure 7–2. Notice that the latitude is the angle between the line of the equator and the other side of the angle.

Points on the earth's surface that have the same latitude lie on an imaginary circle called a *parallel of latitude*. Lines of latitude are identified by degrees north or south of the equator. The equator is

Figure 7-2. **Measuring latitude.**

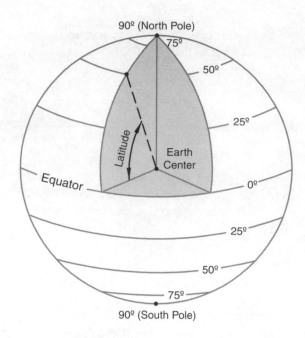

0° latitude. The north pole is 90° *north latitude*, and the south pole is 90° *south latitude*.

Length of a degree of latitude   Parallels of latitude are constructed approximately the same distance apart. Due to the bulging of the earth near the equator, each degree of latitude is not absolutely the same in distance. A degree of latitude varies from 69.4 statute miles near the poles to 68.7 statute miles at the equator. For all but very detailed maps, it is satisfactory to refer to each degree of latitude as being 69 statute miles in length. A *statute mile* is established as an international standard and intended as a permanent rule. A statute mile equals 5280 feet.

Location on Maps

On flat maps, meridians and parallels can appear as either curved or straight lines. Most maps are drawn so north is at the top, south at the bottom, west at the left, and east at the right. Look for the north arrow for the exact orientation.

To determine directions or locations on any map, you must use the coordinates of parallels and meridians. For example, if you want to know which city is farther north, Portland or Salem, you can look at the map in Figure 7-3 to see that Portland is north of Salem. Which city is farther east? Portland or Salem? Again, the map shows Salem on the 123° meridian, with Portland east of Salem. Any location on the earth can be identified by locating its intersecting lines of longitude and latitude.

Finding Distances Between Locations

There are different ways to calculate the distance between two points on the earth's surface with specified latitudes and longitudes given, depending on how far away the points are located from each other. When two points lie on either the same meridian or the same parallel

Figure 7–3. **Using coordinates of parallels and meridians to find locations.**

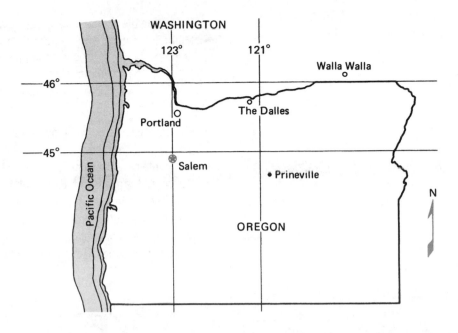

of latitude, you can use the length of a degree to find the distance between the points. If the points are fairly close, such as a few hundred miles or less from each other, you can image the earth's surface as being flat and use the Pythagorean theorem to find distance. Generally, when points are a great distance away from each other, the shape of the earth becomes an issue, and a spherical triangle must be solved in order to identify distance.

Most civil drafting projects involve relatively short distances that are established with the surveying methods discussed in Chapter 5. The following is valuable information and gives you important background knowledge. However, determining distances on the earth's surface is generally reserved for aeronautical, nautical, space navigation, and astronomical applications. Calculating these distances is generally beyond what might be considered normal use in most civil engineering projects.

Finding Distances Between Locations on the Same Meridian or the Same Parallel of Latitude

When two points lie on either the same meridian or the same parallel of latitude, you can use the length of a degree to find the distance between the points.

If the points are on the same meridian, first calculate the number of degrees of latitude between the points and then multiply by the length of a degree of latitude, which is 69 statute miles. The following are two examples:

Example:

- Find the distance between point *A* at 30° north latitude, 110° east longitude, and point *B* at 42° north latitude, 110° east longitude, as shown in Figure 7–4.
- The points have the same longitude, so they are on the same meridian.

- Determine the number of degrees of latitude between the points: 42°—30° = 12°.
- Multiply the number of degrees of latitude between the points by the length of a degree of latitude: 12° × 69 statue miles = 828 statute miles.

Example:

- Find the distance between point *A* at 22° south latitude, 65° west longitude, and point *B* at 22° south latitude, 79° west longitude, as shown in Figure 7–5.
- The points have the same latitude, so they lie on the same parallel of latitude.
- Determine the number of degrees of longitude between the points: 79° − 65° = 14°.
- Calculate the length of a degree of longitude at 22° latitude, as previously discussed: 69 statute miles × cosine 22° = 69 × 0.92718 = 64 statute miles.
- Multiply the number of degrees of longitude between the points by the length of a degree of longitude at 22° latitude: 14° × 64 statue mile = 896 statute miles.

Figure 7–4. Finding the distance between point *A* at 30° north latitude, 110° east longitude, and point *B* at 42° north latitude, 110° east longitude.

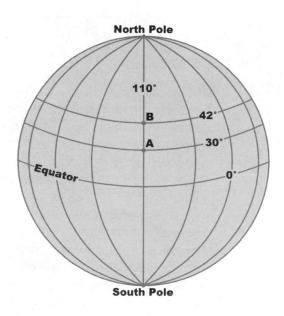

Figure 7–5. Finding the distance between *A* at 22° south latitude, 65° west longitude, and point *B* at 22° south latitude, 79° west longitude.

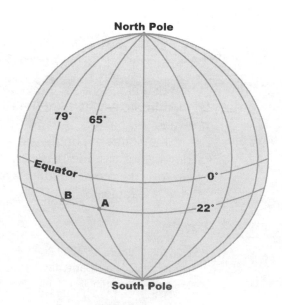

Finding Distances Between Close Locations on Different Meridians and Parallels of Latitude

If the points are fairly close, such as a few hundred miles or less from each other on a different longitude and latitude, you can image the surface of the earth as being flat and use the Pythagorean theorem to find distance. Figure 7–6 shows an example of this situation.

The following is a plane geometry refresher on the Pythagorean theorem:

- The Pythagorean theorem states that in a right triangle, the square of the length of the *hypotenuse* is equal to the sum of the squares of the lengths of the sides.
- The Pythagorean theorem formula is $a^2 + b^2 = c^2$, where a and b are sides of the right triangle, and c is the hypotenuse.
- The hypotenuse is the longest side of a right triangle, opposite the 90° angle.
- A right triangle has one 90° angle. (See Figure 7–7.)

Figure 7–6. **If the points are fairly close, such as a few hundred miles or less from each other on a different longitude and latitude, you can image the surface of the earth as being flat and use the Pythagorean theorem to find distance.**

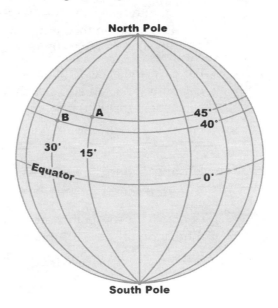

Figure 7–7. **The hypotenuse is the longest side of a right triangle, apposite the 90° angle. A right triangle has one 90° angle.**

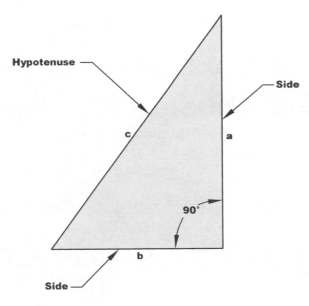

Using points A and B in Figure 7–6 as an example, calculate the distance between the points as follows:

- Find the number of degrees of latitude from point A to the longitude where point B is found; $45° - 40° = 5°$.
- Calculate the distance in the previous step: $5° \times 69$ statute miles = 345 statute miles.
- Determine the number of degrees of longitude from point B to the longitude where point A is located. $30° - 15° = 15°$.
- Find the length of a degree of longitude at 40° latitude: 69 statute miles $\times$ cosine $40° = 69 \times 0.76604 = 52.857$ statute miles.
- Establish the distance between 15° on 40° latitude: $15° \times 52.857$ statute miles = 792.86 statute miles.
- Now, use the Pythagorean theorem formula, $a^2 + b^2 = c^2$, where a and b are sides of the right triangle, and c is the hypotenuse, which is the distance between points A and B, as shown in Figure 7–8. From the previous calculations, $a = 345$ statute miles and $b = 792.86$ statute miles. Continuing with the Pythagorean theorem formula: $345^2 + 792.86^2 = c^2$, $119.025 + 628.626.98 = c^2$, $c = 864.67$ statute miles.

For ease and accuracy, you should use a calculator to make these calculations. You can also search the Internet for Pythagorean theorem calculators, using the search words "Pythagorean theorem calculator." For example, see **www.1728.com/pythgorn.htm**.

Finding Distances Between Locations of Great Distances on a Different Meridian and Parallel of Latitude

Generally, when points are a great distance away from each other, the shape of the earth becomes an issue, and a spherical triangle must be solved in order to identify distance. Although you can solve

Figure 7–8. Using the Pythagorean theorem formula, $a^2 + b^2 = c^2$, to calculate the distance between points A and B, where a and b are sides of the right triangle and c is the hypotenuse, which is the distance between points A and B.

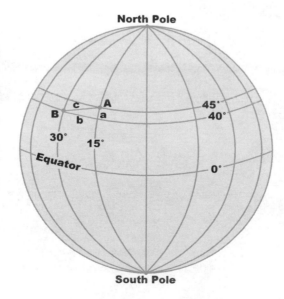

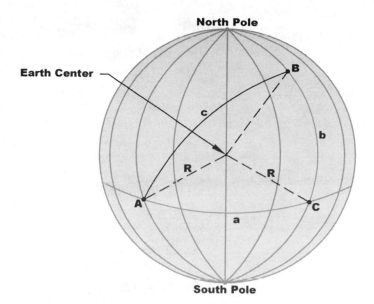

Figure 7-9. A spherical triangle is shown on the earth's surface between points *A*, *B*, and *C*. Notice how the sides *a*, *b*, and *c* of the spherical triangle are arcs rather than straight lines, as discussed when using the Pythagorean theorem and shown in Figure 7-8.

a spherical triangle equation manually, typically a calculator or computer program is used to quickly and accurately solve it. The following provides a brief introduction to the spherical triangle. Making spherical triangle calculations is math intensive and beyond the scope of this textbook.

A spherical triangle is a three-sided geometric object formed on the surface of a sphere by three *great circular arcs* intersecting at three vertices. Great circular arcs are arcs with their centers coinciding with the center of the sphere. A spherical triangle has angles *A*, *B*, and *C*, measured in *radians* at the vertices along the surface of the sphere, and the sphere on which the spherical triangle sits has radius *R*. Radius *R* is the radius of the sphere. The earth's mean radius is approximately 3959 statute miles (6371.3 kilometers). A radian is an angular unit of measure in which 2π radians $= 360°$, and π radians $= 180°$. A spherical triangle is shown on the earth's surface in Figure 7-9. Notice how the sides *a*, *b*, and *c* of the spherical triangle are arcs rather than straight lines, as discussed when using the Pythagorean theorem and shown in Figure 7-8. The sum of the angles of a triangle with straight sides is equal to 180°, while the sum of the angles of a spherical triangle is 180° or greater. The amount by which the sum of the angles of a spherical triangle exceeds 180° is called the *spherical excess*. The spherical excess exists because the sides of the spherical triangle are arc shaped rather than straight. The study of angles and distances on spherical surfaces is called *spherical trigonometry*.

Direction

A **direction**, in surveying, refers to the angular relationship of one line to another. When a number of lines radiate from a point, the direction of these lines is expressed with reference to one of the lines that is designated as having zero direction. In most cases a north–south or east–west line carries the zero designation.

Units of Angular Measure

The units of angular measure most commonly used in civil drafting are degrees. Degrees are identified with the symbol °, as in 30°. There are 360° in a complete circle, a quarter circle has 90°, a half circle has 180°, and three-quarter's of a circle has 270°. Each degree is made up of 60 minutes. The minutes symbol is '. Minutes are divided into 60 seconds, which are identified with the symbol ". So, a complete degree, minute, and second designation reads like this 50°30'45". It is important when you are doing calculations with degrees and parts of degrees that you keep this information in mind. Consider these two examples:

Example:

$$48°40'25''$$
$$+25°38'40''$$
$$73°78'65''$$

In this example, the solution must be reduced because there are only 60' in a degree and 60" in a minute:

$$73°78'65'' = 73°79'5'' = 74°19'5''$$

The final solution is 74°19'5".

Example:

$$75°32'10''$$
$$-34°45'8''$$

In this example, you must borrow a degree from 75°32'10":

$$75°32'10'' = 74°92'10''$$
$$74°92'10''$$
$$-34°45'8''$$
$$40°47'2''$$

Calculating degrees and parts of degrees can usually be done manually. However, if you must make multiple calculations, you may find that a calculator or computer program with degree, minute, and second functionality allows you to quickly and accurately solve problems. In fact, some CADD software programs eliminate the need to calculate by converting angular measurements.

Surveyor's Compass

A surveyor's compass is used in mapping to calculate the direction of a line. The reading taken is usually a bearing angle or an included angle. Bearings and included angles are described throughout this chapter. Figure 7–10 shows the differences between two commonly used compasses: a mariner's compass and a surveyor's compass.

Azimuth

An azimuth is a direction, measured as a horizontal angle from a zero line, generally north–south, in a clockwise direction (see Figure 7–11).

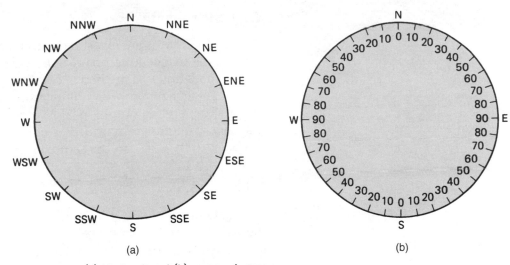

Figure 7–10.   (a) Mariner's and (b) surveyor's compass.

Figure 7–11.   **Azimuth.**

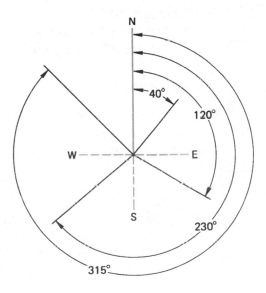

True North (Geographic North)

Abbreviated TN, true north is the location of the north pole. *Geographic north, geographic meridian,* and *true meridian* are terms that are all used to designate the same meaning as true north.

True Azimuth

A true azimuth (TA) is a horizontal angle measured using true north as the reference line.

Magnetic North

Magnetic north (MN) is where the compass north arrow points. Magnetic north is about 1000 miles away from true north. Sometimes the terms *magnetic compass* and *magnetic meridian* are used to mean magnetic north.

Magnetic Azimuth

Magnetic azimuths are measured with magnetic north as the zero line. Actually, the magnetic compass is used only as a check on more accurate methods and as a method to obtain approximate values for angles. The magnetic azimuths may differ from the true azimuth by several degrees, depending on the local magnetic attractions. Occasionally, magnetic azimuths are specified as east or west of magnetic north. For example, 10°W indicates the same direction as 350°.

Grid System

Grid systems are used to establish points of reference for features of the earth's surface when preparing map drawings. Coordinate systems have been developed to help ensure that the curvature of the earth coincides with the rectangular grid on a map drawing. The most commonly used grid systems are the Universal Transverse Mercator (UTM), the Universal Polar Stereographic (UPS), and the State Plane Coordinate (SPC). When you see a note on a drawing, such as UTM grid and 1994 magnetic north, this means that the grid north given refers to the UTM grid system.

Grid North

Grid north (GN) consists of the north–south lines of a grid mapping system previously discussed. The angular variation between true north and grid north is often given in a map legend.

Grid Azimuth

A **grid azimuth** is established for a rectangular survey system so that the north–south grids of the survey are used as the reference, or zero line. You can see this used when you work with the township section system.

Bearings

The **bearing** of a line is its direction with respect to one of the quadrants of the compass. Bearings are measured clockwise or counterclockwise, depending on the quadrant, and starting from north or south (see Figure 7–12).

A bearing is named by identifying the meridian, north or south; the angle; and the direction from the quadrant, east or west. For example, a line in the northeast quadrant with an angle of 30° from the north meridian has a bearing of N30°E. Consider a line in the northwest quadrant that is 40° from north; the bearing is N40°W. Look at the other examples of bearings and azimuths in Figure 7–13.

Magnetic Declination

The meridian indicated by the needle of a magnetic compass seldom coincides with the true meridian. So, the horizontal angle between the magnetic meridian and the true meridian, at any

Figure 7-12. **Bearing.**

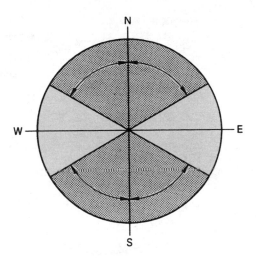

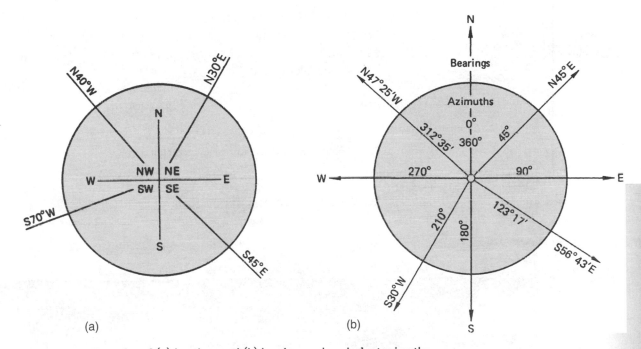

(a)

(b)

Figure 7-13. **Examples of (a) bearings and (b) bearings and equivalent azimuths.**

point, is called the **magnetic declination**. The magnetic declination is either east or west, depending on the direction the arrow of the compass points from true north. The magnetic declination of a map is updated periodically because of continuous changes in its value. Figure 7-14 shows an example of a compass reading displaying the angle between geographic north and magnetic north as the magnetic declination. Magnetic declination is measured in degrees and mils. *Mils* are units of angular measure, where 1 mil equals 1/6400 of the circumference of a circle. Figure 7-15 shows grid north and magnetic north in relationship to true north. This example was taken from the legend of an actual map. Figure 7-16 shows a representation of how the magnetic declination changes in different locations in the United States.

Figure 7-14. **Sample of magnetic declination.**

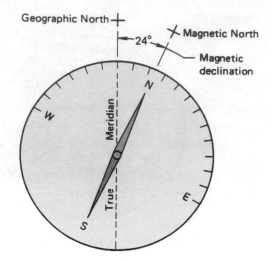

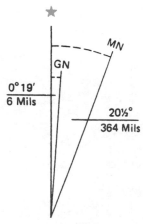

Figure 7-15. **UTM grid and 1994 magnetic north declination at center of sheet.**

Resources are available such as the National Geophysical Data Center's Web site (**www.ngdc.noaa.gov**). Use this Web site to calculate estimated magnetic declination values based on entry of a zip code or latitude and longitude.

Following are some abbreviations and terms associated with making magnetic declination calculations:

MD—magnetic declination
EMD—east magnetic declination
WMD—west magnetic declination
EMA—east magnetic azimuth
WMA—west magnetic azimuth
TA—true azimuth

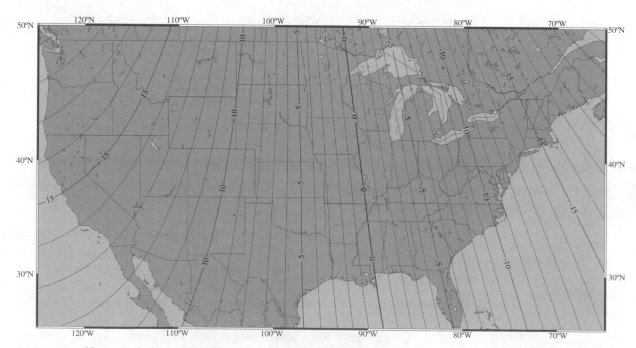

Figure 7-16. **Magnetic declination changes throught the United States.**
(Courtesy of the National Geophysical Data Center, NGDC)

Figure 7–17. Formulas used to calculate true azimuth, given magnetic azimuth and magnetic declination.

$$TA = EMA + EMD$$
$$TA = EMA - EMD$$
$$TA = WMA + WMD$$
$$TA = WMA - EMD$$

Figure 7–17 shows formulas that are used to calculate true azimuth.

The following examples show how to calculate true azimuth, given magnetic azimuth and magnetic declination:

Example: Calculate the true azimuth, given the following information:

East magnetic azimuth = $30°$
Magnetic declination = $20°E$

Substituting the values into TA = EMA + EMD, TA = $30° + 20° = 50°$. So, the true azimuth is $50°$.

Example: Calculate the true azimuth, given the following information:

West magnetic azimuth = $70°20'30''$
Magnetic declination = $20°5'40''E$

Substituting the values into TA = WMA – EMD, TA = $70°20'30'' - 20°5'40''$. Use borrowing to complete the subtraction, $70°19'90'' - 20°5'40'' = 50°14'50''$ W. Because this direction is referenced west from north, you must subtract it from $360°$ to get a true azimuth: $359°59'60'' \quad 50°14'50'' - 309°45'10''$.

Example: Calculate the true azimuth, given the following information:

East magnetic azimuth = $14°$
Magnetic declination = $24°E$

Substituting the values into TA = WMA – EMD, TA = $14° - 24° = -10°$. The negative sign indicates the direction of the azimuth has changed, in this case, from west to east. The true azimuth is $10°$. Refer to Figure 7–14, which shows a $24°$ east magnetic declination.

When you draw bearing lines from a surveyor's notes, the values are either true bearings or magnetic bearings. If they are true bearings, the surveyor identifies this in the field book with a note such as "Bearings are referred to the true (north–south) meridian." The bearings are corrected by applying the magnetic declination for the correct time (year and day). You plot the corrected bearings as given in the field notes. The completed map should indicate with a note that the bearings are true bearings. Surveyor notes and the field book are discussed in Chapter 5.

Most maps carry the magnetic declination for a specific year and the amount of annual change in degrees. The change is indicated as easterly or westerly, and records whether the compass is pointing east of true north (easterly), or west of true north (westerly). After calculating the annual change, the amount must be either added to or subtracted from the angle of declination.

Most maps can be updated frequently, thanks to current map reproduction technology. For example, radar maps can be updated about every 5 minutes, and satellite maps can be updated about every 30 minutes. The frequency of map update schedules is generally determined by the specific agency, the technology, and the number of maps in the system used by the agency or organization where the maps are created. For example, some agencies update their maps quarterly, and some update a certain percentage of maps each year. The U.S. Geological Survey (USGS) currently has no standard updating system for its maps. However, it is gradually moving toward the National Map (see **http://nationalmap.gov**). An out-of-date map is a map that is later than the date that has been revised and reprinted with corrections. You can use the USGS map list at **http://erg.usgs.gov/maplists/index.html** to find map dates.

Local Attraction

A local attraction is any local influence that causes the magnetic needle to deflect away from the magnetic meridian.

Local attractions include steel and iron structures such as underground utilities, power lines, buildings, and iron ore deposits. Sometimes these local attractions greatly alter compass readings.

Location and Direction on a Quadrangle Map

Location and direction can be seen on a quadrangle map such as the one shown in Figure 7–18. This is the SW portion of the Mount Hood North Quadrangle, which shows part of the Mount Hood Wilderness and the NW portion of Mount Hood. The geographic coordinates are shown at the lower-left corner of the quadrangle. This lower-left point is 45°22′30″ north of the equator and 121°45′ west of the prime meridian. Notice the number toward the right side on the bottom that reads 42′30″ and notice the tick mark above that number. At this point, the coordinates are 45°22′30″ north of the equator and 121°42′30″ west of the prime meridian. The tick mark is a small vertical or horizontal line segment on the margin.

Notice the north arrows below the quadrangle. The UTM grid is 0°56′ to the east of true north, and the magnetic declination is 20°E. Also notice that this is based on the 1980 magnetic north.

The UTM grid is shown in groups of 1000 m, or 1 km. At the bottom of the quadrangle in Figure 7–18, the UTM grid is shown as 599, 600, 601, and 602. Along the left side, the UTM grid is shown as 5031, 5030, 5029, 5028, 5027, and 5026. The north–south UTM (on the left side of the quadrangle) indicates the number of kilometers to the equator. Because 1 km is equal to approximately 0.62 mi, you can calculate that the equator is about 3116.12 mi south of Yocum Ridge. Yocum Ridge is located at the north UTM of 5026; and 5026 multiplied by 0.62 = 3116.12 mi.

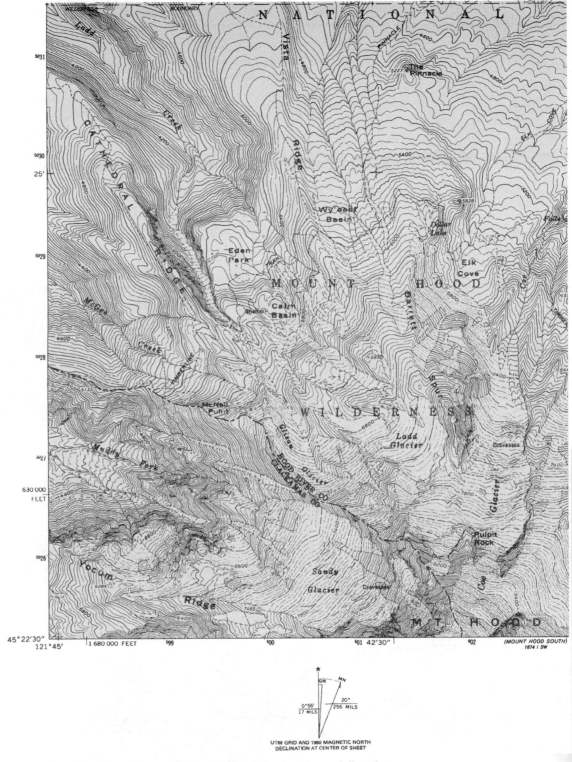

Figure 7-18. A portion of a quadrangle map providing location and direction.

The State Plane Coordinates (SPC) are given in feet. Along the bottom near the lower-left corner in Figure 7-18 is the notation[1] "1 680 000 FEET." The SPC is shown in groups of 10,000 feet. The tick mark to the right of the notation 99 is the SPC mark, and it is 10,000 ft from the mark of 1 680 000 FEET, or approximately 1.89 mi.

Map Geometry

The information that you have learned concerning longitude, latitude, azimuth, and bearing can be put to use in the construction of plats or plots of land. Plots of property are drawn with border lines showing the starting point for location, bearing for direction, and dimensions for size. The following discussion shows how these three components are put together to form the boundaries for a plot. The term *traverse*, used in the following discussion, refers to a line or series of lines connecting a number of points.

Polygon

A **polygon** is a closed figure with at least three sides. The sides of a polygon are straight line segments. A *regular polygon* has equal-length sides and equal-internal angles.

In plotting a traverse, remember that a closed traverse is a polygon. A four-sided polygon closes if all included angles equal 360°, as in Figure 7-19. The total number of included angle degrees in polygons with more than four sides can be calculated using the formula:

$$(n-2) \times 180° = \text{Total degrees}$$

where n = number of sides. For example, the total included angle degrees of an eight-sided polygon is calculated like this:

$$(n-2) \times 180° = \text{Total degrees}$$
$$(8-2) \times 180° =$$
$$6 \times 180° = 1080°$$

Intersecting Lines

When two lines intersect, the opposite angles are equal. In Figure 7-20, angle $X = X$ and $Y = Y$.

Figure 7-19. **All angles of a four-sided polygon will equal 360° when added.**

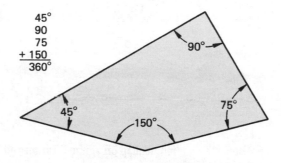

Figure 7-20. **Opposite angles of intersecting lines are equal.**

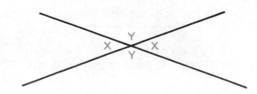

Plotting a Traverse

The previous concepts of polygon angles and intersecting lines become important when you attempt to plot a traverse without all bearings given. The term *plot*, as used here, means to draw.

You may find a situation similar to this example. Given angles *A*, *B*, *C*, and *D*, plot the traverse and determine the bearings. Be sure you understand the definition of *bearing*. Make your calculations in a clockwise direction, beginning at the point of beginning (POB), as shown in Figure 7–21. Use the following steps to plot the traverse in Figure 7–21.

Step 1: Begin by determining the bearing of one line at a time, starting with line *AB*. The bearing of line *AB* is due north. You can reason this because line *AB* is on the section line that is parallel to the north–south line.

Step 2: Determine the bearing of line *BC*, as shown in Figure 7–22. The bearing is in the northeast quadrant. The included angle *ABC* is subtracted from 180°, and the bearing is N69°22′ E.

Figure 7–21. **Example of a typical traverse. Included angles and distances are given.**

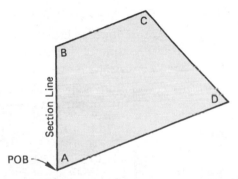

Line	Dist.	Angle	Included degrees
AB	170.1′	DAB	69°10′
BC	131.2′	ABC	110°38′
CD	173.2′	BCD	111°49′
DA	255.0′	CDA	68°23′

Figure 7–22. **Calculating bearings: line *BC*.**

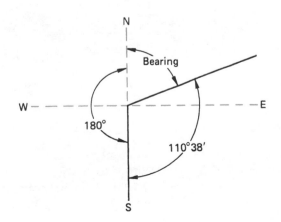

Figure 7–23. Calculating bearings: line CD.

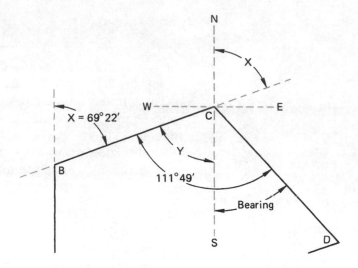

Step 3: Calculate the bearing of *CD*, as shown in Figure 7–23. First, consider everything that you know:
- Angle *BCD* = 111°49′.
- Angle *X* = 69°22′, the bearing of line *BC* that you just calculated.
- Angle *X* = angle *X* because if two parallel lines are cut by another line, the exterior–interior angles on the same side of the line are equal.
- Angle *X* = angle *Y* because when one straight line intersects another, the opposite angles are equal.
- In conclusion, *Y* = 69°22′, so the bearing is:

$$111°49′$$
$$\underline{-69°22′}$$
$$42°27′$$

The bearing is in the southeast quadrant, so it reads S42°27′ E.

Step 4: Determine the bearing of *DA*, and you are back to the POB, as shown in Figure 7–24.

You know from the previous information that angle $Z = 42°27′$. You also know from elementary geometry that $Z = Z_1 = Z_2$. Calculate the angle between north and line *DA* like this:

$$68°23′$$
$$\underline{+42°27′(Z_2)}$$
$$110°50′$$

Now, calculate the bearing of *DA* like this:

$$179°60′$$
$$\underline{-110°50′}$$
Bearing $\quad 69°10′$

With this bearing in the southwest quadrant, the reading is S69°10′ W. Your complete plot layout should look like the drawing shown in Figure 7–25.

Figure 7–24. Calculating bearings: line *DA*.

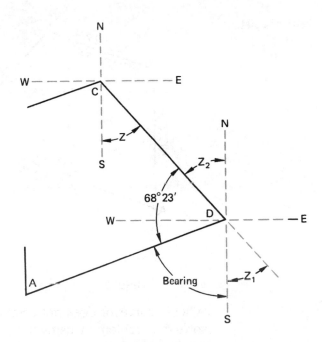

Figure 7–25. **Bearings and distances shown on a plat.**

Plotting a Traverse with CADD

Many of the manual calculations are done for you if you are plotting a traverse with a CADD system. However, it is advisable that you first completely understand the concepts previously discussed before you rely on a computer system to do work for you. Being knowledgeable about the expected outcome of a survey or a traverse allows you to better detect errors even if the computer system is able to process erroneous information.

Coordinate geometry (COGO) is a means used in CADD systems for laying out survey data. The methods for laying out this data include setting individual point coordinates and setting lines and arcs by distance and bearing. Labeling survey points, lines, and curves with lengths and bearings is often an option with COGO software programs.

The typical traverse with included angles and distances shown in Figure 7–21 can be accomplished easily with COGO. The information can be inserted into the computer system as is, from existing survey information, or it can be entered using a keyboard.

Plotting a Closed Traverse

Plotting a traverse is a method of checking the accuracy of a survey. This consists of a series of lines and angles from the survey. Starting at a given point, these angles and lines are plotted to form a closed polygon. When the polygon closes, you know the traverse is accurate, and you have what is called a *closed traverse*. Figure 7–26 is a surveyor's rough sketch of a surveyed plot. The sketch includes all line lengths and bearings. You can be given azimuths or interior angles that you convert to bearings. An *open traverse* can occur when the ends do not close.

Another way to present the information is in a plotting table such as the one shown in Table 7–2. If you are given a plotting table, the information may not be on the sketch.

Figure 7-26.   Rough sketch of a plat.

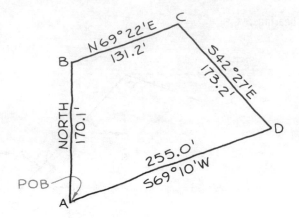

Error of Closure

When a surveyor does not establish a closed traverse, he or she can solve the problem by using the **error of closure** method. As a drafter, you can also have an error due to the small inaccuracies involved in layout. These errors can result in a plot that does not quite close, as shown in Figure 7–27.

After checking all information for accuracy, you can do this to make the correction:

Step 1: Lay out the perimeter of the plot along a straight line and label the corners, as in Figure 7–28.

Step 2: Extend the error of closure above point A'.

Table 7-2. **Plotting table**

Line	Bearing	Distance	Angle
AB	North	170.1'	69°10'
BC	N69°22' E	131.2'	110°38'
CD	S42°27' E	173.2'	111°49'
DA	S69°10' W	255.0'	68°23'

Figure 7-27.   **Error of closure.**

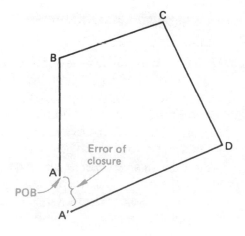

Figure 7–28. **Correcting the error of closure.**

Figure 7–29. **Closed traverse.**

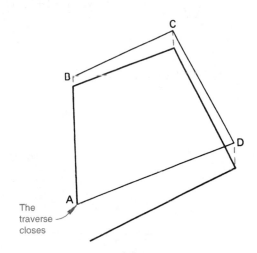

The traverse closes

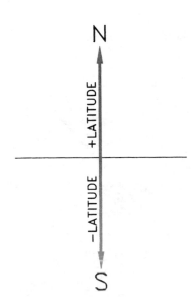

Figure 7–30. **Positive and negative latitude.**

Step 3: Connect a line from A'' to A'.

Step 4: Connect perpendicular lines from points B, C, and D to line A–A''.

Step 5: The distance from the horizontal line to the angle line at each point can be used to compensate for the problem. The proportioned distance corrections as determined by Figure 7–28 are applied to each point in Figure 7–27 at the same angle as A is from A'. Notice how this is done in Figure 7–29.

Plotting Property Using Latitudes and Departures

Plotting a closed traverse is often done by calculating latitude and departure. Calculating latitude and departure is especially important when using manual drafting techniques because the actual calculations are more accurate than the calculations obtained by using a protractor to lay out a line and angle. The *latitude* of a property line relates to the distance the line extends in a north or south direction. A *positive latitude* extends in a northerly direction, while a *negative latitude* runs southerly. See Figure 7–30.

The **departure** of a property line is the distance the property line extends in an east–west direction. Lines running easterly have a *positive departure*, while *negative departures* run westerly, as shown in Figure 7–31.

A right triangle is created by a property line and its latitude and departure. The latitude of a property line is the vertical side of the right triangle, and the departure is the horizontal side, as shown in Figure 7–32.

Figure 7–31.   Positive and negative departures.

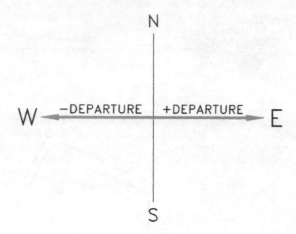

Figure 7–32.   A right triangle created by property lines with latitude and departure.

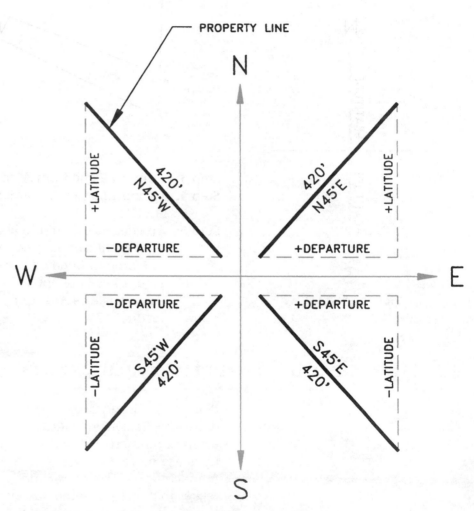

The latitude and departure values are calculated as follows:

$$\text{Latitude} = \text{Distance} \times \cos \text{Bearing}$$
$$\text{Departure} = \text{Distance} \times \sin \text{Bearing}$$

The latitude and departure of the N45°E property line shown in Figure 7–32 are calculated like this:

$$\text{Latitude} = 420' \times \cos 45° = 420' \times 0.70711 = 296.9862$$
$$\text{Departure} = 420' \times \sin 45° = 420' \times 0.70711 = 296.9862$$

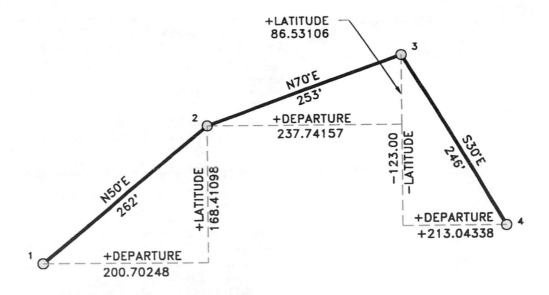

Figure 7–33. Setting up a table for latitude and departure calculations.

COURSE	BEARING	DISTANCE	COS	SIN	LATITUDE	DEPARTURE
1-2	N50°E	262'	.64279	.76604	168.41098	200.70248
2-3	N70°E	253'	.34202	.93969	86.53106	237.74157
3-4	S30°E	246'	.86603	.5000	-123.0000	213.04338

The latitude and departure of the N45°E property line are the same because the bearing is a 45° angle. These values would be different for property lines with other bearings. With regard to the S45°W bearing, the latitude is –296.9862, and the departure is –296.9862.

It is a good idea to set up a table when working with latitude and departure calculations. This helps you keep the information accurately organized. In Figure 7–33, notice the property lines and resulting latitude and departure calculations placed on the drawing and in a table.

The importance of latitudes and departures lies in the plotting of a closed traverse. When a traverse is closed, the sum of the latitudes and departures is zero. Latitudes and departures are referred to as *balanced* when their sums equal zero. When the sum of the latitudes and departures does not equal zero, the resulting amount is the error of closure, and the data is called *unbalanced*. Unbalanced latitudes and departures require that slight changes be made to the latitude and departure of each property line in order to close the traverse and balance the calculations at zero.

Computer programs are available that process the information about a plot based on the bearings and distances of each property line and automatically calculate the latitudes, departures, and azimuths. If the resulting data is unbalanced, automatic adjustments are made in property lines to balance the latitudes and departures and to close the traverse. A set of calculations of this type is shown in Figure 7–34.

Figure 7–34. Plot information processed by a computer automatically calculates and balances latitudes, departures, and azimuths.

Traverse Computation
Problem Number 1: Polygon traverse.

Course	Length	Azimuth	Cos(Az)	Sin(Az)
1–2	284.800	21 3 0.0	+0.93326741	+0.35918251
2–3	210.000	93 35 0.0	−0.06250017	+0.99804503
3–4	240.150	93 3 0.0	−0.05320745	+0.99858356
4–5	278.750	201 3 0.0	−0.93326730	−0.35918263
5–1	452.000	272 34 0.0	+0.04478198	−0.99899679
	1,465.700 = total distance			

| Unbalanced | | Balanced | | | Coordinates | |
Lat	Dep	Lat	Dep	Point	X	Y
+265.795	+102.295	+265.797	+102.290	1	0.000	0.000
−13.125	+209.589	−13.123	+209.586	2	102.290	265.797
−12.778	+239.810	−12.775	+239.806	3	311.876	252.675
−260.148	−100.122	−260.145	−100.127	4	551.682	239.899
+20.241	−451.547	+20.246	−451.554	5	451.554	−20.246
−0.015	+0.026					

Linear error of closure = .029 ft.
Precision = 1 in 49117
Area = 2.7677 acres

TEST

Part I

Multiple choice: Circle the response that best finishes each statement or access this test on the Student Web site and follow the instructions to respond electronically.

7–1 The line that represents 0° longitude is also called:

    a. The international date line
    b. The prime meridian
    c. The equator
    d. Greenwich, England

7–2 Lines of latitude:

    a. Are measured as an angular distance from the point at the center of the earth
    b. Connect the north and south poles
    c. Are called parallels
    d. Are approximately the same distance apart

7–3 $45°26'14'' + 15°10'52'' =$

    a. $60°36'6''$
    b. $60°37'66''$
    c. $60°37'6''$
    d. $61°13'6''$

7–4 A direction measured clockwise from a given zero is called:

    a. A bearing
    b. An azimuth
    c. A magnetic declination
    d. A local attraction

7–5 A direction measured clockwise or counterclockwise with respect to quadrants of a compass is called:

    a. A grid azimuth
    b. An azimuth
    c. A bearing
    d. A magnetic declination

7–6 Refer to Figure 7–18. What is the distance from Elk Cove to the equator?

    a. 5,020,000 m
    b. 5,029,000 mi
    c. 5029 km
    d. 8,111.3 mi

7-7 What is the length of a degree of latitude?

    a. 64 statute miles
    b. 69 nautical miles
    c. 69 statute miles
    d. 690 statute miles

7-8 What is the Pythagorean theorem formula?

    a. $a^2 + b^2 = c^2$
    b. $a^2 \times b^2 = c^2$
    c. $a^2 + b^2 = c$
    d. $a^2 \times b^2 = c$

7-9 What is the length of a degree of longitude at 22° latitude?

    a. 69 statute miles
    b. 65 statute miles
    c. 64 statute miles
    d. 62 statute miles

7-10 What is the name of the longest side of a right triangle, opposite the 90° angle?

    a. Acute triangle
    b. Leg
    c. Side
    d. Hypotenuse

Part II

7-1 Give the azimuths of the following lines on the spaces provided or access this test on the Student Web site and enter your answers electronically. North is zero.

Line *A* _____
Line *B* _____
Line *C* _____
Line *D* _____

7-2 Give the bearings of the lines featured in question 7–1.

Line *A* _____
Line *B* _____
Line *C* _____
Line *D* _____

Figure T7-1.

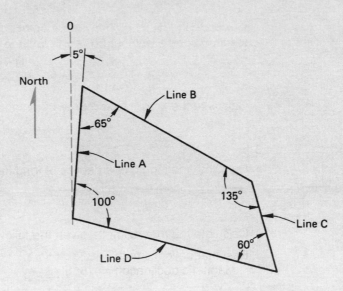

Part III

True or false: Circle the "T" if the statement is true or the "F" if the statement is false. Reword all false statements so that the meaning is true or access this test on the Student Web site and follow the instructions to enter your answers electronically.

7-1   T   F   Magnetic azimuths may differ from true azimuth by several degrees.

7-2   T   F   The horizontal angle between the magnetic meridian and the true meridian is called the magnetic declination.

7-3   T   F   Magnetic azimuth + Magnetic declination = True azimuth.

7-4   T   F   The magnetic declination does not change.

7-5   T   F   The included angles of a four-sided polygon equal 360°.

7-6   T   F   When drawing a plat based on angular information, you must convert bearings to azimuths or interior angles.

Part IV

Given the following groups of information, determine the distances on the earth's surface. Use your knowledge of lengths of a degree of longitude and latitude. Make sketches or use CADD to make drawings of the earth showing the points given to help you establish location; show calculations where appropriate.

7-1   Calculate the distance between a point at 45° north latitude, 20° west longitude and a point 30° north latitude, 20° west longitude.

7-2   Calculate the distance between a point at 16° north latitude, 60° east longitude and a point at 28° south latitude, 60° east longitude.

7-3 Calculate the distance between a point at 50° north latitude, 80° west longitude and a point at 50° north latitude, 20° west longitude.

7-4 Calculate the length of a degree of longitude at 45° north latitude.

7-5 Calculate the length of a degree of longitude at 75° south latitude.

7-6 Calculate the true azimuth, given the following information:

East magnetic azimuth = 32°
Magnetic declination = 15°E

7-7 Calculate the true azimuth, given the following information:

East magnetic azimuth = 46°
Magnetic declination = 5°W

7-8 Calculate the true azimuth, given the following information:

East magnetic azimuth = 18°
Magnetic declination = 7°E

7-9 Calculate the true azimuth, given the following information:

East magnetic azimuth = 27°
Magnetic declination = 12°W

7-10 Calculate the true azimuth, given the following information:

East magnetic azimuth = 19°45'12"
Magnetic declination = 4°50'39"E

7-11 Find the distance between a point at 10° north latitude, 80° west longitude and a point at 10° north latitude, 20° west longitude.

7-12 Determine the distance between a point at 72° north latitude, 28° west longitude and a point at 18° north latitude, 28° west longitude and a point at 18° north latitude, 42° west longitude.

7-13   Find the distance between point *A* at 30° north latitude, 110° east longitude and point *B* at 42° north latitude, 110° east longitude.

7-14   Find the distance between point *A* at 22° south latitude, 65° west longitude and point *B* at 22° south latitude, 79° west longitude.

7-15   Calculate the distance between point *A* at 45° north latitude, 15° west longitude and point *B* at 40° north latitude, 30° west longitude.

PROBLEMS

P7-1   Use one of the following instructions to solve this problem based on your course objectives:

Option 1:

Tape Figure P7–1 to your drawing board. With your drafting machine protractor or handheld protractor, determine the azimuth and bearing for each line. Place your answer in the table provided, using your best freehand lettering. Accuracy to ±15′ is possible.

Option 2:

Use AutoCAD to open file P07–1.dwg on the Student Web site and determine the azimuth and bearing of each line. Place your answers in the given table using your best freehand lettering or enter the answers electronically in a table created using CADD.

P7-2   Given the partial traverse in Figure P7–2, place the following items in the table:

Bearing of each property line (course)

Distance of each course

Cosine of each bearing angle

Sine of each bearing angle

Latitude of each course

Departure of each course

P7-3   Given the traverse in Figure P7–3, place the following items in the table:

Bearing of each property line (course)

Distance of each course

Cosine of each bearing angle

Sine of each bearing angle

Latitude of each course

Departure of each course

Figure P7-1.

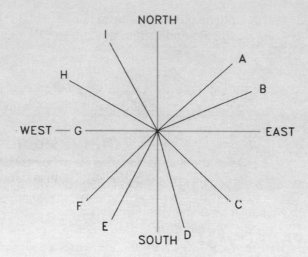

Line	Azimuth	Bearings
A		
B		
C		
D		
E		
F		
G		
H		
I		

P7-4   Draw a traverse from the calculations and information given in Figure P7-4.

P7-5   Given the northing and easting information in the table in Figure P7-5, use your CADD system to plot the subdivision boundary. Identify the length (to one-hundredth of a foot) and bearing of each property line and place the information in the table. Plot the traverse at a scale of 1 in. = 50 ft on a B-size sheet and place the following items on your plot:

Bearing of each line (course)

Distance of each course

Small circles at intersections of courses, similar to the example in Figure P7-2

Figure P7–2.

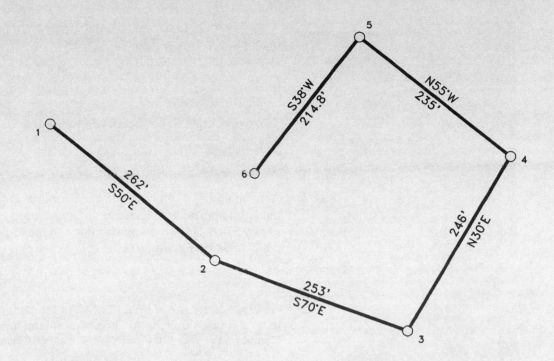

COURSE	BEARING	DISTANCE	COS	SIN	LATITUDE	DEPARTURE
1–2						
2–3						
3–4						
4–5						
5–6						

Figure P7–3.

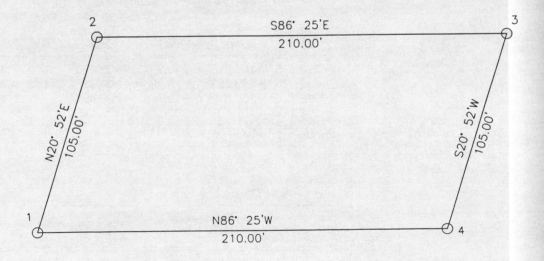

COURSE	BEARING	DISTANCE	COS	SIN	LATITUDE	DEPARTURE
1–2						
2–3						
3–4						
4–1						

A point number at the end of each course, similar to the course numbering in Figure P7–2

POB

Scale

North arrow

Title block: Erika Subdivision, Quincey Lane at Christopher Blvd., Jean, Wisconsin

P7–6   Refer to Figure 7–18. Using the coordinates found on that quadrangle, mark the approximate location of Mount Hood on the map shown in Figure P7–6. Draw the approximate magnetic declination line of the quadrangle on Figure P7–6.

P7–7   A site manager wants data from different sources to be combined into a table that gives both bearings and azimuths from a bench mark. Complete the table of Figure P7–7 to accomplish this task.

Figure P7–4.

Traverse Computation
Problem Number 1: Polygon traverse.

Course	Length	Azimuth	Cos(Az)	Sin(Az)
1–2	284.800	21 3 0.0	+0.93326741	+0.35918251
2–3	210.000	93 35 0.0	−0.06250017	+0.99804503
3–4	240.150	93 3 0.0	−0.05320745	+0.99858356
4–5	278.750	201 3 0.0	−0.93326730	−0.35918263
5–1	452.000	272 34 0.0	+0.04478198	−0.99899679

1,465.700 = total distance

Unbalanced		Balanced			Coordinates	
Lat	Dep	Lat	Dep	Point	X	Y
+265.795	+102.295	+265.797	+102.290	1	0.000	0.000
−13.125	+209.589	−13.123	+209.586	2	102.290	265.797
−12.778	+239.810	−12.775	+239.806	3	311.876	252.675
−260.148	−100.122	−260.145	−100.127	4	551.682	239.899
+20.241	−451.547	+20.246	−451.554	5	451.554	−20.246
−0.015	+0.026					

Linear error of closure = .029 ft.
Precision = 1 in 49117
Area = 2.7677 acres

POINT NO.	NORTHING	EASTING	LENGTH	BEARING
1 (POB)	71394.4238	176534.3439		
2	71368.0963	176968.3491		
3	71127.4345	176950.6149		
4	71028.9085	176905.4732		
5	70969.1469	176571.7470		
6	71143.5863	176510.4833		

Figure P7–5.

P7-8   Using the formulas in Figure 7-17, complete the table of Figure P7-8.

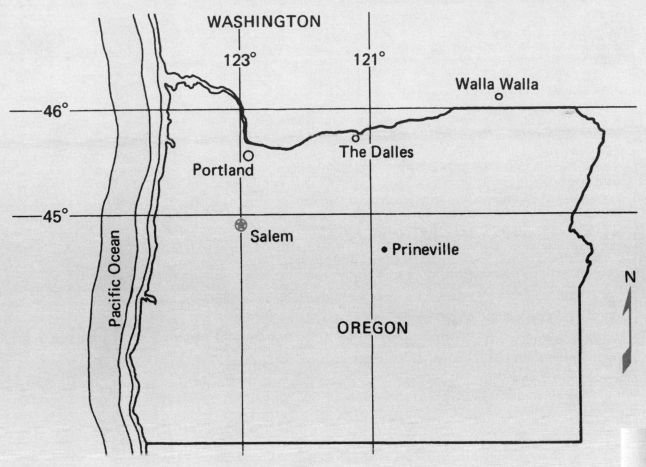

Figure P7-6.

Figure P7-7.

Point	Azimuth	Bearing
A		N15°45'30"E
B		S20°W
C	270°	
D	135°30'	
E		N35°14'45"W

Figure P7-8.

Magnetic Azimuth	Magnetic Declination	True Azimuth
20°30'E	2°15'E	
170°E	10°20'W	
	15°20'E	11°15'
	20°20'15"W	210°30'
10°E	15°W	

Legal Descriptions and Plot Plans

Learning Objectives

After completing this chapter, you will be able to:

- Define terms related to legal descriptions and plot plans.
- Provide the legal description and number of acres in given rectangular system areas.
- Sketch plot plans that display specific characteristics.
- Draw complete plot plans from given engineering sketches.
- Draw plot plans from written information.
- Convert plat map drawings to formal drawings.
- Review a given legal description and edit it as necessary for accuracy and closure verification.
- Write a legal description from a given plot plan.

Key Terms

Metes and bounds
Lot and block
Rectangular system
Great survey
Base line
Principal meridian
Township
Section
Plot plan
Site plan
Plat
Easement
Manhole
Vicinity map
Plan
Profile
Legend
Utilities
Delta angle

This chapter shows the three typical ways of identifying property. Each individual property must be completely described in a survey. A survey becomes the legal description that keeps your land or property separate from your neighbor's property.

The topics covered include:

- Metes and bounds
- Lot and block
- Public land surveys
- Basic reference lines
- Rectangular system
- Plot plans
- Methods of sewage disposal

Metes and Bounds

Metes and bounds is a method of describing and locating property by measurements from a known starting point called a *monument*. *Metes* can be defined as being measurements of property lines expressed in units of feet, yards, rods, or meters. *Bounds* are boundaries, such as streams, streets, roads, or adjoining properties. The monument, or *point of beginning (POB)* of the system, is a fixed point such as a section corner, a rock, a tree, or an intersection of streets.

The metes and bounds system is often used for describing irregularly shaped plats and, while used in all areas of the country, it is the primary method of describing plats in states east of the Mississippi River. A typical plat using metes and bounds is shown in Figure 8–1.

The following is a sample legal description using metes and bounds:

> BEGINNING at the intersection of the centerline of W. Powell Boulevard, formerly Powell Valley Road and the centerline of S.W. Cathey Road; thence running East along the centerline of W. Powell Boulevard 184 feet; thence South on a line parallel with S.W. Cathey Road, 200 feet; thence West on a line parallel with W. Powell Boulevard, 184 feet; thence North along the centerline of S.W. Cathey Road to the place of beginning; EXCEPTING therefrom, however, the rights of the public in and to that portion of the herein described property lying within the limits of W. Powell Boulevard and S.W. Cathey Road.

Lot and Block

Lot and block is a method that describes land by referring to a recorded plat, the lot number, the county, and the state. A legal lot and block must be filed with the county clerk or recorder as part of a plat, which is a map or plan of a subdivision. See Figure 8–2.

The lot and block system is commonly used to describe small units of property in a subdivision. The exact boundaries of the subdivision can be described by the rectangular system, which is discussed next, or the metes and bounds system. For example, the property lines of the lots in the small subdivision shown in Figure 8–1 are established using metes and bounds; but the lots can additionally be

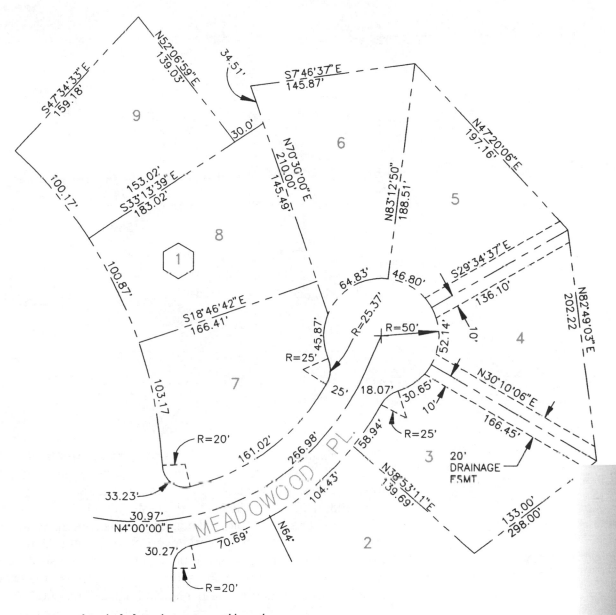

Figure 8–1.   A typical plat using metes and bounds.

identified with a lot and block system. Just remember that a necessary part of a plot plan, or plat, is the inclusion of an accurate legal description.

The following is an example of a lot and block description:

Lot 7, Block 135, Oregon City Subdivision, City of Oregon City, Clackamas County, State of Oregon.

Rectangular System

Public Land Surveys

In some of the southern, midwestern, and far western states, referred to as *public land states*, or *public land survey*, the U.S. Bureau of Land Management devised a rectangular system for describing land.

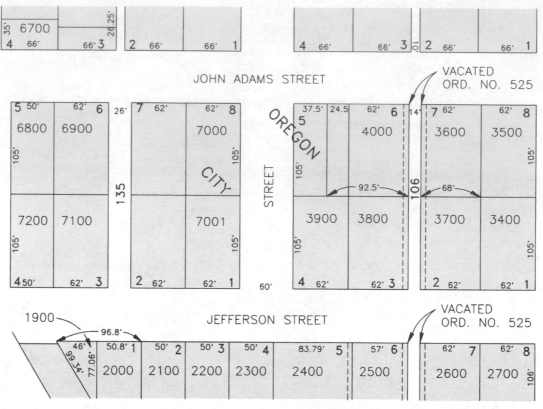

Figure 8–2. **Lot and block.**

The states involved in the public land surveys are Alabama, Alaska, Arizona, Arkansas, California, Colorado, Florida, Idaho, Illinois, Indiana, Iowa, Kansas, Louisiana, Michigan, Minnesota, Mississippi, Missouri, Montana, Nebraska, Nevada, New Mexico, North Dakota, Ohio, Oklahoma, Oregon, South Dakota, Utah, Washington, Wisconsin, and Wyoming. In 1850, the federal government bought 75 million acres from Texas, and these, too, are public lands. In the list of public land states, notice that some southern, and even one southeastern state (Florida), are included in the public land states. The public land states begin with Ohio. Its west boundary is the first principal meridian.

Basic Reference Lines

Each large portion of the public domain is a single great survey, and it takes on as much as it can use of one parallel of latitude and one meridian of longitude. The initial point of each great survey is where these two basic reference lines cross. This must be determined astronomically. The parallel is called the base line, and the meridian is called the principal meridian. There are 31 pairs or sets of these standard lines in the United States proper and 5 in Alaska.

Initially, each principal meridian was numbered. However, the numbering stopped with the sixth principal meridian, which passes Nebraska, Kansas, and Oklahoma. The rest of the 31 sets of standard lines took on local names. For example, in Montana, the public land surveys use the *Montana meridian* for the principal meridian. The principal meridians and base lines of the great land survey, not including Alaska, are shown in Figure 8–3.

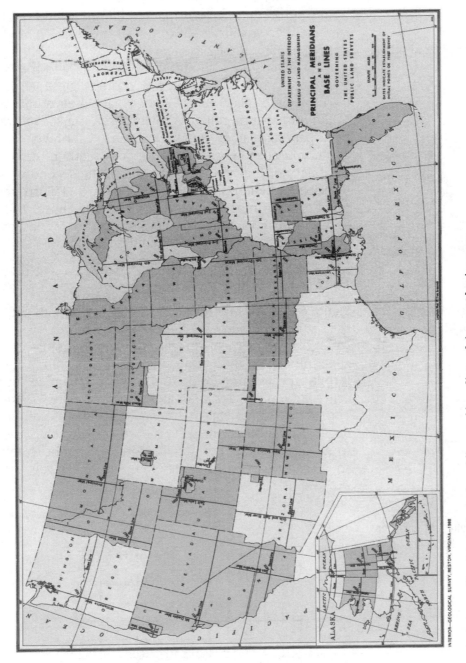

INTERIOR—GEOLOGICAL SURVEY, RESTON, VIRGINIA—1988

Figure 8–3.   The states principal meridians and base lines of the great land survey. (Courtesy U.S. Bureau of Land Management, www.blm.gov)

Rectangular-Township/Section System

Using base lines and meridians, an arrangement of rows of blocks, called **townships**, is formed. Each township is 6 miles square. Townships are numbered by rows or tiers that run east–west. These tiers are counted north and south from the base line. But instead of saying "tier one, "tier two, tier three, . . . ," the term "township" is used. For example, a township in the third tier north of the base line is named "Township No. 3 North," abbreviated "T.3N." Similarly, the third tier south of the base line is named "T.3S."

Townships are also numbered according to the vertical, north–south, column in which they are located. These vertical columns of townships are called *ranges*. Ranges take their numbers east or west of the principal meridian. A township in the second range east of a principal meridian is "Range No. 2 East," abbreviated "R.2E."

If you put townships and ranges together, the township in the third tier north of the base line and in the second range east of the principal meridian is "T.3N.,R.2E." Figure 8–4 illustrates the arrangement of townships about the two reference lines. The tiers number as far north and south and ranges number as far east and west as the great public land survey in which they are located.

The Division of Townships

Figure 8–5 shows the division of a township into sections and how the sections are numbered in each township.

A township is a square with sides approximately 6 miles long. At each mile along the 6-mile sides of a township, a line cuts across, forming a checkerboard of 36 squares, each a mile square. Each parcel of land, being approximately 1 mile square, contains 640 acres. These squares are called **sections**. Sections are numbered 1 to 36, beginning at the northeast corner of the township and going across from right to left, then left to right, and right to left, until all 36 squares or sections are numbered. Sections always start numbering

Figure 8–4. **Arrangement of townships about the base line and principal meridian.**

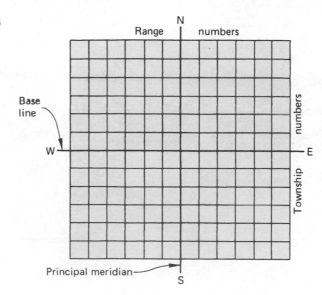

with 1 in the upper-right corner, and 36 is always in the lower-right corner. There are 43,560 square feet in an acre.

The Subdivision of Sections

Figure 8–6 illustrates some typical *subdivisions* of a section. The smallest subdivision shown in Figure 8–6 is 10 acres. However, even smaller subdivisions can be made, such as a residential subdivision of lots less than an acre in size.

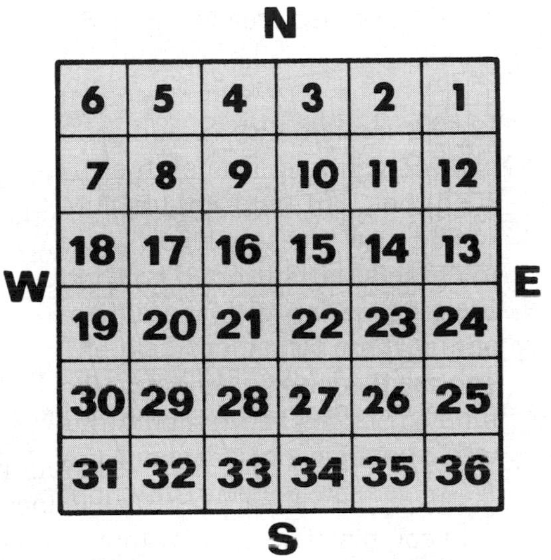

Figure 8–5. **Correct method of numbering sections within a township.**

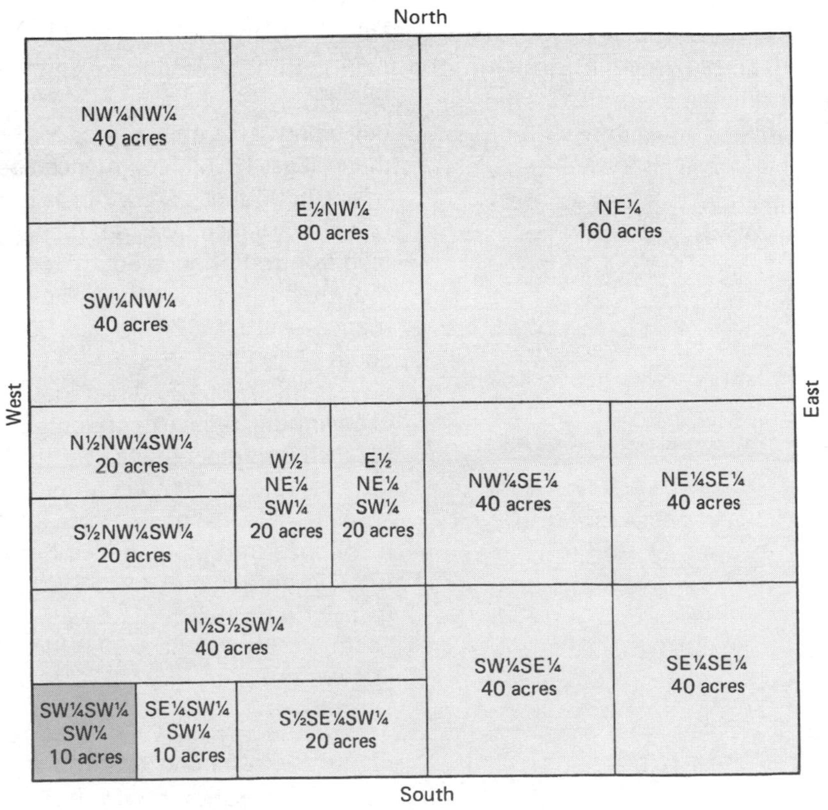

Figure 8–6. **Some typical subdivisions of a section.**

Each section, as shown in Figure 8–6, can be subdivided into *quarter sections*. These are sometimes called *corners*; for example, the "northwest corner of Section 16" is abbreviated "NW 1/4 of Sec.16."

A quarter section can be further divided into *quarter-quarters* (e.g., "NW 1/4, NW 1/4 of Sec. 36"). Further subdivisions of a quarter-quarter are shown in Figure 8–6.

In a written description of a portion of land, the smallest portion is written first, followed by the next larger portion, and so on. In Figure 8–6, the smallest portions are two 10-acre subdivisions. Notice that the description begins with the smallest division and progresses to the largest; for example, "SW 1/4, SW 1/4, SW 1/4" is represented in the shaded area in Figure 8–6.

The Complete Description

The description of a small subdivision must include its relationship with the township and relate to the reference lines of the great survey. Always remember that a complete description begins with the smallest division and progresses to the largest. An example of a legal description reads like this:

The SW 1/4, SE 1/4 of Section 9 in Township 3 South, Range 2 East of the Willamette meridian, all being in Clackamas County, Oregon.

The following legal description demonstrates that a complete description of real property can include all three types of descriptions in combination. This example uses the rectangular system to identify the point of beginning, metes and bounds to describe the boundary lines, and a lot and block description as an alternate description:

Part of the Stephen Walker D.L.C. No. 52 in Sec.13 T. 2 S. R. 1E., of the W.M., in the County of Clackamas and State of Oregon, described as follows:

Beginning at the one-quarter corner on the North line of said Section 13; thence East 111.65 feet; thence South 659.17 feet; thence South 25°35′ East 195.00 feet to a 5/8-inch iron rod; thence South 56° West 110.0 feet to a 5/8-inch iron rod; thence South 34° East 120.79 feet to a 5/8-inch iron rod; thence South 19°30′ East 50.42 feet to a 5/8-inch iron rod; thence South 40°32′ East 169.38 feet to a 5/8-inch iron rod; thence South 49°29′ West 100.0 feet to a 5/8-inch iron rod; thence South 65°00′50″ West 51.89 feet to a 5/8-inch iron rod; thence South 52°21′30″ West 125.0 feet to a 1/2-inch iron pipe, being the true point of beginning; thence continuing South 52°21′30″ West 124.91 feet to a 1/2-inch iron pipe; thence North 21°30′1.2″ West 94.480575′ to a half inch iron pipe on the arc of a circle with a radius of 50.0 feet, the center point of which bears North 22°01′30″ West 50.0 feet from said last-mentioned iron pipe; thence Northeasterly along the arc of said circle, through an angle of 69°53′29″, 60.99 feet to a 1/2-inch iron pipe; thence North 88°05′01″ East 51.00 feet to a 1/2-inch iron pipe; thence South 39°55′35″ East 80.0 feet to the true point of beginning. ALSO known as *Lot 6, Block 3, CHATEAU RIVIERE*, in Clackamas County, Oregon.

Figure 8–7 displays a small subdivision drawn with a CADD system. Lot lines are shown with lengths and bearings. The survey can be

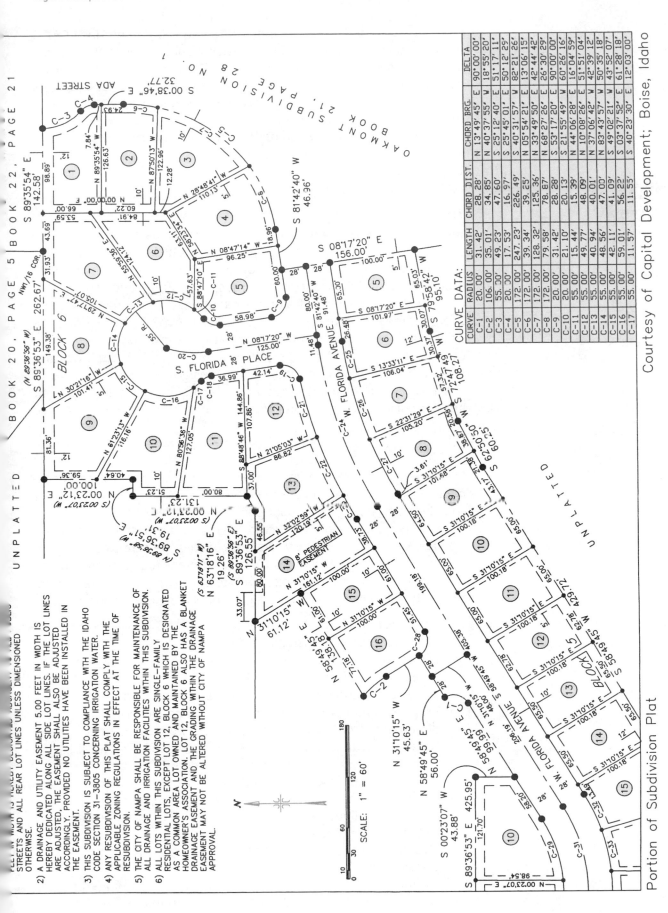

CURVE DATA:

CURVE	RADIUS	LENGTH	CHORD DIST.	CHORD BRG.	DELTA
C-1	20.00'	31.42'	28.28'	N 13°49'45" E	90°00'00"
C-2	106.00'	35.01'	34.85'	N 40°37'55" W	18°55'20"
C-3	55.00'	49.23'	47.60'	S 25°12'40" E	51°17'11"
C-4	20.00'	17.53'	16.97'	S 25°45'01" E	50°12'29"
C-5	172.00'	247.23'	226.49'	S 40°31'57" W	82°21'26"
C-6	172.00'	39.34'	39.25'	N 05°54'21" E	13°06'15"
C-7	172.00'	128.32'	125.36'	N 33°49'50" E	42°44'42"
C-8	172.00'	79.58'	78.87'	N 68°27'26" E	26°30'29"
C-9	20.00'	31.42'	28.28'	S 53°17'20" E	90°00'00"
C-10	20.00'	21.10'	20.13'	N 21°55'49" W	60°26'16"
C-11	55.00'	49.77'	48.09'	N 44°06'28" E	51°51'04"
C-12	55.00'	40.94'	40.01'	N 10°08'26" E	42°39'12"
C-13	55.00'	48.56'	47.03'	N 37°06'42" W	50°35'18"
C-14	55.00'	42.11'	41.09'	N 83°43'57" W	43°52'07"
C-15	55.00'	59.01'	56.22'	N 49°02'21" W	61°28'18"
C-16	55.00'	11.57'	11.55'	S 03°37'52" E	12°03'00"
C-17				S 40°23'30" E	

Courtesy of Capital Development; Boise, Idaho

Portion of Subdivision Plat

Figure 8–7. **Part of subdivision drawn using a CADD system.**
(Courtesy of Capital Development, Boise, Idaho)

combined with aerial photography or 3D modeling to produce CADD drawings that have added realism. When a subdivision is drawn with a CADD system, true north for the preliminary drawing is shown pointing to the top of the screen. This allows the greatest degree of accuracy when entering lengths and bearings. It also allows map information from other sources—such as aerial photography, which also uses north pointing to the top of the screen—to be imported exactly.

Plot Plans

A plot plan, also known as a site plan, or plat, is a map of a piece of land. A plot plan becomes a legal document containing an accurate drawing and a legal description of the land. It is not always necessary to show relief as contour lines, and often, only arrows are used to show direction of slope. In some specific situations, however, contour lines are established and drawn. Contour lines are used when the land has unusual contours, is especially steep, or has out-of-the-ordinary drainage patterns or when contour lines are required by local code officials or for design purposes. Be sure to check with your local jurisdiction for specific requirements. Contour lines are discussed in Chapter 9.

Plot Plan Requirements

Many items are necessary to make a plot plan a legal, working document. As a drafter, you can use the information as a checklist for proper completion of a plot plan. A plot plan is often referred to as a *site plan* when it shows a proposed structure and other proposed construction features, such as driveways, walks, and utilities. Be sure to check your local city or county regulations for any different requirements. Many building departments require plot plans to be drawn on an 8 1/2 × 14-in. sheet. The following is a list of possible plot plan requirements:

- Legal description of the property.
- Property lines, dimensions, and bearings.
- Direction of north.
- All existing and proposed roads.
- Driveways, patio slabs, parking areas, and walkways.
- Proposed and existing structures, including location dimensions from property lines and between structures.
- Location of water well and/or water service line.
- Location of water wells on adjacent properties.
- Location of proposed gas and power lines.
- Location of septic tank, drainfield, drainfield replacement area, and/or sewer lines. Sewage disposal methods are discussed next.
- Dimensions and spacing of soil absorption field, or leach lines. This item is part of the septic sewage disposal system, discussed next.
- Location of soil test holes. Soil test holes can be required for a variety of reasons, including geological conditions, soil compaction, and soil absorption.

- Proposed location of rain drains, footing drains, and method of storm water disposal.
- Ground elevation at lot corners and street elevation at driveway centerline.
- Slope of ground.
- Proposed elevations of main floor, garage floor, and basement or crawl space.
- Number of bedrooms proposed.
- Proposed setback from all property lines.
- Utility and drainage easements.

An **easement** is a legal right-of-way given by a property owner to allow others access to or over the property. An easement can be for access to and from another property, for utilities, or for other uses. When used for utilities, an easement is called a *utility easement*, which is generally a portion of land, shared by a property owner and a public agency, that contains a public utility, such as electrical power, telephone, or a sewer line. Detailed specifications about the easement are included in the property legal description.

Figure 8–8 shows a typical plot plan. Notice that not all of the information previously described is identified. Be sure to confirm

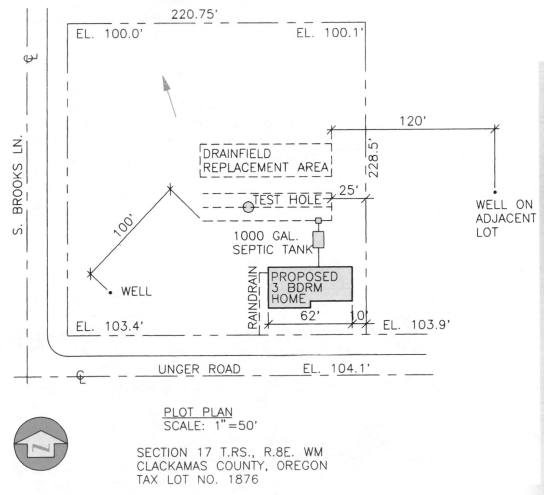

Figure 8–8.   **A typical plot (site) plan.**

local requirements so you use all the information needed to describe your plot completely. The plot plan should also include:

- Natural drainage channels
- Total acreage
- Drawing scale: for example, 1 in. = 50 ft (1″ = 50′)

Sewage Disposal Methods

Septic Tank Sewage Disposal

A conventional *septic tank* is usually a concrete or steel box where the wastewater from a house collects. Wastewater from toilets, bathtubs, showers, laundry, and kitchen is fed into this tank. It is designed to hold the water for two or three days, which is long enough for most heavy suspended material to sink to the bottom of the tank to form a sludge. Lighter, floating materials float to the top of the tank, where they remain trapped between the inlet and outlet pipes. After a couple days, the wastewater portion leaves the tank as effluent. *Effluent* is discharged to the underground piping network, called a *soil absorption field*, *drainfield*, or *leach lines*.

The soil absorption field is an underground piping network buried in trenches usually less than 2 ft below the surface of the ground. This field distributes the effluent over a large soil area, allowing it to percolate through the soil. The soil usually acts as an excellent filter and disinfectant by removing most of the pollutants and disease-causing viruses and bacteria found in the effluent. Figure 8–9 shows a section through a septic tank and a partial absorption field.

Figure 8–10 shows how the septic system is drawn on a plot plan. Keep in mind that specific lengths of drainfield and minimum specifications are determined by local requirements, but drainfield lines must run parallel to the contour lines because each drain line must be level.

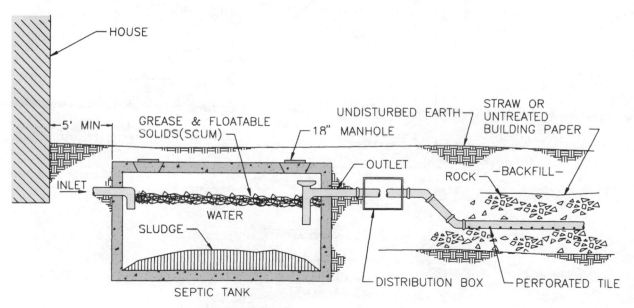

Figure 8–9.   **Cross section through a typical septic tank.**

Figure 8–10. **Sample plot plan showing a house and septic system.**

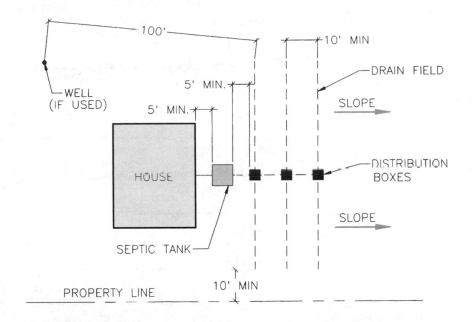

Cesspool Sewage Disposal

Cesspools have the same purpose as septic systems, which is to break down and distribute waste materials to an area of earth. The soil then acts as a filter to disperse pollutants. Cesspools are used in locations where the soil bearing strata is very porous—an area of gravel or similar material of considerable depth. The cesspool structure is a large concrete cylinder. This cylinder can be of precast concrete, concrete block, or other materials. The cesspool has slots at the bottom for the effluent to escape into a layer of gravel around the tank and then into the porous soil. Your local soils department can advise you as to the type of system that should be used. A cross section of a typical cesspool is shown in Figure 8–11.

Figure 8–12 shows how a cesspool drawing looks on a plot plan.

Public Sewers

In locations where public sewers are available, the plot plan should show a sewer line from the house to the public sewer, usually located in the street or in an easement provided somewhere near the property. Construction of this method of sewage disposal is often easier than the construction of a cesspool or septic system. See Figure 8–13 for a cross section of a public sewer hookup.

Figure 8–14 shows an example of how a conventional sewer hookup is drawn on a plot plan.

The sewer line can be drawn using a hidden line and labeled SEWER LINE as shown, or the representation can be a line broken along its length with the abbreviation "S" for sewer or "SAN" for sanitary sewer inserted in the space provided by the break. Storm sewers are a system of pipes that carry only water runoff from building and land surfaces. The storm sewer is separate from the sanitary sewer. Storm sewers are generally shown in or at the edge of the street adjacent to the property, and they can have drainage lines connected to

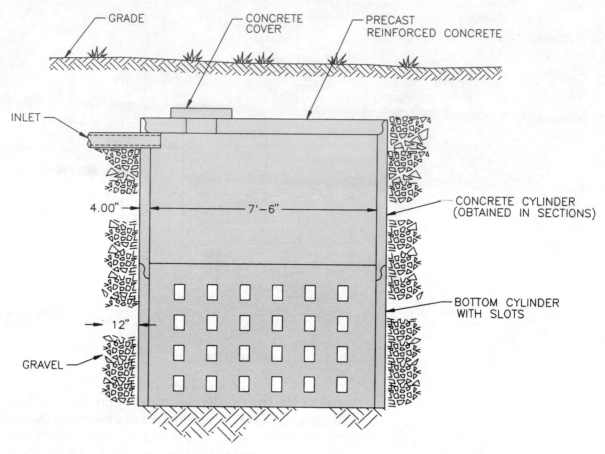

Figure 8–11. Cross section of a typical cesspool.

Figure 8–12. Sample plot plan showing a house and cesspool.

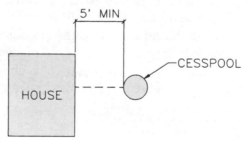

the building or site for rain water distribution. Specific requirements depend on local regulations and specific site conditions. The storm sewer can be drawn as a line broken along its length with the word "STORM" inserted in the space provided by the break. Confirm specific drawing requirements with your instructor or company standards. The drawing in Figure 8–14 also shows the centerline of the street, the street name, and the main sewer line, which is generally found in the street or in an easement. The small circles placed periodically along the main sewer and labeled with the abbreviation MH indicate manholes. A manhole is an underground structure used for maintenance access or for making connections to underground utilities and other services, including sewers, telephone, electricity, storm drains, and gas. The manhole is protected by a manhole cover, which is a metal or concrete cover designed to prevent accidental or unauthorized access to the manhole. The manhole cover is the round steel

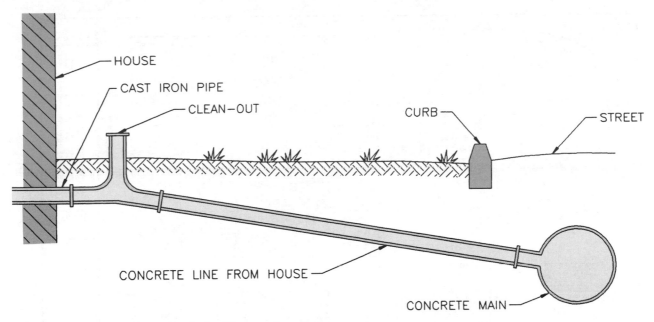

Figure 8–13.   Cross section of a typical public sewer installation.

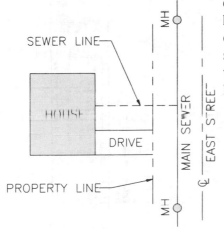

Figure 8–14.   Sample plot plan showing a house and public sewer layout.

or cast iron plate that you typically see in streets and roads. A manhole is sometimes referred to as a maintenance hole. A sewer hookup could be easily incorporated in a CADD drawing such as the one shown in Figure 8–7. Figure 8–15 shows a portion of a neighborhood with a public sewer layout. The drawing in Figure 8–15 has the following features:

■ *Vicinity map*   The **vicinity map**, in the upper-right corner of Figure 8–15, is a map showing the project site in relation to the surrounding area. This map provides information for access to the site.

■ *Site area*—The drawing in the lower-right corner of Figure 8–15 shows a construction site in relationship to the immediately surrounding area. Notice the thicker building outline on the right side of this drawing. This building is detailed in the plan view, discussed next.

■ *Plan*—The **plan** drawing, in the lower-left portion of Figure 8–15, shows the detailed construction information in plan view. The *plan view* is created looking down from above and can display buildings, roads, curbs, walks, and subsurface construction features, such as sewers and utilities. Look at the building outline on the left side of the plan and find this same building that was identified in the site area.

■ *Profile*—The **profile** is an outline of a cross section of the earth. The profile in Figure 8–15 is found in the upper-left corner of the drawing and provides a cross section through the site showing the existing ground and sewer construction. Profiles are explained in detail in Chapter 11.

■ *Legend*—Near the lower-right of center in Figure 8–15. The **legend** shows the variety of symbols and their names, as used on this drawing. Below the legend are general notes related to the entire drawing.

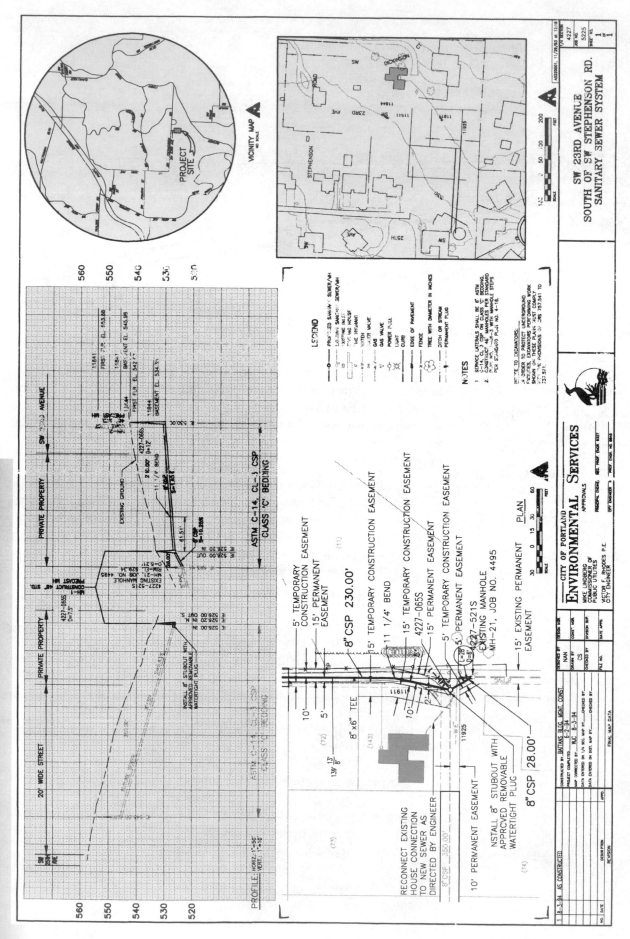

Figure 8-15. Part of residential sanitary sewer system drawing. (Courtesy of City of Portland, Oregon, www.portlandonline.com.)

Utilities on the Plot Plan

In addition to sewage disposal, other utilities are normally drawn on the plot plan, from the main lines existing in a street or utility easement. These utilities can include electrical, gas, phone, and cable. Some utilities are overhead, such as electrical. However, all utilities could be brought to the property from underground. Before you complete the plot plan, determine utility locations and where the utilities will enter the property so they can be identified on the proposed plan.

Utilities can be drawn a variety of ways, such as by using hidden lines, thin lines, or thick lines. The lines can be labeled with notes designating their use, or lines can be broken along their length with an abbreviation designating the utility type inserted in the space provided by the break. Look at Figure 8–15 to find the following features in the plan view:

- *80″ CSP 230.00′*—This is a thick line labeled to specify an 8-in. concrete sewer pipe that is 230 ft long.
- *Medium thick hidden (dashed) line connecting the building to the sewer manhole*—See the note RECONNECT EXISTING HOUSE CONNECTION TO NEW SEWER AS DIRECTED BY ENGINEER.

Site Design Considerations

When you design a plot plan for a proposed home, addition, or commercial building, many issues need to be considered to make sure the design blends well within the existing environment, allows for good access, protects adjacent properties, and maintains the integrity of the surrounding area. Several issues that can affect the quality of the construction project and adjacent properties should be considered during site design. Some of these factors are outlined in the following and are presented as suggested recommendations to consider. The use of any one or more depends on the specific site:

- Provide a minimum driveway slope of 1/4″ per foot. The maximum slope depends on surface conditions and local requirements.
- Provide a minimum lawn slope of 1/4″ per foot if possible.
- Single-car driveways should be a minimum of 10′ (3 m) wide, and double-car driveways should be a minimum of 18′ (5.5 m) wide but can taper to a minimum of 10′ wide at the entrance if necessary. Any reduction of driveway width should be centered on the garage door. A turning apron is preferred, when space permits. This allows the driver to back into the parking apron and then drive forward into the street, which is safer than backing into the street.
- The minimum turning radius for a driveway should be 15′ (4.5 m). The turning radius for small cars can be less, but

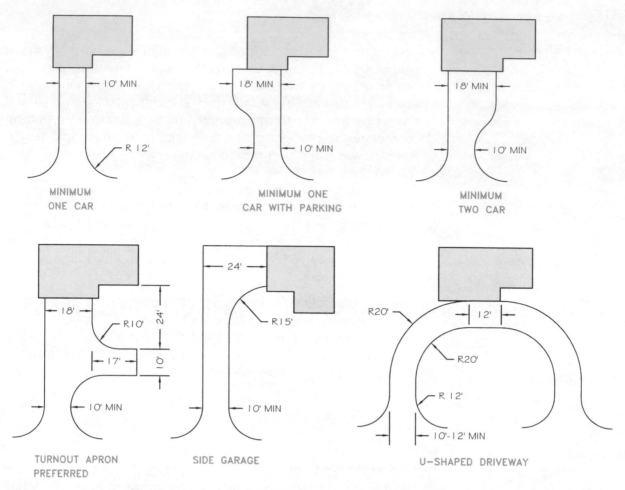

Figure 8-16. A variety of driveway layouts to use as examples. The dimensions are given as commonly recommended minimums for small to standard-sized cars. Additional room should be provided, if available.

more should be considered for trucks. A turning radius of 20′ (6 m) is preferred if space permits. Figure 8–16 shows a variety of driveway layouts as examples. The dimensions are given as commonly recommended minimums for small to standard-sized cars. Additional room should be provided, if available.

- Provide adequate room for the installation of and future access to water, sewer, and electrical utilities.
- Do not build over established easements. Easements were defined earlier in this chapter.
- Follow basic grading rules, which include not grading on adjacent property. Do not slope the site so as to cause water drainage onto adjacent property. Slope the site away from the structure. Adequate drainage of at least 10′ away from the building is recommended.
- Identify all trees that are to remain on the site after construction.
- Establish retaining walls where needed to minimize the slope, control erosion, and level portions of the site.

Rural Residential Fire Department Access and Site Planning

Special considerations need to be made when designing driveways and turnarounds in rural areas. In urban and suburban areas, fire truck access is normally designed into the subdivision plan, and each residence should be fairly easy to access for firefighting purposes. Rural locations can present special problems for firefighting because they are often larger pieces of property that frequently have long gravel driveways where access can be limited. Check the regulations for your location. The guidelines governing site design can differ from one location to the next, but the following are common standards for your consideration:

- For road clearances, a 15′ minimum width *all-weather* surface driveway must be provided, with an additional 5′ width clear of vegetation. The driveway should also be clear of vegetation to a height of 13′-6″. *All-weather* means gravel or paved surface. Figure 8–17 shows several basic driveway design options.
- The driveway should be engineered for a 12,500-lb wheel load and 50,000-lb gross vehicle load.
- A 10% average maximum road grade is preferred, but up to 15% for 200′ is acceptable.
- Provide a turnaround, at the end, if the driveway is longer than 150′.
- Provide a 20′ wide by 40′ long passage space at the midpoint of every 400′ length.
- Bridges and culverts should be designed to support a minimum of 50,000 lb.
- Provide a *firebreak* of at least 30′ around all structures. A firebreak requires ground cover no more than 24″ in height, with all dead vegetation removed. Steep terrain around the structure can require a greater firebreak.
- The property address should be posted on a fire department–approved sign where the driveway meets the main road.
- On-site water supplies, such as a swimming pool, pond, or water storage tank, should be accessible within 15′ for fire suppression. A fire sprinkler system designed and installed in the home can be substituted for a water supply.
- The use of wood roofing material or other combustible materials is restricted in *wildfire zones*. Wildfire zones are heavily wooded areas and can be confirmed at the local building official or zoning office.

Property Line Layout

The property lines of each lot and the boundaries of the plat are commonly labeled with distances and bearings. Figure 8–18 shows a small subdivision plat and the individual lots or plots found in the plat. An example of property line labeling can be seen on the west property line of Lot 2, which is 112.93′ for the length and S34′09′ 220″W for the bearing. This property line is set up to be drawn as

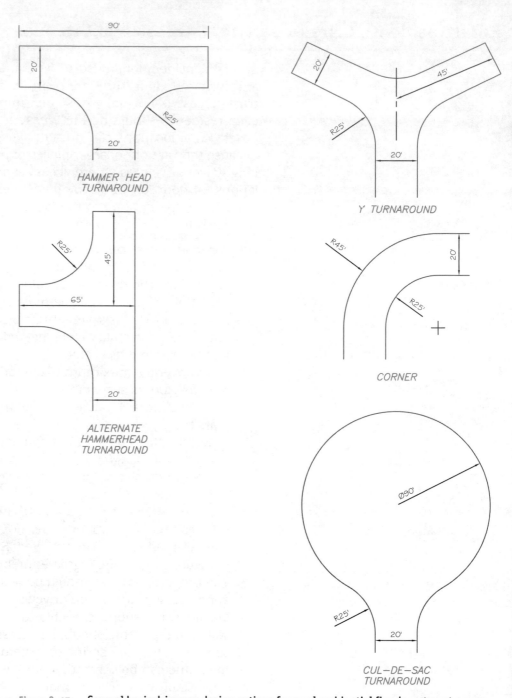

Figure 8–17. Several basic driveway design options for rural residential fire department access.

shown in Figure 8–19a. After the property lines are drawn, they are labeled with the distance and bearing, as shown in Figure 8–19b.

Many plats have property lines that are arc shaped, such as the lines around the cul-de-sac in Figure 8–18. For example, the largest curve is labeled R = 50.00′ L = 140.09′. R is the radius of the curve, and L is the length of the curve. There are three sub-lengths in this curve: L = 48.39′ is for Lot 4, L = 68.92′ is for Lot 6, and L = 22.78′ is for Lot 8. Figure 8–20a shows the setup for drawing this curve using the radius and arc lengths. Plats also typically show a **Delta angle** for curves, which is represented by the symbol Δ. The Delta angle is the included angle of the curve. The included angle is the angle formed

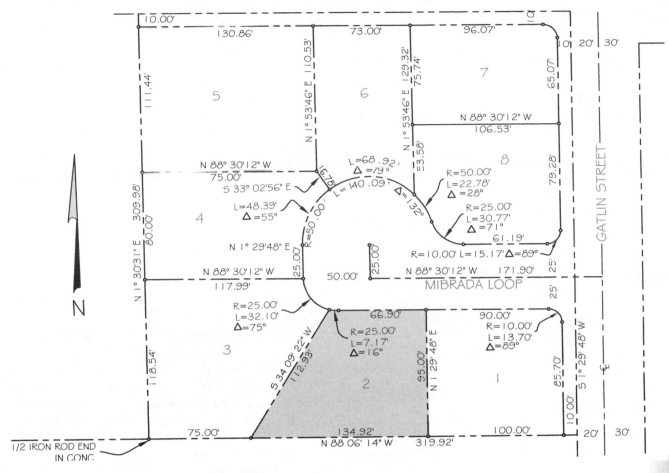

Figure 8-18. A small subdivision plat and the individual lots or plots in the plat.

Figure 8-19. Drawing and labeling a straight property line.

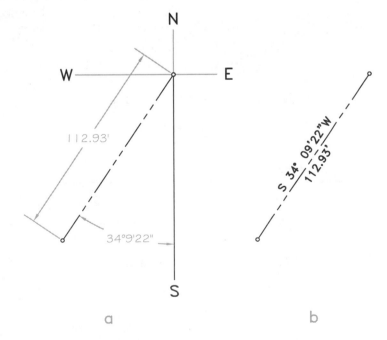

a

b

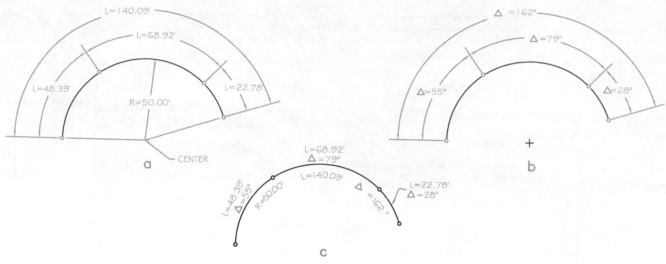

Figure 8-20. Drawing and labeling an arced property line.

between the center and the end points of the arc, as shown in Figure 8-20b. Figure 8-20c shows the final labeling of the curve.

Generally the plat or legal description provides metes and bounds coordinates for property line boundaries. For example, the south property line for Lot 2 has the coordinates given, with the bearing and distance of N 88°06'14" W and 134.92'. CADD systems that are used for either general or architectural applications have a surveyor's units setting. When the CADD system is set to draw lines based on surveyor's units, the south property line of Lot 2 is drawn with this computer prompt: @134.92' < N 88d06'14" W. Notice that the degree symbol (°) is replaced with the lowercase letter d when entering a bearing at the computer prompt. Most CADD programs have options for drawing arcs that allow you to create the curves in Figure 8-20. The commands typically allow you to draw arcs with a combination of radius, arc length, and included angle. This provides you with the flexibility needed to use the R, L, and Δ information provided on the plat or in the surveyor's field notes. Surveyor's field notes are discussed in Chapter 6.

Steps in Site Plot Layout

The recommended steps used to create a plot plan allow you to design the plot and then add structures, utilities, and dimensions in a typical sequence. Follow these steps to draw a plot plan:

Step 1. Select the sheet size. In this example, the selected sheet size is 8 1/2 × 11 in. Evaluate the plot to be drawn. Use Lot 2 of Sandy Estates, shown in Figure 8-18, as an example. Determine the scale to use by considering how the longest dimension, 134.92', fits on the sheet. Always try to leave at least a 1/2" margin around the sheet or between any border line and the drawing elements.

Figure 8–21. **Step 2: Laying out the plot plan property lines.**

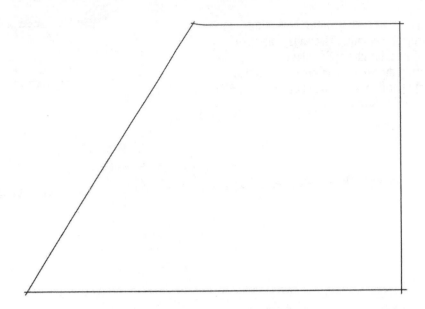

Step 2. Use Lot 2 in Figure 8–18 as an example to lay out the proposed plot plan. If a plat is not available, then the plot plan can be laid out from the legal description by establishing the boundaries using the given bearings and dimensions. Lay out the entire plot plan using construction lines. If errors are made, the construction lines are very easy to erase. Another way to lay out proposed plot plans is to use CADD layers. See Figure 8–21.

Step 3. Lay out the proposed structure using construction lines. The proposed structure in this example is 60′ long by 36′ wide. The house can be drawn on the site plan with or without showing the roof. A common practice is to draw only the outline of the floor plan or foundation. In some cases, the roof overhang is considered in the setback. In these situations, the house outline can be drawn as a hidden (dashed) line under the roof, and dimensions are given for the house and roof overhang. The front setback is 25′, and the east setback is 15′ in this example. Be sure the structure is inside or on the minimum setback requirements. *Setbacks* are imaginary boundaries beyond which the structure cannot be placed. Think of setbacks as property line offsets that are established by local regulations. Minimum setbacks can be confirmed with local zoning regulations. The minimum setbacks for the sample property are 25′ front, 10′ sides, and 35′ back from property lines to the house, as shown in Figure 8–22.

Step 4. Darken all property lines, structures, roads, driveways, walks, and utilities, as shown in Figure 8–23. Some drafters use a thick line or shading for the structure.

Step 5. Add dimensions, corner and floor level elevations, and contour lines, if required. (Contour lines are discussed in Chapter 9.) Contour lines are not required for this example. The property line dimensions are generally placed on the inside of the property lines in decimal feet, and the bearing is placed on the outside of the property

Figure 8-22. Step 3: Laying out the structures, roads, driveways, walks, and utilities. Be sure the structure is on or within the required minimum setbacks. Apply proper layers when using CADD.

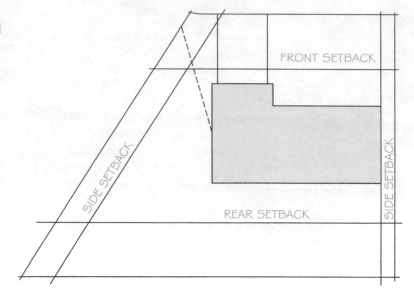

FRONT SETBACK

SIDE SETBACK

SIDE SETBACK

REAR SETBACK

Figure 8-23. Step 4: Darken property boundary lines, structures, roads, driveways, walks, and utilities. Apply proper layers when using CADD.

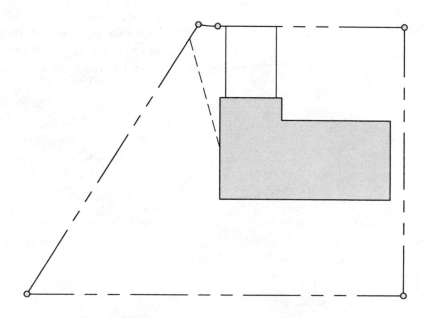

lines. The dimensions locating and giving the size of the structure are commonly provided in feet and inches or in decimal feet. All proposed and existing structures should be located with dimensions from property lines and dimensions provided between structures. Try to keep the extension and dimension lines to a minimum on the site plan. One way to do this is to dimension directly to the building outline and place size dimensions inside the structure outline. Add all labels, including the road name, property dimensions and bearings (if used), utility names, walks, and driveways, as shown in Figure 8-24.

Step 6. Complete the site plan by adding the north arrow, legal description, title, scale, client's name, and other title block

Figure 8–24. **Step 5: Add dimensions and elevations. Label all roads, driveways, walks, and utilities. Apply proper layers when using CADD.**

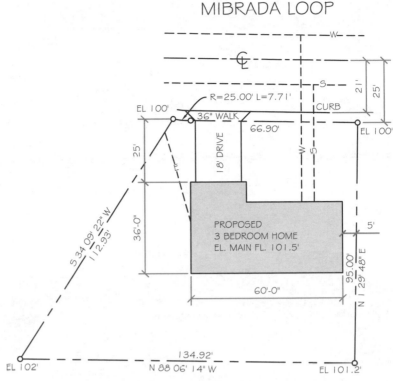

Figure 8–25. **Step 6: Complete the plot plan. Add the sheet layout, such as border and title block, drawing title, scale, north arrow, legal description, and other information, such as owner's name. Apply proper layers when using CADD.**

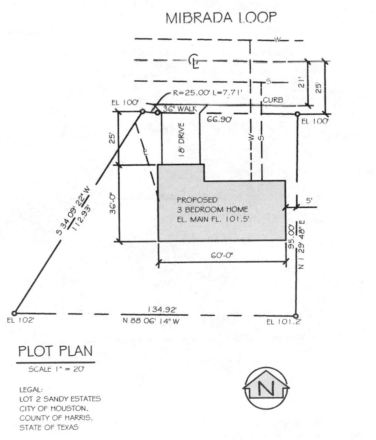

information. Figure 8–25 shows the complete plot plan. The term *site plan* is commonly substituted for the term *plot plan* when creating a plot with structures for a proposed construction site.

TEST

Part I

Define the following terms using concise statements. Use Microsoft Word to open the file "Chapter 08 test" on the Student Web site.

8-1   Metes and bounds

8-2   Lot and block

8-3   Township

8-4   Section

8-5   Plot plan

8-6   Septic tank

8-7   Cesspool

8-8   Base line

8-9   Principal meridian

8-10   Acre

Part II

Given the section shown in Figure T8–1 with areas labeled by letters, provide the legal description and the number of acres for each area.

Figure T8-1.

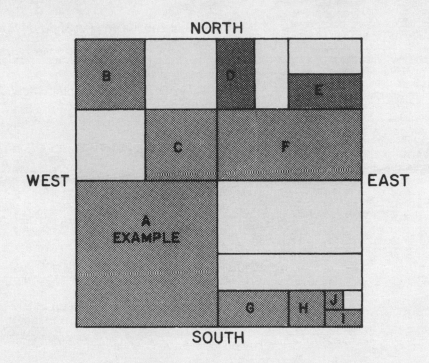

	Area	Legal Description	Acres
8-1	A	SW 1/4	160
8-2	B		
8-3	C		
8-4	D		
8-5	E		
8-6	F		
8-7	G		
8-8	H		
8-9	I		
8-10	J		

Part III

Carefully sketch or use CADD to create examples of plot plans that display each of the following characteristics. Verify the use of sketches or CADD with your instructor. You may wish to use a separate sheet of paper.

8-1 Public sewer to house on plot. Show driveway to house from street.

8–2   Cesspool to house on plot. Show driveway to house from street.

8–3   Septic system to house on plot. Show driveway to house from street.

SUBDIVISION PLAT

Study the portion of a subdivision plat in Figure 8–7 to answer the following questions. Use Microsoft Word to open the file "Ch 08 Subdivision plat" on the Student Web site and use AutoCAD to open file "plat."

1. The public utility, drainage, and irrigation easements are _____ ft wide along all rear lot lines.

2. The 8'-ft-wide area marked between Lot 13 and 14 of Block 6 is for a _____.

3. The delta of curve C-15 is _____ and borders Lot _____, Block _____.

4. The bearing of the west lot line of Lot 5, Block 5 is _____ _____.

5. The common area lot is Lot _____, Block _____, and this lot also has a _____ easement.

6. Curve C–5 borders portions of Lots _____ of Block _____.

7. The diameter of the cul-de-sac is _____.

8. The _____ is responsible for maintaining the irrigation facilities within the subdivision.

9. Lot 5, Block 5 is bordered on the east by _____.

10. Lot 1, Block 6 is accessed by _____ Street.

11. Curve C–2 borders Lot _____, Block _____. The chord distance is _____, and the chord bearing is _____.

12. There are seven legal description callouts around the perimeter of Lot _____, Block _____.

PROBLEMS

Part I: Drawing Plot Plans from Sketches

Use one of the following drafting methods and media, as specified by your instructor:

     Use pencil, with freehand lettering and proper line technique on vellum.

     Use ink and mechanical lettering equipment on vellum.

Use ink and mechanical lettering equipment on polyester film.

Use computer-aided drafting and make a print or plot of your drawing.

Use AutoCAD to open one of the drawing templates files on the Student Web site. Open the "Title block info" file to see examples of title block that can be used on your drawings.

P8–1   Given the rough sketch shown in Figure P8–1, draw a plot plan on an 8 1/2- × 14-in. sheet or your selected template. The sketch is not to scale. Scale your drawing to fit the sheet with a 1/2-in. minimum margin to the edge of the sheet. Use the following information:

1. You select the scale (e.g., 1 in. = 20 ft, 1 in. = 50 ft). The scale you select should make the plot plan as large as possible within the limits of the sheet.

Figure P8–1.

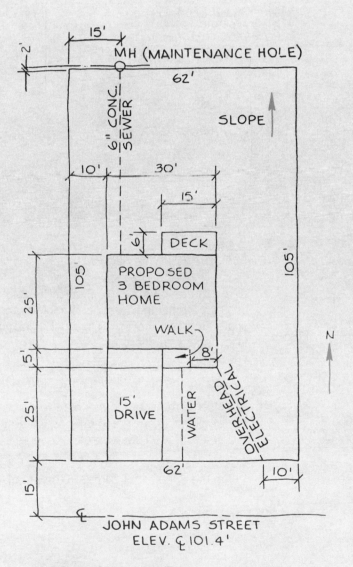

OREGON CITY ADDITION
LOT 7, BLOCK 2, OREGON CITY, OREGON
ELEV. MAIN FL. 101.8'
ELEV. BSMT. FL. 92.8'

2. Label the plot plan, scale, legal description, elevations given, and north arrow.

3. Use as many of the plot plan requirements described in this chapter as possible.

4. Property lines run north–south and east–west.

Figure P8–2.

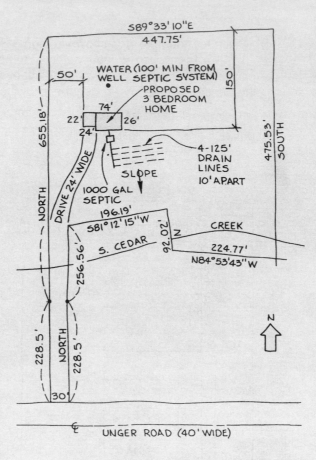

P8-2   Given the rough sketch in Figure P8–2, draw a plot plan on 18- × 24-in. or 17- × 22-in. media or your selected template. The sketch is not to scale. Scale your drawing for best utilization of the paper size. Use the following information:

1. Construct your own title block, with title, legal description, your name, the scale, and a north arrow.

2. Use as many of the plot plan requirements described in this chapter as possible, including but not limited to title, north arrow, graphic scale, legend, total acres, and legal description.

3. Create a vicinity map of your own location and design and place it in the upper-right corner of the sheet.

Part II: Drawing Plot Plans from Written Information

Draw the following property boundaries from the given legal descriptions or property line data. Use one of the following drafting methods and media, as specified by your instructor:

Use pencil, with freehand lettering and proper line technique on vellum.

Use ink and mechanical lettering equipment on vellum.

Use ink and mechanical lettering equipment on polyester film.

Use computer-aided drafting and make a print or plot of your drawing.

Use the appropriate scale and sheet size unless otherwise specified. Give the general legal description, scale, a north symbol, and other information requested with each problem.

P8-3   All that portion of Lot 140, commencing at the southwesterly corner and thence continuing along said parallel line, North 0 Degrees 22 Minutes East, 50.00 feet; thence South 89 Degrees 38 Minutes East, 270.85 feet to a point in the center line of Hillside Drive; thence South 58 Degrees 28 Minutes West, 12.98 feet to an angle point in said center line; thence continuing along said center line, South 36 Degrees 42 Minutes West, 102.0 feet; thence leaving said center line, North 78 Degrees 34 Minutes West, 203.46 feet to the TRUE POINT OF BEGINNING.

P8-4   SITE DESCRIPTION

Starting at a point on the west side of the 35′ right of way of El Corto Street, San Marcos, California:

Station	Bearing	Distance
1 P.O.B.	S 75 00 E	310.01′
2	N 23 00 E	276.06′
3	N 27 30 W	221.63′
4	S 23 30 W	420.07′
5	N 75 00 W	143.32′
6	S 02 45 W	22.23′

Legal Description:

A portion of Lot #9, in block "L" of Charles Victor Hall Tract Unit #2, Map No. 2056 filed in the office of the County Recorder of San Diego County, State of California, on September 22, 1927.

P8-5   That portion of Lot 6, commencing at the most Northerly corner of that parcel of land delineated and designated as "1.17 Acres (Net)"; thence South 55 Degrees 17 Minutes 37 Seconds East, 203.85 feet to the Northwesterly boundary of County Road (Highland Drive) being a point on the arc of a 165.88 foot radius curve concave Northwesterly, a radial line of said curve bears South 13 Degrees 38 Minutes 13 Seconds East to said point; thence along said Northwesterly boundary as follows: Westerly along the arc of said curve through a central angle of 10 Degrees 17 Minutes 13 Seconds a distance of 29.78 feet to the beginning of a reverse 170.0 foot radius curve; Southwesterly along the arc of said curve through a central angle of 52 Degrees 40 Minutes a distance of 156.27 feet to the point of tangency in the Southeasterly line of said Lot 6; and along said Southeasterly line tangent to said curve South 33 Degrees 59 Minutes West, 37.91 feet to the most Southerly corner of said land; thence north 56 Degrees 01 Minute West, 115.00 feet to a line which bears South 33 Degrees 59 Minutes West from the True Point of Beginning; thence North 33 Degrees 59 Minutes East, 195.73 feet to the TRUE POINT OF BEGINNING.

Part III: Converting Plat Map Drawings to Formal Drawings

Draw the following formal plat drawings from the given plat maps. The plat maps are not to scale, so you will have to select a scale such as 1 in. = 10 ft or 1 in. = 50 ft. Select the paper size to fit each problem. Use one of the following drafting methods and media, as specified by your instructor:

Use pencil, with freehand lettering and proper line technique on vellum.

Use ink and mechanical lettering equipment on vellum.

Use ink and mechanical lettering equipment on polyester film.

Use computer-aided drafting and make a print or plot of your drawing.

Use the appropriate scale and sheet size, unless otherwise specified. Give the correct line representation, all curve data, general legal description, scale, a north symbol, and other information requested with each problem. Make a print for instructor evaluation. Problems P8–6 through P8–10 follow.

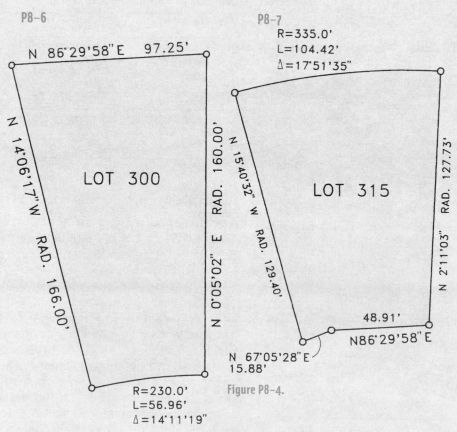

P8–6

Figure P8–3.

P8–7

Figure P8–4.

P8-8

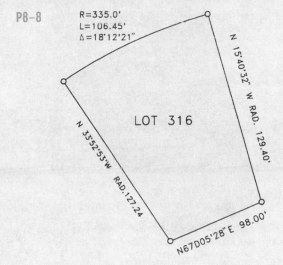

R=335.0'
L=106.45'
Δ=18°12'21"

N 15°40'32" W RAD. 129.40'

N 33°52'53" W RAD. 127.24

LOT 316

N67D05'28" E 98.00'

Figure P8-5.

P8-9

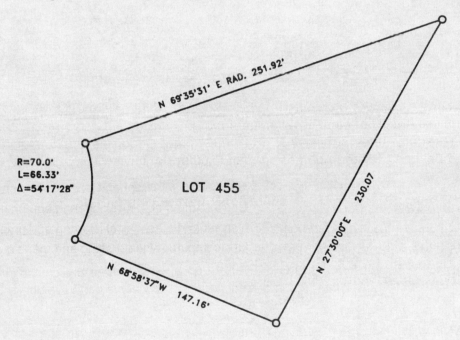

N 69°35'31" E RAD. 251.92'

R=70.0'
L=66.33'
Δ=54°17'28"

LOT 455

N 27°30'00" E 230.07

N 68°58'37" W 147.16'

Figure P8-6.

P8–10

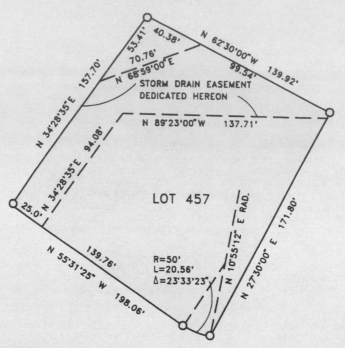

Figure P8–7.

Part IV: Advanced Drawing Plot Plans from Written Information

Draw the following property boundaries from the given legal descriptions or property line data. Use one of the following drafting methods and media, as specified by your instructor:

> Use pencil, with freehand lettering and proper line technique, on vellum.
>
> Use ink and mechanical lettering equipment on vellum.
>
> Use ink and mechanical lettering equipment on polyester film.
>
> Use computer-aided drafting and make a print or plot of your drawing.

Use the appropriate scale and sheet size unless otherwise specified. Give the general legal description, scale, a north symbol, and other information requested with each problem.

P8–11   Legal Description

Starting at a point on the north side of the 66 feet right of way of Edgewood Drive; thence N 61°56′33″ E for a length of 184.24 feet; thence N 1°16′55″ W for a length of 715.37 feet; thence S 89°44′40″ W for a length of 164.51 feet; thence South 1°16′55″ E for a length of 801.32 feet to the point of beginning.

P8–12   All that portion of Lot Four (4) in Block One Hundred Forty-nine (149) of the City of Escondido, as per Map thereof No. 336, filed in the office of the County Recorder of said San Diego County, July 10, 1886, described as follows:

Beginning at a point on the center line of Grant Avenue, North 69°43′ East, a distance 240.0 feet from the center line intersection of North Broadway and Grant Avenue, which said letter point is the Northwest corner of said Lot Four (4) of Block One Hundred Forty-nine (149); thence North 69°43′ East along the center line of said Grant Avenue, a distance of 317.0 feet to a point; thence South 00°57′ East 96.0 feet; thence South 10°40′ W. 166.0 feet; thence South 69°43′ W. 200.0 feet; thence North 20°17′ W. 233.0 feet; more or less, to the point of beginning, and containing 1.42 acres, more or less.

P8-13   LEGAL PROPERTY DESCRIPTION: PLOT AT SCALE 1″ = 100.0′
P.O.B. is the center of Bear Road, which is 66.0 feet wide.

Bearing	Distance
N 3 45 E	560.5
N 0 15 W	619.2
N 45 00 E	425.3 Top of river bank
N 45 00 E	80.6 Center of Indian River
S 78 10 E	232.0
S 59 45 E	238.5
S 50 45 E	270.7
S 23 15 E	318.8
S 71 30 E	200.4
S 7 45 W	430.5 Top of river bank
S 7 45 W	114.5 Center of Indian River
DUE WEST	451.3
S 0 10 W	397.3
N 79 00 W	465.1
N 88 47 W	365.0 To P.O.B.

Acreage computation: 1 acre = 43,560 SF

P8-14   Property Legal Description
Flemming Property
Corner of Birmingham and MacKinnon
Cardiff, California
File No. SB5501

Point No	Bearing		Distance
47	N 0° 52′ 0 E		95.0
39	N 27° 28′ 50″ E		19.875
42	N 25° 36′ 2″ E		102.60
165	ARC CENTER R = 102.60 S 38° 15′ 3″ W	DELTA = 12 39 1 102.60	L = 22.556
112	S 38° 15′ 3″ W		130.00
162	ARC CENTER R = 130.0 N 14° 48′ 54″ E	DELTA = 23 26 9 130.0	L = 53.174
116	S 63° 53′ 58″ W		25.04
117	S 73° 22′ 11″ W		23.25
118	S 77° 50′ 6″ W		23.51
119	S 68° 44′ 46″ W		23.41
120	S 1° 24′ 39″ W		52.23
124	N 89° 53′ 24″ E		99.00
129	S 2° 5′ 19″ W		64.988
45	N 89° 56′ 50″ E		50.00
47			

Plot the above description in the best scale and compute the total area in square feet and in acres.

P8-15 All that portion of Lot 12 of MARTIN'S ADDITION TO VISTA, in the County of San Diego, State of California, as shown on Map No. 1472, on file in the Office of the County Recorder of said San Diego County, described as follows:

Beginning at a point of intersection of the Southeasterly line of said Lot 12, with a line drawn parallel with and distant 140.00 feet, measured at right angles Northeasterly from the Northeasterly line of Citrus Avenue, 60 feet wide, as shown on said Map No. 1472, said point being the Southeasterly corner of the land conveyed to William Allington by deed dated February 02, 1933, and recorded in Book 188 Page 391 of Official Records of said San Diego County; thence North 30 Degrees 18 Minutes West along the Easterly line of land so conveyed, being also the aforementioned parallel line, 186.45 feet to an angle point in said Easterly line; thence continuing along said Easterly line, being parallel with and distant 140.00 feet at right angles Easterly from the Easterly line of said Citrus Avenue, North 0 Degrees 22 Minutes East 141.97 feet to the TRUE POINT OF BEGINNING; thence continuing along said parallel line, North 0 Degrees 22 Minutes East, 50.00 feet to a point distant thereon South 0 Degrees 22 Minutes West, 100.00 feet from the Southerly line of the Northerly 4.0 Acres of said Lot 12, as said Northerly 4.0 Acres were conveyed to H. B. Morris, et ux, by deed dated April 14, 1930, and recorded in Book 1784 Page 187 of Deeds; thence parallel with and 100.00 feet Southerly at right angles from said Southerly line of said Northerly 4.0 Acres as conveyed to said Morris, South 89 Degrees 38 Minutes East, 270.85 feet to a point in the center line of Hillside Drive as shown on said Map No. 1472; thence along said center line of said Hillside Drive, South 58 Degrees 28 Minutes West, 12.98 feet to an angle point in said center line; thence continuing along said center line, South 36 Degrees 42 Minutes West, 102.0 feet; thence leaving said center line, North 78 Degrees 34 Minutes West, 203.46 feet to the TRUE POINT OF BEGINNING.

P8-16   That portion of Lot 6 in Block 4 of Keeney's Marine View Gardens, in the County of San Diego, State of California, according to Map thereof No. 1774, filed in the office of the County Recorder of San Diego County, December 31, 1923, lying within the following described boundary:

Commencing at the most Northerly corner of that parcel of land delineated and designated as "1.17 Acres (Net)" on Record of Survey Map No. 4270, filed in the office of the County Recorder of San Diego County, April 18, 1957, being also the most Northerly corner of land described in deed to John R. Minton, et ux, recorded December 23, 1964, as File No. 232023; thence along the Northeasterly line of said Minton's land, South 55° 17' 379" East, (Record South 55 52'0" East) 115.01 feet to the TRUE POINT OF BEGINNING; thence continuing along said Northeasterly line South 55 17'37" East, 203.85 feet to the Northwesterly boundary of County Road Survey No. 821 (Highland Drive) as described in Parcel 2 in deed to the County of San Diego, recorded April 21, 1949, as Document No. 35757 in Book 3179, Page 154 of Official Records; being a point on the arc of a 165.88 foot radius curve concave Northwesterly, a radial line of said curve bears South 13°38'13" East to said point; thence along said Northwesterly boundary as follows: Westerly along the arc of said curve through a central angle of 10°17'13" a distance of 29.78 feet to the beginning of a reverse 170.00 foot radius curve; Southwesterly along the arc of said curve through a central angle of 52°40'00" a distance of 156.27 feet to the point of tangency in the Southeasterly line of said Lot 6; and along said Southeasterly line tangent to said curve South 33°59'00" West, 37.91 feet to the most Southerly corner of said Minton's land; thence along the Southwesterly line of said Minton's land North 56°01' 00" West, 115.00 feet to a line which bears South 33°59'00" West from the True Point of Beginning; thence North 33°59'00" East, 195.73 feet to the TRUE POINT OF BEGINNING.

ALSO that portion of Lot 6 adjoining the above described land as shown on said Record of Survey Map No. 4270 that lies Westerly of the Southeasterly prolongation of the Northeasterly line of the above described land.

Part V (Advanced): Study a Given Legal Description for Accuracy

Study the wording and verify closure of the following legal description and make corrections as needed:

P8-17   Beginning at the one-quarter corner on the North line of said Section 13; thence East 111.65 feet; thence South 659.17 feet; thence South 25° 35' East 195.00 feet to a 5/8-inch iron rod; thence South 56° West 110.00

feet to a 5/8-inch iron rod; thence South 34° East 120.79 feet to a 5/8-inch iron rod; thence South 19°30′ East 50.42 feet to a 5/8-inch iron rod; thence South 40°32′ East 169.38 feet to a 5/8-inch iron rod; thence South 49°29′ West 100.00 feet to a 5/8-inch iron rod; thence South 65°00′50″ West 51.89 feet to a 5/8-inch iron rod; thence South 52°21′30″ West 125.00 feet to a 1/2-inch iron pipe, being the true point of beginning; thence continuing South 52°21′30″ West 124.91 feet to a 1/2-inch iron pipe on the arc of a circle with a radius of 50.0 feet, the center of which bears North 22°01′30″ West 50.00 feet from said last-mentioned iron pipe; thence Northeasterly along the arc of said circle, through an angle of 69°53′29″, 60.99 feet to a 1/2-inch iron pipe; thence North 88°05′01″ East 51.00 feet to a 1/2-inch iron pipe; thence South 39°55′35″ East 80.00 feet to the true point of beginning. ALSO known as Lot 6, Block 3, Chateau Riviere, in Modesto, California.

Part VI (Advanced): Write a Complete Legal Description from a Given Lot

P8-18   Given the partial subdivision in Figure P8–8 select one or more fully displayed lots, or your instructor will assign a specific lot or lots. Write the complete legal description for the selected lot or lots. The subdivision name is Pinecrest, located in Section 33, T3N, R2W, Boise Meridian. Use the NW 1/16 corner at the top right as the point of beginning.

Part VII (Advanced): Use CADD to Draw complete Plats

Use a sheet size and format appropriate for the required drawing content. Use a title block, border, line types, and text styles as discussed in this textbook or as specified by your instructor or company. Sample templates and symbols are provided on the Student Web site. Draw the complete plats shown in Figure P8–9 and P8–10 unless otherwise specified by your instruction.

Plat Name: same as your last name, your school name, or as desired.

County or Parish: the county or parish where you live.

City: the city where you live.

State: the state where you live.

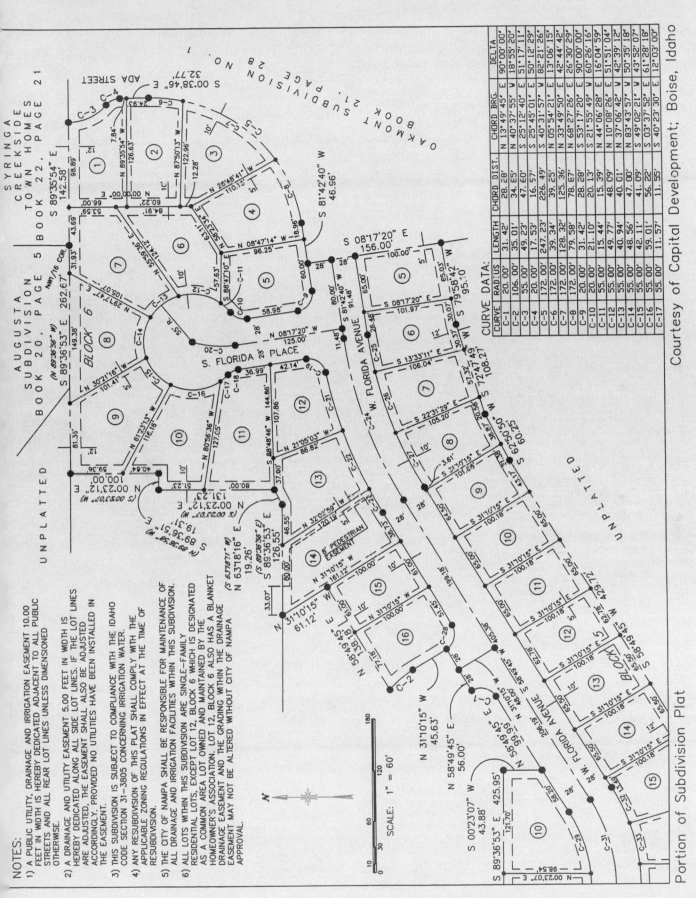

NOTES:
1) A PUBLIC UTILITY, DRAINAGE AND IRRIGATION EASEMENT 10.00 FEET IN WIDTH IS HEREBY DEDICATED ADJACENT TO ALL PUBLIC STREETS AND ALL REAR LOT LINES UNLESS DIMENSIONED OTHERWISE.

2) A DRAINAGE AND UTILITY EASEMENT 5.00 FEET IN WIDTH IS HEREBY DEDICATED ALONG ALL SIDE LOT LINES. IF THE LOT LINES ARE ADJUSTED, THE EASEMENT SHALL ALSO BE ADJUSTED ACCORDINGLY. PROVIDED NO UTILITIES HAVE BEEN INSTALLED IN THE EASEMENT.

3) THIS SUBDIVISION IS SUBJECT TO COMPLIANCE WITH THE IDAHO CODE SECTION 31-3805 CONCERNING IRRIGATION WATER.

4) ANY RESUBDIVISION OF THIS PLAT SHALL COMPLY WITH THE APPLICABLE ZONING REGULATIONS IN EFFECT AT THE TIME OF RESUBDIVISION.

5) THE CITY OF NAMPA SHALL BE RESPONSIBLE FOR MAINTENANCE OF ALL DRAINAGE AND IRRIGATION FACILITIES WITHIN THIS SUBDIVISION.

6) ALL LOTS WITHIN THIS SUBDIVISION ARE SINGLE-FAMILY RESIDENTIAL LOTS, EXCEPT LOT 12, BLOCK 6 WHICH IS DESIGNATED AS A COMMON AREA LOT OWNED AND MAINTAINED BY THE HOMEOWNER'S ASSOCIATION. LOT 12, BLOCK 6 ALSO HAS A BLANKET DRAINAGE EASEMENT AND THE GRADING WITHIN THE DRAINAGE EASEMENT MAY NOT BE ALTERED WITHOUT CITY OF NAMPA APPROVAL.

CURVE DATA:

CURVE	RADIUS	LENGTH	CHORD DIST.	CHORD BRG.	DELTA
C-1	20.00'	31.42'	28.28'	N 13°49'45" E	90°00'00"
C-2	106.00'	35.01'	34.85'	N 40°37'55" W	18°55'20"
C-3	55.00'	49.23'	47.60'	S 25°12'40" E	51°17'11"
C-4	20.00'	17.53'	16.97'	S 25°45'01" E	50°12'29"
C-5	172.00'	247.23'	226.49'	N 40°31'57" W	82°21'26"
C-6	172.00'	39.34'	39.25'	N 05°54'21" E	13°06'15"
C-7	172.00'	128.32'	125.36'	N 33°49'50" E	42°44'42"
C-8	172.00'	79.58'	78.87'	N 68°27'26" E	26°30'29"
C-9	20.00'	31.42'	28.28'	S 53°17'20" E	90°00'00"
C-10	20.00'	21.10'	20.13'	S 21°55'49" W	60°26'16"
C-11	55.00'	15.44'	15.39'	N 44°06'28" E	16°04'59"
C-12	55.00'	49.77'	48.09'	N 10°08'26" E	51°51'04"
C-13	55.00'	40.94'	40.01'	S 37°06'42" W	42°39'12"
C-14	55.00'	48.56'	47.00'	N 83°43'57" W	50°35'18"
C-15	55.00'	42.11'	41.09'	S 49°02'21" W	43°52'07"
C-16	55.00'	59.01'	56.22'	S 03°37'52" E	61°28'18"
C-17	55.00'	11.57'	11.55'	S 40°23'30" E	12°03'00"

Portion of Subdivision Plat

Courtesy of Capital Development; Boise, Idaho

Figure P8-8.

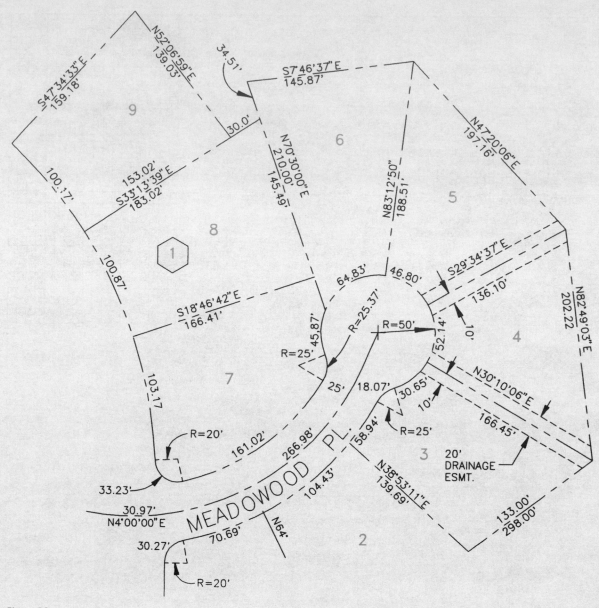

Figure P8-9.

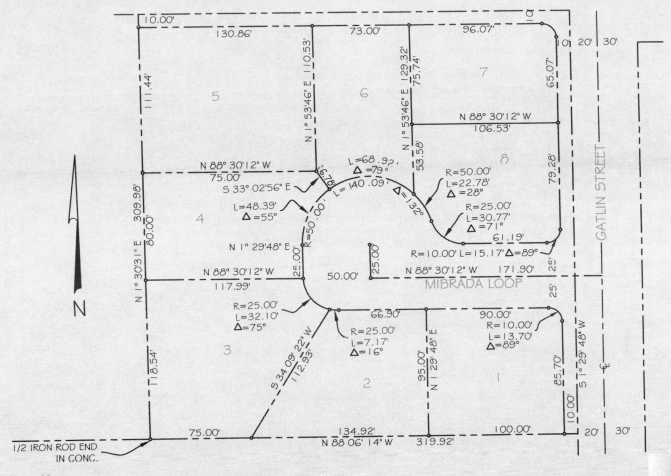

Figure P8 10.

Contour Lines

Learning Objectives

After completing this chapter, you will be able to:

- Describe topographical features using contour line characteristics.
- Identify different types of contour lines.
- Create contour map field notes and use the interpolation method.

Key Terms

Contour interval
Contour line
Concave slope
Convex slope
Saddle
Index contour
Intermediate contour
Supplementary contour
Mean sea level
Control point survey
Interpolation
Interfluve
Uniform slope theory
Grid survey
Stations
Radial survey
Base line
Transit line
Triangulated irregular network (TIN)

The topography of a region is best represented by contour lines. The word *topography* comes from the Greek words *topos*, a place, and *graphein*, to draw. The most common method of "drawing a place" for mapping purposes is to represent differences in elevation with contour lines. These lines connect points of equal elevation. They can also reveal the general lay of the land and describe certain geographical features to those trained in topographical interpretation.

This chapter provides instruction in the basic theory and concepts of contour lines and their creation. Keep in mind that civil engineering software provides the capability to use data obtained directly from surveying instruments and automatically convert that to contour maps with only minor input from the CADD user. You may wonder why it is necessary to study the techniques for creating contour maps. In order for you to be able to read, interpret, and edit contour maps, it is critically important that you have an understanding of how contour lines are created and what topographical characteristics they represent.

This chapter describes and illustrates the characteristics of contour lines and the features they represent. Detailed instructions are provided for constructing contour maps when given a minimum of elevation data.

The topics covered include:

- Contour line characteristics
- Types of contour lines
- Plotting contour lines from field notes
- Plotting contour lines with a CAD system

Contour Line Characteristics

A good example of a contour line is the shore of a lake or reservoir. The water level represents one contour line because the level of the lake is the same in all places. By late summer, many reservoirs are lowered considerably, and previous water levels are seen as lines: contour lines. The space between these lines is termed the contour interval.

If you closely observe the contour lines of a reservoir, you can see that they do not touch, and they run parallel to each other. One line can be followed all the way around the reservoir until it closes on itself. This basic characteristic is shown in Figure 9–1. Note also that the contour lines are generally parallel, and they never cross one another.

Slopes

The steepness of a slope can be determined by the spacing of the contour lines. A gentle slope is indicated by greater intervals between the contours (see Figure 9–2), whereas a steep slope is evident when there are closely spaced contours (see Figure 9–3).

Slopes are not always uniform. A concave slope flattens toward the bottom, as shown in Figure 9–4. The steepness of the upper part of the slope is represented by the close contour lines. A convex slope is just the opposite and develops a steeper gradient as it

Figure 9–1. **Contour lines formed by lapping water at different levels in a reservoir.**
(Reproduced by permission of City of Portland Oregon)

Figure 9–2. **Uniform gentle slope.**

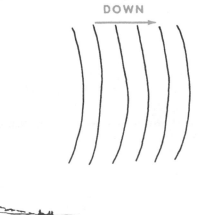

Figure 9–3.   **Uniform steep slope.**

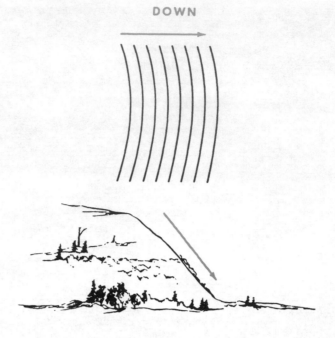

Figure 9–4.   **Concave slope.**

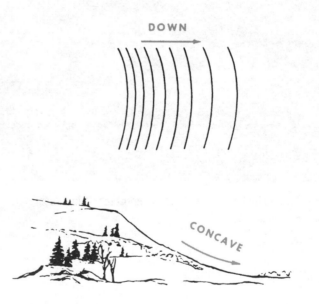

progresses. The contour lines are closer together near the bottom of the slope, as shown in Figure 9–5.

An exception exists to the rule that contours never touch. In Figure 9–6 the contours are obviously touching. Can you determine the type of landform shown in Figure 9–6? It is a cliff. Sheer cliffs and vertical rock walls of canyons are easy to spot on topographical maps because of the sudden convergence of contour lines.

Streams and Ridges

If you have taken hikes in the mountains, you know that as a level trail traverses a hill, you find yourself walking in a large "U," or horse-shoe. As you approach a stream between two hills, the trail begins to form a "V" with the bottom of the V pointing upstream, as shown in

Figure 9–5. **Convex slope.**

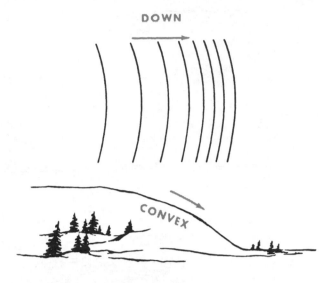

Figure 9–6. **Contours merge to form a cliff.**

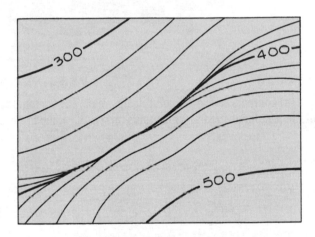

Figure 9–7a. Near stream junctions, an "M" is often formed, as shown in Figure 9–7b. The peaks of the M point upstream.

The characteristics shown in Figure 9–7 can quickly reveal slope, stream flow, and slope directions to an experienced map reader. Notice that the bottom of the V points upstream. Contour lines form a U around a hill or ridge, and the bottom of the U points downhill, as shown in Figure 9–7c.

Relief Features

The features shown in Figure 9–8 are easily spotted on contour maps. The peak of a hill or mountain in Figure 9–8a is a common feature and may be accompanied by an elevation. Here, the contour lines form circles of ever-decreasing diameter. Two high points or peaks side by side form a saddle, such as that shown in Figure 9–8b. A saddle is a low spot between two peaks.

The special contour line in Figure 9–8c is used to represent a depression in the land. The contour line has short lines pointing into the depression and is used to identify human-made features such as quarries and pits, or natural features such as the limestone sinkholes common in the southeastern United States.

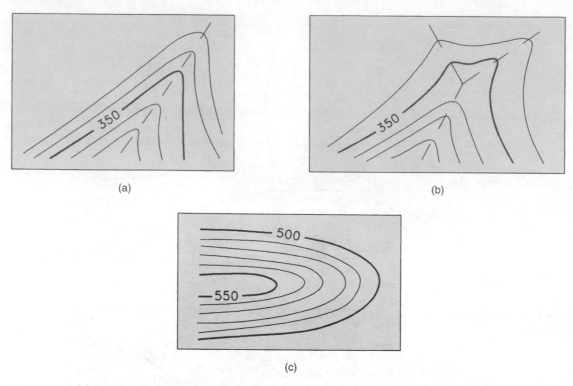

(a)

(b)

(c)

Figure 9-7. (a) Contours form a "V" pointing upstream. (b) Contours form an "M" above stream junctions. The tops of the M point upstream. (c) Contours form a "U" around ridges. The bottom of the U points downhill.

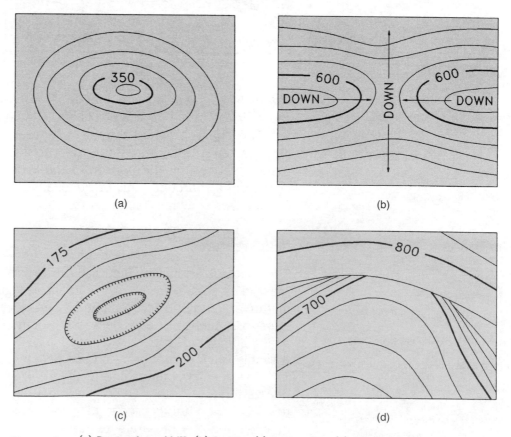

(a)

(b)

(c)

(d)

Figure 9-8. (a) Dome-shaped hill. (b) Saddle. (c) Depression. (d) Overhang.

The feature shown in Figure 9–8d is similar to a cliff, but the lower contour lines actually seem to go under the higher ones. In reality they do, and they portray an overhang, a feature found in rocky, highly sculpted, and mountainous terrain.

Types of Contour Lines

Index Contours

Every fifth line on a topographic map is an index contour. This aids the map reader in finding references and even-numbered elevations. The index contour is normally a thick line and is broken at intervals and labeled with its elevation (see Figure 9–9).

Intermediate Contours

The remaining contours in Figure 9–9 are intermediate contours and represent the intervals of elevation between the index lines. There are four of these lines between index contours. These lines are not normally labeled but can be if the scale and function of the map dictate that they be.

Supplementary Contours

A supplementary contour is not as common as the others. It is used when the normal contour interval is too large to clearly illustrate significant topographic features on land with a gentle slope. They are usually given the value of half the contour interval (see Figure 9–9).

Determining Contour Line Values

When constructing contour maps, you have to assign values to index contours. This should not be an arbitrary decision but one based on a constant reference. That reference is sea level. Imagine that the first index contour is at mean sea level and has a value of zero (0) feet elevation. Mean sea level is the average elevation between high and low tides. Next, there are four intermediate contours, and the fifth line is an index contour. Given the contour interval to be used

Figure 9–9.   Types of contour lines.

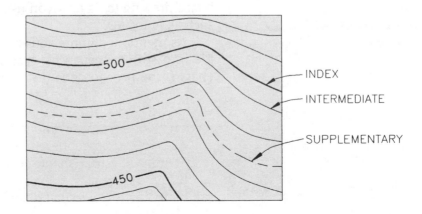

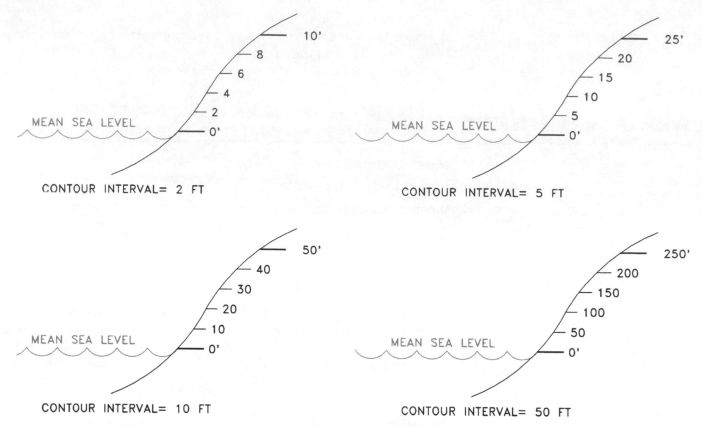

Figure 9–10. **Every fifth line is an index contour, and the contour interval determines the value of the index.**

for the map, it should be an easy process to determine the index contour values. Figure 9–10 provides examples of index contour values at a variety of contour intervals.

Constructing Contour Lines from Field Notes

The discussion of laying out a contour map in this section provides a background on constructing contour lines from field notes. It covers traditional and manual techniques used in locating survey points on a map and interpolating (estimating) the location of contours between survey points. These techniques are useful if you are using board drafting tools or if you use manual CADD tools with software such as AutoCAD.

As mentioned in previous chapters, importing a surveyor's point file into software such as AutoCAD Civil 3D or Carlson Software enables the user to generate and display contour lines on the new DTM at any contour line spacing (contour interval) and from any viewpoint. For a more detailed discussion of this process, see the section "Plotting Lines with a CAD System" later in this chapter.

As a rule, topographic maps tend to be somewhat inaccurate in representing the true shape of the land. General features and large landforms can be shown accurately, but small local relief (elevation variation) is often eliminated. This is especially true of contour maps

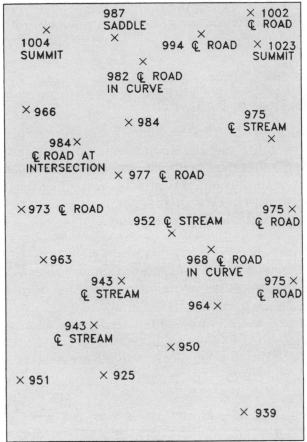

Figure 9–11. Contour map plotted using control point survey.

created from aerial photographs. Trees and vegetation may hide the true shape of the land.

A more accurate view of the land can be obtained through ground survey. This process of mapping establishes spot elevations from known points. Field notes are then plotted as contour lines on the new map. Let us take a closer look at this process.

Control Point Survey

Plots of land may often be surveyed in such a manner that contour maps can be created from the survey or field notes. The creation of these maps depends on a certain amount of guesswork, but a good knowledge of landforms, slopes, roads, and stream characteristics may ensure a greater degree of success in the mapping operation.

The control point survey is a common method of establishing elevations for use in contour mapping. Figure 9–11 is an example of the two basic steps in the mapping process. The surveyor's field notes (elevations) are plotted on the map and labeled. Next, a contour interval is chosen. This depends on the purpose of the map and the elevation differential within the plot. Contour lines are then drawn to connect equal elevation points. Notice in Figure 9–11 that prominent features on the landscape are surveyed. These are the control points. Their elevations may not be an even number. In this case, the mapper must use one of two methods to "interpolate" between two control points to find the even number. While we are on the subject, let us discuss interpolating a little further.

Interpolating Contour Lines by Estimation

Interpolation involves inserting missing values between numbers that are given. A drafter must often interpolate when plotting field notes. Inserting missing values may seem like guesswork, but it can be accomplished with a certain amount of accuracy if five basic steps are followed. Only a surveyor or mapper with experience should use this method for establishing contour lines:

Step 1: Establish elevations at stream junctions. Given the elevations at points *A* and *B* in Figure 9–12a; we must determine the elevation of the stream junction at *C*. With dividers or scale, we find that *C* is two-thirds of the distance from *A* to *B*. The elevation difference between *A* and *B* is 60 ft. Because 2/3 of 60 is 40, the elevation of point *C* is 170 ft. Using this method, determine the elevation of the stream junction at *F*.

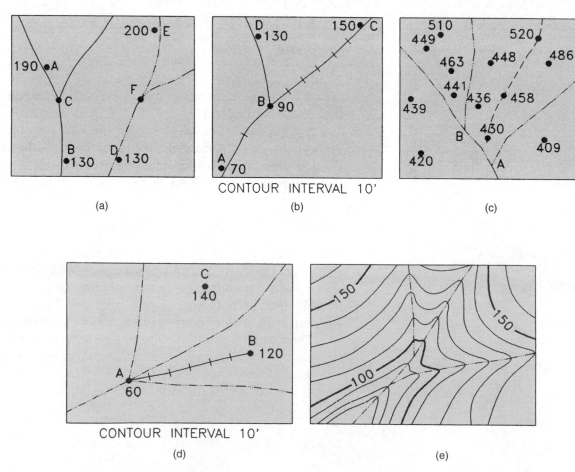

Figure 9–12. **Interpolating contour lines.**

Step 2: Locate points where contours cross streams. Given a contour interval of 10 ft in Figure 9–12b and spot elevations at points *A, B, C,* and *D,* we must locate stream crossings of all contour lines. The vertical elevation between points *A* and *B* is 20 ft. Divide the distance between *A* and *B* in half, and the 80-ft contour can be located at that point. The vertical distance between points *B* and *C* is 60 ft. The line between these two points must be divided into six equal segments. The first new point above *B* is 100 ft in elevation. Determine the stream crossings of the contour lines between points *B* and *D.*

Step 3: Locate Ridges as Light Construction Lines. Areas of higher elevation usually separate streams except in swamps and marshes. To locate these ridges, or interfluves (Figure 9–12c), sketch a light dashed line beginning at the stream junction and connecting the highest elevation points between the two streams. Begin at stream junction *A* and sketch a line through the 430-, 458-, and 520-ft elevation points. Repeat the process at stream junction B. Sketch a line from *B* through the 441-, 463-, and 510-ft elevation points.

Step 4: Determine the Points on the Ridge Lines Where Contours Cross. This step is performed in exactly the same manner as step 2. In Figure 9–12d the space between point *A* and the spot elevation of 120 ft is 60 ft. The line is divided into six equal parts, as in step 2. Locate the contour crossings between points *A* and *C.*

Step 5: Connect the Points of Equal Elevation with Contour Lines. As you do this, keep in mind the characteristics of contour lines discussed previously (see Figure 9–12e).

Be aware that interpolating distances is necessary in situations other than those discussed in the five steps. Keep in mind that by interpolating contour lines, we are using an assumption termed uniform slope theory. This is based on equal spacing of contours between known points. Some do's and don'ts are illustrated in Figure 9–13.

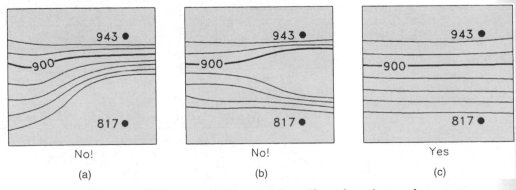

Figure 9–13. When interpolating contour lines using the uniform slope theory, always space contours evenly as in part c of the figure.

Mathematical Interpolation of Contour Lines

You can apply the theory of uniform slopes in an exact manner by using the mathematical interpolation method. There are two variations of this method. The first method is good for control point surveys and requires that you measure the distance between two points, using the scale of the map. Look at Figure 9–14 as you read. In this example, the measured distance on the map is 2.6″. This measurement is taken on the map and is shown in the plan, or map view, at the top of Figure 9–14. This is a horizontal measurement on the map and is not a measurement on a slope. The lower portion of Figure 9–14 is the section (profile), cut along *A–A* in the plan (map) view. The map distance of 2.6″ shown in the section view is the same horizontal measurement that is given in the plan view.

Next, calculate the difference in elevation between points *A* and *B* by subtracting the elevation of *A* (343.8′) from the elevation of *B*

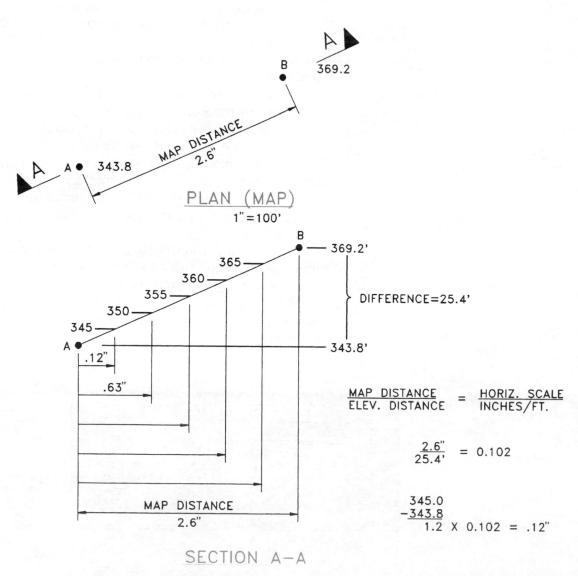

Figure 9–14. Mathematical interpolation of contour lines allows you to calculate the distance between two points.

(369.2′). This is 25.4 ft. Now divide the map distance of 2.6 in. by the difference in elevation, 25.4 ft, to get the horizontal scale distance in inches per foot of vertical rise:

$$\frac{\text{Map distance}}{\text{Elevation difference}} = \text{in./ft of vertical rise}$$

$$\frac{2.6 \text{ in.}}{25.4 \text{ ft}} = 0.102 \text{ in./ft of vertical rise}$$

If the contour interval is 5 ft, the first contour above point A is 345 ft. The difference between this contour and point A is 1.2 ft. Multiply 1.2×0.102, and the result is 0.12 in. This is the distance that you would measure from point A on the map view to find the 345-ft contour line.

Continue in this manner to locate the 350-ft contour on the map. The difference between 350 and the 343.8 value of point A is 6.2. Multiply this by 0.102, and the result is 0.63 in. This is the distance you would measure from point A on the map to find the 350-ft contour line. Find the remaining contours using this method and record your answers in the spaces provided in Figure 9–14.

The second method uses the map distance between two points to find a percent of slope. The slope can then be converted to an actual map distance from the given elevation to contour lines. Look at the section view in Figure 9–15 as you follow this explanation. The elevation difference between points A and B is 25.4 ft. Divide 25.4 ft by the map distance of 260 ft:

$$25.4 \text{ft} \div 260 \text{ ft} = 0.098$$

This gives a percent of slope of 0.098. Next, subtract the elevation of point A from the nearest contour, 345. To solve for the distance from point A to the 345-ft contour (x), divide 1.2 by 0.098:

$$0.098x = 1.2 \text{ ft}$$
$$x = 12.24 \text{ ft}$$

Figure 9–15. The map distance between two points can be used to determine the percent of slope. The slope is converted to a distance between a given elevation and a contour line.

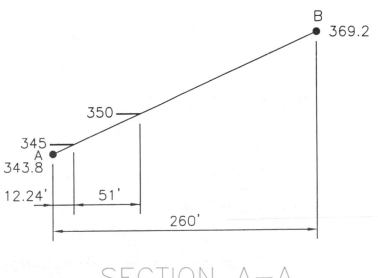

SECTION A—A

The result of 12.24 ft is the distance to measure on the map view from point *A* to find the 345-ft contour. Use this method to solve for the location of each additional contour from point *A*.

Another variation of mathematical interpolation is best used for grid surveys and is discussed in the next section of this chapter.

Grid, or Checkerboard, Surveys

Using a grid, a surveyor divides a plot of land into a checkerboard. Stakes are driven into the ground at each grid intersection. Elevations are measured at each stake and recorded in the field book. Additional stakes may be placed and recorded if significant elevation changes occur between grid intersections. The drafter plots this grid as shown in Figure 9–16a The surveyor determines the size of the squares based on the land area, topography, and elevation differential. The vertical lines of the grid in Figure 9–16 are labeled with letters and are 20 ft apart. The horizontal lines, labeled 0 + 00, 0 + 20, 0 + 40, 0 + 60, and so on, are called stations. The stations are also 20 ft apart. The first number in the station label is hundreds of

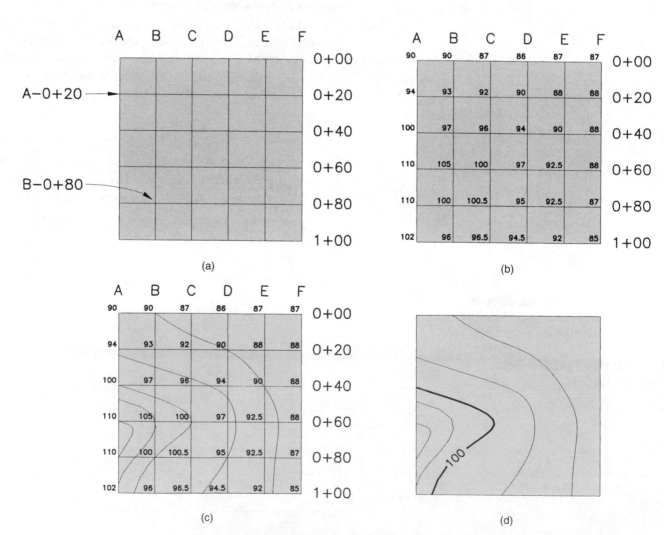

Figure 9-16. (a) For a grid survey, land is divided into a checkerboard and labeled. (b) All grid intersections are labeled. (c) Connect the elevations with curved lines or splines. (d) Completed contour map of grid survey.

Table 9–1. **Grid survey field notes for the map in Figure 9–16**

Station	Elev.	Station	Elev.	Station	Elev.
A–0 + 00	90.0	C–0 + 00	87.0	E–0 + 00	87.0
A–0 + 20	94.0	C–0 + 20	92.0	E–0 + 20	88.0
A–0 + 40	100.0	C–0 + 40	96.0	E–0 + 40	90.0
A–0 + 60	110.0	C–0 + 60	100.0	E–0 + 60	92.5
A–0 + 80	110.0	C–0 + 80	100.5	E–0 + 80	92.5
A 1 + 00	102.0	C–1 + 00	96.5	E–1 + 00	92.0
B–0 + 00	90.0	D–0 + 00	86.5	F–0 + 00	87.0
B–0 + 20	93.0	D–0 + 20	90.0	F–0 + 20	88.0
B–0 + 40	97.0	D–0 + 40	94.0	F–0 + 40	88.0
B–0 + 60	105.0	D–0 + 60	97.0	F–0 + 60	88.0
B–0 + 80	100.0	D–0 + 80	95.0	F–0 + 80	87.5
B–1 + 00	96.0	D–1 + 00	94.5	F–1 + 00	85.0

feet, and the second number to the right of the plus sign (+) is tens of feet. For example, the station number 5 + 45 is 5 hundreds and 45 tens, or 545 ft from the point of beginning.

The elevation of each grid intersection is recorded in the field notes shown in Table 9–1. Using the surveyor's field notes, we see that grid point A − 0 + 40 has an elevation of 100.0 ft. What is the elevation of point C − 0 + 60?

To begin plotting the elevations, draw a grid at the required size or use grid paper. Next, using the field notes, label all the grid intersections with elevations (see Figure 9–16b). Connect the elevations with lines. The drafter is aware of the required contour interval at this point and must decide which elevation points to connect and when to interpolate between uneven elevation points (Figure 9–16c). Figure 9–16d shows the finished contour map.

Interpolating Contours for Grid Surveys

A mathematical interpolation method can be used to plot contours in a grid survey, using the theory of uniform slopes. Look at Figure 9–17a as you follow this example.

The formula requires three values: (1) the amount over the whole foot contour of the highest point you are working from; (2) the difference in elevation between the point you are working from and the next lowest grid elevation; (3) the distance between the point you are working on and the next lowest grid intersection. The formula is written as follows:

$$\frac{\text{Amount above whole foot contour}}{\text{Difference in elevation}} \times \text{Distance between grid intersections}$$

Use the formula to calculate where the 601-ft contour will fall along side 1 in Figure 9–17a. The following examples begin calculating at the

Figure 9–17a. **The theory of uniform slopes is used to calculate contours in a grid survey.**

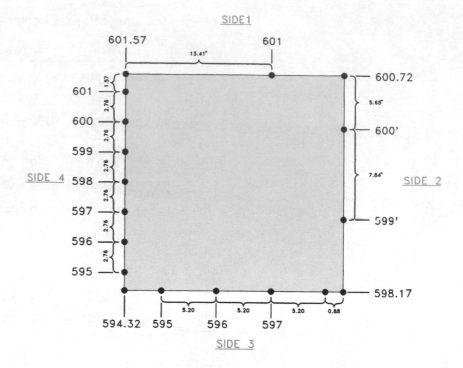

highest elevation of the two grid intersections in question. (The number 20 in the following formula represents the distance in feet between grid intersections.)

Side 1

$$\frac{A}{B} = \frac{601.57 - 601}{601.57 - 600.72} = \frac{0.57}{0.85} = 0.67 \times 20 = 13.41$$

In this formula the numerator (A) is the difference in elevation between 601.57 and 601, or 0.57 ft. The denominator (B) is the difference in elevation between the two corners of side 1, 601.57 and 600.72, or 0.85 ft. Next, divide 0.57 by 0.85 to find the percentage of the distance of contour 601 from the grid intersection 601.57. The result is 0.67. This means that the 601 contour is 67% of the distance between grid intersection 601.57 and grid intersection 600.72. To find the actual distance in feet, multiply 0.67 by 20 because the total length of side 1 is 20 ft. The answer is 13.41. Notice in Figure 9–17a that the distance from grid intersection 601.57 to contour 601 is 13.41 ft.

Measure 13.41 ft from the 601.57-ft point to find the 601-ft contour. Calculate side 2 using the following formulae:

Side 2

$$\frac{600.72 - 600}{600.72 - 598.17} = \frac{0.72}{2.55} = 0.28 \times 20 = 5.65$$

$$= 20 - 5.65 = 14.35$$

$$\frac{600 - 599}{600 - 598.17} = \frac{1.00}{1.83} = 0.55 \times 14.35 = 7.84$$

Notice that only two calculations are required per side if more than two contours cross a side. The second formula calculates the horizontal

Figure 9–17b. **After elevation values are located on the grid, points of the same value are connected to form contour lines.**

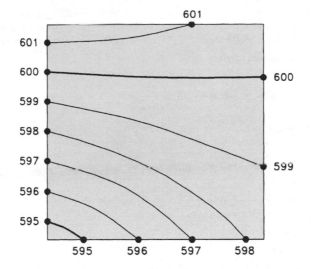

distance for 1 ft of elevation. Therefore, no additional calculations are needed. The same process is used for the third and fourth sides:

Side 3

$$\frac{598.17 - 598}{598.17 - 594.32} = \frac{0.17}{3.85} = 0.044 \times 20 = 0.88$$

$$= 20 - 0.88 = 19.12$$

$$\frac{598 - 597}{598 - 594.32} = \frac{1.00}{3.68} = 0.27 \times 19.12 = 5.20$$

Side 4

$$\frac{601.57 - 601}{601.57 - 594.52} = \frac{0.57}{7.25} = 0.0786 \times 20 = 1.57$$

$$= 20 - 1.57 = 18.43$$

$$\frac{601 - 600}{601 - 594.32} = \frac{1.00}{6.68} = 0.15 \times 18.43 = 2.76$$

After you have located the contour line elevations on the edges of the grid, connect points of the same value with lines, as shown in Figure 9–17b.

Radial Survey

A **radial survey** can be used for locating property corners, structures, natural features, and points to be used in contour mapping. Control points are established using a method called *radiation*, in which measurements are taken from a survey instrument located at a central point called a *transit station*. From this point, a series of angular and distance measurements are made to specific points. Readings such as this, taken from a transit station to specific control points, are called *side shots*. This technique is also used when an instrument setup (station) cannot be located on a point such as a property corner or section marker.

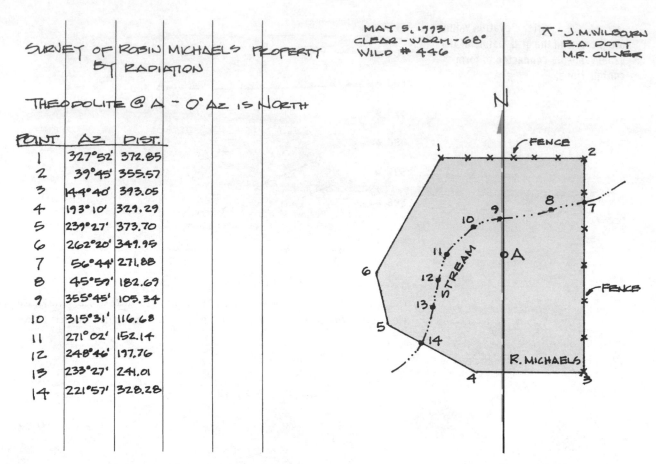

Figure 9–18. Field notes of a radial survey contain azimuths and distances, property corners, and additional control points.

From the transit station, the azimuths and distances of each point are recorded in the field notes. See Figure 9–18. This information can later be used to construct a property plat or a contour map. If the property is too large to sufficiently map using a single transit station, additional transit stations can be established. When two transit stations are used, the line between the two is called a **base line**. When more than two stations are used, the lines between them are called **transit lines**. Several transit lines can form an open or closed traverse, or a centerline survey.

Any of the interpolation techniques previously discussed can be used to construct a contour map. The field notes in Figure 9–18 were used to create the map shown in Figure 9–19.

Contour Labeling

Most topographic maps show written elevations only on index contour lines. These labels are normally enough to give the map reader sufficient reference values to work with. Figure 9–20 shows the method in which labeling is done. The elevation numbers are placed so that they are not upside down. Contour line labels are located at regular intervals along the contour line.

Property plats, highway maps, and special maps of many other kinds may require every contour to be labeled. In this case, the

Figure 9-19. A property plat can be constructed from the radial survey field notes.

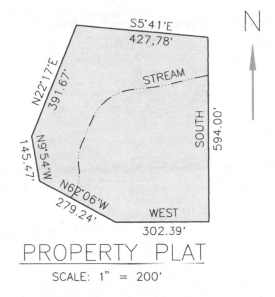

Figure 9-20. Contour line labeling should be on index contours, placed at regular intervals, and should not appear upside down.

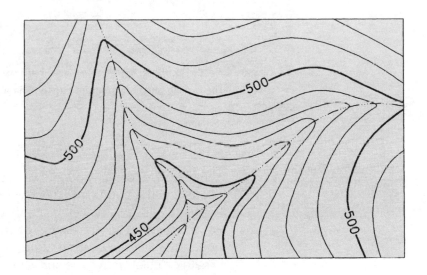

drafter must use good layout and spacing techniques to achieve a balanced and uncluttered appearance.

Plotting Contour Lines with a CADD System

In the CADD environment, contours are actually a by-product of surfaces, also known as digital terrain models (DTMs). The data to build a DTM is originally gathered in the field at the project site by surveyors, using equipment such as an electronic total station. A surveyor must be careful in the field to collect data that accurately represents all significant features of the site, such as edges of pavement, centerlines of roads, tops and toes of slopes, and the flow lines of ditches or streams. Information for each point is stored in a point file, which is then imported into the CADD software. Figure 9–21 shows the SurvCom program developed by Carlson Software, which is used to transfer data between a survey instrument or data

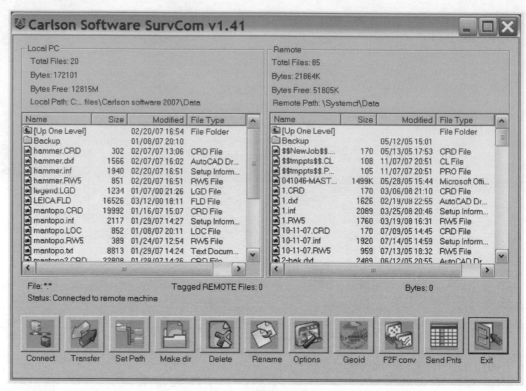

Figure 9–21. The Carlson SurvCom program transfers data from a survey instrument to an office computer.
(Courtesy Carlson Software)

collector/recorder and an office computer. The CADD software connects the points into a network of triangles, called a **triangulated irregular network (TIN)**. Each triangle represents a face on the surface, and the elevations of the corners of the face are known quantities. Interpolating along the face edges is a straightforward math calculation for the software. Then it is just a matter of connecting points of the same elevation along different edges to draw the contours at the desired contour interval. Once a surface has been built within a civil CADD application, it is a simple matter for the software to generate contours from the surface at any user-specified interval.

The contours are typically represented as basic CADD geometry, such as lines or polylines, at the specified elevation. It is for this reason that the addition of contour labels is also an easy task. Once the characteristics of the text to be used are established, either a specified number of labels per contour can be automatically added by the software, or labels can be added in a semi-automatic mode by manually indicating the desired locations for labels.

In some CADD applications, custom objects represent the contours with unique properties beyond those of standard geometry, so instead of lines or polylines, actual "contour objects" are created. One benefit of these is the ability to slide contour labels along the contours to adjust their position.

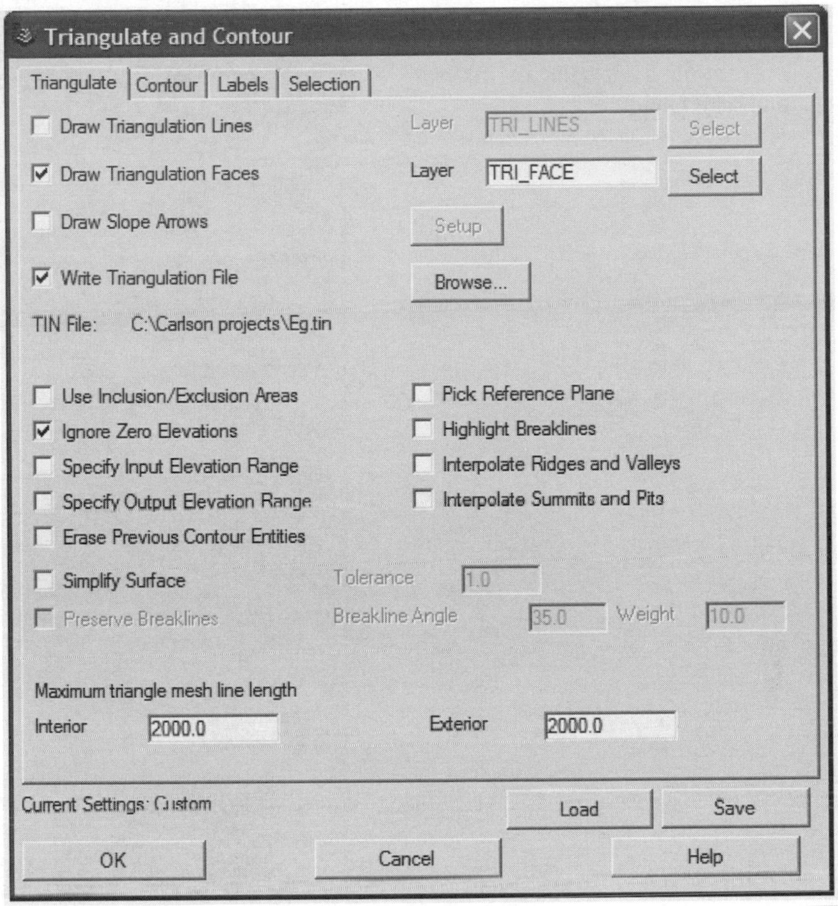

Figure 9–22. **Options in the Triangulate tab control how the triangulated mesh is represented in the drawing as well as the naming and placement of the external TIN file.**
(Courtesy Carlson Software)

One of the newest approaches to contours is to have them appear as just another way to visualize a surface, without actually generating individual contour objects of any kind.

After a set of data is collected and saved as a file, it is available to produce a surface, or DTM, in CADD. Each civil/survey software program has its own method of producing that digital model and, subsequently, a set of contours in the drawing to represent it visually. Although different brands of software may vary in the manner in which they handle the details, the process of producing a contour map is similar. Figures 9–22 through 9–25 are provided as an example. These figures show the four tabs in the Carlson Software Triangulate and Contour dialog box that are used for this purpose. The process requires that the user select a number of options in order to effectively display the finished contour map:

- Representation of the triangulated mesh and treatment of the TIN file (see Figure 9–22).
- Contour line features (see Figure 9–23).
- Contour line labeling (see Figure 9–24).
- Type of data used to generate the model surface (see Figure 9–25).

Figure 9–26 shows an example of a contour map that was created from field observations and generated from a raw data file.

Figure 9-23. The Contour tab is where all aspects of the generated contours are controlled, including the interval and smoothing.
(Courtesy Carlson Software)

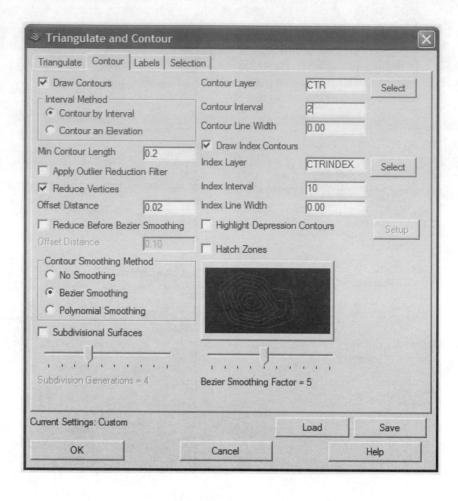

Enlarging Maps in CADD

The fundamental difference between drafting on paper and working in a CADD environment is that on paper, all the line work that represents objects in the real world is drawn to a scale, such as 1″ = 50′, and all the annotation, such as text and dimensions, is drawn on the paper at actual size, 1/8″ or 1/10″. In CADD, the reverse is true: All the geometry that represents real-world objects is created at actual full size, sometimes called one-to-one. If a lot measures 120′ on a side, a line is created in CADD that is 120′ long. Annotation, therefore, must be scaled to be appropriate for this full-sized map. If text were entered into the drawing at a height of 1/10″, it would of course be nearly invisible on a lot that measures 120′ on a side. So in CADD, the annotation is scaled, and the line work is entered full size. The scaling factor that is to be used for the annotation is determined by the scale at which the drawing is to be plotted on paper. Different plot scales require different text heights. Enlarging maps in CADD is therefore "simply" a matter of giving a different scale to the drawing when it is plotted, keeping in mind that the annotation will need to be adjusted for different plot scales. See Chapter 3 for detailed information on map scales, scale factors, and text heights.

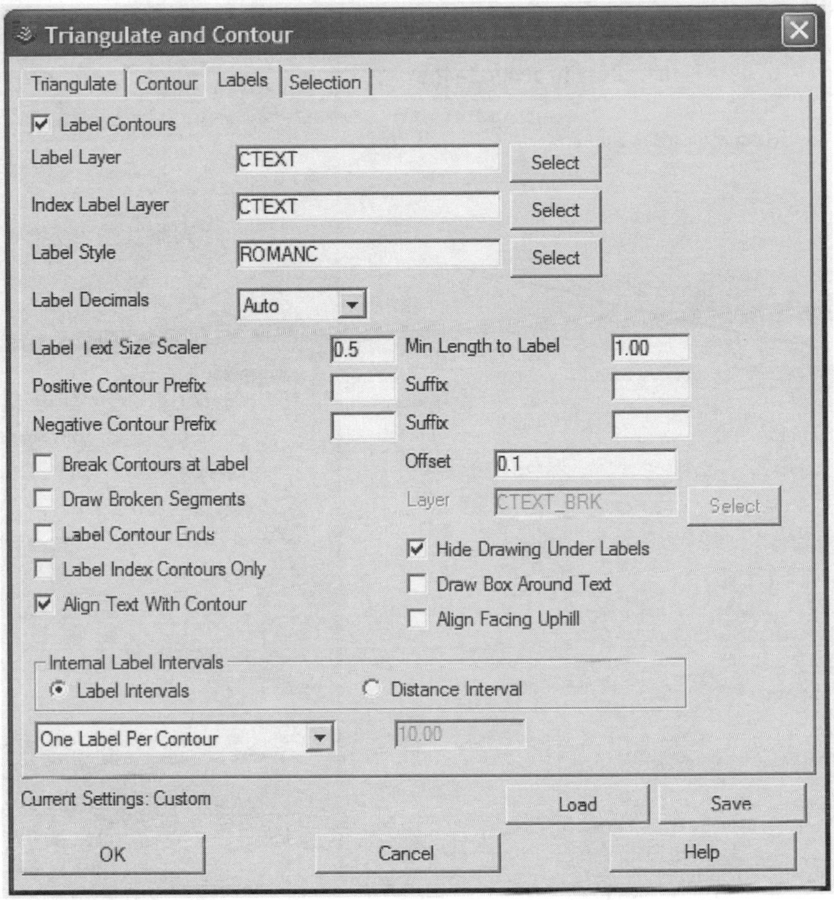

Figure 9-24. **In the Labels tab, the user specifies the details of the creation of contour labels.**
(Courtesy Carlson Software)

Digitizing and Scanning

Information on paper drawings, such as contours, roads, lots, etc., can be transferred to a CADD drawing through a process known as digitizing. In one method, the paper drawing is placed on a digitizing table, the drawing is calibrated to the scale at which it was drawn, and the line work is traced, or digitized, creating CADD geometry that duplicates the information on the paper drawing in a digital drawing file.

Paper drawings can also be scanned, which essentially takes a picture of the drawing and stores it as a digital image, or raster file, consisting of many dots, or pixels. The number of pixels per square inch is called the *resolution* of the image file. The *depth* of the image file refers to whether it is a black-and-white image, in which each pixel is either black or white; grayscale, in which each pixel is one of 256 shades of gray; or color, which has several depth options, depending on how many different colors are used. The more depth, the larger the file size of the raster files.

Once scanned, an image can be viewed in a CADD environment and either traced or digitized manually, simply by drawing over the lines in the image with CADD geometry, known as vector data. Raster-to-vector conversion software can also be used to accomplish

Figure 9–25.   The Selection tab is where the user specifies what type(s) of data is to be used to generate the surface.
(Courtesy Carlson Software)

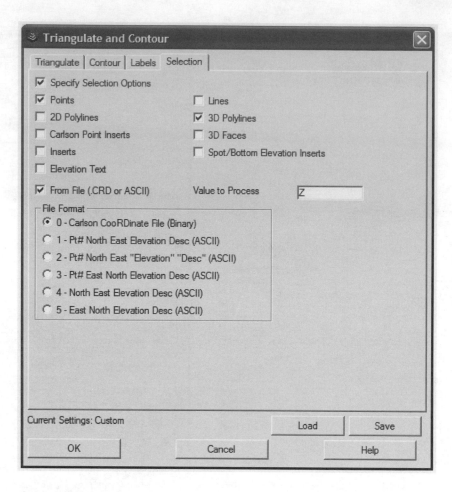

Figure 9–26.   An example of a contour map generated from a raw data file and displayed in the Carlson Survey program.
(Courtesy Carlson Software)

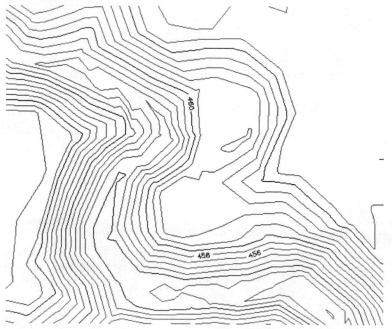

the digitizing automatically. Automatic conversion of raster to vector is a very tricky process, however, and misinterpretations are frequent, producing CADD geometry that is not usable. Conversion software technology has steadily improved over the years but by definition remains an imperfect science.

TEST

Use Microsoft Word to open the file "Chapter 09 test" on the Student Web site.

9-1 What do contour lines represent?

9-2 List four characteristics of contour lines.

9-3 Sketch the following features using contour lines:

Mountain peak   Saddle   Depression

9-4 What is the function of index contours?

9-5 Briefly define *control point survey*.

9-6 What is interpolation?

9-7 What type of survey divides the land into a checkerboard?

9-8 Explain the grid system of map enlarging.

9-9 What letter of the alphabet is formed when a contour line crosses a stream? _____ In which direction does the letter point? _____

9-10 What letter is formed when a contour line wraps around a hill or ridge? _____ In which direction does the letter point? _____

9-11 What is a radial survey?

9–12   What measurements are taken in a radial survey?

9–13   Explain how a manually drawn contour map could be transferred to a CAD system.

9–14   What is the difference between a raster drawing and a vector drawing?

TOPOGRAPHIC PLAN

Use Microsoft Word to open the file "Ch 09 topographic plan" on the Student Web site.

Study the topographic plan in Figure T9–1 to answer the following questions.

1. Parcel 1 is located in the _____ Quarter of Section _____.

2. The most noticeable topographic feature at the south edge of Parcel 1 is a/an _____, with an actual elevation at the center of just below _____.

Name three restrictions to building along the south side of West Moss Avenue.

3. _____

4. _____

5. _____

6. The flattest area of the plan shown is the _____. The elevation of this area is between _____ and _____.

7. The highest elevation of the plan is at the _____ corner.

8. The parallel contour lines along the west property line of Parcel 1 indicate the location of a/an _____. Another similar feature is located _____.

9. How many trees are located within Parcel 1? _____

10. Where is a traffic signal located? _____

11. The elevation of TBM #3 is _____, and it is located in the _____ corner of Parcel 1.

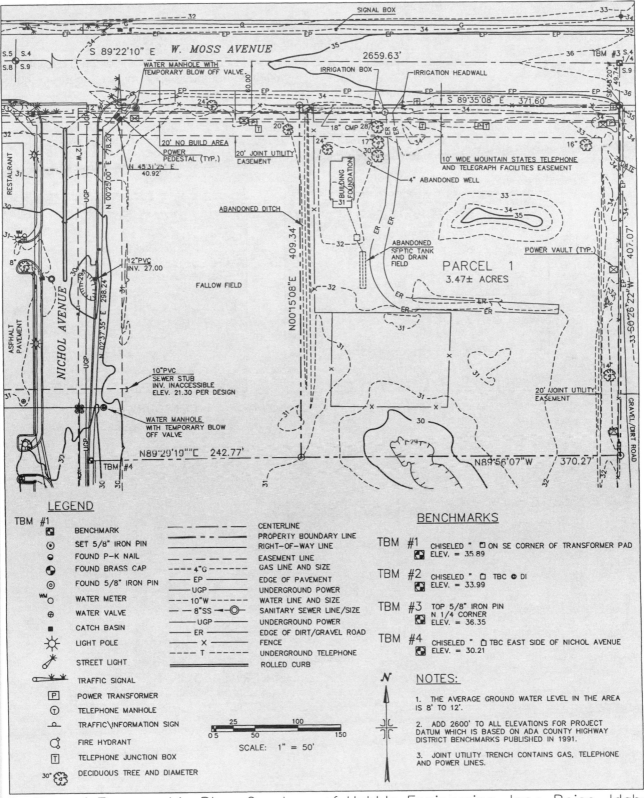

Portion of Topographic Plan Courtesy of Hubble Engineering, Inc.; Boise, Idaho

Figure T9-1.

(Courtesy of Hubble Engineering, Inc., Boise, Idaho)

PROBLEMS

P9-1   Using proper methods of contour line interpolation, establish contour lines for the problems given in Figure P9–1. Use indicated contour intervals. Label all index contours and keep in mind the characteristics of contours discussed in this chapter.

Use AutoCAD to open the file "P09–1" on the Student Web site.

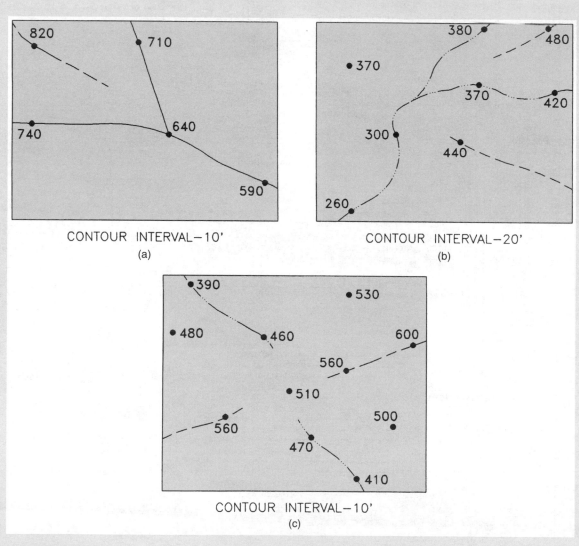

CONTOUR INTERVAL—10'
(a)

CONTOUR INTERVAL—20'
(b)

CONTOUR INTERVAL—10'
(c)

Figure P9–1.

Pg–2 **a.** Given the surveyor's field notes from a control point survey, establish contour lines at the contour interval indicated in Figure P9–2. Index contours should be a heavy line weight and should be labeled. Use interpolation where required.

b. Assume that the drawing shown in Figure P9–2 is at a scale of 1 in. = 200 ft. With your CAD system, digitize the drawing, also transferring all the elevation points. Interpolate and construct contours within CAD at an interval of 5 ft. Index contours should be a heavy line weight and should be labeled. Place labels of road, driveway, and other features where appropriate and give them a finished plotted height of 1/8 in. Elevation labels should have a finished plotted height of 1/8 in. Plot at 1 in. = 50 ft on a D-size sheet of paper and submit the drawing to your instructor for approval.

Use AutoCAD to open the file "P09–2" on the Student Web site.

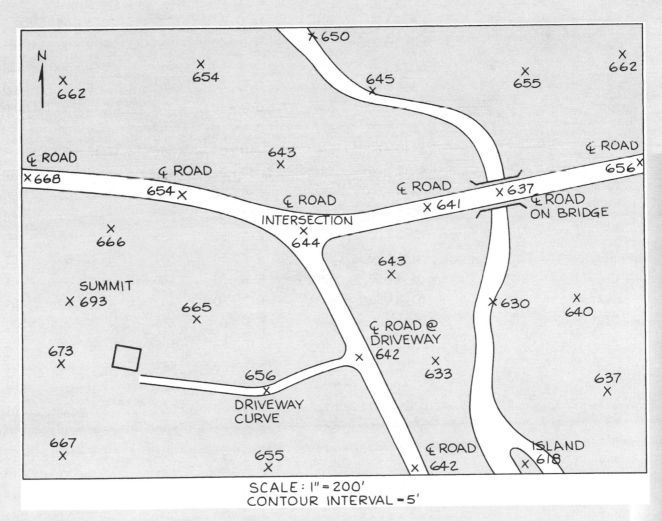

Figure P9–2.

P9-3 **a.** A grid survey produced the field notes given in Table P9–1. Using the grid of Figure P9–3, first locate the elevations of all grid intersections. Then plot contour lines at an interval of 10 ft. Index lines should be labeled and should contrast in line weight with intermediate contours. Use a scale of 1″ = 100′.

b. With your CAD system, construct a grid similar to the one in Figure P9–3, labeling all station points. Use the information given in Table P9–1 to then locate the elevations of all grid intersections. Draw the contour lines at an interval of 10 ft. Index lines should be labeled and should contrast in line weight with intermediate contours. Plot at a scale of 1 in. = 200 ft and submit your grid to your instructor for evaluation.

Table P9–1. **Grid survey field notes**

Station	Elev.	Station	Elev.	Station	Elev.
A–0 + 00	592	D–0 + 00	577	G–0 + 00	602
A–1 + 50	595	D–1 + 50	536	G–1 + 50	592
A–3 + 00	599	D–3 + 00	531	G–3 + 00	561
A–4 + 50	583	D–4 + 50	519	G–4 + 50	529
A–6 + 00	560	D–6 + 00	468	G–6 + 00	460
A–7 + 50	558	D–7 + 50	475	G–7 + 50	380
A–9 + 00	577	D–9 + 00	492	G–9 + 00	395
A–10 + 50	589	D–10 + 50	496	G–10 + 50	422
A–12 + 00	594	D–12 + 00	498	G–12 + 00	437
B–0 + 00	587	E–0 + 00	579	H–0 + 00	584
B–1 + 50	600	E–1 + 50	562	H–1 + 50	568
B–3 + 00	648	E–3 + 00	535	H–3 + 00	536
B–4 + 50	594	E–4 + 50	507	H–4 + 50	507
B–6 + 00	537	E–6 + 00	450	H–6 + 00	441
B–7 + 50	543	E–7 + 50	437	H–7 + 50	381
B–9 + 00	561	E–9 + 00	463	H–9 + 00	372
B–10 + 50	563	E–10 + 50	465	H–10 + 50	406
B–12 + 00	565	E–12 + 00	464	H–12 + 00	427
C–0 + 00	571	F–0 + 00	602	I–0 + 00	555
C–1 + 50	576	F–1 + 50	586	I–1 + 50	537
C–3 + 00	563	F–3 + 00	560	I–3 + 00	513
C–4 + 50	578	F–4 + 50	532	I–4 + 50	483
C–6 + 00	500	F–6 + 00	461	I–6 + 00	442
C–7 + 50	518	F–7 + 50	394	I–7 + 50	382
C–9 + 00	536	F–9 + 00	428	I–9 + 00	359
C–10 + 50	535	F–10 + 50	444	I–10 + 50	391
C–12 + 00	534	F–12 + 00	451	I–12 + 00	417

Use AutoCAD to open the file "PO9–3" on the Student Web site.

P9–4 Construct a grid enlargement of Figure P9–2 or P9–3. Increase the scale four times. Label all contours. Include a north arrow and legend. Use C-size paper. Use either CAD, pencil, or ink (check with your instructor). Make a print and submit it to the instructor for evaluation, unless otherwise indicated.

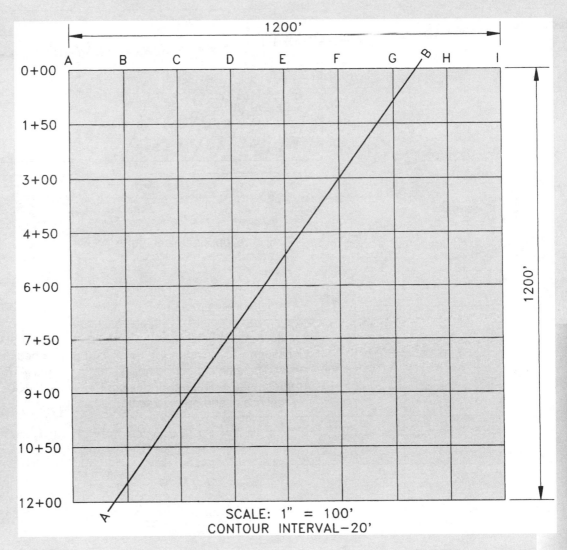

Figure P9–3.

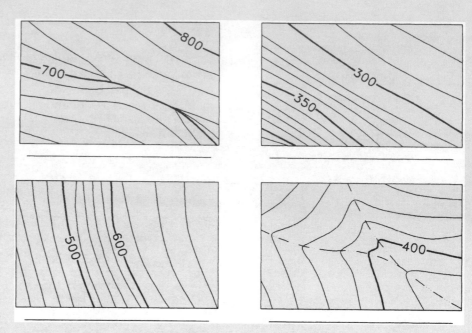

Figure P9–5.

P9–5 Identify the topographic features shown in Figure P9–5.

P9–6 A radial survey produced the site notes shown in Figure P9–6. Using the elevation points given, create a contour map of the site with a contour interval of 2 ft. In the completed contour plan, show all set nail locations and elevations, as well as the road bed and concrete meter vault. The side cut on the north side of the gravel road should also be represented. Label only index contour lines. Include a north arrow, verbal scale, and graphic scale.

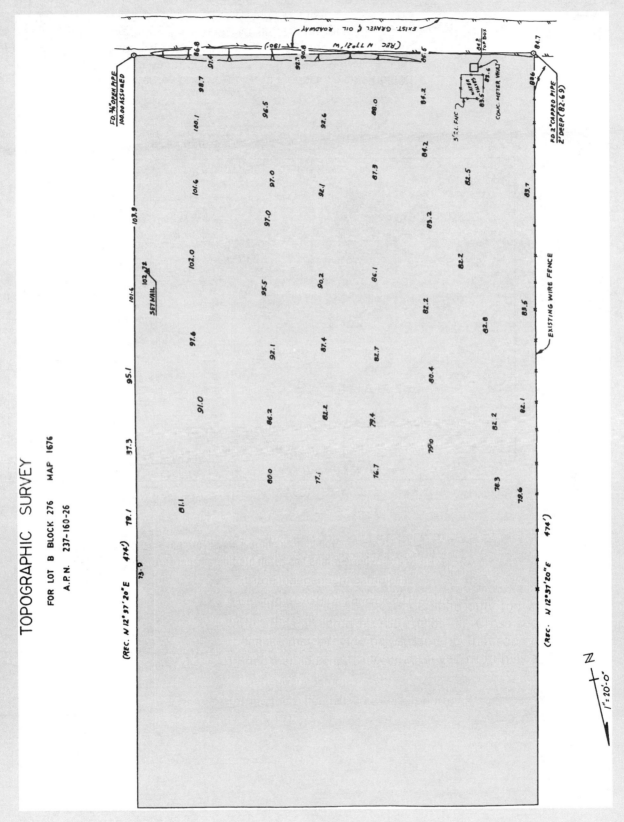

TOPOGRAPHIC SURVEY
FOR LOT B BLOCK 276 MAP 1676
A.P.N. 237-160-26

Figure Pg-6.

Pg-7   A radial survey produced the site notes shown in Figure P9–7. Using
        the elevation points given, create a contour map of the site with a
        contour interval of 5 ft. Draw the map using a scale of 1 in. = 20 ft.
        Locate the elevation points by measuring in Figure P9–6 from the
        lower-left corner horizontally and vertically to each point. The scale of
        Figure P9–6 is 1 in. = 60 ft. Label all features indicated and label all
        contour lines. Include a north arrow and verbal scale.

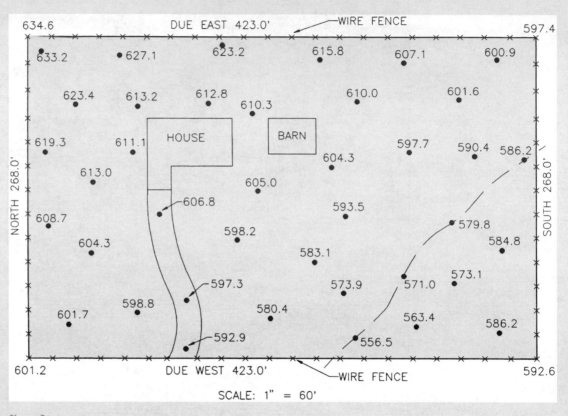

Figure P9–7.

Note: Problems 9–8 through 9–10 provide information that was provided with traditional methods of surveying and mapping, without the use of CADD software and electronic data collection. The use of these problems will provide practice in the layout of survey data and the creation of contour maps using manual methods. But the techniques of electronic data collection coupled with powerful CADD software used today are much more automatic and can quickly produce contour maps and surface models viewed from any angle. If you have access to software such as Autodesk Land Desktop, it would be worthwhile to acquire point files created by a surveyor and use them to generate contour maps.

P9–8 A radial survey produced the field notes in Figure P9–8. Use these notes to construct a site map with a contour interval of 1 ft. Label all the control points and each index line. Show all features indicated in the field notes. Include a north arrow, representative fraction scale, and graphic scale.

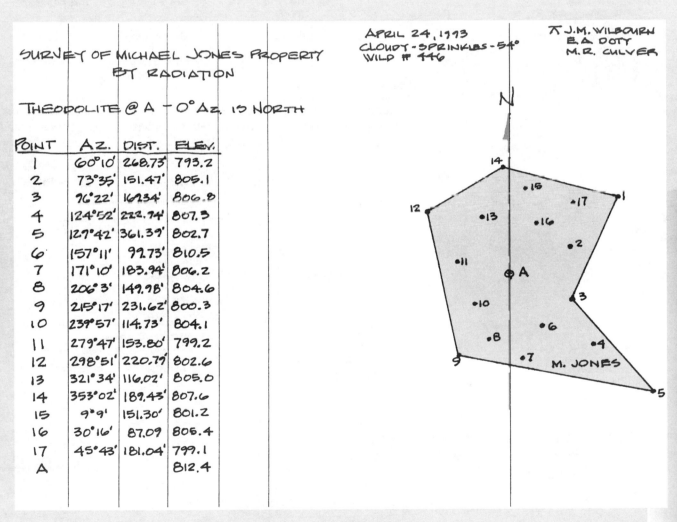

Figure P9–8.

P9-9   Refer to Figure 9–18 for this problem. Plot the piece of property using
        the field notes given in Figure 9–18. Draw the stream as intermittent.
        Construct a contour map of the property using the elevations of each of
        the following points. These points correspond to the points in the field
        notes. Use a contour interval of 2 ft and label the index contour lines.
        Draw a verbal scale and north arrow. Use a scale appropriate for a
        B-size sheet of paper.

Point	Elevation	Point	Elevation
A	421.2		
1	423.5	8	413.6
2	418.9	9	409.1
3	437.3	10	407.9
4	426.4	11	401.3
5	389.7	12	394.6
6	412.5	13	386.5
7	416.2	14	372.8

P9-10   A second radial survey of the site used in problem P9–9 produced the
        following list of points and their elevations. Revise the map constructed
        in problem P9–9, using this new survey.

Point	Azimuth	Distance	Elevation
15	20°50′	228.75′	418.3′
16	344°59′	197.30′	419.6′
17	302°48′	282.61′	416.7′
18	291°10′	200.73′	410.2′
19	271°20′	271.39′	411.9′
20	250°11′	276.97′	406.0′
21	204°2′	204.65′	414.7′
22	172°33′	116.33′	423.5′
23	149°15′	246.61′	428.1′
24	113°35′	248.07′	427.0′
25	78°40′	123.11′	412.8′

Horizontal Alignment Layout

Learning Objectives

After completing this chapter, you will be able to:

- Create a highway layout drawing using the point of curve and point of intersection methods.
- Construct a vertical curve profile drawing.
- Calculate tangent distances for a vertical curve.

Key Terms

Transit line
Point of curve
Radius
Delta angle
Curve length
Degree of curve
Point of reverse curve
Point of tangency
Point of intersection

The layout of a proposed highway or road usually begins on a contour map or an aerial photograph. Road designers and engineers, with input from government officials, determine the location of the road by using maps and information gathered from field study. The engineer's initial design and centerline location are given to the surveyors, who then locate the proposed road's centerline and right-of-way boundaries. The drafter then plots the surveyor's field notes on a contour map. When the initial layout is completed, the construction details can begin. This chapter discusses the initial layout of roads and highways.

The topics covered include:

- Plan layout
- Plan layout with a CADD system
- Profile layout
- Drawing conversions for CADD

Plan Layout

Centerline (Route) Survey

Before a drafter can begin the actual drawing of a road, a survey crew must physically locate the centerline on the ground and record bearings, distances, and station points as field notes. The drafter uses these notes to plot the highway. The initial function of the survey crew is to mark the centerline of the highway. Subsequent surveys establish right-of-way, actual road widths, cross sections, and other details.

Plan Layout

The plan and profile is an important drawing in highway layout. Using the surveyor's field notes, the drafter first constructs the plan view. This can be done on an existing map, or the drafter may have to draw a new one. The plan view shows trees, fences, buildings, other roads, and cultivated areas. The centerline, or transit line, is then drawn using bearings and distances. Station points are located every 100 ft. Figure 10–1 shows a plan layout. Notice that the road is to have curves. The information needed to construct a curve is given under the heading "Curve Data." Let us examine this information.

Point of curve (P.C.) is the point at which the curve begins. The station value is also written at the point of curve.

Radius (R) is a curve radius. To find the center point of the radius, you must project a line perpendicular to the centerline and measure the required distance on this line (see Figure 10–2).

Delta angle (Δ) is the central or included angle of the curve between the point of curve (P.C.) and the point of tangency (P.T.). From the perpendicular line projected to find the radius center, measure the delta angle. This point is the end of the curve (see Figure 10–2).

Curve length (L) is the centerline length of the arc from the P.C. to the P.T. or the end of the curve (see Figure 10–2).

Degree of curve (D) is the angle of the 100-ft arc that connects station points. The degree is measured from the previous station (see Figure 10–3).

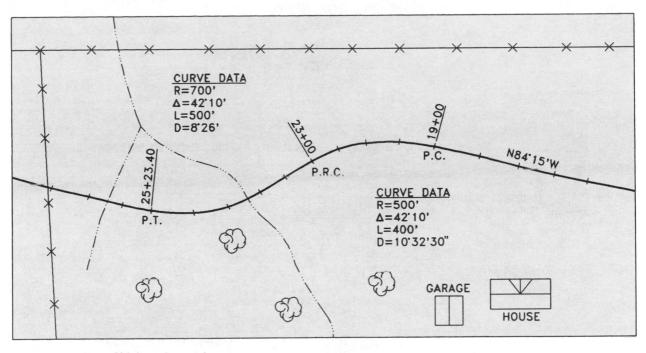

Figure 10-1. Plan of highway layout data.

Figure 10-2. Basic curve data for highway layout.

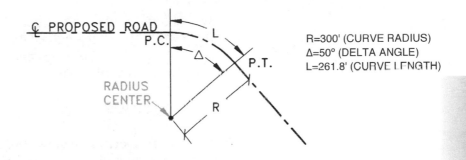

Figure 10-3. Degree of curve on a 100-ft arc.

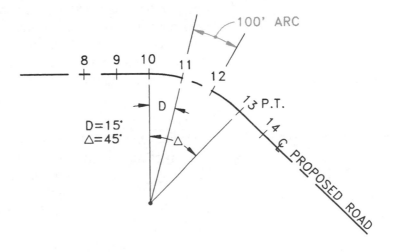

Point of reverse curve (P.R.C.) is the point at which one curve ends and the next curve begins. A *reverse curve*, known as an "S" curve in racing terminology, contains no straight section between curves. The station value is given after "P.R.C." (see Figure 10-1).

Point of tangency (P.T.) is the end of the curve. The station value is also written at this point.

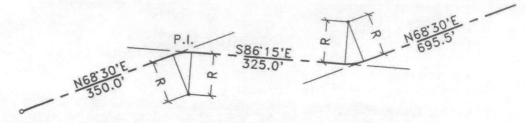

Figure 10-4.   Highway curve layout using bearings, distances, and curve radii.

Figure 10-5.   Method of locating highway curve radius center.

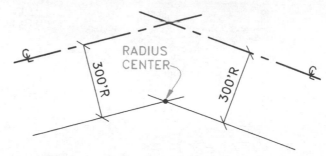

Curve Layout: A Second Method

The survey crew may only establish centerlines and points of inter-section (P.I.). A point of intersection on a plan view is the junction of two centerlines of different bearings. Curves are constructed at P.I.s. Figure 10–4 shows the curve layout method using bearings and P.I.s. The drafter is given bearings and distances and also suggested curve radii. Using this information, the drafter must plot the road center-line and curves.

To find the center point of the radius, measure perpendicularly from each leg of the road to the inside of the curve the exact radius distance, as shown in Figure 10–5. Then draw a line parallel to each leg through the radius point just measured. The intersection of these two parallel lines is the center point for the radius curve. You can now construct the curve and road outline, using the radius point.

Once the centerlines of the road have been plotted and the curves are laid out, the width of the road and right-of-way can be easily drawn by measuring from the centerline.

Plan Layout with a CADD System

Constructing a plan view of a highway layout can be done with a CADD system in much the same way as with manual drafting. Data in the form of curve lengths, bearings, and distances can be entered when drawing the transit line. Some CADD software packages rou-tinely put in the centerline stationing.

In a CADD environment, first a digital terrain model is generated for the project area. This can be done from a ground survey, an aerial survey, or even published data from a government agency such as the U.S. Geological Survey (USGS), which has digital 2D and 3D maps available of the entire country. When the layout of the proposed align-ment is established, a profile of the existing conditions can be auto-matically generated.

TEST

Use Microsoft Word to open the file "Chapter 10 test" on the Student Web site.

10-1   What type of survey is initially used to lay out a road?

10-2   What is the point at which a curve begins?

10-3   What is the delta angle?

10-4   How is the degree of curve measured? Show your answer in a sketch.

10-5   What is the point at the end of a curve called?

10-6   Define *point of intersection* (P.I.).

10-7   Briefly describe how you would locate the center point of a 400-ft-radius horizontal curve, given two centerlines and a P.I.

SEWER PLAN AND PROFILE

Study the portion of a sewer plan and profile in Figure T10–1 to answer the following questions. Use Microsoft Word to open the file "Ch 10 sewerprofile" on the Student Web site and use AutoCAD the to open the file "sewerprofile."

1. The highest elevation on the profile is just north of Lot _____, Block _____ at Station _____.

2. At sewer manhole B-3, the invert out elevation is _____.

3. Keynote 6 refers to _____.

4. At Station 3 + 95.03, the invert out is located _____ below the manhole.

5. At Lot 9, Block 5, the sewer connection is at Station _____, and the invert elevation at the end is _____.

6. On the profile, the maximum slope for a sewer line is _____%.

7. On Florida Avenue, the sewer line is typically located _____ from the centerline of the street.

8. Station 2 + 75.78 is the location of SSMH _____.

9. SSMH B-1 has two invert in _____" PVC pipes at elevations
   of _____ and _____ and one invert out
   _____" PVC pipe at an elevation of _____.

10. The average slope of the sewer line between station $6 + 90.00$ and station
    $2 + 75.78$ is _____%.

PROBLEMS

P10–1 **a.** For this problem you will lay out a 40-ft-wide road using the
           information given in Figure P10–1. Plot the centerline bearings on
           Figure P10–1 and then construct the curves and road outlines.
           Label all points, bearings, and radius curves.

       b. If you have access to a scanner and a CAD system, scan the infor-
           mation given in Figure P10–1. If you have a CAD system only, then
           digitize the information given in Figure P10–1. Be sure that the con-
           tours and existing road have real-world coordinates. Construct the
           centerline bearings on Figure P10–1 first and then construct the
           curves and road outlines. Label all points, bearings, and radius
           curves. Show centerline stationing along the road. Plot at a scale of
           1 in. = 200 ft on an 8 1/2- × 11-in. sheet of paper and submit it to
           your instructor.

       Use AutoCAD to open the file "P10–1" on the Student Web site.

P10–2 **a.** This exercise involves the layout of a road using some different
           information. A 40-ft-wide street is to be plotted using the information
           given in Figure P10–2. The street begins at point *A*, which is 100 ft
           east along Holgate Avenue.

       b. If you have access to a scanner and a CAD system, scan the
           information given in Figure P10–2. If you have only a CAD system,
           then digitize the information given in Figure P10–2. Be sure that the
           contours and existing road have real-world coordinates. To repeat, a
           40-ft-wide street is to be constructed using the information given in
           Figure P10–2. The street begins at point A, which is 100 ft east
           along Holgate Avenue. Show centerline stationing along the road.
           Plot at a scale of 1 in. = 50 ft on an 11 × 17-in. sheet of paper and
           submit it to your instructor.

       Use AutoCAD to open the file "P10–2" on the Student Web site.

P10–3 For this project, use the completed problem 9–3. First you will plot a
       highway on the existing contour map. Next, you will construct and plot
       cut and fill along the highway.

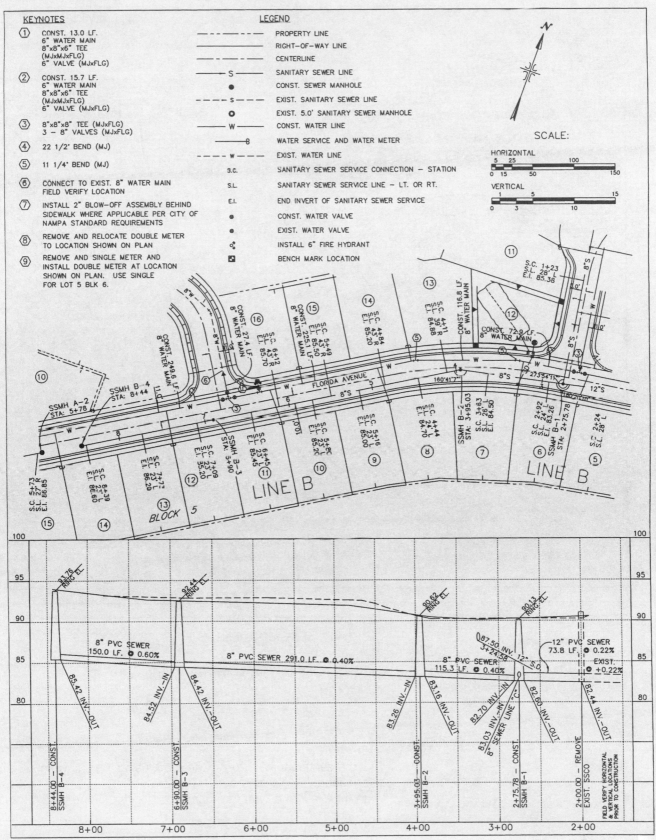

Portion of Sewer Plan and Profile   Courtesy of Capital Development: Boise, Idaho

Figure T10-1.
(Courtesy of Captial Development, Boise, Idaho)

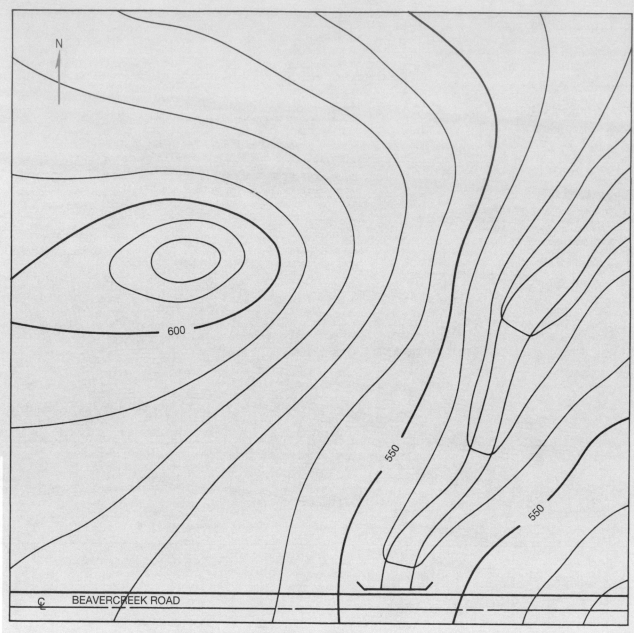

SCALE:1" = 200

Point A: 710' west from right edge of map on ℄ of Beavercreek Rd.

Point B: N24°30'E, 200'radius curve

Point C: N39°25'W, 620', 300'radius curve, then due north to edge of map.

Road to be 40' wide.

Figure P10–1.

Road Layout

a. Plot the centerline of a 20-ft-wide road, using the following information:

- Point A is 225 ft East from station A 12 + 00 along the bottom of the map.
- Point B (P.I.) is N26°14′E, 756 ft from point A.
- N13°15′W to top of map.

b. The road has 6-ft-wide shoulders and a 300-ft radius curve.

c. The road centerline is at 530-ft elevation.

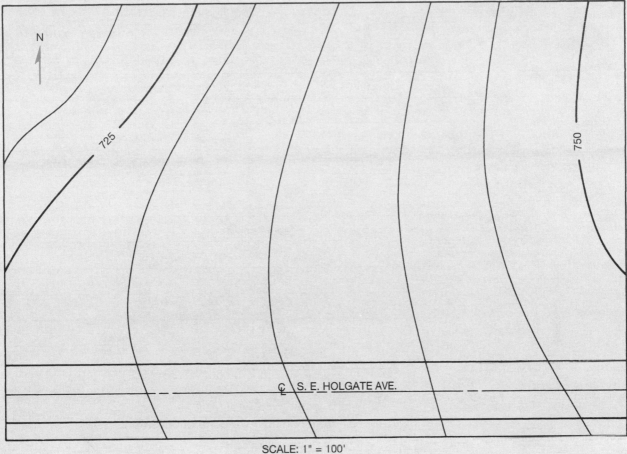

SCALE: 1" = 100'

Point A: 100' east from left edge of
map on ℄ S.E. Holgate Ave.
Point B: Due north 110'
Point C: Δ angle—30° (NE)
Radius curve — 150' to point C

Point D: 170' from C
Point E: Δ angle—60° (NE)
Radius curve — 100' to point E
Point F: 160' from E

Point G: Δ angle—90°
Radius curve —
120' to point G
Point H: Due south to ℄
Holgate Ave.
Plot A 40' wide street.

Figure P10–2.

Cut and Fill

a. Draw a cut-and-fill scale below the bottom edge of the map. Use separate layers for the cut-and-fill scale.

b. Cut angle of repose is 1 1/2:1, and fill angle of repose is 2:1.

c. Draw the outline of the cut and fill along the road as a spline.

d. Use different hatch patterns for the cut-and-fill patterns.

e. Label inside all cuts and fills or outside with a leader if space is limited.

f. Plot the drawing on a C-size sheet of paper.

P10–4 The purpose of this problem is to create a partial street layout map, working from an engineering sketch and survey data. Using the sketch as a basic guide (Figure P10–4), construct the drawing with the detailed information given. Choose an appropriate scale and paper size for this problem.

Bearings and Distances		
Line *AD*	S6°45′32″W	280′
Line *DC*	S6°45′32″W	80′
Line *AB*	N6°45′32″E	70′
Line *AE*	N83°14′28″W	120′
Line *FG*	S78°48′43″W	216′
Line *DH*	N83°14′28″W	185′

Curve Data	
Curve *EF*	Radius 413′
	Delta angle 17°56′49″
	Length 129.37′
Curve *HI*	Radius 120′
	Delta angle 90°
	Length 188.50′

Street Data
Street width 40′ (20′ from centerline to edge of pavement, EOP)
Curb width 80 from EOP to grass strip
Grass strip from curb to sidewalk 4′
Sidewalk 5′ wide
Sidewalk radius at street intersections 15′

Figure P10–4.

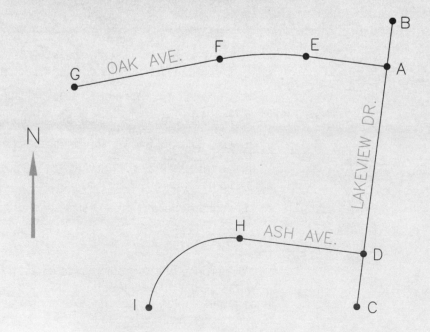

P10-5 A grid survey produced the field notes shown in Table P10–1. Construct the grid shown in Figure P10–5 and then locate the elevations of all grid intersections. Plot contour lines at an interval of 10 ft. Index lines should be labeled, and their thickness should be greater than the intermediate contours. Use a scale of $1'' = 100'$.

Lay out roads on the map, using the point of intersection method and the road data given below. When labeling curves, give the radius, delta angle, and length of curve, as shown in Figure 10–1. The road is 24 ft wide, with a 4-ft-wide shoulder on each side.

Point *A:* 217.21′ north from lower-left corner of grid

Point *B:* N68°56′59″E, 135.14′, 300′ radius curve

Point *C:* N87°26′51″E, 449.07′, 200′ radius curve

Point *D:* N47°25′53″E, 337.54′, 350′ radius curve

Point *E:* N19°33′9″E, 281.75′, 300′ radius curve, then N23°56′23″E to edge of map

Point *G:* N15°42′41″W, 284.84′, 240′ radius curve

Point *H:* N66°28′17″W, 243.09′, 200′ radius curve, then N78°44′6″W to edge of map

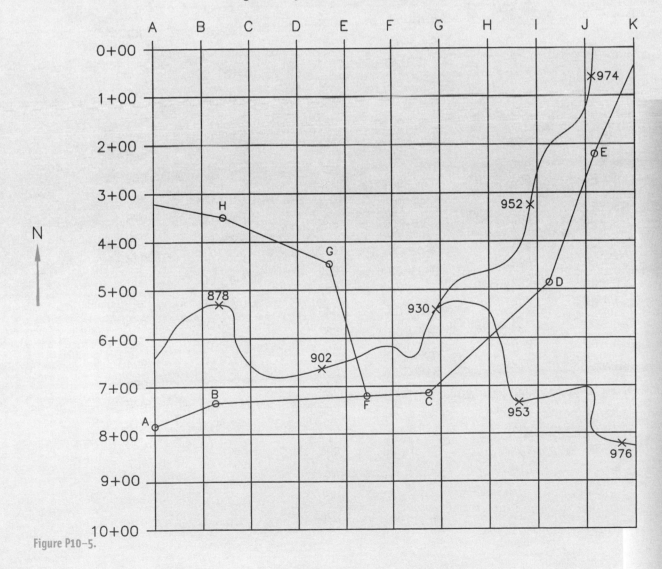

Figure P10–5.

Table P10-1 Grid survey field notes

Station	Elev	Station	Elev	Station	Elev
A–0 + 00	987	D–7 + 00	902	H–3 + 00	954
A–1 + 00	970	D–8 + 00	927	H–4 + 00	941
A–2 + 00	942	D–9 + 00	953	H–5 + 00	939
A–3 + 00	918	D–10 + 00	982	H–6 + 00	939
A–4 + 00	904	E–0 + 00	1012	H–7 + 00	943
A–5 + 00	887	E–1 + 00	985	H–8 + 00	960
A–6 + 00	869	E–2 + 00	960	H–9 + 00	1000
A–7 + 00	877	E–3 + 00	930	H–10 + 00	1013
A–8 + 00	896	E–4 + 00	922	I–0 + 00	1030
A–9 + 00	920	E–5 + 00	916	I–1 + 00	987
A–10 + 00	946	E–6 + 00	909	I–2 + 00	962
B–0 + 00	993	E–7 + 00	913	I–3 + 00	953
B–1 + 00	973	E–8 + 00	928	I–4 + 00	950
B–2 + 00	939	E–9 + 00	960	I–5 + 00	954
B–3 + 00	919	E–10 + 00	977	I–6 + 00	955
B–4 + 00	905	F–0 + 00	1021	I–7 + 00	952
B–5 + 00	887	F–1 + 00	987	I–8 + 00	967
B–6 + 00	878	F–2 + 00	965	I–9 + 00	1010
B–7 + 00	893	F–3 + 00	937	I–10 + 00	1022
B–8 + 00	909	F–4 + 00	928	J–0 + 00	987
B–9 + 00	942	F–5 + 00	922	J–1 + 00	970
B–10 + 00	960	F–6 + 00	911	J–2 + 00	968
C–0 + 00	997	F–7 + 00	917	J–3 + 00	966
C–1 + 00	976	F–8 + 00	942	J–4 + 00	969
C–2 + 00	946	F–9 + 00	964	J–5 + 00	984
C–3 + 00	924	F–10 + 00	967	J–6 + 00	978
C–4 + 00	912	G–0 + 00	1030	J–7 + 00	963
C–5 + 00	898	G–1 + 00	1000	J–8 + 00	968
C–6 + 00	887	G–2 + 00	977	J–9 + 00	1011
C–7 + 00	894	G–3 + 00	947	J–10 + 00	1026
C–8 + 00	924	G–4 + 00	937	K–0 + 00	996
C–9 + 00	949	G–5 + 00	931	K–1 + 00	995
C–10 + 00	972	G–6 + 00	923	K–2 + 00	994
D–0 + 00	1003	G–7 + 00	929	K–3 + 00	993
D–1 + 00	983	G–8 + 00	955	K–4 + 00	1005
D–2 + 00	954	G–9 + 00	988	K–5 + 00	1014
D–3 + 00	929	G–10 + 00	996	K–6 + 00	1002
D–4 + 00	918	H–0 + 00	1032	K–7 + 00	987
D–5 + 00	914	H–1 + 00	1008	K–8 + 00	982
D–6 + 00	905	H–2 + 00	978	K–9 + 00	1005
				K–10 + 00	1016

Profiles

Learning Objectives

After completing this chapter, you will be able to:

- Construct profile drawings using contour maps.
- Construct profile drawings using profile measurement field notes.
- Construct plan and profile drawings using field notes and engineering sketches.

Key Terms

Profile
Plan and profile
Intermediate foresight
Invert elevation
Vertical curve

A profile is an outline. An *artistic profile* is the outline of a face from the side, and a *map profile* is the outline of a cross section of the earth. Profiles are drawn using the information given on contour maps. Their uses include road grade layout, cut-and-fill calculations, pipeline layouts, site excavations, and dam and reservoir layout. This chapter examines basic profile construction from contour maps and the plan and profile commonly used by civil engineering firms for underground utility location and layout and for highway designs.

Three techniques are possible for the construction of profiles and for many other types of civil engineering drawings. The first is traditional manual drafting, which is, for the most part, a historical method and seldom, if ever, used. See Appendix B for creating contour map profiles using traditional methods. The second is to manually construct the profile using a general drafting CADD system such as AutoCAD. While this method is feasible, it does not utilize the full power of the third method, which is fully integrated civil engineering data collection and CADD software. You should base your view of drawing creation on the methods and software you will be using.

This chapter discusses the purposes and types of map profiles. Instructions and illustrations are provided to show how map profiles can be used in a variety of situations. The topics covered include:

- Profile leveling
- Plan and profile
- Profile layout—vertical curves
- Plan and profiles with CADD

Profile Leveling with Traditional Methods

Before a project such as a highway, a utility line, a railroad, a canal, or another linear feature can be built, the elevation characteristics along the route must be surveyed. In *profile leveling*, surveyors measure a number of elevations along the centerline of the route.

Surveying Procedure

Profile leveling is similar to standard differential leveling, but additional intermediate shots are taken along the route. The instrument is set up in a position from which several shots along the centerline can be taken. The rod is placed on a known elevation, such as a bench mark (BM), and a backsight (B.S.) is taken to determine the height of the instrument (H.I.). The rod can then be placed at intervals along the route's centerline and elevations measured at each point. These rod shots are called intermediate foresight (IFS) readings, or *ground rod* readings.

The location of IFS readings is determined by the topography. Normally, stakes are set at 50- or 100-ft intervals. Stations set at 100-ft intervals are called *full stations*. They are labeled 0 + 00, 1 + 00, 2 + 00, and so on. Intermediate readings taken between full stations are referred to as *plus stations*. For example, a point that is 463.25 ft from station 0 + 00 is labeled 4 + 63.25. Plus stations are located at

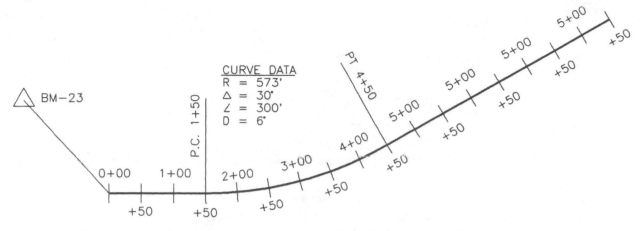

Figure 11–1. **Profile leveling measurements are taken at the station points indicated on the map.**

sudden elevation changes such as bank and stream edges, road edges and centerlines, and the tops and bottoms of ditches.

When IFS readings can no longer be taken from the instrument setup, a new instrument station is needed. The rod is placed on a turning point (T.P.), and a foresight (F.S.) reading is taken. The instrument is then moved ahead to a location from which additional IFS readings can be made. Figure 11–1 shows an example of what a typical profile leveling setup would look like on a map.

To check the profile leveling survey, it is necessary to close on another BM. Remember from the leveling discussion in Chapter 5 that the difference between the totals of the B.S. readings and the F.S. readings is the elevation difference between the beginning and end points. For example, if the totals of the B.S. readings are +14.65 and the totals of the F.S. readings are −6.79, the difference is +7.86 (+14.65 − 6.79 = +7.86). This value should be the H.I. reading when the rod is placed on the final BM.

Profile Leveling Field Notes

Field notes for profile leveling are similar to those for differential leveling, with the addition of station values and IFS readings. Figure 11–2 shows an example of profile leveling field notes.

Plotting Field Notes

Profile field notes can be plotted manually using a grid or profile paper or using a CAD system with a similar prototype drawing containing a grid, or series of horizontal and vertical guidelines. The bottom line of the profile represents the horizontal distance on the route of the survey and can be labeled with the station point values. The vertical aspect of the profile is an exaggerated scale labeled with elevation values. The elevation values of each station are taken from the field notes and plotted on the profile. An example is the profile created from the field notes in Figure 11–2 that is shown in Figure 11–3.

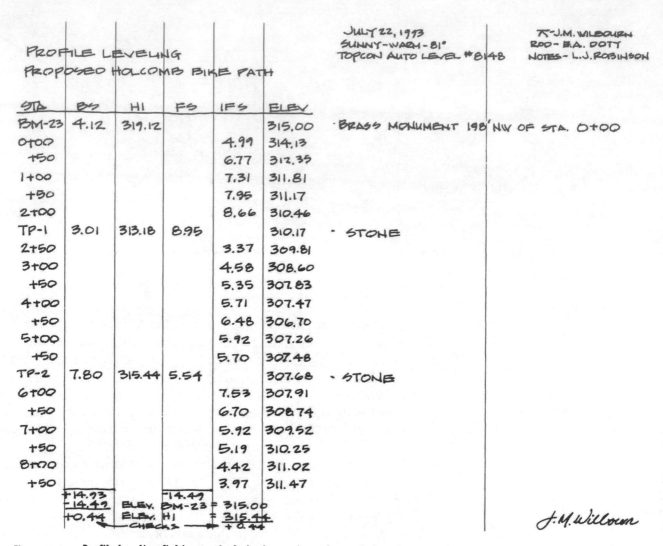

PROFILE LEVELING
PROPOSED HOLCOMB BIKE PATH

JULY 22, 1973
SUNNY-WARM-81°
TOPCON AUTO LEVEL #8148

π-J.M. WILBOURN
ROD- B.A. DOTT
NOTES- L.J. ROBINSON

STA	BS	HI	FS	IFS	ELEV	
BM-23	4.12	319.12			315.00	BRASS MONUMENT 198' NW OF STA. 0+00
0+00				4.99	314.13	
+50				6.77	312.35	
1+00				7.31	311.81	
+50				7.95	311.17	
2+00				8.66	310.46	
TP-1	3.01	313.18	8.95		310.17	STONE
2+50				3.37	309.81	
3+00				4.58	308.60	
+50				5.35	307.83	
4+00				5.71	307.47	
+50				6.48	306.70	
5+00				5.92	307.26	
+50				5.70	307.48	
TP-2	7.80	315.44	5.54		307.68	STONE
6+00				7.53	307.91	
+50				6.70	308.74	
7+00				5.92	309.52	
+50				5.19	310.25	
8+00				4.42	311.02	
+50				3.97	311.47	

+14.93
-14.49 ELEV. BM-23 = 315.00
+0.44 ELEV. HI = 315.44
CHECKS = + 0.44

J.M.Wilbourn

Figure 11-2. Profile leveling field notes include the station value and elevation at each station.

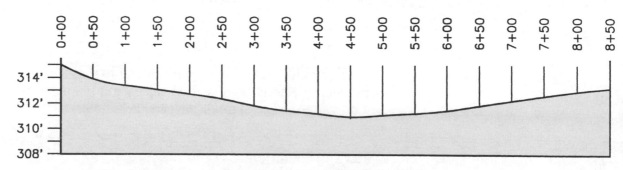

Figure 11-3. This profile drawing was created using the field notes shown in Figure 11-2.

Profiles can be created for projects that consist of a single straight line, a series of connected straight lines (utilities), or straight lines connected by curves, such as highways. The profile information is plotted in the same manner, but the plan drawing or map indicates the true appearance of the feature. This is illustrated by the plan and profile drawing, discussed later in this chapter.

Profile Leveling with CADD

Profile leveling is commonly done by conducting a topographic survey of the area to be developed. The surveyors generate as many points as are needed to produce a digital terrain model with appropriate detail. The resulting point file is then used as the data source to generate and display the existing ground in contour or grid format, surface models, or profiles.

Once the point file is generated by the surveyors, it is possible to create and display any type of profile automatically. Software does this by combining surface elevation data with any alignment that is drawn on the map.

Plan and Profile

A plan and profile, as used by civil engineers and state highway departments, can be compared to a top and front view in mechanical drafting, where the front view is a section. This type of drawing is often much more detailed than a leveling profile because it represents a completed project. The drawing is convenient to use because it allows both the plan and cross section of a specific area to be shown on the same sheet. The plan is always placed above the profile. The uses of this type of map are many. Transportation departments use the plan and profile extensively for layout and design of roads and transit systems, as shown in Figure 11–4. The profile view is often done along the centerline of a road to illustrate gradient and curves. Civil engineering firms employ the plan and profile when designing subdivision street layouts and underground utility locations (see Figure 11–5). One utility that is displayed in plan and profile format is sanitary sewer lines.

The following discussion on layout and construction goes through the procedure for manually constructing a plan and profile using a CADD system. Keep in mind that civil engineering software can automatically generate profiles along any alignment that is drawn or selected on the map or terrain model.

Layout and Construction

The scales most commonly used for a plan view are 1 in. = 100 ft and 1 in. = 50 ft. All pertinent information necessary for the map is drawn on the plan. The plan is normally long and narrow because it illustrates linear features, such as roads and sewer lines. Refer to Figure 11–5 for proper layout of the plan and profile. Before locating the plan on a drawing, it is important to know how much vertical elevation is to be shown in the profile. Keep in mind that the profile is one of the few CADD drawings not drawn full size. Its scale is related to the elevation difference in the profile view.

The vertical scale of the profile is normally a ratio of 10:1 or 1 in. = 10 ft when the plan scale is 1 in. = 100 ft, and 1 in. = 5 ft when the plan scale is 1 in. = 50 ft. Using the appropriate scale, a drafter determines

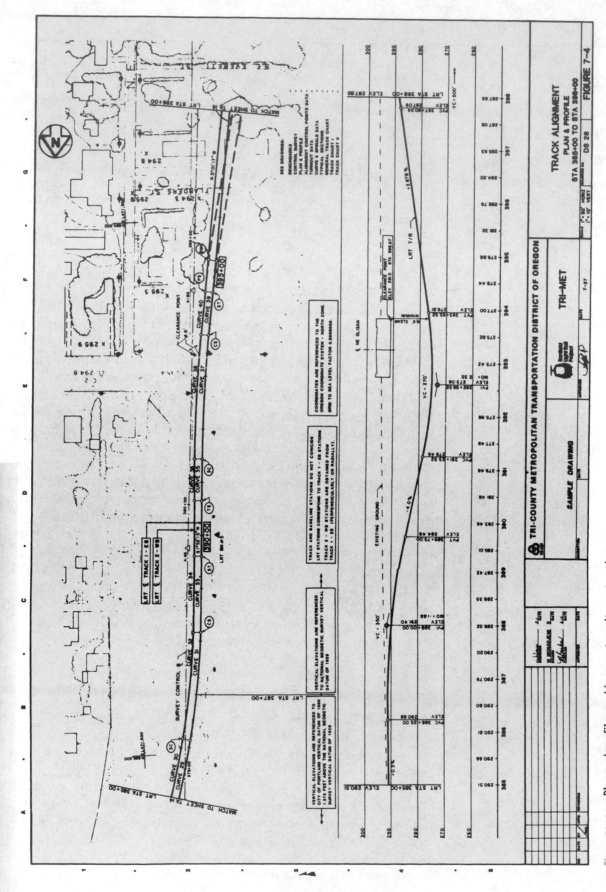

Figure 11–4. Plan and profile used in mass transit construction.
(Courtesy of Tri-Met, Tri-County Metropolitan Transportation District of Oregon)

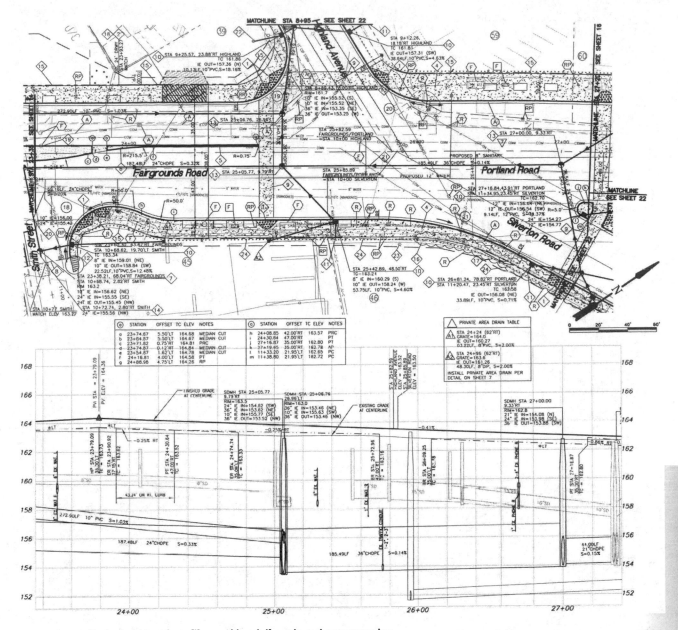

Figure 11-5. Typical plan and profile used by civil engineering companies.
(Courtesy of Otak, Inc.)

from the field notes the amount of elevation to be shown in the profile. This information allows the drafter to decide what size of paper or CAD drawing limits to use and where to locate the views. Because the profile is projected from the plan, the horizontal scales of the two views are the same.

The following step-by-step procedure is provided as an example of profile layout and construction. This example shows the layout of a small section of sewer line and two manholes. The annotations at each manhole provide all the information necessary to construct the profile. Refer to Figure 11-6a-e.

1. Create the plan layout. See Figure 11-6a.

2. Project end points of the sewer line into the new profile area. Project other features, such as manholes, into the profile.

Figure 11–6a. **Begin the profile with the plan layout.**

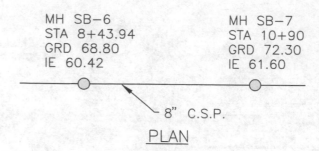

Figure 11–6a. **Begin the profile with the plan layout.**

Figure 11–6b. **Project end points of the sewer line and manhole center points into the area of the new profile.**

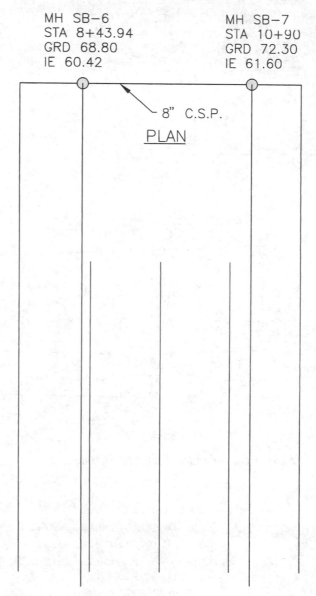

Create vertical grid lines based on the distance required between station points. This example uses 50-ft stations. See Figure 11–6b.

3. Using the elevation data given, determine the lowest and highest elevations and then establish the bottom outline of the profile. Construct horizontal lines at appropriate reference

Figure 11–6c. **Establish the bottom outline of the profile. Construct horizontal lines at appropriate reference elevation values in the profile view.**

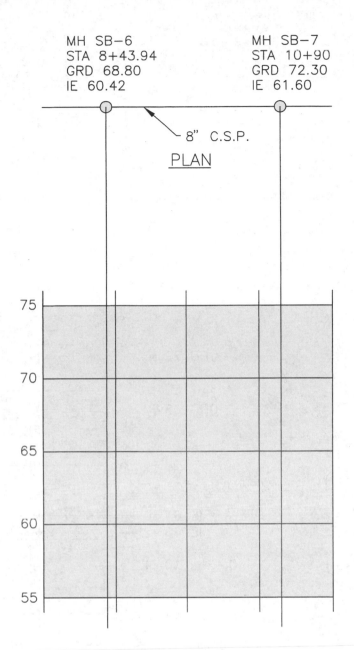

MH SB–6
STA 8+43.94
GRD 68.80
IE 60.42

MH SB–7
STA 10+90
GRD 72.30
IE 61.60

8" C.S.P.

PLAN

75

70

65

60

55

elevation values in the profile view. The lowest pipe elevation is 60.42 ft at MH SB-6, so 55 ft is used as the lowest elevation in the profile. Allow some space between the highest and lowest elevations of the profile. This example uses 5-ft vertical spacing between labeled horizontal grid lines. Apply elevation text labels at this point for easy reference. See Figure 11–6c.

Important Note: Remember that the vertical scale is almost always exaggerated in the profile view, but the horizontal scale in the profile is the same as in the plan view. In this example, the plan scale is 1" = 50', and the vertical profile scale is 1" = 5', a ratio of 10:1. This means that the vertical profile measurements on your drawing should be 10 times their actual value. In this example, the distance between the 70- and 75-ft grid lines will actually measure 50 ft.

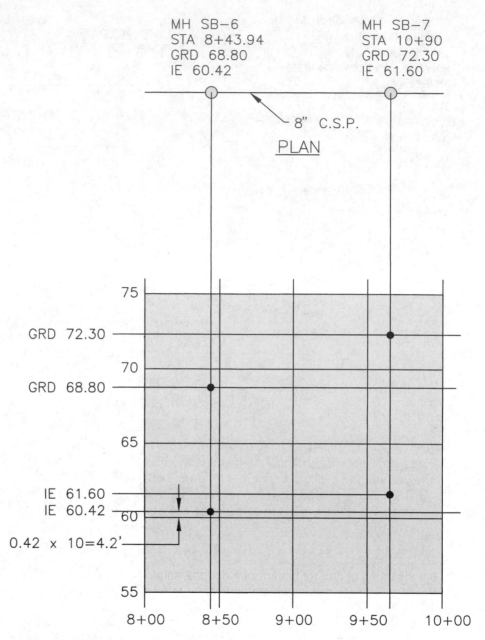

Figure 11-6d. In the profile, locate all elevations required at manholes, such as grade (GRD) and invert elevation (I.E.).

4. In the profile, locate all elevations required at manholes, such as grade (GRD) and invert elevation (I.E., bottom inside of pipe). For example, the elevation of MH SB-6 is 60.42. This is 0.42 above the 60-ft grid. To properly locate this point, multiply 0.42 by 10. The result, 4.20, is the distance above the 60-ft grid to locate the I.E. Project these elevations to intersect the appropriate vertical line projected from the plan. For illustration purposes, only the grade and invert elevations needed to construct the profile are shown to the left of the grid line elevations in Figure 11-6d. Within the profile, dots indicate where these elevations apply.

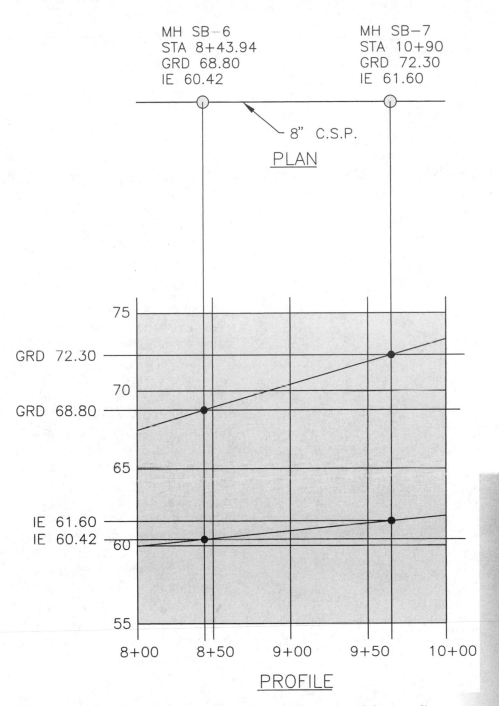

Figure 11–6e. Draw lines representing features such as the grade and the sewer line.

5. Draw lines representing features such as the grade and the sewer line. Be sure to determine whether the grade is natural ground or a flat surface, such as a street or sidewalk. The angle at which these lines extend past the manholes to the edges of the profile are determined by the elevations of features not shown on this drawing. See Figure 11–6e.

6. Apply symbols and labels as required. A similar completed example is shown in Figure 11–7.

Figure 11-7. Profile terms and symbols.

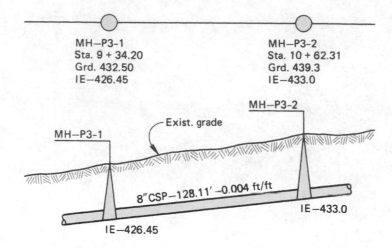

Terms and Symbols

The drafter should keep in mind that certain standard symbols and terms exist that are used frequently throughout the industry. But standards are sometimes modified, and each company may alter things to suit its needs. With this in mind, a drafter should always be aware of the company standards in use at the time.

Full station points are established by surveyors every 100 ft. The first station point is 00 + 00, then 1 + 00, 2 + 00, and so on. The example in Figure 11-5 shows a profile divided every 20 ft by vertical grid lines. At intervals along the plan view, manholes are located, and their specific location is given as a station point value. The manhole symbol and station point value are shown in Figure 11-7, as they appear in both plan and profile. Manholes are abbreviated MH, followed by an assigned number.

An important number called the invert elevation, always found on the profile view and abbreviated I.E., represents the bottom inside of the pipe (see Figure 11-7). This value is established in the design layout of the pipe or sewer line and is important in the surveying, excavating, and construction aspects of the job. Make it a habit to check the invert elevations on your drawing with either the engineer's sketch or the surveyor's field notes.

The distance between station points and the amount of slope are often indicated in the profile just above the pipe (see Figure 11-7). The size of the pipe is given first, and then the distance between manholes, followed by the slope—in this case, vertical drop in feet to horizontal run per foot.

Grade is a common term that means an established elevation such as road grade. This is given with the manhole number and station value in the plan view. The drafter can use this number to plot grade elevation in the profile view.

Not all profiles are located directly under the plan, although this is the ideal situation. Some pipelines or sewers may take several turns through a new subdivision, and the plan itself may not be a linear shape. In this case, the plan may be located to the left of the drawing, with the profile on the right. The profile always appears as a straight line or flat plane, but the plan view may show several turns in the pipe. The profile is constructed in the same manner as we discussed, but the drafter is not able to project points from one view to the next.

Profiles of Curved Lines with CADD

By using a CADD system to manually construct a profile along a linear alignment, you can obtain the exact length of the curve segments from the plan view and transfer those measurements directly to a profile line at the appropriate elevations.

Software such as Autodesk LandDesktop automatically picks up surface elevations along the alignment, be they straight lines or curves, and stores them in a file. This alignment can then be displayed as a profile and enhanced with any additional data and symbols required. If the alignment drawn on the terrain model touches symbols and components such as manholes, drains, or utilities, these will also be displayed on the profile view.

Profile Layout—Vertical Curves

The plan view shows all necessary horizontal control: bearings, distances, radii, and angles. But as in the location and construction of a sewer line, a road requires vertical control. The ground does not remain flat, and the road must reflect this. All necessary vertical information is shown on the profile. The layout of the profile is done in the manner discussed previously.

A vertical curve is the shape of the road or highway as it crests a hill or reaches the bottom of a valley and creates a "sag." These features are calculated mathematically by the engineer or computer program. The drafter is given all necessary elevation points and then plots the curve. In Figure 11–8, the B.V.C. (begin vertical curve) is

Figure 11–8.   **Vertical curve layout.**

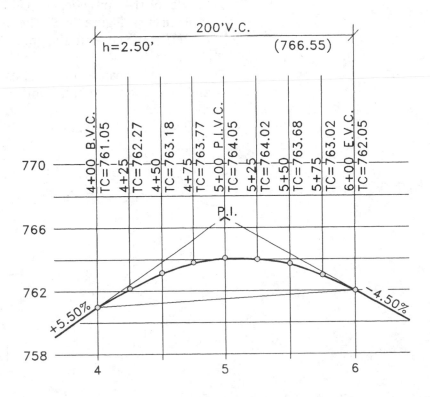

labeled, as is the E.V.C. (end vertical curve). The vertical curve occupies this entire distance and is labeled on the profile as 200 ft V.C.

Keep in mind that a vertical curve is measured as a horizontal distance and not a radius.

The P.I. (point of intersection) on the profile is the intersection of the projected grade lines or grade slopes. The elevation of this point can be calculated using the elevations of the B.V.C. and E.V.C. and grade slopes. Remember that grades are given as percentages.

The vertical curve is tangent to two points, stations 4 + 00 and 6 + 00. A straight line connecting these two stations has an elevation of 761.55 ft directly below the P.I., and the vertical distance between the P.I. and the straight line is 5.00 ft. The vertical curve will pass midway through this distance and have an elevation of 764.05 ft. The distances from the grade line to the curve at each station point can be calculated using this formula:

$$\frac{(D_1)^2 h}{(D)^2} = TD$$

The tangent distance (TD) is the measurement from the grade line to the profile of the curve at a station point. Once you have solved the formula for this distance, the TD can be subtracted from the elevation of the grade line to give you the elevation of the road profile at a specific station point.

Figure 11–9 graphically identifies all the components of the formula. The distance between the B.V.C. and the P.I. is labeled D, and the distance from the B.V.C. to the required station is D_1. The height of the midway point directly below the P.I. is termed h. It can be stated that the distances from the grade line to the road profile are proportional to the squares of the horizontal distances from the tangent points.

Table 11–1 provides the calculations for all the points of the vertical curve in Figure 11–8. The *ordinate* is the tangent distance from the top of the curve to the grade (tangent) line at each horizontal station point.

A drafter can plot the points of the vertical curve at each station and then connect those points to create the curve. This line becomes the profile of the proposed road. Elevations of the road are written vertically at each station point.

Figure 11–9. Components of the vertical curve formula.

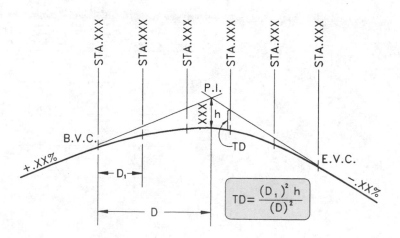

Table 7–1. **Points of the vertical curve in Figure 11–8**

Station	Tangent Elevations	Ordinate	Curve Elevations
4 + 00	761.05	0	761.05
4 + 25	762.43	0.16	762.27
4 + 50	763.81	0.63	763.18
4 + 75	765.18	1.41	763.77
5 + 00	766.55	2.50	764.05
5 + 25	765.43	1.41	764.02
5 + 50	764.31	0.63	763.68
5 + 75	763.18	0.16	763.02
6 + 00	762.05	0	762.05

Figure 11–10. **Visibility studies are useful in highway design.**

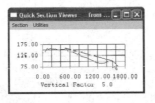

Figure 11–10 shows a visibility study done with a CADD system. These kinds of studies can be useful and efficient when used in conjunction with highway design. Besides using a visibility study, it is possible to use CADD to design highway layouts by including user-defined input such as stopping sight distance (the distance needed to stop safely), passing sight distance (the distance needed to pass safely), and vertical curve limitations.

Profiles with CADD

In a CADD environment, profiles are derived from a combination of digital terrain models (DTMs) and horizontal alignments through a process often referred to as sampling. An alignment is defined and stored as a series of lines and arc segments. They are strictly 2D, but their coordinates, critical geometry, and sequence are known quantities. The beginning of the alignment is assigned a numerical value known as a station, and subsequently all points along the alignment also have stations derived from the beginning station and the distance along the alignment. The surface, or DTM, is also defined and stored by the application, but as a network of 3D data. Comparing the two produces an easily derived list of stations along the alignment and elevations from the surface. This list is utilized to automatically generate a profile. The profile itself can be generated using any user-specified combination of horizontal and vertical scales. A wide range of annotation options is typically available, including text and graphics along the bottom and top of the profile.

CADD packages enable you to work effectively with sewer pipe design and layout, as well as pipe profiles and cross sections. Refer to Figure 11–5 for an example of a plan and profile sheet of a sewer system drawn using CADD software.

The process of designing a proposed finished grade for a roadway has been dramatically enhanced with the advent of sophisticated CADD software. This software recognizes all the critical design considerations, and it offers a dynamic graphical computer environment that is extraordinarily powerful. In Figure 11–11, the condition of the existing ground along the proposed alignment of the new roadway is shown as the jagged line, and the sloping straight line segments show the proposed design of the top of the center of the new road. Vertical curves are locations where the grade changes to provide for driving comfort and safety. The tabular data below the graphical image shows all the mathematical details of the proposed

Figure 11–11. The Carlson Civil user interface for vertical profile design includes both graphical and tabular data.
(Courtesy Carlson Software)

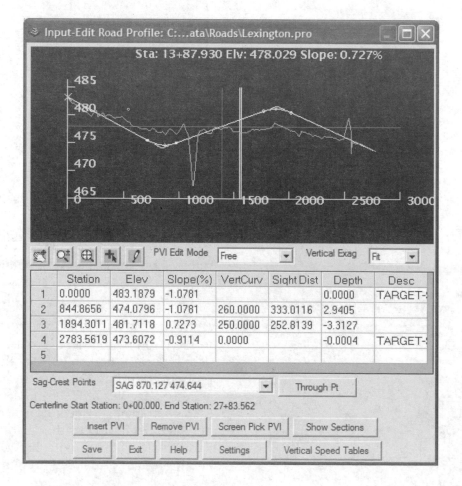

profile. If edits are made in either area of the dialog box, both the graphical and tabular elements will change to reflect the edits.

Plan and Profiles with CADD

A civil CADD engineering drawing typically contains a plan map of the area of a project, showing the existing conditions, along with the proposed design. For a roadway or pipe design project, there are also a profile of the existing conditions along the roadway or pipe alignment and a proposed vertical design for either or, often, both. With these components in place, plan and profile sheets can be easily generated; the desired section of the plan is displayed in one viewing window, and the corresponding section of the profile is displayed in another, and both are placed on a virtual sheet with a title block, notes, and details. A site plan with a proposed road profile is shown in Figure 11–12.

Figure 11–12. **A plan view of a site with a proposed roadway and profile created using Autodesk Land Desktop software.**

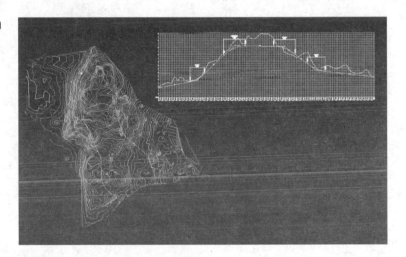

TEST

Use Microsoft Word to open the file "Chapter 11 test" on the Student Web site.

11-1   What is a map profile?

11-2   What are the uses of a map profile?

11-3   Why is the vertical scale of a map profile exaggerated?

11-4   Which points are projected from a map to the profile?

11-5   Define *profile leveling*.

11-6   How is the location of an IFS determined?

11-7   Write the following values in the proper station format.

300 – _____
567 – _____
298.43 – _____

11-8   What type of feature would require a profile leveling of connected straight lines and curves?

11-9   Who uses a plan and profile and for what purpose?

11-10   What scales are common for a plan and profile?

11-11   A point established every 100 ft in a linear survey is called a _____.

11–12   What is invert elevation?

11–13   What information is found next to a manhole symbol on a plan and profile?

11–14   What is an established elevation called?

11–15   Why is a profile necessary for road construction?

11–16   What type of information does a vertical curve show?

11–17   What use does a visibility study have?

STREET PLAN AND PROFILE

Study the portion of a street plan and profile in Figure T11–1 to answer the following questions. Use Microsoft Word to open the file "Ch 11 streetprofile" on the Student Web site, and use AutoCAD to open file "streetprofile."

1. The highest point on the profile is Station _____, at elevation _____.

2. Keynote 2 refers to _____ that crosses through Lots _____, Block _____ and Lots _____, Block _____.

3. The surface drainage flow along Florida Avenue changes direction at Station _____.

4. The elevation at the intersection of Edwards Avenue and Florida Avenue is _____.

5. The shallowest slope indicated on the profile is _____%.

6. The steepest slope indicated on the profile is _____ %.

7. The vertical scale of the profile is _____ times that of the horizontal scale.

8. The elevation at Station 7 + 41.20 is _____ and indicates the corner between Lots _____, Block _____.

9. The dashed line across the rear of Lots 10 through 15, Block 8, indicates the location of _____.

10. The distance from the west subdivision boundary to the centerline of Edwards Avenue is _____.

11. The existing sidewalk on Edwards Avenue ends at Station _____, elevation _____.

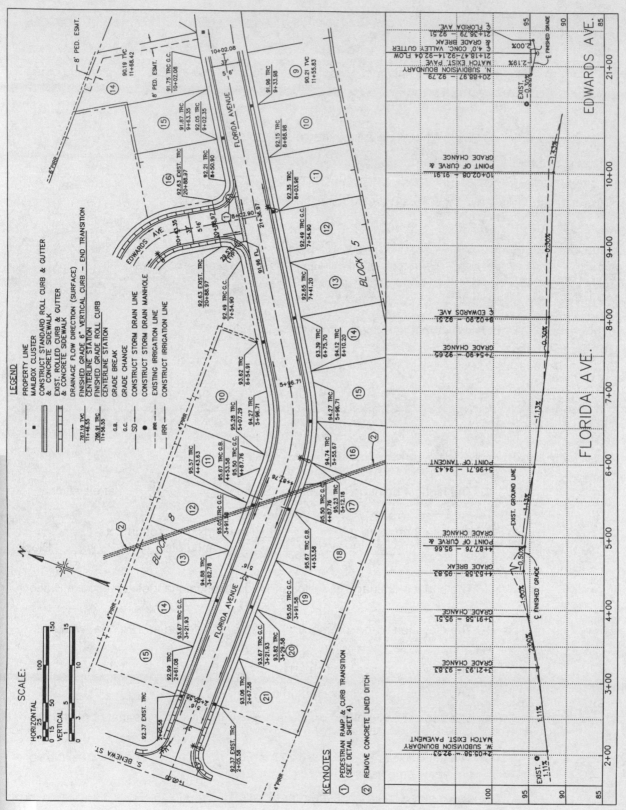

Portion of Street Plan and Profile   Courtesy of Capital Development; Boise, Idaho

Figure T11-1.

(Courtesy of Captial Development, Boise, Idaho)

PROBLEMS

P11–1 Construct a map profile along line *AB* in the map shown in Figure P9–3. The vertical scale should be exaggerated. Use an A- or B-size sheet of vellum. Label vertical elevations and indicate scales. Use a proper sectioning symbol to indicate earth. Make a print and submit it to your instructor for evaluation, unless otherwise indicated.

P11–2 a. This problem requires you to plot a profile of a curved road. Construct your profile in the space provided on Figure P11–2 or on a separate sheet of paper. Use the steps discussed in this chapter.

b. Using your CADD system, digitize or scan the plan view of Figure P11–2. Plot the profile of the curved road using the steps discussed in this chapter. Plot at a horizontal scale of 1 in. = 200 ft and a vertical scale of 1 in. = 20 ft on C-size paper and submit it to your instructor for evaluation.

Use AutoCAD to open the file "P11–2" on the Student Web site.

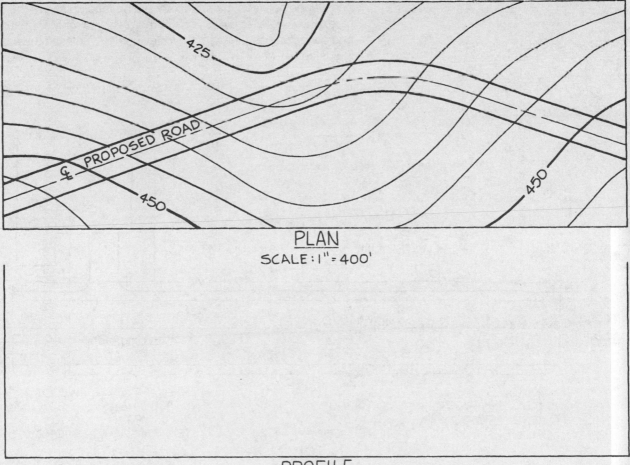

PLAN

SCALE : 1" = 400'

PROFILE

Figure P11–2.

P11-3   Survey stakes have been located along the centerline of a proposed street. A shot from the instrument to BM-1 has established an H.I. of 567.28 ft. Beginning at station 0 + 00, IFS shots have been taken at full stations for the length of the street, and their values are 0.8, 2.6, 3.1, 3.8, 4.5, 5.1, 6.4, 7.1, 7.5, 8.3, 7.7, 7.5, 7.0, 6.2, 5.4, 9.6, 8.1, 4.7, 3.9, 3.5. Plot the profile for these stations. The final drawing should be plotted on a C-size piece of paper. Select the appropriate scales and label the station and elevation values.

P11-4   a. Figure P11–4 is an engineering sketch of the plan view of a road and underground utilities. Remember that engineering sketches, by their nature, may not accurately reflect proper drafting and layout techniques. That is true of this sketch. The dimensions, however, are accurate. Using the information given, construct a plan and profile on C-size paper. Show all necessary information discussed in the text. Distances and slope between manholes should be labeled above the sewer pipe, as shown in Figure 11–7. Show water and gas lines in the plan view only. Make a print and submit it to your instructor for evaluation, unless otherwise indicated.

   b. Using your CADD system and the information given in Figure P11–4, construct a plan and profile on a separate sheet of C-size paper. Show all necessary information discussed in the text. Distances and slopes between manholes should be labeled above the sewer pipe. Show water and gas lines in the plan view only. Plot at $1'' = 50'$ and submit it to your instructor for evaluation, unless otherwise indicated.

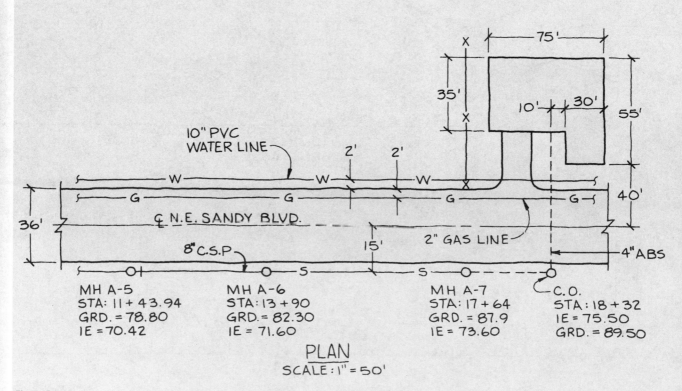

PLAN
SCALE : 1" = 50'

Figure P11–4.

P11-5 Figure P11–5 is the plan view of a survey line of 1500 ft. Using C-size paper, draw the survey in scale of 1 in. = 50 ft and plot all the existing features. Make proper note of the curve data and the points where the curve begins and ends. Show all data for location and the beginning transit line bearing. Show the north arrow with the scale of the drawing below.

Draw the survey line on the top half of the C-size paper and record the survey line elevations on a grid on the lower half of the sheet. The grid should reflect the vertical elevation changes and the horizontal station locations.

Survey Line Elevations

Sta.	Elev.	Sta.	Elev.
15 + 00	119.0	22 + 60	124.0
15 + 30	120.0	23 + 00	123.0
15 + 70	120.5	23 + 50	121.0
16 + 00	120.0	23 + 75	120.0
16 + 60	118.0	24 + 00	119.0
17 + 00	117.0	25 + 00	117.75
18 + 00	119.0	25 + 50	117.25
18 + 70	120.0	26 + 00	117.75
19 + 00	120.5	26 + 50	118.0
19 + 60	121.0	27 + 00	119.0
20 + 00	121.5	27 + 50	119.0
20 + 50	122.0	28 + 00	118.0
20 + 80	124.0	29 + 00	114.0
21 + 00	125.0	29 + 50	112.0
22 + 00	126.0	30 + 00	110.0

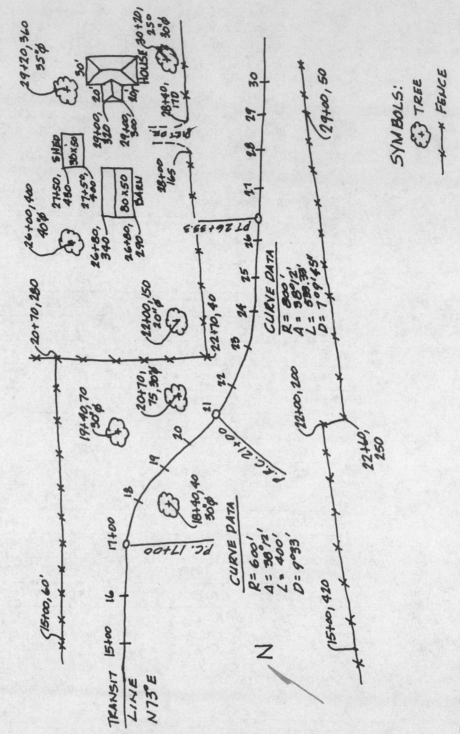

SURVEY FIELD NOTES

SYMBOLS:
TREE
FENCE

Figure P11-5.

P11-6 Construct a set of six profiles across the piece of property shown in Figure P9–8. One profile cuts through the transit station, Point *A*. The other profiles are 50 ft apart (see Figure P11–6). Show all profiles on a single sheet of paper. Horizontal scale should be 1 in. = 100 ft, and the vertical scale should be 10 times the horizontal. Each profile should be only as long as the distance between property lines along the profile. Show elevation values for each profile. Label each profile with a subtitle, such as PROFILE A.

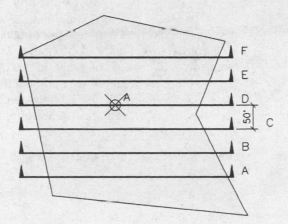

Figure P11-6.

P11-7 Construct a series of profiles across the stream in Figure P9–7. The first profile should be 50 ft from the southern property line, along the stream, and should be labeled PROFILE A. Label each profile consecutively. Each profile should be cut perpendicular to the stream and extend for 100 ft beyond the stream, or to the edge of the property. Profiles should be 25 ft apart and cover the entire length of the stream on the property. Determine the best horizontal and vertical scales to use in order to arrange all profiles on a D-size sheet of paper. Use a 10:1 ratio for horizontal and vertical scales. Label elevations on all profiles.

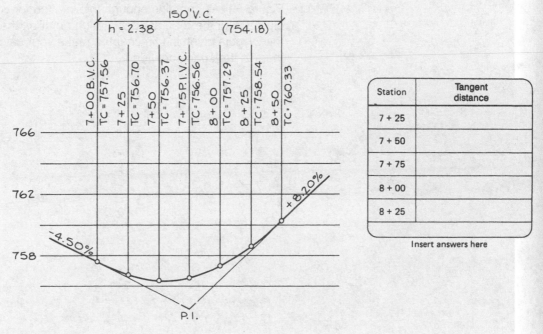

Figure P11-7.

P11-8   Cut a profile along the stream in the drawing created in problem P11–7.
         Determine the best location for a small dam and pond with a water level
         that keeps the pond inside the property line. Construct any needed
         profiles to show the height of the dam and the water line. Add the dam
         and pond to the map. The drawings submitted for this problem should
         include the map and profiles and should provide enough information to
         fully describe the size and location of the dam and pond.

P11-9   A sewer line is to be added to the house in Figure P9–7. Run the sewer
         30 ft from the west edge of the house. The new sewer connects with a
         main sewer 30 ft south of the southern property line. Keep the new
         sewer 10 ft east of the driveway. Show a cleanout (CO) 10 ft from the
         house. Show an additional CO between the house and the main
         connection, no farther than 100 ft from the nearest CO. Use the
         following information for this problem:

         House sewer pipe is 4-in. ABS.

         Sewer main is 8-in. CSP.

         Grade at house is 608 ft.

         Sewer line IE at house is 603 ft.

         IE at house CO is 602.5 ft.

         Grade above sewer main is 584 ft.

         Sewer IE at connection point is 574.80 ft.

         Create a plan and profile for the sewer installation. Do not show all the
         property. Show contours on the plan. Construct the drawing so it is
         similar to the one in Figure P11–4. In the profile along the sewer, note
         the type of pipe, distance between cleanouts, and slope in FT/FT.
         Choose appropriate scales and size of paper for this problem.

P11-10   Figure P11–7 contains enough information for you to calculate the
         elevation of the road at each station point on the vertical curve. Using
         the formula given in this chapter, make your calculations and record
         them in the space provided.

Earthwork

Learning Objectives

After completing this chapter, you will be able to:

- Define and use *angle of repose* in a cut-and-fill drawing.
- Create an accurate cut-and-fill drawing of a proposed highway.
- Construct cross-section drawings using cross section survey data.
- Construct an accurate cut-and-fill drawing of a proposed building site.
- Calculate quantities of earth removed from borrow pits.
- Construct borrow pit excavation grids.
- Calculate earthwork volumes of cross sections using the *average end* method.

Key Terms

Earthwork
Cut and fill
Borrow pit
Angle of repose
Percent of grade
Frequency
Cross section

Earthwork is a term used in construction to describe quantities of earth either excavated from areas or filled into low spots. Cut and fill represents earth that is cut from hillsides and filled into valleys and low areas. Borrow pits are excavations along highways or construction projects from which material is removed and used as fill elsewhere. This chapter describes how earthwork can be plotted on maps for highways and site plans and how the volumes of earth can be calculated with mathematical formulae.

The topics covered include:

- Establishing the cross section profile
- Locating cut-and-fill boundaries
- Plotting cuts and fills for an inclined road
- Highway cut-and-fill layout with a CADD system
- Site plan cut-and-fill layout
- Borrow pit calculations

Highway Cut-and-Fill Layout—Traditional Method

The following discussion of laying out highway cut and fill was used prior to the advent of today's powerful civil engineering software. These methods could be used with board drafting or completed manually with generic CADD software. Readers who do not have the use of software such as Autodesk Land Desktop can still use AutoCAD to complete this type of civil drawing.

Level Roads

In designing or planning the location of a road, it is necessary to accurately determine how far the cuts and fills will extend beyond the sides of the road. This is important in determining the proper amount of land to be purchased for the right-of-way.

The road is first plotted on a contour map using surveying field data and one of the highway layout techniques discussed in Chapter 10 (see Figure 12–1a). The engineer establishes an angle of repose, which is the slope of the cut and fill from the road. The angle of repose is basically the ratio of run to rise (Figure 12–2), and it is determined primarily by the type of soil or rock to be cut through or used as fill material. An angle of repose of 2:1 means that for every 2 ft of horizontal distance, the slope rises or drops 1 ft vertically.

A cross-sectional view, or profile, is established off the end of the road. Then the angle of repose slope is plotted. Using an angle of repose of 1 1/2:1 for an area of cut, the slope is determined by measuring from the edge of the road 1 1/2 units horizontally and then measuring 1 unit vertically and marking that point. A straight line connecting the edge of the road and the point just measured reflects the 1 1/2:1 angle of repose. See Figure 12–1b.

The location of contour lines on this slope is determined by measuring vertically from the road using the horizontal scale of the map. Mark each contour value above and below the road and then project these marks to the slope lines to find the contour locations. See Figure 12–1b.

Figure 12-1a. Begin cut-and-fill layout by plotting the new road on the map.

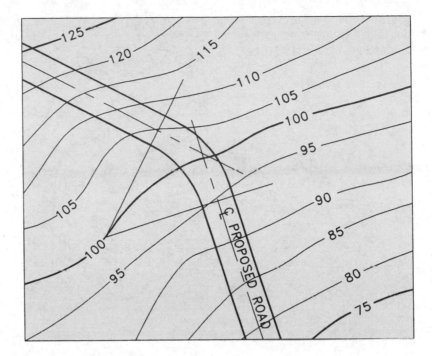

Figure 12-1b. Cut-and-fill cross section is added to the map perpendicular to the road.

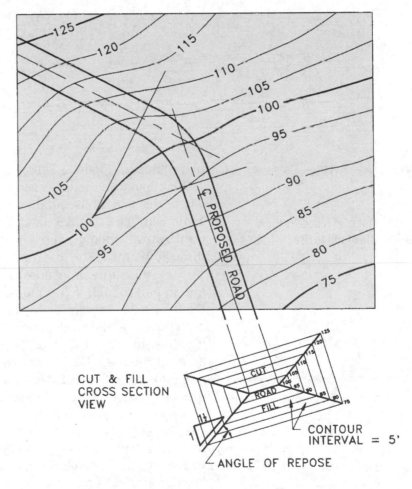

The points at which the contour values intersect the angle of repose in the cross section are projected onto the map and parallel to the road. Project all lines as shown in Figure 12-1c. Cut-and-fill boundaries, such as the top of a cut and the toe of a fill, are located next. To

Figure 12–1c. Intersection of cross section values with map contour lines permits outlines of cut and fill to be drawn.

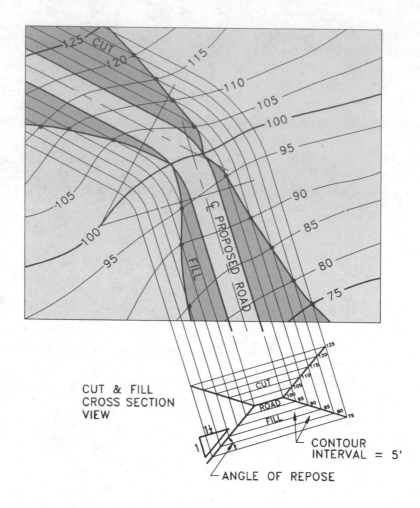

CUT & FILL
CROSS SECTION
VIEW

CONTOUR
INTERVAL = 5'

ANGLE OF REPOSE

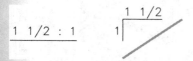

1 1/2 : 1

Figure 12–2. Angle of repose is the same as the ratio of run to rise.

plot the cut in Figure 12–1c, first follow the line projecting from the 105-ft contour in the cross section up into the map and make a mark where this line intersects the 105-ft contour line on the map. Do the same with the 110-, 115-, and 120-ft contour marks in the cross section. Always follow each line from the cross section completely through the map. The line may cross its contour more than once.

Use this same procedure to plot the cut on both sides of the road and to plot the fill. If cut and fill are the same angle of repose, as in Figure 12–1c, the lines projected from the cross section represent both the cut and the fill values. But if cut and fill are different angles, it is best to project the cut lines from the cross section only along areas of the map that are above the level of the road. In a like manner, project scale lines for fill from the cross section only into areas of the map that are below the level of the road. This prevents the confusion of having two sets of lines along the entire length of the road.

To complete the cut-and-fill boundaries, begin drawing a line at the intersection of the road and the contour line having the same elevation as the road. Keep the cut-and-fill boundary line between the lines projected from the cross section until you reach the next mark on a contour line. See Figure 12–1c.

Figure 12–3 is a pictorial representation of the map in Figure 12–1.

If you are using a CADD system such as AutoCAD, you may not need to create the cut-and-fill profile scale below the map. Using the

Figure 12–3.   **Pictorial view of a cut and fill.**

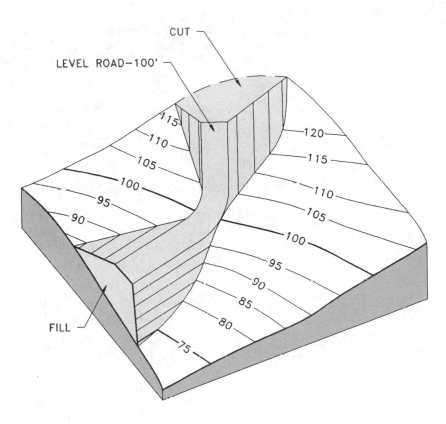

following procedure enables you to quickly plot the outlines of cut and fill with just a few commands:

1. Create two layers named Cut Scale and Fill Scale.

2. Determine the angle of repose for the cut—for example, 1 1/2:1—and the contour interval. This example uses a contour interval of 5 ft.

3. Multiply the angle of repose by the contour interval:

$$1\ 1/2 \times 5 = 7.5\ \text{ft}$$

4. Using a command such as OFFSET in AutoCAD, offset the sides of the road 7.5 ft several times on each side of the road. Be sure to change these offset lines to the Cut Scale layer. Turn off this layer so it is not visible.

5. Determine the angle of repose for fill—for example, 2:1—and multiply this by the contour interval:

$$2 \times 5 = 10\ \text{ft}$$

6. Offset the sides of the road 10 ft several times on each side of the road. Be sure to change these offset lines to the Fill Scale layer.

7. Now you will have cut-and-fill scale lines such as those shown in Figure 12–1c, and you can use these lines to plot the outline of cut and fill.

Inclined Roads

The amount of cut and fill for an inclined road can best be established with a plan and profile. The road is plotted on the contour map as for a level road, but a profile of the existing grade along the entire centerline is drawn as shown in Figure 12–4.

The *grade* of the road is determined and plotted on the profile. The grade is termed percent of grade. A 1-percent grade rises 1 ft vertically for every 100 ft of horizontal distance. Therefore, a 100-percent grade is a 45° angle.

The road in Figure 12–4 has a 2.5-percent grade and an angle of repose of 2.1 for both cut and fill. To establish cut and fill, first project the intersections of each contour line and road centerline from the map to the profile drawing. At the point where the line projected from the road centerline on the map intersects the road grade in the profile, measure from the road to the surface of the natural ground line. For example, the intersection of contour 185 is projected from the road centerline in the map to the profile. The measurement along this line in the profile from the road to the natural ground elevation is 5 ft. Multiply this figure by the angle of repose (2) and place that measurement

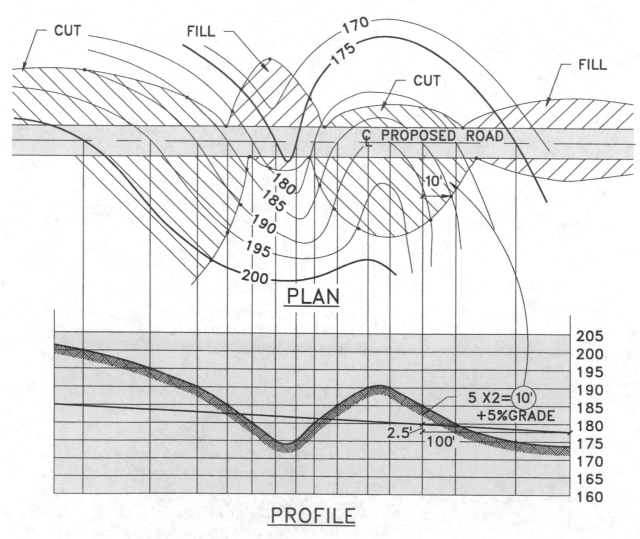

Figure 12–4.   Cut-and-fill layout for an inclined road.

perpendicular to the edge of the road in the map plan, point *A*. Project this point parallel to the road to the 185′ contour, point *B*, as shown in Figure 12–4. Do this for all the contours that cross the road in the profile. The points can then be connected to delineate the areas of cut and fill.

Highway Cut-and-Fill Layout with a CADD System

A 3D model of a proposed roadway can be constructed using civil engineering CADD software. The designer or engineer must first designate a horizontal alignment, a vertical alignment, the shape of the roadway corridor—sometimes called a template or a typical cross section—and the angle of repose of the slopes that project perpendicularly from the edge of the roadway. These projections interact with a surface, or digital terrain model, of the existing conditions, to calculate horizontally and vertically, where they intersect the existing ground. The interval along the alignment at which the projections are calculated is often referred to as the frequency.

By developing a model of a proposed roadway and having it interact with a model of the existing conditions at the site, the limits of slope work are calculated and drawn, as are the cut-and-fill volumes of earthwork needed to build the roadway. If the typical cross section of the roadway is designed with detail, the volumes of select materials, such as asphalt, gravel, and curbing, can be calculated by the software as well.

Cross Sections

The previous discussion of highway cut-and-fill layout covers a method used for plotting cut and fill using only route survey data of a road centerline. After laying out the highway, the angles of repose were used to plot the cut and fill.

The cross section method of plotting cut and fill is based on field surveys, or lines of levels run perpendicular to the road. These level lines are often short and span only the width of the highway and areas affected by the cut or fill. Cross sections are important because they provide measurements that can be used for calculating the amounts of earth to be removed from hills and filled into valleys and areas below road grade.

Cross Section Surveys

Profiles perpendicular to the road centerline are usually measured at full stations (every 100 ft), at 50-ft stations, and at breaks, or changes in the profile of the centerline. The sections extend far enough from the centerline to include any cut or fill.

The level instrument is set up at a station that allows several profile measurements to be made from one instrument location. Each foresight reading along the centerline is noted as an *intermediate foresight (IFS)*. The IFS is located at a station or elevation change.

Additional rod readings are taken at set distances perpendicular to the centerline. For example, an IFS reading of 6.4 is recorded on the centerline. Then the rod is moved 15 ft perpendicular from the centerline and a rod reading, or foresight (F.S.), of 7.9 is recorded. The elevation difference is −1.5 ft (6.4 − 7.9 = −1.5). A second F.S. of 9.2 is measured 35 ft perpendicular from the centerline, and the elevation difference from the centerline is −2.8 ft (6.4 − 9.2 = −2.8). See Figure 12–5. This process is used on both sides of the centerline.

Cross Section Field Notes

Field notes for level profiles and cross sections contain all the information required to construct cross section drawings. Figure 12–6 shows an example of cross section field notes. Surveyors try to measure several cross sections before moving to another instrument setup. A T.P. measurement is taken to relocate the instrument. Several IFS readings can then be taken from one station. Surveyors may also begin their cross section notes at the bottom of the page. This places measurements on the right side of the centerline on the right side of the page.

The elevation notes for the profile are usually given on the left side of the page, and the measurements for the cross section appear on the right. Notice that the cross section notes contain what appear to be positive and negative fractions. The numerator is the elevation difference from the centerline IFS. The denominator represents the distance of that point from the centerline. The plus or minus indicates whether the point is above or below the elevation of the IFS on the centerline.

Cross Sections with a CADD System

After a vertical design for a proposed roadway has been produced, CADD software can develop a digital 3D model of the proposed road. Then slices of the proposed roadway model and the existing conditions model can be taken at regular intervals along the roadway to better visualize the design of the roadway and its interconnection with the existing conditions along the path of construction. These slices are known as cross sections. In Figure 12–7, the Carlson Civil

Figure 12–5. Cross section surveys are composed of several elevation measurements taken perpendicular to the centerline.

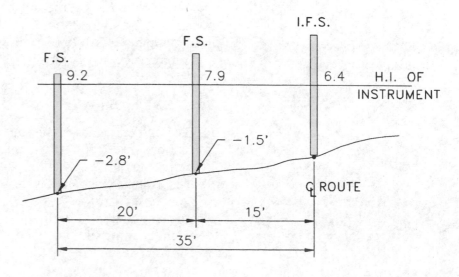

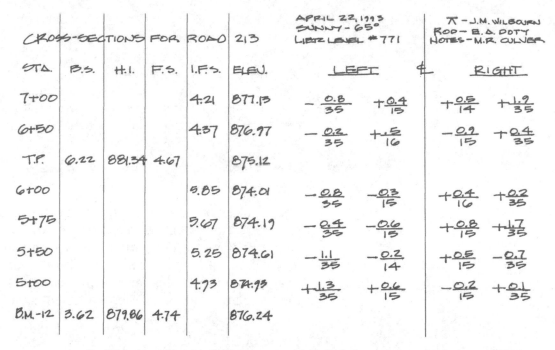

Figure 12-6. Traditional cross section field notes contain all the information required to construct cross section drawings. Current surveying methods use electronic data collectors to store field notes.

Figure 12-7. The Carlson Civil dialog box displays roadway cross sectional data and graphics for analysis and/or editing.
(Courtesy Carlson Software)

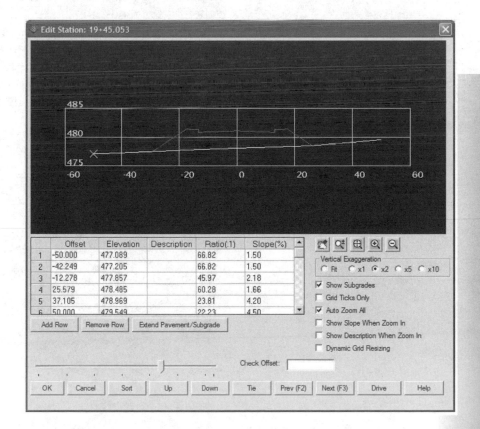

roadway design software is displaying a cross sectional view for Station 19+45.053. The existing ground slopes gently from the lower left, and the proposed roadway sits atop the existing grade. The tabular data displayed below the graphical window displays the actual mathematical data occurring at this location.

Site Plan Cut-and-Fill Layout

The following discussion outlines the procedure that can be used to plot the cut and fill surrounding a site without using surveyors' profile notes or cross section notes. This procedure can be used to estimate the approximate limits of cut and fill. A series of profile cross sections can be surveyed at the site to determine more exact areas of cut and fill.

Site Plan Layout

The property boundaries for the proposed site are plotted on a contour map using surveyors' notes. The elevation of the site (after excavation or filling) is determined by the engineer, as is the required angle of repose. This information may be given on the plan as well as bearings and distances for the property lines. Figure 12–8 depicts the site plan layout before application of cut and fill.

Cut and Fill

The drafter should first determine the areas of cut and fill. Then the appropriate scales for each can be plotted on the map. In Figure 12–9, the angle of repose for cuts is 2:1 and 1 1/2:1 for fills. The contour interval is 2 ft. In areas of fill, measure perpendicular to the property lines 1 1/2 times the contour interval and draw a line parallel to the property line. For the areas of cut, measure perpendicular to the property lines 2 times the contour interval, or 4 ft, and draw lines parallel to the site boundaries. Closely study the example in Figure 12–9.

Figure 12–8. **Site plan layout before application of cut and fill.**

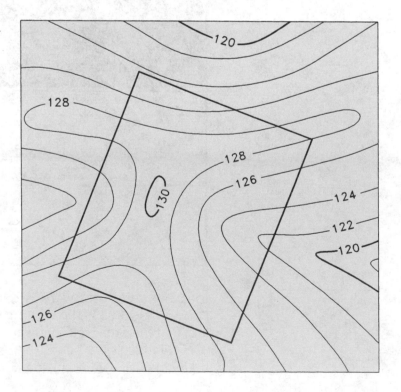

The elevation for the site is to be 126 ft. Areas below this elevation are fill, and areas above are cut. Where the first line of the fill scale intersects the 124-ft contour, make a mark. The second line of the fill scale is the 122-ft contour. Find all the intersections of like contours and then connect those points, as shown in Figure 12–10. Use the same technique when finding the required points for the cut. The first line parallel to the property line on the cut scale is 128 ft.

The cut-and-fill scale lines can be added quickly using a CADD system in the same manner previously discussed for highway cut

Figure 12-9. Site plan layout with cut-and-fill scales added.

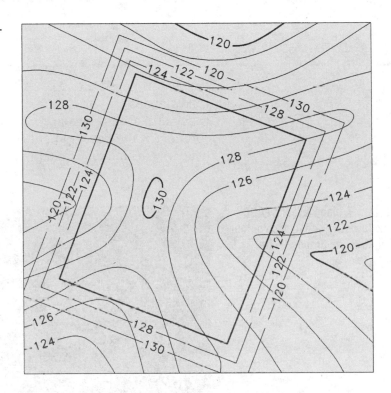

Figure 12-10. Completed site plan layout showing areas of cut and fill.

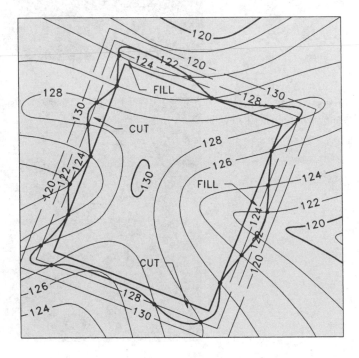

and fill. Create layers called Cut Scale and Fill Scale. Then offset the sides of the property for both cut and fill, using the formula:

Angle of repose × Contour interval = Offset distance

Be sure that the lines you offset are changed to the appropriate layer before you begin plotting the cut-and-fill outlines.

From this map, the amounts of excavation and fill can be estimated. Any profiles that are needed can be taken directly from the map. Legends and additional information can be placed on the map as required.

Site Plan Cut-and-Fill Layout with a CADD System

Just as it is possible to use CADD software to enhance the process of roadway design, site design can also be performed using CADD. The main similarity between roadway and site design in a CADD environment is the development of two digital terrain models that interact with each other. One represents existing conditions and the other

Figure 12–11. A plan view of a CADD terrain model with grading and contour lines applied to the proposed site.

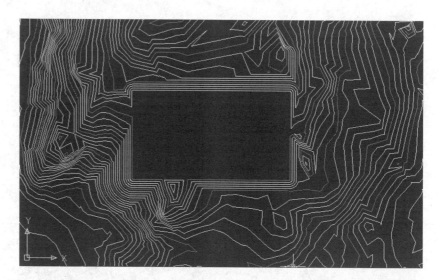

Figure 12–12. The same site shown in Figure 12–11 is shown here in a 3D view.

proposed improvements. Their interaction determines the limits of slope work and the volume of material needed to construct the design. The main difference is that a roadway design is based on an alignment, and a site design is not. Other than that, many of the same calculations are derived from the process. Figure 12–11 shows a 2D plan view of a terrain model with contour lines applied to the proposed site. Figure 12–12 displays the same site in a 3D view. Notice the cut at the rear of the site and the fill at the front.

Earthwork Calculations

Drainage Considerations

When developing site grading plans, the most essential factor to consider is drainage. Determining how water will flow on the site and exit the site is of foremost concern. A *hydrologic* study of the existing conditions of the site would include the type of soils and ground cover present, how water flows on the site, how much water is absorbed, and the volume and direction of water leaving the site.

An analysis of these factors must also be assembled based on the proposed design. When a field or forest is replaced with a paved parking area, there are major impacts to consider. Much less water is absorbed into the ground and hence exits the site. The water is also contaminated from flowing across the asphalt. Drainage collection basins and pools are often constructed to prevent contaminants from flowing into watersheds. These collection basins are often landscaped with plants that absorb and clean pollutants from the water. In addition, ponds and basins hold water long enough to allow for evaporation of some pollutants.

The effects of different amounts of rain are calculated to determine what are known as 1-year, 10-year, 50-year, and 100-year storms. A 1-year storm is the worst storm that is likely to occur in a 1-year period, a 10-year storm is the worst storm that is likely to occur in that time period, and so on. Careful design assessments are also made to impacts on wetland areas, including direct impact from earthwork on the site and drainage from a site flowing into existing wetland areas.

Borrow Pits

A *borrow pit* is an area from which quantities of earth are excavated to construct embankments and fills. Borrow pits are often visible at interchanges along interstate highways. They can appear as square, rectangular, or trapezoidal ponds because they often fill with water.

Accurate calculations of borrow material are important because the contractor is paid based on the amount of earth removed. The price per cubic yard is multiplied by the number of yards excavated and hauled.

A borrow pit is defined by laying out a grid. The size of the grid is determined by the amount of material needed, the type of soil, and the land available. The grid is composed of squares with sides of

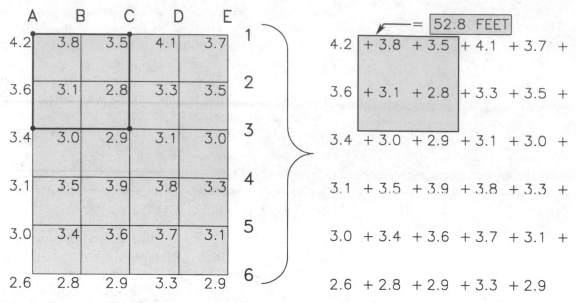

Figure 12–13. The borrow pit is laid out as a grid, and the final excavation depths are labeled at each grid intersection.

20, 40, 50, or 100 ft. See Figure 12–13. The elevations of each grid intersection are determined by running levels. Reference points, or hubs, are established on extension lines beyond the limits of the grid. Using these reference hubs, the grid can be easily relocated after the excavation.

The elevations of the grid intersections are determined after excavation by running levels again. The heights of the cut are recorded for each intersection, as shown in Figure 12–13. These values can then be used to determine the quantity of borrow material. The quantity of earthwork in one of the squares is calculated by multiplying the area of the section by the average of cut depths at each corner. For example, in Figure 12–13, the square $A1$, $A2$, $B1$, $B2$ is 50 ft × 50 ft, or 2500 sq ft. The average depth of its four corners is:

$$\frac{4.2 + 3.8 + 3.6 + 3.1}{4} = 3.675$$

Multiply 2500 × 3.675 and the result is 9187.5 cu ft. Divide cubic feet by 27 to obtain cubic yards:

$$\frac{9187.5}{27} = 340.28 \text{ cu yd}$$

The most accurate calculations can be obtained by following this procedure for each square in the grid. The procedure can be simplified by combining squares of the same dimensions. For example, to find the material in the larger square of $A1$, $A3$, $C1$, $C3$, you must find the average of all the corner depths for four squares. Corners that are common to more than one square must be added for each square. The total of the corner depths for the large square just defined is 52.8 (see Figure 12–13). Divide this by 4, and the average cut depth is 13.2 ft. Finally, the average cut depth multiplied by the area of the square (2500 ft) is 33,000 cu ft, or 1222 cu yd. One cu yd is equal to 27 cu ft.

The formula for determining the amount of material is:

Area of section × Average of corner depths = Cubic feet

The number of cubic yards is then calculated as follows:

$$\frac{\text{Cubic feet}}{27} = \text{Cubic yards}$$

The values in the previous example are calculated as follows:

13.2 × 2500 = 33,000 ÷ 27 = 1222 cu yd

Cut and Fill by Average End Method

Maps that are constructed using CADD programs and specialized application software can contain enough data for calculating earthwork volumes. These procedures, based on computer-generated data, are often sufficient for construction and estimating purposes. But it is important for surveyors and civil drafters to understand the nature of cross section area calculations and to be able to calculate volumes of earthwork in cut and fill.

A *level* cross section is one in which the ground is basically level, and the height, or depth, of the cut is constant across the profile. The area (A) of a level cross section is calculated by figuring the average of the top and bottom widths (d and w) and multiplying this by the height (h) of the cut (or fill) (see Figure 12–14):

$$A = h\left(\frac{2d + w}{2}\right)$$

$$A = h\left(d + \frac{w}{2}\right)$$

A cross section that is not level but has three distinct levels, is calculated by finding the area of triangles. See Figure 12–15. The following formula can be used for these calculations:

$$A = \left(\frac{1}{2}\right)\left(\frac{w}{2}\right)(h_1 + h_2) + \left(\frac{1}{2}\right)(c)(d_1 + d_2)$$

$$A = \frac{w}{4}(h_1 + h_2) + \frac{c}{2}(d_1 + d_2)$$

These two formulae allow you to calculate the area of a cross section. These areas can then be used to calculate earthwork volumes. The *average end method* uses the averages of the two end cross sections to compute the volume of earth between the sections. The volume (V) is equal to the average area of the two cross sections (A_1

Figure 12–14. The area of a level cross section is calculated by using the dimensions of the profile.

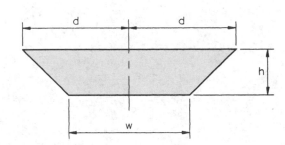

Figure 12-15. The area of cross
sections that are not level but that have
three distinct levels are calculated by
finding the area of triangles.

Figure 12-15. The area of cross
sections that are not level but that have
three distinct levels are calculated by
finding the area of triangles.

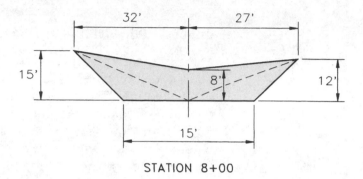

Figure 12-16. The volume of earth
between these two cross sections is
1161.36 cu yd.

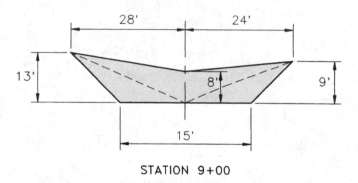

STATION 8+00

STATION 9+00

and A_2) multiplied by the distance between the two (D). The number
of cubic yards is determined by dividing the result by 27:

$$V = \left(\frac{A_1 + A_2}{2}\right)\left(\frac{D}{27}\right)$$

The following examples illustrate how averages can be calculated for the two cross sections shown in Figure 12–16. The averages
are then used to calculate the earthwork volumes between the two
sections.

Section 8+00

$$A = \left(\frac{1}{2}\right)\left(\frac{w}{2}\right)(h_1 + h_2) + \left(\frac{1}{2}\right)(c)(d_1 + d_2)$$

$$A = \frac{w}{4}(h_1 + h_2) + \frac{c}{2}(d_1 + d_2)$$

$$A = \frac{15}{4}(15 + 12) + \frac{8}{2}(32 + 27)$$

$$A = 101.25 + 236 = 337.25 \text{ sq ft}$$

Section 9+00

$$A = \frac{w}{4}(h_1 + h_2) + \frac{c}{2}(d_1 + d_2)$$

$$A = \frac{15}{4}(13 + 9) + \frac{8}{2}(28 + 24)$$

$$A = 82.5 + 208 = 290.5 \text{ sq ft}$$

Now that the areas of the two sections have been determined, an earthwork calculation for the volume of material between the two sections can be made. The following formula allows you to find the volume in cubic yards. In this formula, A equals the area of a cross section, and D is the distance between cross sections:

$$V = \left(\frac{A_1 + A_2}{2}\right)\left(\frac{D}{27}\right)$$

$$V = \left(\frac{337.25 + 290.5}{2}\right)\left(\frac{100}{27}\right)$$

$$V = 313.88 \times 3.70 = 1161.36 \text{ cu yd}$$

TEST

Use Microsoft Word to open the file "Chapter 12 test" on the Student Web site.

12-1   What is cut and fill?

12-2   Why is it necessary that cuts and fills be accurate?

12-3   What determines the slope of a cut?

12-4   What is the slope of a cut and fill called?

12-5   What is percent of grade?

12-6   Why might industrial sites require the calculation of cuts and fills?

12-7   What is a cross section?

12-8   What is an intermediate foresight?

12-9   How many IFS readings can be taken from a single instrument setup?

12-10   Write the correct field notes notation for an IFS reading that is 25 ft from the centerline and 2.6 ft below the elevation of the centerline.

12-11   What determines the size of a borrow pit?

12-12   What is the meaning of the numbers recorded at the intersections of a borrow pit grid?

12-13   Write the formula for obtaining the cubic feet in a borrow pit and the formula for converting cubic feet into cubic yards.

12-14   Describe the average end method of computing earth volumes.

STREET AND SIDEWALK DETAILS

Study the portion of street and sidewalk details in Figure T12–1to answer the following questions. Use Microsoft Word to open file "Ch 12 details" on the *Civil Drafting Technology Web site*, and use AutoCAD to open the file "details."

1. The thickness of the street asphalt is _____.
2. The mailboxes are to be mounted by _____ to the _____.
3. The concrete sidewalk is _____ thick.
4. The distance from the sidewalk flare to the right-of-way is _____.
5. The type of curb and gutter specified is _____.
6. The depth of the concrete at the back of the curb is _____.
7. The flare added to the sidewalk plan allows room for _____.
8. The underlayment for the sidewalk is specified as _____.
9. The roadway slopes _____ percent toward the gutter.
10. A typical concrete flare on the sidewalk measures a total of _____ long.
11. The typical width of the sidewalk is _____, and if a flare is added, the typical width is _____.
12. If Alternative "A" is used, the concrete will be a _____ pour, and a _____ will be added to the concrete.

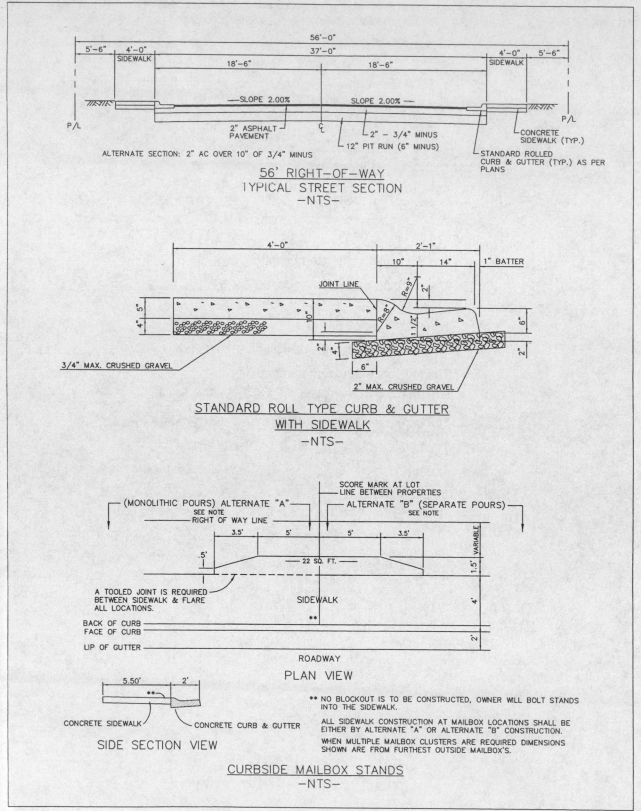

Details   Courtesy of Capital Development ; Boise, Idaho

Figure T12-1.

(Courtesy of Captial Development, Boise, Idaho)

PROBLEMS

P12–1   **a.** Figure P12–1 shows a proposed road layout. It will be a level road at an elevation of 270 ft. The angle of repose for cut and fill is 2:1. Construct the required cut and fill directly on the map. Your cut-and-fill scale may be placed in the space provided. Show all your work. Use different shading techniques for cut and fill.

b. Transfer the graphics shown in Figure P12–1 to a CADD system, either by digitizing or by scanning. Using the information given in P12–1a, construct the required cut and fill along the road. Use different hatching patterns for cut and fill. Plot at 1 in. = 50 ft on an 11- × 17-in. sheet of paper and submit it to your instructor.

Use AutoCAD to open the file "P12–1" on the Student Web site.

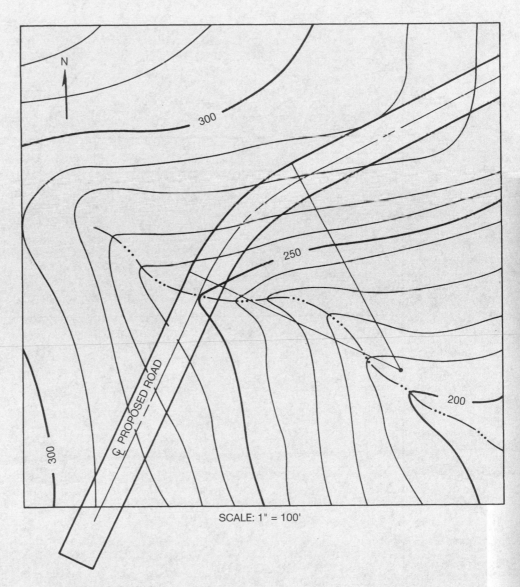

Figure P12–1.

P12–2 **a.** This exercise requires you to plot the cut and fill for an inclined road. You are given the plan shown in Figure P12–2 and must construct a profile from which to calculate cut and fill. Refer to Figure 12–4 if you encounter problems. The road is to have a 6-percent grade, and the cut and fill begins at elevation 1500 ft. The angle of repose for both cut and fill is 2:1. Use shading and labels to identify the cut and fill in the plan view.

b. Transfer the graphics shown in Figure P12–2 to a CADD system, either by digitizing or by scanning. Follow the directions given in P12–2a. Plot at 1 in. = 50 ft on an 11- × 17-in. sheet of paper and submit it to your instructor.

Use AutoCAD to open the file "P12–2" on the Student Web site.

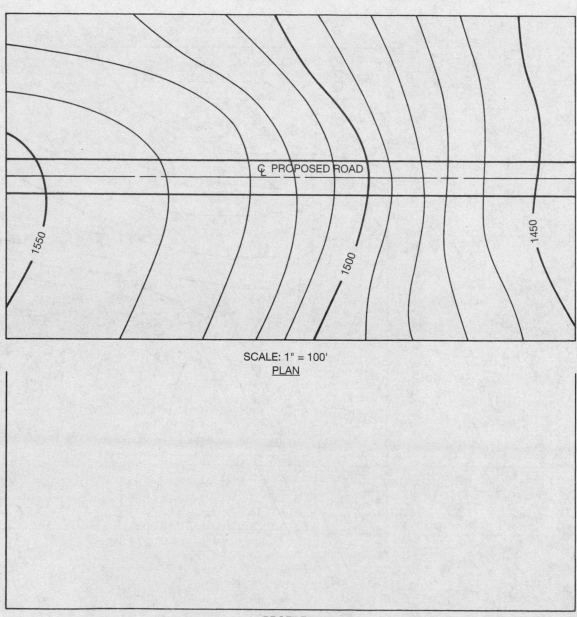

SCALE: 1" = 100'
PLAN

PROFILE

Figure P12–2.

P12-3 **a.** The cut and fill for a proposed industrial site must be determined in this problem. The site is shown in Figure P12–3. The elevation of the site is to be 640 ft. The angle of repose for the cut is 2:1, and it is 1 1/2:1 for the fill. Plot the areas of cut and fill directly on the map and label them.

b. Transfer the graphics shown in Figure P12–3 to a CADD system, either by digitizing or by scanning. Follow the directions given in Problem P12–3a. Use CADD software, if available, to construct the areas of cut and fill. Plot at 1 in. = 100 ft on an 8 1/2- × 11-in. sheet of paper and submit it to your instructor.

Use AutoCAD to open the file "P12–3" on the Student Web site.

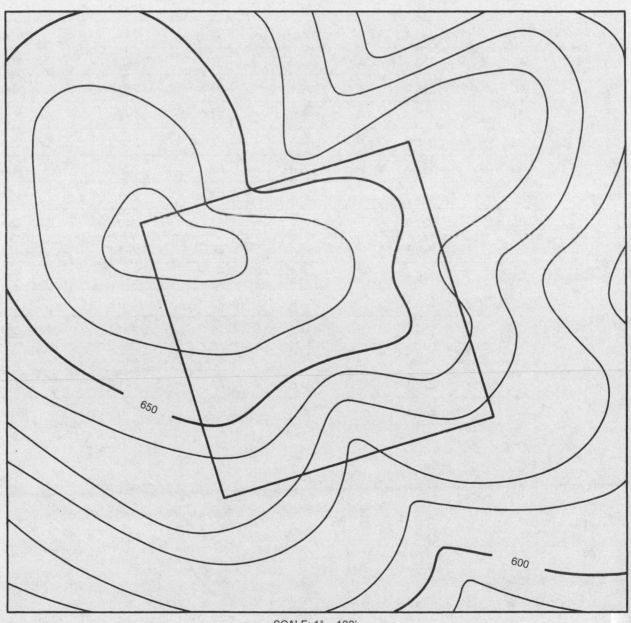

SCALE: 1" = 100'
CONTOUR INTERVAL -10'

Figure P12–3.

P12–4 The measurements in the table below were surveyed on a grid for a borrow pit. The first column in the table represents the grid location. "Existing Elevation" is the elevation before excavation, and "Finish Elevation" is after excavation. The grid spacing is 50 ft. Grid lines A–F run north and south. Draw the borrow pit grid to scale on a B-size sheet. Label the grid values and label the cut depths at each grid intersection. Calculate the total amount of excavated material in cubic yards. Place this number on your drawing.

Grid	Existing Elevation	Finish Elevation	Grid	Existing Elevation	Finish Elevation
A1	236.2	233.1	D1	238.3	231.5
A2	235.8	232.8	D2	237.6	232.2
A3	237.0	233.1	D3	236.9	231.8
A4	236.9	234.5	D4	239.2	234.1
A5	237.1	233.9	D5	240.2	235.4
A6	238.2	234.1	D6	238.7	234.1
B1	237.1	233.0	E1	238.3	234.0
B2	238.2	234.0	E2	239.2	235.6
B3	239.4	235.3	E3	237.5	233.2
B4	238.7	233.9	E4	239.7	234.2
B5	239.6	235.2	E5	240.8	235.2
B6	240.1	236.4	E6	241.3	235.9
C1	240.8	235.4	F1	241.3	236.5
C2	239.8	234.5	F2	240.6	236.1
C3	239.5	234.2	F3	239.8	235.3
C4	240.3	236.1	F4	240.7	236.2
C5	239.1	234.8	F5	241.3	237.8
C6	240.6	236.0	F6	240.6	235.9

P12–5 The following measurements were surveyed on a grid for a borrow pit. The grid spacing is 20 ft. Draw the borrow pit grid to scale on a B-size sheet. Label the grid values and label the cut depths at each grid intersection. Calculate the total amount of excavated material in cubic yards. Place this number on your drawing.

Grid	Existing Elevation	Finish Elevation	Grid	Existing Elevation	Finish Elevation
A1	547.3	543.1	D1	546.3	542.8
A2	546.7	542.6	D2	546.9	543.1
A3	546.8	541.9	D3	547.3	544.0
A4	546.3	541.5	D4	547.6	543.8
A5	547.4	542.8	D5	547.9	544.2
A6	547.7	543.1	D6	547.5	543.8
B1	548.3	544.2	E1	548.4	544.3
B2	548.5	544.8	E2	548.2	543.7
B3	548.9	544.6	E3	548.0	544.3
B4	548.2	543.9	E4	547.8	543.4
B5	547.4	543.7	E5	547.9	544.0
B6	547.8	543.6	E6	547.5	543.2
C1	547.3	543.1	F1	547.8	543.1
C2	547.0	542.8	F2	548.2	543.9
C3	547.0	542.5	F3	548.5	544.6
C4	546.8	542.3	F4	548.3	544.0
C5	546.4	542.0	F5	548.8	544.7
C6	546.1	542.1	F6	548.3	544.8

P12–6 Plot cross sections for each of the profiles listed in the field notes in Figure 12–6. Use a single D-size sheet or two C-size sheets for the layout. In each cross section, plot a 24-ft-wide level road with 4-ft-wide shoulders. The road elevation is 875 ft. The angle of repose for the fill is 1 1/2:1, and it is 1:1 for the cut.

Label the road centerline and dimension road and shoulder widths. The road should slope 0.04 ft/ft from the centerline to the edge of road. The shoulder slope is 0.06 ft/ft. Label these values on your drawing. Draw the cut and fill beginning at the outside edge of the road shoulder. Label the cut and fill with the appropriate symbol and values. Draw the existing grade as a dashed line in the areas of cut and fill. Use the earth sectioning symbol in areas of undisturbed earth.

P12-7   Plot cross sections for each of the profiles listed in the field notes in
        Figure 12–6. Use a single D-size sheet or two C-size sheets for the
        layout. In each cross section, plot a 24-ft-wide level road with 4-ft-wide
        shoulders. The road elevation is 872 ft. The angle of repose for the cut
        is 1:1. After drawing each cross section, determine the elevation at the
        intersection of the grade line and cut line. Use these elevations to
        calculate the earthwork involved between stations 5 + 00 and 7 + 00.
        Use the average end method illustrated in Figure 12–14 to calculate
        volumes of material in cubic yards. Record your answers below or on
        the drawing by each cross section.

Station	Area
5 + 00	_____
5 + 50	_____
6 + 00	_____
6 + 50	_____
7 + 00	_____
	Cubic yards = _____

P12-8   Use completed problem P10–3 to create three cross sections through
        the new road and determine the cut and fill.

Road Cross Sections

a. Remember that cross sections are cut perpendicular to the road.
   Cut three cross sections through the road and cut and fill at the following locations: cross section A, 220 ft along the road centerline
   from point A; cross section B, 415 ft from cross section A, or at
   widest area of fill; cross section C, 450 ft along the road centerline
   from the P.I. at point *B*.

b. Locate completed cross sections on separate C-size sheets, one
   section per sheet.

c. The vertical scale of the cross sections is to be the same as the
   horizontal scale.

d. The road surface has a slope of 0.02 ft/ft from the road centerline.

e. The shoulder surface has a slope of 0.06 ft/ft from the edge of pavement (EOP).

f. Road and shoulder surface slope angle can be exaggerated on the
   drawing for clarity.

g. Composition of the road is as follows: 12-in.-thick base of gravel
   (show as dashed line); 6-in.-thick sand–asphalt hot mix (show as
   solid line); road surface is 1 1/4-in.-thick asphaltic–concrete (show
   as thick solid line).

h. Draw cross sections with an appropriate scale that allows the drawing, especially the area of cut and fill, to be shown as large as possible on the sheet. Each cross section sheet may have a different
   scale, but each scale should be one that can be checked with a civil
   engineer's scale.

Additional Details and Labeling

a. Label the centerline of proposed road, bearings and distances, and location points on the road.

b. Label the road width, shoulder width, road surface and shoulder surface slopes, and centerline of the road in all cross sections.

c. Road composition can be labeled in all cross sections as local notes or called out on one sheet in general notes, with local note references on each drawing.

d. Indicate cut and fill in cross sections with a note and show the angle of repose symbol and values on each side of the road, along the appropriate slope.

e. Below all three cross section viewing arrow symbols on the base drawing, place a drawing reference in parentheses. For example, section A-A, if shown on sheet number P12–5–02, should have the label (P12–5–02) below one of the viewing arrows. Place a similar cross-reference label on the cross section drawing just below the section name.

f. Use the earth hatch symbol to indicate areas of *undisturbed* earth only. Place patches of this symbol at angular changes of undisturbed earth and several places along slopes.

g. Title all cross section drawings HWY. CROSS SECTION.

h. Change the title of original map (problem P8–3) to HIGHWAY CUT AND FILL.

i. Begin drawing numbers with P12–5–01 on the HIGHWAY CUT AND FILL drawing and continue in sequence with cross sections.

j. Label the sheets as a set, such as 1 of 4, 2 of 4, etc.

k. Submit drawings plotted to scale on C-size paper, complete with border and title block.

Civil Engineering Detail Drawings

Learning Objectives

After completing this chapter, you will be able to:

- Name the civil engineering drawing disciplines.
- Identify the different kinds of drawing standards.
- Describe the civil engineering drawing process.
- Identify and describe the different kinds of civil engineering drawings and detail drawings.
- Describe the importance and the process of standards checking.

Key Terms

Vicinity map
Site plan
Profile
Combined sewerage outlet (CSO)
Concrete masonry units (CMUs)
Symbol library
Legend
Standards checking

As you learned in Chapter 1, civil engineering deals with the design and construction of projects related to the land, such as roads, subdivisions, light rail systems, bridges, waterworks, waste treatment, railroads, canals, and any building site. Throughout this text you have seen the wide variety of disciplines and drawings that are involved in civil engineering and civil drafting. Each design and drafting discipline requires its own specific types of drawings and details.

This chapter provides a general discussion of the nature of details found on civil engineering drawings. The topics covered include:

- Civil engineering drawing disciplines
- Civil engineering drawing standards
- The civil engineering drawing process
- Plan drawings
- Section, cross section, and profile drawings
- Detail drawings
- Standard details
- Symbol libraries
- Checking drawing standards

Civil Engineering Drawing Disciplines

Civil engineering is one of the broadest fields of engineering. It encompasses surveying, aerial photography, map making, earthwork, grading, contouring, drainage, structural, architectural, piping, mechanical, electrical, and landscaping work. Civil engineering companies are most often involved in all phases of a construction project and either create drawings, or contract with companies that develop a wide variety of civil engineering drawings.

Except in large civil firms, surveying is often contracted out to licensed surveyors. As discussed in Chapter 6, the surveyor will provide a text file of points at the job site from which civil drafters and designers will develop drawings. Departments within the civil firm will then work on site preparation, street and parking layout, earthwork grading and drainage, and foundation and structural work. Architectural design and drawings may be handled by the civil firm or may be contracted to an architectural company. Architects may be given appropriate base drawings from which to work, such as site plans, contour maps, road layout, and structural drawings.

Projects involving mechanical, piping, and electrical work such as waterworks, sewage treatment, power generation, and other process industry work may require specialized design and engineering efforts. Again, except in large civil firms, these aspects of a project may be contracted out to engineering companies that specialize in the disciplines listed above.

Final stages of a project may involve finished site preparation and landscape design. Depending on the size of the company, this aspect of the project can be completed in-house or contracted to landscape architects.

Civil Engineering Drawing Standards

Within the design, engineering, and construction industry, it is often said that standards are great things, it's just too bad that more companies don't use them properly. Standards, when adhered to, enable everyone involved in a project to know the exact specifications of all aspects of the project. This in turn leads to a reduction in errors and cost overruns.

One of the most important things for any new drafter to understand is the role that standards play in the company. This means studying any standards documentation that is available and learning how the standards are used within the design, engineering, and drawing process.

Five types of standards may be at play when a drafter constructs a drawing:

- **National and international organizations' standards:** These standards are created by the members of organizations such as the American Institute of Architects (AIA), the Construction Specification Institute (CSI), and the International Organization for Standardization (ISO). These are, in turn, used to create company standards. A publication titled *The U.S. National CAD Standard*, available through the CSI, includes CAD-related documents from various organizations. The American Public Works Association (APWA) is a North American organization that provides public works goods and services. Refer to the Student Web site for links to these organizations.

- **Company standards:** Some standards are developed by an engineering firm. Every company eventually creates and maintains its own standards library of details, sections, and symbols. These are most often proprietary and may or may not be created based on national organization standards, and they often reflect the clients and governments with which the company works.

- **Client standards:** The client is the organization for which the project is being developed. This can be a government municipality or private concern. A private company such as a land developer may have detail drawings representing methods of layout, design, and construction; cities and counties may have similar details. It is critically important that you know where one set of standards ends and the other begins.

- **Government standards:** City, county, state, and federal codes and details may apply to many aspects of a project, and these must be adhered to even if national organization and company standards are available. Municipalities and counties may have thousands of standards reflected in CADD detail and symbol drawings, and it is important for a CADD drafter to know the location and proper use of these files.

- **Project standards:** These standards may comprise a combination of all the above, and they are the final documents that are used to design and build a project. Depending on the size and scope of the project, a document with a title such as Project Specifications may be printed and made available for reference.

The Civil Engineering Drawing Process

Civil engineering is based on projects that are built on or under the ground. Therefore, some of the first drawings that are created for a project are maps and site plans. A vicinity map places a project site within an area of several square miles and provides a good overview of the site relative to the surrounding area. See Figure 13–1. A site plan is a drawing that shows the layout of a project on the land. It is a larger-scale drawing than the vicinity map, and it depicts the overall site and all buildings and site work. Several site plans may be included in the project drawing set, each illustrating a specific component of the project. An example of a subdivision composite utility site plan is shown in Figure 13–2.

Plan views illustrate all aspects of a project, such as utilities, water, storm sewer, sanitary sewer, street alignments, and landscaping. Profiles along linear, or horizontal, alignment features, such as streets, sewers, and water lines, can then be produced. Cross sections are then generated across features such as streets, drainage basins, and railway beds. Detail drawings are then created to fully describe features that do not show on all other drawings.

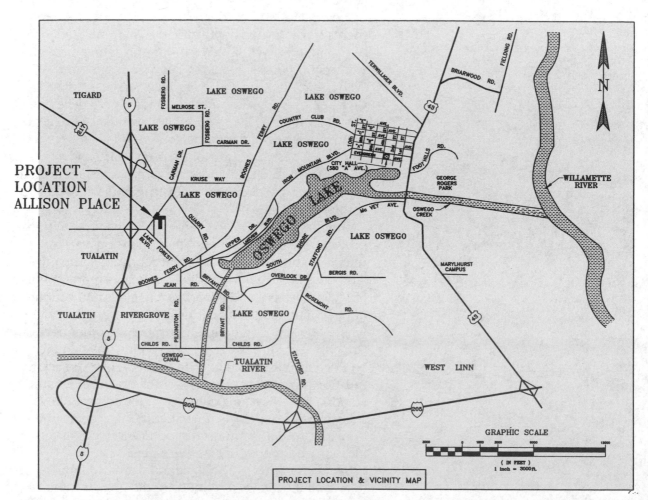

Figure 13–1. A vicinity map places a project site within an area of several square miles and provides a good overview of the site relative to the surrounding area.
(Courtesy Lee-Pace Engineering, Inc.)

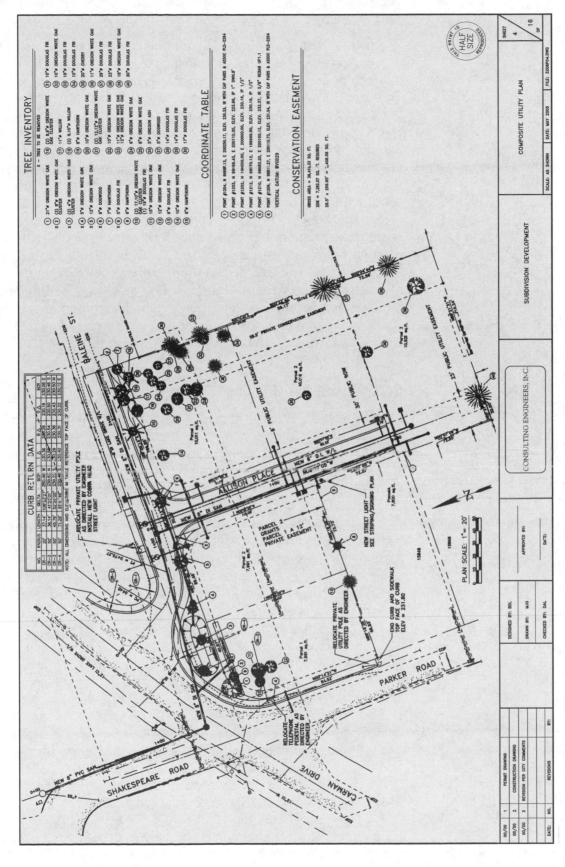

Figure 13-2.   A subdivision composite utility site plan shows the utilities layout of the project on the land.
(Courtesy Lee-Pace Engineering, Inc.)

Plan Drawings

A plan is a view from above. Depending on the size and complexity of a project, a variety of plan drawings may be created. Using layering techniques, all the site information can be added to a drawing, and then individual plan sheets for utilities, sanitary sewer, water lines, storm drainage, street signage, and landscaping can be plotted.

As you learned in Chapter 6, survey data in the form of a text file can be imported into software such as Autodesk LandDesktop and used as the foundation from which to develop site drawings. Once the survey data has been imported into the drawing, it is just a matter of using the project design specifications and software tools to create the drawing layout. For example, after the drafter provides some basic location, elevation, slope, and dimensional data, the software can quickly generate features such as streets, curbs, gutters, and sidewalks. The drafter can then request the creation of profiles of existing grade or new features, such as streets or utilities, and cross sections of roads and other horizontal alignments.

A utility site plan for a subdivision is shown in Figure 13–2. A site plan of water and sanitary sewer is shown in Figure 13–3.

Section, Cross Section, and Profile Drawings

All drawing disciplines use drawing techniques to view objects and areas as if they are cut through and viewed from the side. The resulting views are called *sections*. Civil companies may use the terms *section* and *cross section* interchangeably. Technically, a section cuts through something partially or completely, whereas a cross section cuts all the way across a feature such as a highway, street, canal, utility trench, or runway.

Sections are called out on plan views with symbols such as the circle with the stylized arrow shown in Figure 13–4. This figure is a zoomed-in portion of a storm drainage plan view. The arrow points in the direction of the view. Note that the letter in the top part of the symbol is the identification for the section, and the number in the lower half of the circle indicates the sheet number the section is shown on. Figure 13–4 shows section A, which is on sheet 6, and the view is to the right.

A project will have a set of drawings, and the sheets in the set are numbered sequentially. To find section A in Figure 13–4, you must go to sheet 6 of the drawing set. Sometimes sections and details can be shown on the sheet on which they are called out. This is the case with section A. See Figure 13–5. Notice that the symbol for the section is an ellipse, and the section identification is shown in the top half. The two numbers in the bottom of the ellipse indicate the sheet the section was cut on and the sheet it is shown on, in this case sheet 6.

A section will have one scale or may be indicated as not to scale, with "N.T.S." by the title, as shown in Figure 13–5.

A typical cross section is shown in Figure 13–6. In this case, a cutting plane line for a section is not shown on the plan drawing, and a section identification symbol is not shown because this is a typical cross section that is common to any location along the street. Specific cross sections may be shown if features such as drains and underground utilities must be shown.

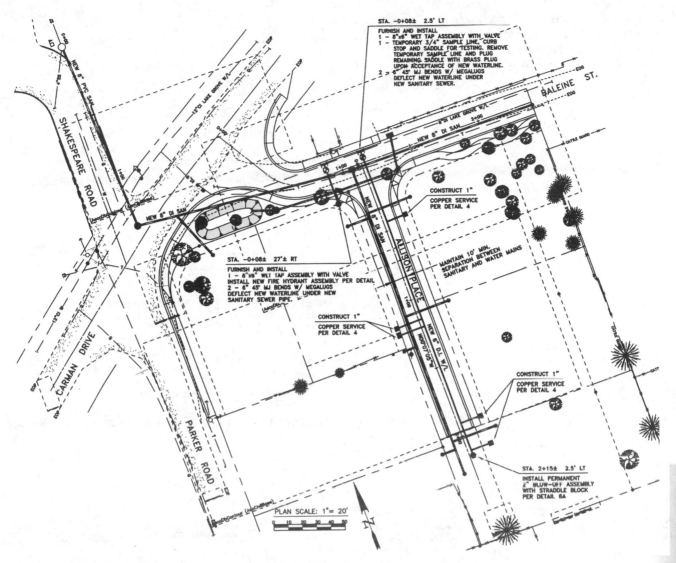

Figure 13-3. This site plan shows the proposed layout of water and sanitary sewer systems.
(Courtesy Lee-Pace Engineering, Inc.)

Figure 13-4. A section symbol shown on a plan view. This is section A, shown on sheet 6, and the view is to the right.
(Courtesy Lee-Pace Engineering, Inc.)

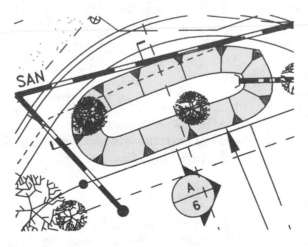

A **profile** is a section that is cut along the length of a linear feature such as a road, sewer line, power line, or stream. See Chapter 11 for a discussion of profiles. A profile normally has horizontal and vertical scales that are different. See Figure 13-7.

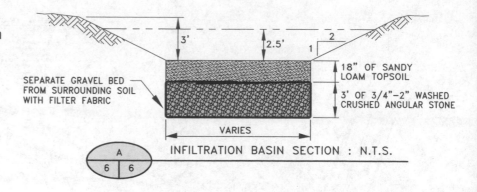

Figure 13-5. This is section A, and it was cut on sheet 6 and is also shown on sheet 6. It is not to scale (N.T.S.).
(Courtesy Lee-Pace Engineering, Inc.)

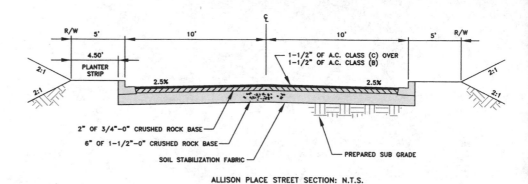

Figure 13-6. A typical cross section common to any location along the street of a subdivision project.
(Courtesy Lee-Pace Engineering, Inc.)

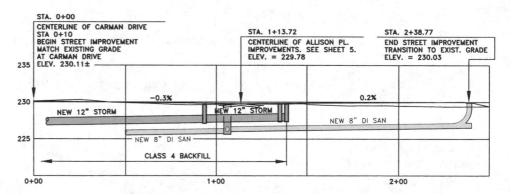

Figure 13-7. A profile is a section that is cut along the length of a linear feature, such as this sewer line, and normally has different horizontal and vertical scales.
(Courtesy Lee-Pace Engineering, Inc.)

Detail Drawings

Detail drawings are normally the documents that are used to guide construction because these are most often the standards that govern the project. Details may be shown on one of the plan sheets if it is a common feature and the subject of a specific plan. In addition, if the detail is not a typical construction standard, it may also be shown on plan sheets or with other sections. For example, the drawing shown

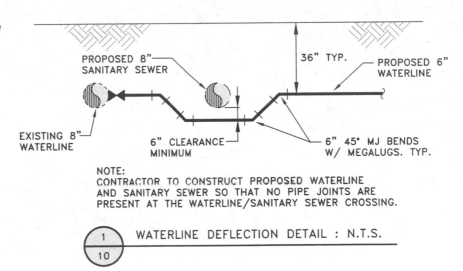

Figure 13–8. This detail illustrates how the new water lines are to be deflected around the proposed sewer line. (Courtesy Lee-Pace Engineering, Inc.)

in Figure 13–3 is a water line plan for a new subdivision. A detail shown on the complete drawing illustrates how the new water lines are to be deflected around the proposed sewer line. See Figure 13–8.

It is important for a civil drafter to be aware of the kinds of detail drawings that are archived in drawing and symbol libraries. A project may utilize many standard details, some requiring minor changes in dimensions, materials, and construction methods. Always spend sufficient time at the beginning of a project working with engineers, designers, and clients to become aware of all the existing resources that are available to you. This will decrease your workload and make you more efficient.

Details can be created for any construction feature, and they become the most important drawings for construction purposes. Therefore, most companies and government agencies that deal with civil projects have sizable libraries of standard details. The next section provides a look at a variety of typical details used in civil projects.

Standard Details

The following detail drawing examples are provided to give you an idea of the wide variety of drawing types that are developed and maintained by civil engineering firms, government agencies, and client companies. These examples, and many others, can be found on the Student Web site.

As you study the drawings in this chapter, remember that they are examples of one company's methods for constructing civil engineering details and represent the different types of things for which details are typically provided. As with any other type of drawing in the wide range of engineering and drafting disciplines, national and professional organizational standards are always superseded by company, client, and local agency standards. Therefore, the treatment of the various drawings shown in this chapter will vary from one locale to another. In addition, the presentation of detail drawings as simple as those for fire hydrant connections can vary between towns and cities in the same county.

Road/Street Details

Common details for roads and streets can include cul-de-sac plan views, curbs, sidewalks, sidewalk ramps, medians, and utilities. Figures 13–9 through 13–13 provide a sampling of road and street details.

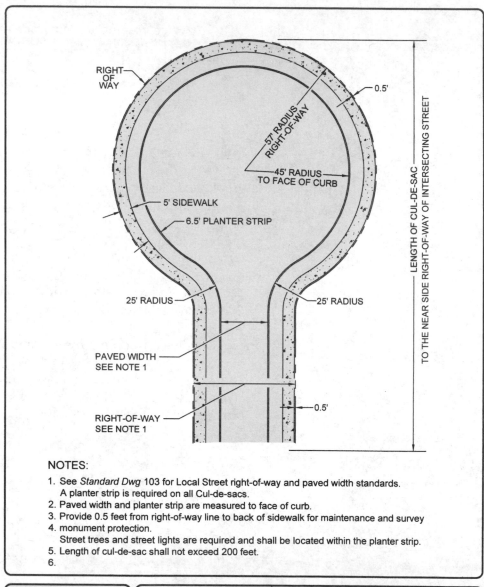

NOTES:

1. See *Standard Dwg* 103 for Local Street right-of-way and paved width standards.
   A planter strip is required on all Cul-de-sacs.
2. Paved width and planter strip are measured to face of curb.
3. Provide 0.5 feet from right-of-way line to back of sidewalk for maintenance and survey
4. monument protection.
   Street trees and street lights are required and shall be located within the planter strip.
5. Length of cul-de-sac shall not exceed 200 feet.
6.

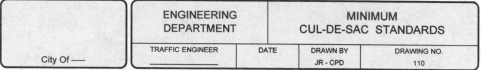

	ENGINEERING DEPARTMENT	MINIMUM CUL-DE-SAC STANDARDS
	TRAFFIC ENGINEER	DATE	DRAWN BY	DRAWING NO.
City Of ——			JR - CPD	110

Figure 13–9. This detail drawing provides minimum standards for a cul-de-sac layout. (Courtesy Lee-Pace Engineering, Inc.)

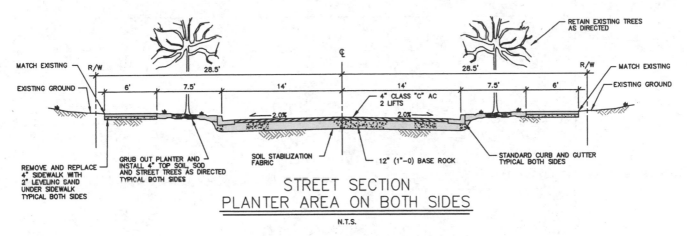

STREET SECTION
PLANTER AREA ON BOTH SIDES
N.T.S.

Figure 13-10. Sidewalks, planter strips, and street width are shown in this cross section.
(Courtesy Lee-Pace Engineering, Inc.)

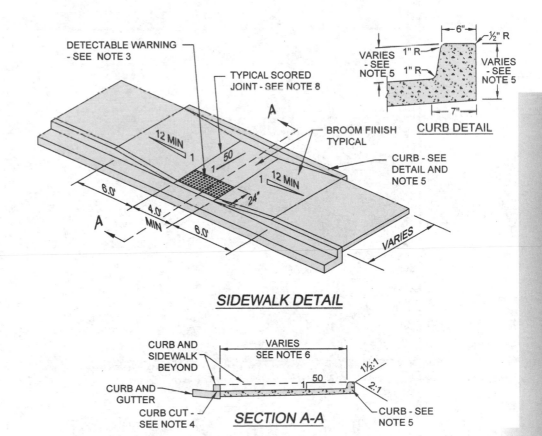

SIDEWALK DETAIL

SECTION A-A

Figure 13-11. Detail of sidewalk curb cut for handicap access.
(Courtesy Lee-Pace Engineering, Inc.)

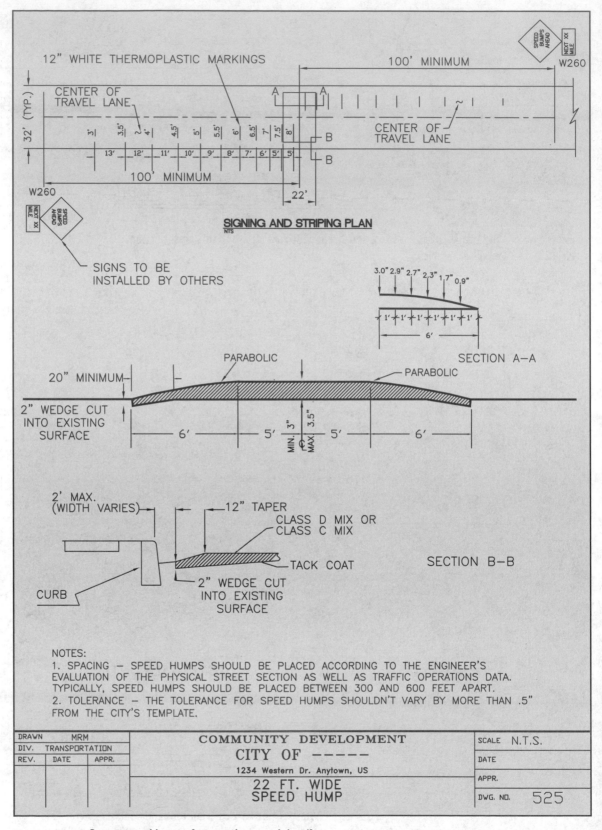

12" WHITE THERMOPLASTIC MARKINGS

CENTER OF
TRAVEL LANE

100' MINIMUM

32' (TYP.)

3' 3.5' 2' 4' 4.5' 5' 5.5' 6' 6.5' 7' 7.5' 8'

13' 12' 11' 10' 9' 8' 7' 6' 5' 5'

CENTER OF
TRAVEL LANE

100' MINIMUM

22'

W260

SPEED BUMPS AHEAD / NEXT XX MILE

SIGNING AND STRIPING PLAN
NTS

SIGNS TO BE
INSTALLED BY OTHERS

3.0" 2.9" 2.7" 2.3" 1.7" 0.9"

1' 1' 1' 1' 1' 1'

6'

SECTION A–A

20" MINIMUM

PARABOLIC

PARABOLIC

2" WEDGE CUT
INTO EXISTING
SURFACE

6'   5'   MIN. 3"   MAX. 3.5"   5'   6'

2' MAX.
(WIDTH VARIES)

12" TAPER

CLASS D MIX OR
CLASS C MIX

TACK COAT

SECTION B–B

CURB

2" WEDGE CUT
INTO EXISTING
SURFACE

NOTES:
1. SPACING – SPEED HUMPS SHOULD BE PLACED ACCORDING TO THE ENGINEER'S
EVALUATION OF THE PHYSICAL STREET SECTION AS WELL AS TRAFFIC OPERATIONS DATA.
TYPICALLY, SPEED HUMPS SHOULD BE PLACED BETWEEN 300 AND 600 FEET APART.
2. TOLERANCE – THE TOLERANCE FOR SPEED HUMPS SHOULDN'T VARY BY MORE THAN .5"
FROM THE CITY'S TEMPLATE.

DRAWN	MRM		COMMUNITY DEVELOPMENT	SCALE N.T.S.
DIV.	TRANSPORTATION		CITY OF – – – – –	
REV.	DATE	APPR.	1234 Western Dr. Anytown, US	DATE
			22 FT. WIDE	APPR.
			SPEED HUMP	DWG. NO. 525

Figure 13–12. Street speed hump plan, sections, and detail.
(Courtesy Lee-Pace Engineering, Inc.)

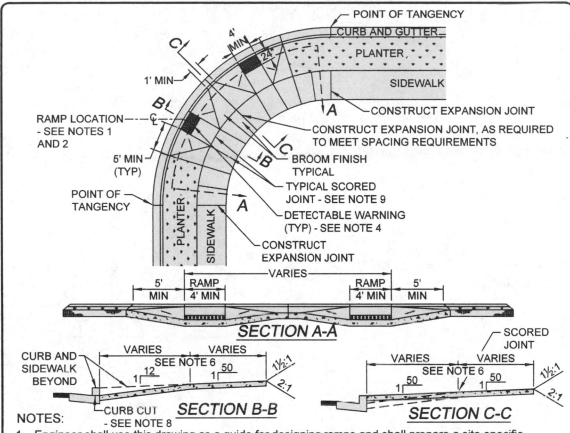

NOTES:
1. Engineer shall use this drawing as a guide for designing ramps and shall prepare a site-specific drawing for each ramp.
2. Engineer shall verify applicability of this drawing to specific locations within the project before using it as a design guide and shall locate each ramp relative to crosswalk or stop line.
3. Sidewalk ramp grades shall meet *ADA Standards*.
4. Detectable warning shall be truncated dome type, 24 inches long in direction of travel and full width of ramp, with domes aligned on a square grid with its gridlines parallel and perpendicular to the centerline of the ramp, "Armor-Tile, Cast-In-Place Tiles".
5. Curb inlet or catch basin shall not be allowed in front of textured ramp.
6. For sidewalk widths, planter strip widths and sidewalk panel dimensions, see *Standard Dwg* 215. Concrete to have compressive strength of 4,000 psi at 28 days.
7. Bevel the curb cut from gutter to back of curb at 8.33% (1:12).
8. Score at grade changes, surface texture changes and at other points shown. Edges shall be shined.
9. Engineer shall accept full responsibility for correcting all unacceptable ramp construction resulting
10. from applying this drawing "as is" and not providing a site-specific drawing for each ramp.
    A single ramp may be used at 'T' intersections at the locations shown in the diagram in section
11. 210.10 of the Engineering Design Manual.

	ENGINEERING DEPARTMENT	STANDARD SIDEWALK RAMPS WITH PLANTER STRIP
	CITY ENGINEER	DATE	DRAWN BY	DRAWING NO.
City Of ----			JR - TD	220

Figure 13-13. This detail provides plan and sections of sidewalk ramps and planter strip.
(Courtesy Lee-Pace Engineering, Inc.)

Storm Sewer Details

Storm sewer details focus on storm drains and all related inlets, grating, manholes and access ways, piping, valves, and pump stations, if required. Storm sewers are normally just surface drainage from streets, parking lots, and roof gutter drains. In some locales, storm drains and sanitary sewer lines are connected in what is termed a combined sewerage outlet (CSO). In this case, storm drains may flow to a sewerage treatment plant and combine with sanitary sewer. A variety of storm sewer details are shown in Figures 13–14 through 13–17.

Figure 13-14. **Plan, section, and isometric view of a storm sewer drain.** (Courtesy Lee-Pace Engineering, Inc.)

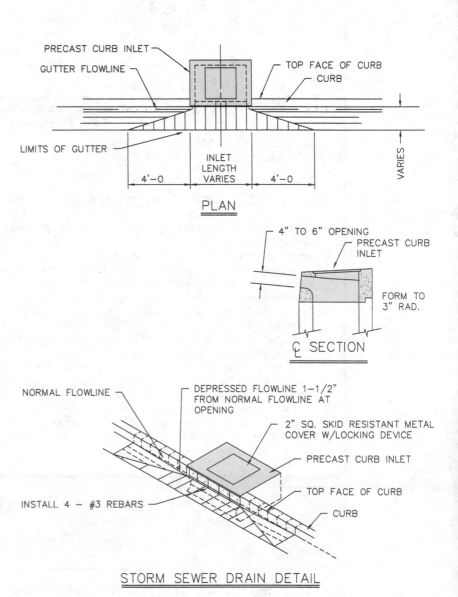

Figure 13-15. **This plan and section details a 72" manhole.**
(Courtesy Lee-Pace Engineering, Inc.)

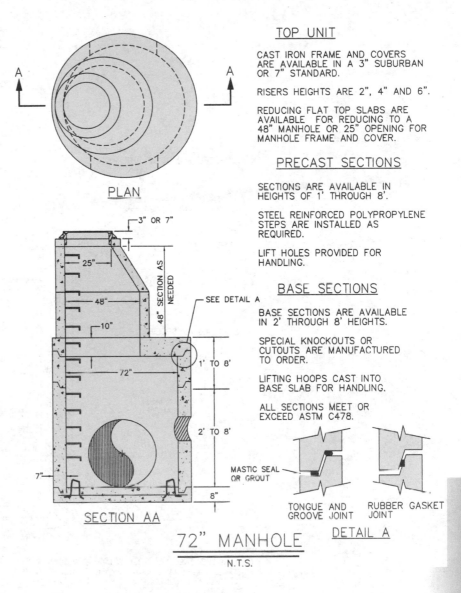

TOP UNIT

CAST IRON FRAME AND COVERS ARE AVAILABLE IN A 3" SUBURBAN OR 7" STANDARD.

RISERS HEIGHTS ARE 2", 4" AND 6".

REDUCING FLAT TOP SLABS ARE AVAILABLE FOR REDUCING TO A 48" MANHOLE OR 25" OPENING FOR MANHOLE FRAME AND COVER.

PRECAST SECTIONS

SECTIONS ARE AVAILABLE IN HEIGHTS OF 1' THROUGH 8'.

STEEL REINFORCED POLYPROPYLENE STEPS ARE INSTALLED AS REQUIRED.

LIFT HOLES PROVIDED FOR HANDLING.

BASE SECTIONS

BASE SECTIONS ARE AVAILABLE IN 2' THROUGH 8' HEIGHTS.

SPECIAL KNOCKOUTS OR CUTOUTS ARE MANUFACTURED TO ORDER.

LIFTING HOOPS CAST INTO BASE SLAB FOR HANDLING.

ALL SECTIONS MEET OR EXCEED ASTM C478.

PLAN

SECTION AA

MASTIC SEAL OR GROUT

TONGUE AND GROOVE JOINT   RUBBER GASKET JOINT

DETAIL A

72" MANHOLE
N.T.S.

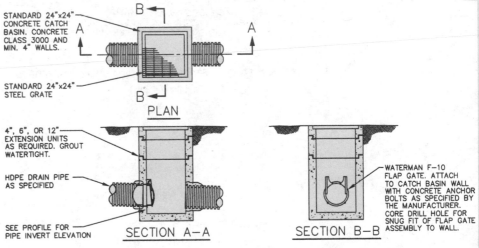

STANDARD 24"x24" CONCRETE CATCH BASIN. CONCRETE CLASS 3000 AND MIN. 4" WALLS.

STANDARD 24"x24" STEEL GRATE

PLAN

4", 6", OR 12" EXTENSION UNITS AS REQUIRED. GROUT WATERTIGHT.

HDPE DRAIN PIPE AS SPECIFIED

SEE PROFILE FOR PIPE INVERT ELEVATION

SECTION A-A

WATERMAN F-10 FLAP GATE. ATTACH TO CATCH BASIN WALL WITH CONCRETE ANCHOR BOLTS AS SPECIFIED BY THE MANUFACTURER. CORE DRILL HOLE FOR SNUG FIT OF FLAP GATE ASSEMBLY TO WALL.

SECTION B-B

CATCH BASIN DETAIL WITH FLAP GATE
N.T.S

Figure 13-16. **Plan and two sections of catch basin details.**
(Courtesy Lee-Pace Engineering, Inc.)

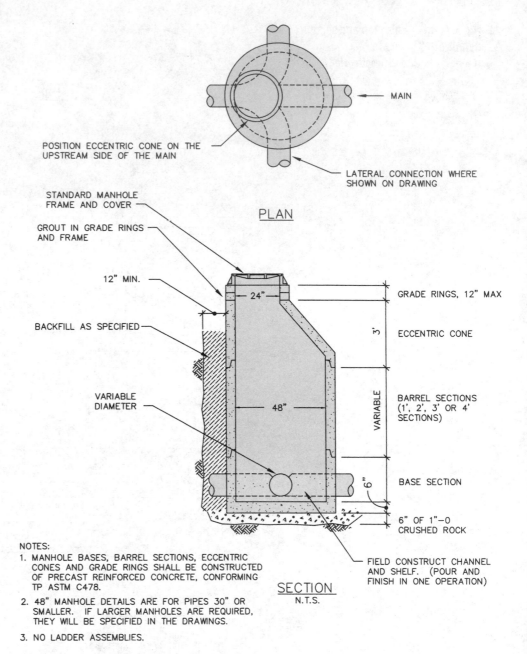

MAIN

POSITION ECCENTRIC CONE ON THE
UPSTREAM SIDE OF THE MAIN

LATERAL CONNECTION WHERE
SHOWN ON DRAWING

PLAN

STANDARD MANHOLE
FRAME AND COVER

GROUT IN GRADE RINGS
AND FRAME

12" MIN.

24"

GRADE RINGS, 12" MAX

BACKFILL AS SPECIFIED

3'

ECCENTRIC CONE

VARIABLE
DIAMETER

48"

VARIABLE

BARREL SECTIONS
(1', 2', 3' OR 4'
SECTIONS)

6"

BASE SECTION

6" OF 1"—0
CRUSHED ROCK

FIELD CONSTRUCT CHANNEL
AND SHELF. (POUR AND
FINISH IN ONE OPERATION)

SECTION
N.T.S.

NOTES:
1. MANHOLE BASES, BARREL SECTIONS, ECCENTRIC
   CONES AND GRADE RINGS SHALL BE CONSTRUCTED
   OF PRECAST REINFORCED CONCRETE, CONFORMING
   TP ASTM C478.

2. 48" MANHOLE DETAILS ARE FOR PIPES 30" OR
   SMALLER. IF LARGER MANHOLES ARE REQUIRED,
   THEY WILL BE SPECIFIED IN THE DRAWINGS.

3. NO LADDER ASSEMBLIES.

Figure 13-17.   Manhole with storm sewer connections.
(Courtesy Lee-Pace Engineering, Inc.)

Sanitary Sewer Details

Sanitary sewer is the waste lines that originate from commercial and residential locations and flow by gravity and pump stations to a waste treatment plant. These types of detail drawings can include components of all of the above related structural, piping, mechanical, and architectural disciplines. A selection of sanitary sewer details is shown in Figures 13–18 through 13–20.

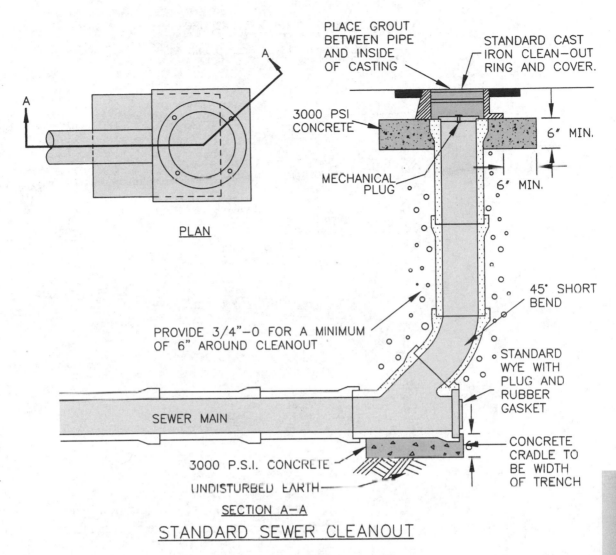

PLACE GROUT
BETWEEN PIPE
AND INSIDE
OF CASTING

STANDARD CAST
IRON CLEAN—OUT
RING AND COVER.

3000 PSI
CONCRETE

6" MIN.

MECHANICAL
PLUG

6" MIN.

45° SHORT
BEND

PROVIDE 3/4"—0 FOR A MINIMUM
OF 6" AROUND CLEANOUT

STANDARD
WYE WITH
PLUG AND
RUBBER
GASKET

SEWER MAIN

CONCRETE
CRADLE TO
BE WIDTH
OF TRENCH

3000 P.S.I. CONCRETE

UNDISTURBED EARTH

PLAN

SECTION A—A

STANDARD SEWER CLEANOUT

NOTES:

1. IF IN GRAVEL STREET PLACE 2" A/C PAVEMENT IN 4' DIAMETER CIRCLE AROUND
   CLEAN—OUT. SLOPE AWAY FROM CLEANOUT.
2. IF IN OPEN AREA & NOT SUBJECT TO STREET USE, USE LOCKING IRRIGATION BOX
   INSTEAD OF STANDARD CAST IRON CLEAN—OUT RING & COVER.
3. UNLESS OTHERWISE APPROVED BY THE CITY ENGINEER CLEANOUTS ARE TO BE
   USED ONLY AS A TEMPORARY TERMINUS.
4. ALL CLEAN—OUT MATERIAL TO BE SAME AS SEWER MAIN PIPE.

Figure 13–18.   Plan and section of sanitary sewer cleanout.
(Courtesy Lee-Pace Engineering, Inc.)

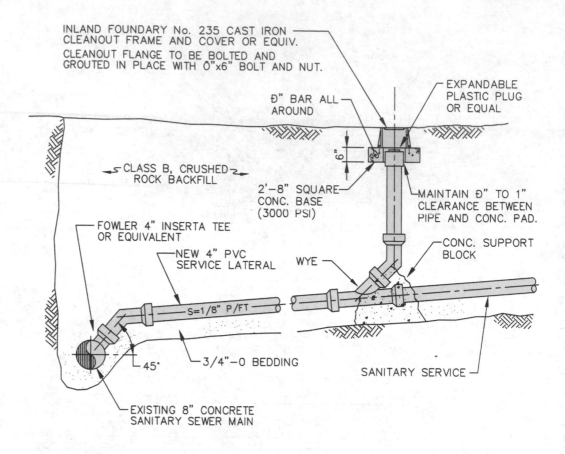

SANITARY SERVICE
LATERAL WITH CLEANOUT

N.T.S.

Figure 13-19. Elevation detail of sanitary sewer cleanout with lateral connection to main sewer.
(Courtesy Lee-Pace Engineering, Inc.)

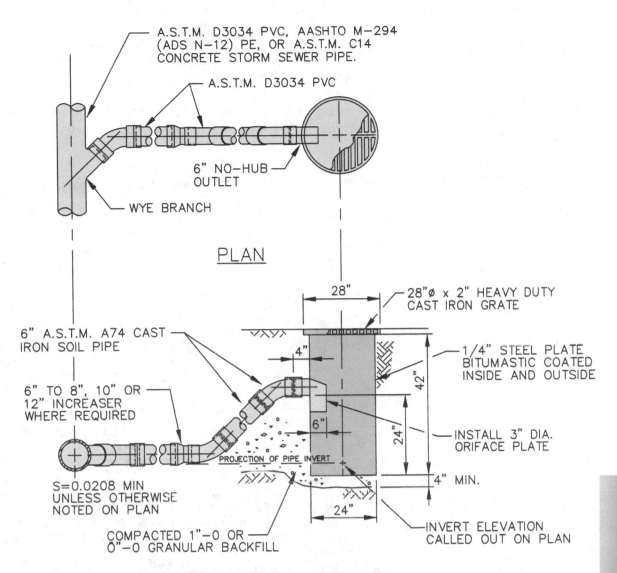

A.S.T.M. D3034 PVC, AASHTO M—294
(ADS N—12) PE, OR A.S.T.M. C14
CONCRETE STORM SEWER PIPE.

A.S.T.M. D3034 PVC

6" NO—HUB
OUTLET

WYE BRANCH

PLAN

28"

28"∅ x 2" HEAVY DUTY
CAST IRON GRATE

6" A.S.T.M. A74 CAST
IRON SOIL PIPE

4"

1/4" STEEL PLATE
BITUMASTIC COATED
INSIDE AND OUTSIDE

42"

6" TO 8", 10" OR
12" INCREASER
WHERE REQUIRED

6"

24"

INSTALL 3" DIA.
ORIFACE PLATE

PROJECTION OF PIPE INVERT

S=0.0208 MIN
UNLESS OTHERWISE
NOTED ON PLAN

4" MIN.

24"

INVERT ELEVATION
CALLED OUT ON PLAN

COMPACTED 1"—0 OR
0"—0 GRANULAR BACKFILL

NOTE: METAL CATCH BASIN FABRICATED
BY LYNCH CO., OR OTHER
APPROVED MANUFACTURER

ELEVATION

SANITARY SEWER
METAL CATCH BASIN DETAIL

N.T.S.

Figure 13–20.   Detail of metal catch basin for sanitary sewer line.
(Courtesy Lee-Pace Engineering, Inc.)

Water Details

Water details are drawn for any kind of water system needs, such as potable water, utility water (non-potable), and fire sprinkler water. Details may include piping, valves, and pump station equipment, mechanical, and concrete and structural drawings. Figures 13–21 through 13–24 show a variety of water details.

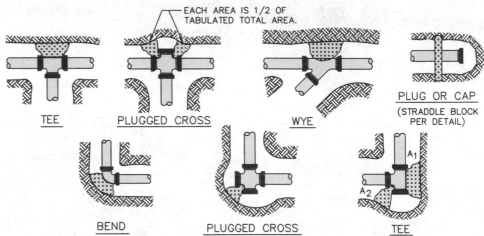

NOTES:

1. CONCRETE THRUST BLOCKING TO BE POURED AGAINST UNDISTURBED EARTH.

2. KEEP CONCRETE CLEAR OF JOINTS AND ACCESSORIES.

3. IF NOT SHOWN ON PLANS, REQUIRED BEARING AREAS AT FITTING SHALL BE AS INDICATED BELOW, ADJUSTED IF NECESSARY, TO CONFORM TO THE TEST PROCEDURE(S) AND ALLOWABLE SOIL BEARING STRESS(ES) STATED IN THE SPECIAL SPECIFICATIONS.

4. BEARING AREAS AND SPECIAL BLOCKING DETAILS SHOWN ON PLANS TAKE PRECEDENCE OVER BEARING AREAS AND BLOCKING DETAILS SHOWN ON THIS STANDARD DETAIL.

5. BUILDING PAPER OR VISQUEEN SHALL BE PLACED BETWEEN CONCRETE AND FITTINGS.

6. ALL POURED IN PLACE CONCRETE SHALL HAVE A 28 DAY STRENGTH OF 3,000 PSI AND 2" TO 4" SLUMP.

7. WHERE UPTHRUST WILL OCCUR, INSTALL HOOKED END NO. 4 REBAR STRAPS IN CONCRETE AT EACH END OF FITTING. COAT STRAP WITH BITUMASTIC.

8. BELOW BEARING AREAS BASED ON TEST PRESSURE OF 150 PSI AND AN ALLOWABLE SOIL BEARING STRESS OF 2,000 PSF. TO COMPUTE BEARING AREAS FOR DIFFERENT TEST PRESSURES AND SOIL BEARING STRESSES, USE THE FOLLOWING EQUATION: BEARING AREA = (TEST PRESSURE/150) X (2,000/SOIL BEARING STRESS) X (TABLE VALUE). BEARING AREAS IN SQUARE FEET.

FITTING SIZE (IN.)	TEE, WYE, PLUG OR CAP	90° BEND PLUGGED CROSS	TEE PLUGGED ON RUN A_1	A_2	45° BEND	22-1/2° BEND	11-1/4° BEND
<3	.05	.7	1.0	.7	.5		
4	1.0	1.4	1.9	1.4	1.0	–	–
6	2.0	3.0	4.3	3.0	1.6	1.0	–
8	3.8	5.3	7.6	5.4	2.9	1.5	1.0
10	5.9	8.4	11.8	8.4	4.6	2.4	1.2
12	8.5	12.0	17.0	12.0	6.6	3.4	1.7
14	11.5	16.3	23.0	16.3	8.9	4.6	2.3
16	15.0	21.3	30.0	21.3	11.6	6.0	3.0
18	19.0	27.0	38.0	27.0	14.6	7.6	3.8
20	23.5	33.3	47.0	33.3	18.1	9.4	4.7
24	34.0	48.0	68.0	48.0	26.2	13.6	6.8

STANDARD THRUST BLOCK DETAILS

Figure 13–21. This table provides the bearing areas for concrete thrust blocks at fittings. Thrust blocks provide structural support and integrity for pressurized water lines.
(Courtesy Lee-Pace Engineering, Inc.)

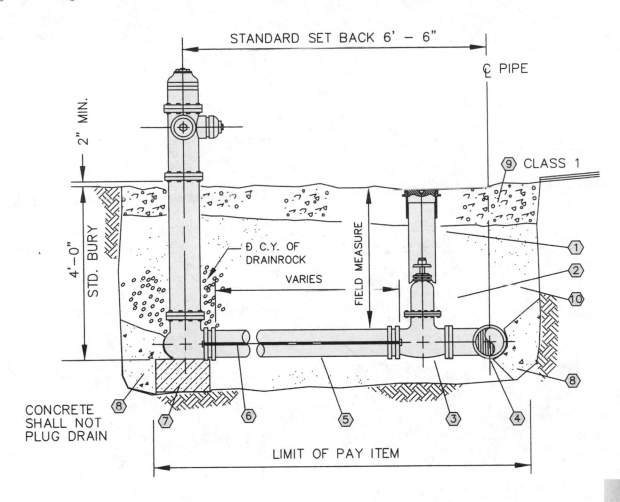

STANDARD SET BACK 6' – 6"

℄ PIPE

2" MIN.

⑨ CLASS 1

4'-0"
STD. BURY

FIELD MEASURE

Ð C.Y. OF
DRAINROCK

VARIES

①

②

⑩

⑧

CONCRETE
SHALL NOT
PLUG DRAIN

⑧

⑦   ⑥   ⑤   ③   ④

LIMIT OF PAY ITEM

① VALVE BOX AND LID

② 2 C.F. CRUSHED ROCK
   UNDER VALVE BOX.

③ 6" FLG. X M.J. GATE VALVE

④ SIZE X 6" M.J. X FLG. TEE

⑤ 6" D.I. SPOOL

⑥ RESTRAIN F.H. W/MIN. (2) 1/2"∅
   ALL THREAD RODDING. COAT
   ALL–THREAD W/ BITUMINOUS
   PAINT.

⑦ 12" SQ. X 3" THICK CONC.
   BLOCK.

⑧ THRUST BLOCK

⑨ SEE TECHNICAL SPECIFICATIONS
   FOR SURFACE RESTORATION.

⑩ SEE TECHNICAL SPECIFICATIONS
   FOR BEDDING AND TRENCH
   BACKFILL REQUIREMENTS.

⑪ ALTERNATIVE BLOCKING, TIES,
   SHACKLES, ETC. SUBJECT TO
   APPROVAL OF ENGINEER.

STANDARD FIRE HYDRANT DETAIL

NOT TO SCALE

Figure 13–22. Standard fire hydrant and valve box detail.
(Courtesy Lee-Pace Engineering, Inc.)

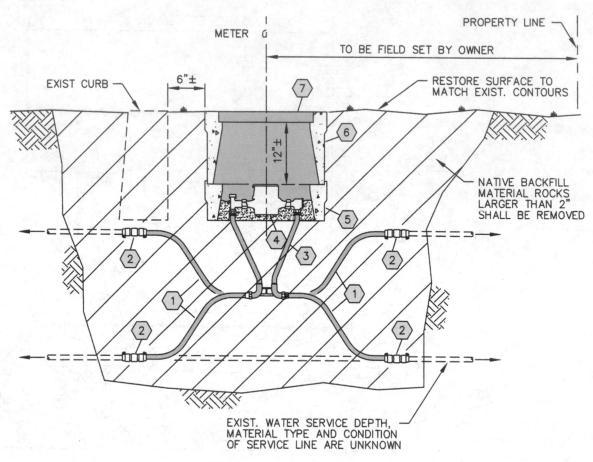

PROPERTY LINE

METER ℄

TO BE FIELD SET BY OWNER

EXIST CURB

6"±

⑦

RESTORE SURFACE TO
MATCH EXIST. CONTOURS

12"±

⑥

NATIVE BACKFILL
MATERIAL ROCKS
LARGER THAN 2"
SHALL BE REMOVED

⑤

④

③

② ① ② ① ②

② ②

EXIST. WATER SERVICE DEPTH,
MATERIAL TYPE AND CONDITION
OF SERVICE LINE ARE UNKNOWN

MATERIAL LIST

① 3/4" COPPER PIPE TAIL – TWO REQ'D PER INSTALLATION.

② TRANSITION COUPLINGS/PACK JOINT OR APPROVED EQUAL – TWO REQ'D PER INSTALLATION.

③ COPPERSETTER, 15" HIGH (AS SPECIFIED).

④ 5/8" X 3/4" METER (SUPPLIED BY OWNER).

⑤ 8" METER BOX EXTENSION.

⑥ BROOK 36 SERIES METER BOX (AS SPECIFIED).

⑦ METER BOX LID – SEE SPECIFICATIONS FOR TYPE.

METER INSTALLATION DETAIL

N.T.S.

Figure 13-23.   Water meter installation detail.
(Courtesy Lee-Pace Engineering, Inc.)

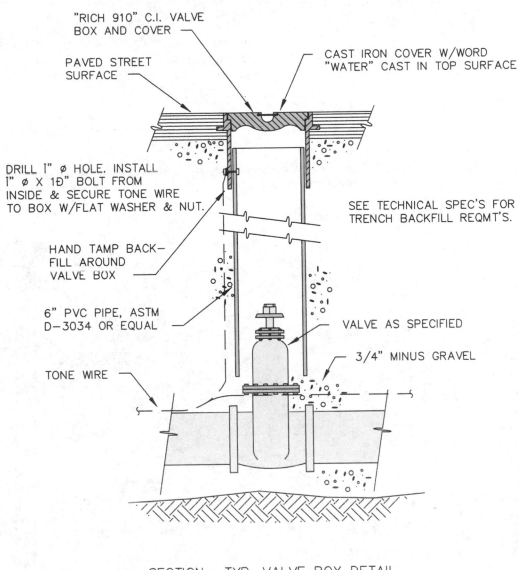

"RICH 910" C.I. VALVE
BOX AND COVER

PAVED STREET
SURFACE

CAST IRON COVER W/WORD
"WATER" CAST IN TOP SURFACE

DRILL 1" ∅ HOLE. INSTALL
1" ∅ X 1Đ" BOLT FROM
INSIDE & SECURE TONE WIRE
TO BOX W/FLAT WASHER & NUT.

SEE TECHNICAL SPEC'S FOR
TRENCH BACKFILL REQMT'S.

HAND TAMP BACK—
FILL AROUND
VALVE BOX

6" PVC PIPE, ASTM
D—3034 OR EQUAL

VALVE AS SPECIFIED

3/4" MINUS GRAVEL

TONE WIRE

SECTION— TYP. VALVE BOX DETAIL
N.T.S.

Figure 13–24.   Valve box detail for a fire hydrant.
(Courtesy Lee-Pace Engineering, Inc.)

Piping Details

Piping details can include pipe, fittings, valves, pumps, and related structural components for any of the previously mentioned disciplines. A variety of piping details are shown in Figures 13–25 through 13–27.

Figure 13–25. **Detail of floor-mounted pipe support.**
(Courtesy Lee-Pace Engineering, Inc.)

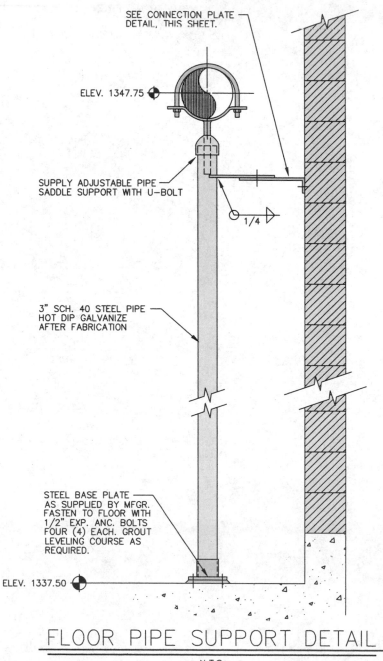

SEE CONNECTION PLATE DETAIL, THIS SHEET.

ELEV. 1347.75

SUPPLY ADJUSTABLE PIPE SADDLE SUPPORT WITH U–BOLT

1/4

3" SCH. 40 STEEL PIPE HOT DIP GALVANIZE AFTER FABRICATION

STEEL BASE PLATE AS SUPPLIED BY MFGR. FASTEN TO FLOOR WITH 1/2" EXP. ANC. BOLTS FOUR (4) EACH. GROUT LEVELING COURSE AS REQUIRED.

ELEV. 1337.50

FLOOR PIPE SUPPORT DETAIL

N.T.S.

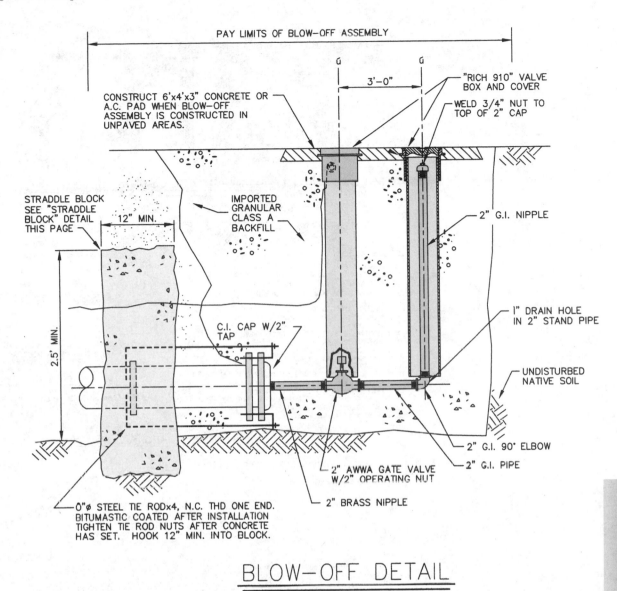

PAY LIMITS OF BLOW-OFF ASSEMBLY

3'-0"

"RICH 910" VALVE BOX AND COVER

WELD 3/4" NUT TO TOP OF 2" CAP

CONSTRUCT 6'x4'x3" CONCRETE OR A.C. PAD WHEN BLOW-OFF ASSEMBLY IS CONSTRUCTED IN UNPAVED AREAS.

STRADDLE BLOCK SEE "STRADDLE BLOCK" DETAIL THIS PAGE

IMPORTED GRANULAR CLASS A BACKFILL

12" MIN.

2" G.I. NIPPLE

2.5' MIN.

C.I. CAP W/2" TAP

1" DRAIN HOLE IN 2" STAND PIPE

UNDISTURBED NATIVE SOIL

2" G.I. 90° ELBOW

2" G.I. PIPE

2" AWWA GATE VALVE W/2" OPERATING NUT

2" BRASS NIPPLE

0"∅ STEEL TIE RODx4, N.C. THD ONE END. BITUMASTIC COATED AFTER INSTALLATION TIGHTEN TIE ROD NUTS AFTER CONCRETE HAS SET. HOOK 12" MIN. INTO BLOCK.

BLOW-OFF DETAIL

N.T.S.

Figure 13–26.   Detail of valve and blow-off line for water line.
(Courtesy Lee-Pace Engineering, Inc.)

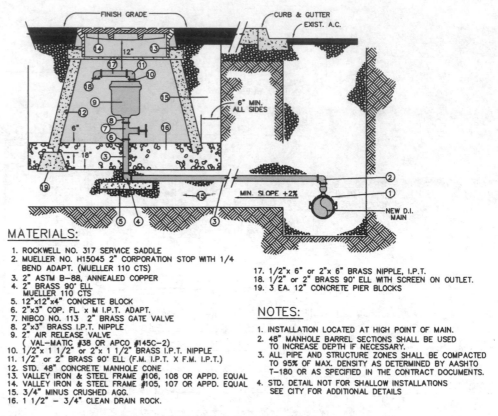

MATERIALS:

1. ROCKWELL NO. 317 SERVICE SADDLE
2. MUELLER NO. H15045 2" CORPORATION STOP WITH 1/4
   BEND ADAPT. (MUELLER 110 CTS)
3. 2" ASTM B-88, ANNEALED COPPER
4. 2" BRASS 90° ELL
   MUELLER 110 CTS
5. 12"x12"x4" CONCRETE BLOCK
6. 2"x3" COP. FL. x M I.P.T. ADAPT.
7. NIBCO NO. 113 2" BRASS GATE VALVE
8. 2"x3" BRASS I.P.T. NIPPLE
9. 2" AIR RELEASE VALVE
   (VAL-MATIC #38 OR APCO #145C-2)
10. 1/2"x 1 1/2" or 2"x 1 1/2" BRASS I.P.T. NIPPLE
11. 1/2" or 2" BRASS 90° ELL (F.M. I.P.T. X F.M. I.P.T.)
12. STD. 48" CONCRETE MANHOLE CONE
13. VALLEY IRON & STEEL FRAME #106, 108 OR APPD. EQUAL
14. VALLEY IRON & STEEL FRAME #105, 107 OR APPD. EQUAL
15. 3/4" MINUS CRUSHED AGG.
16. 1 1/2" - 3/4" CLEAN DRAIN ROCK.

17. 1/2"x 6" or 2"x 6" BRASS NIPPLE, I.P.T.
18. 1/2" or 2" BRASS 90° ELL WITH SCREEN ON OUTLET.
19. 3 EA. 12" CONCRETE PIER BLOCKS

NOTES:

1. INSTALLATION LOCATED AT HIGH POINT OF MAIN.
2. 48" MANHOLE BARREL SECTIONS SHALL BE USED
   TO INCREASE DEPTH IF NECESSARY.
3. ALL PIPE AND STRUCTURE ZONES SHALL BE COMPACTED
   TO 95% OF MAX. DENSITY AS DETERMINED BY AASHTO
   T-180 OR AS SPECIFIED IN THE CONTRACT DOCUMENTS.
4. STD. DETAIL NOT FOR SHALLOW INSTALLATIONS
   SEE CITY FOR ADDITIONAL DETAILS

STANDARD AIR RELEASE VALVE

Figure 13-27. Air release valve detail for water main.
(Courtesy Lee-Pace Engineering, Inc.)

Structural Details

Structural details comprise a range of materials that are used for the structure of a building. These include masonry, steel, and wood.

Masonry. Masonry includes any products used in construction by masons, such as brick, stone, and concrete blocks, often termed **concrete masonry units (CMUs)**. This type of detail often shows how masonry is to be installed and connected to other components of the building system, such as steel, wood, and concrete structural members, walls, and foundations. In addition, common details illustrate the positioning of steel rebar within the masonry. A selection of masonry details are shown in Figures 13-28 through 13-30.

Steel. Steel details most often illustrate the manner in which steel members are connected and anchored to other steel, concrete, masonry, and wood components. This can include a wide variety of fasteners, such as bolts, nuts, rebar, rivets, and welds. A good knowledge of welding symbols is beneficial. A company that deals with structural steel will likely maintain a symbol library of welding symbols. Figure 13-31 through 13-34 provide a sampling of structural steel details.

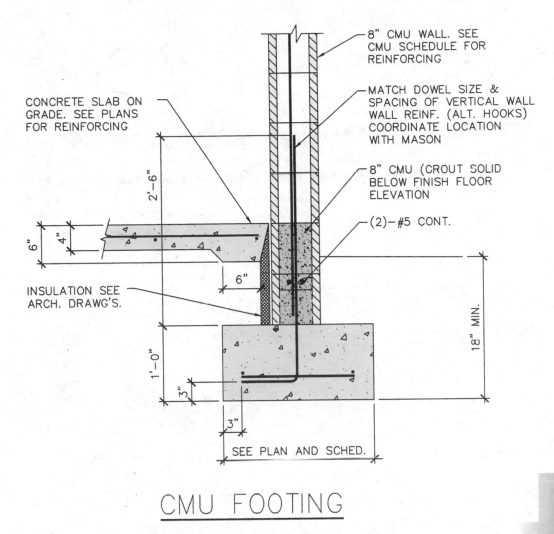

CONCRETE SLAB ON GRADE. SEE PLANS FOR REINFORCING

8" CMU WALL. SEE CMU SCHEDULE FOR REINFORCING

MATCH DOWEL SIZE & SPACING OF VERTICAL WALL WALL REINF. (ALT. HOOKS) COORDINATE LOCATION WITH MASON

8" CMU (GROUT SOLID BELOW FINISH FLOOR ELEVATION

(2)-#5 CONT.

INSULATION SEE ARCH. DRAWG'S.

2'-6"

6"

4"

6"

1'-0"

3"

3"

18" MIN.

SEE PLAN AND SCHED.

CMU FOOTING

Figure 13-28.   Concrete masonry unit detail at footing and slab connections.
(Courtesy Lee-Pace Engineering, Inc.)

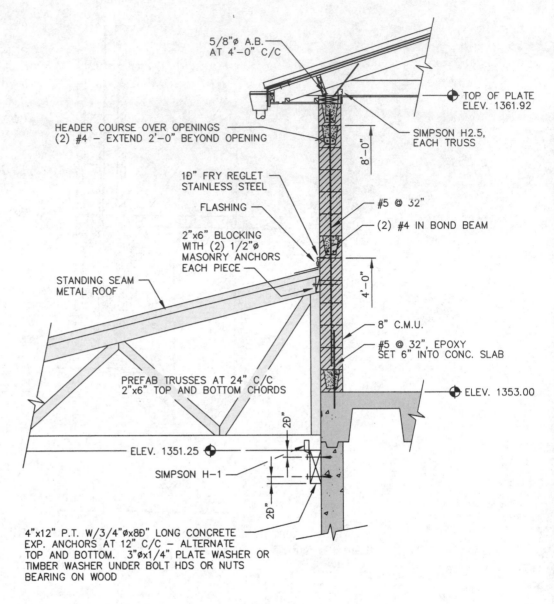

5/8"ø A.B.
AT 4'-0" C/C

TOP OF PLATE
ELEV. 1361.92

HEADER COURSE OVER OPENINGS
(2) #4 - EXTEND 2'-0" BEYOND OPENING

SIMPSON H2.5,
EACH TRUSS

8'-0"

1Ð" FRY REGLET
STAINLESS STEEL

FLASHING

#5 @ 32"

(2) #4 IN BOND BEAM

2"x6" BLOCKING
WITH (2) 1/2"ø
MASONRY ANCHORS
EACH PIECE

4'-0"

STANDING SEAM
METAL ROOF

8" C.M.U.

#5 @ 32", EPOXY
SET 6" INTO CONC. SLAB

PREFAB TRUSSES AT 24" C/C
2"x6" TOP AND BOTTOM CHORDS

ELEV. 1353.00

2Ð"

ELEV. 1351.25

SIMPSON H-1

2Ð"

4"x12" P.T. W/3/4"øx8Ð" LONG CONCRETE
EXP. ANCHORS AT 12" C/C - ALTERNATE
TOP AND BOTTOM. 3"ø×1/4" PLATE WASHER OR
TIMBER WASHER UNDER BOLT HDS OR NUTS
BEARING ON WOOD

CMU/WALL DETAIL
1/2" = 1'-0"

Figure 13-29. Concrete masonry unit detail at wall and roof connections.
(Courtesy Lee-Pace Engineering, Inc.)

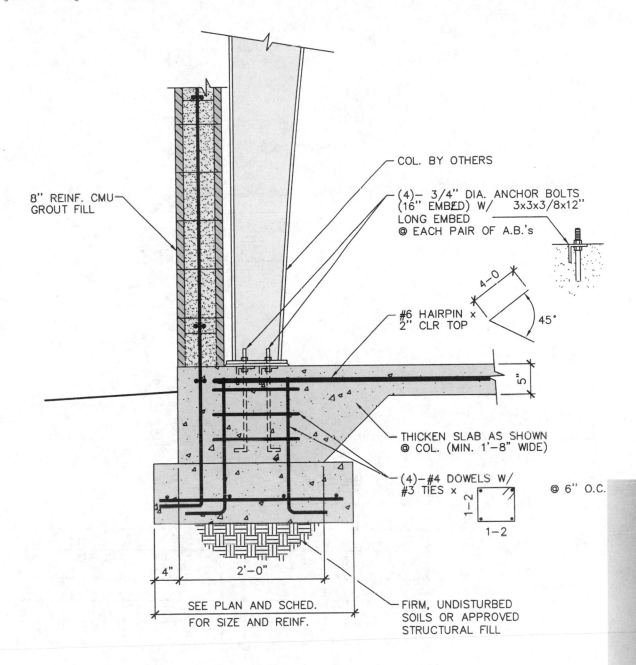

8" REINF. CMU
GROUT FILL

COL. BY OTHERS

(4)– 3/4" DIA. ANCHOR BOLTS
(16" EMBED) W/   3x3x3/8x12"
LONG EMBED
@ EACH PAIR OF A.B.'s

#6 HAIRPIN x
2" CLR TOP

4–0

45°

5"

THICKEN SLAB AS SHOWN
@ COL. (MIN. 1'–8" WIDE)

(4)–#4 DOWELS W/
#3 TIES x

@ 6" O.C.

1–2

1–2

1–2

FIRM, UNDISTURBED
SOILS OR APPROVED
STRUCTURAL FILL

4"   2'-0"

SEE PLAN AND SCHED.
FOR SIZE AND REINF.

FOOTING/CMU WALL
SCALE: 1" = 1'-0"

Figure 13-30. Concrete masonry units and reinforcing bar detail at footing.
(Courtesy Lee-Pace Engineering, Inc.)

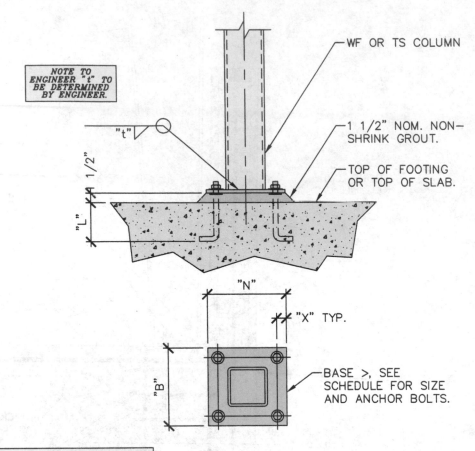

NOTE TO
ENGINEER "t" TO
BE DETERMINED
BY ENGINEER.

"t"

1/2"

"L"

WF OR TS COLUMN

1 1/2" NOM. NON-
SHRINK GROUT.

TOP OF FOOTING
OR TOP OF SLAB.

"N"

"X" TYP.

"B"

BASE >, SEE
SCHEDULE FOR SIZE
AND ANCHOR BOLTS.

NOTE TO ENGINEER:
SEE NOTES ON STEEL 1

COLUMN BASE PLATE SCHEDULE

COL. SIZE	N (IN)	B (IN)	THICK. (IN.)	X (IN)	ANCHOR BOLTS NOxDIA.xL
–	–	–	–	–	–
–	–	–	–	–	–
–	–	–	–	–	–
–	–	–	–	–	–
–	–	–	–	–	–
–	–	–	–	–	–
–	–	–	–	–	–

BASE PLATE DETAIL
N.T.S.

Figure 13–31.   Detail of structural steel column base plate connection to concrete.
(Courtesy Lee-Pace Engineering, Inc.)

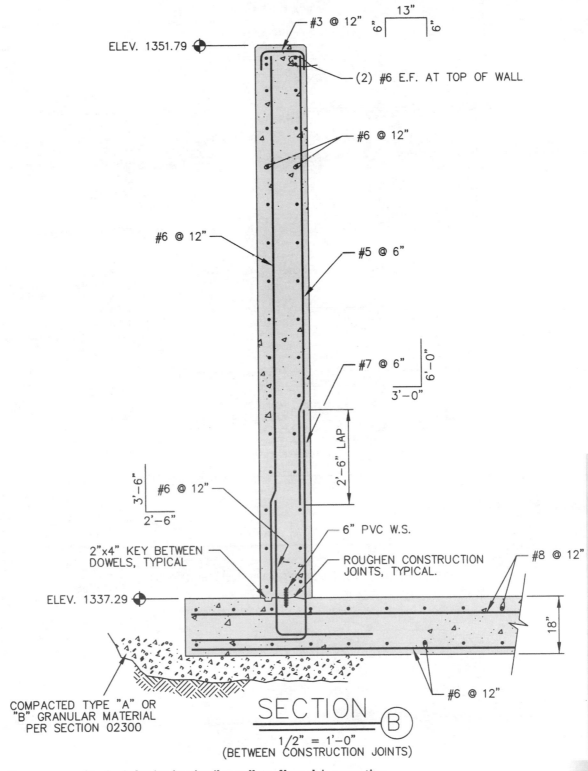

ELEV. 1351.79

#3 @ 12"

13"
6" 6"

(2) #6 E.F. AT TOP OF WALL

#6 @ 12"

#6 @ 12"

#5 @ 6"

#7 @ 6"

6'-0"
3'-0"

2'-6" LAP

#6 @ 12"

3'-6"
2'-6"

6" PVC W.S.

#8 @ 12"

2"x4" KEY BETWEEN
DOWELS, TYPICAL

ROUGHEN CONSTRUCTION
JOINTS, TYPICAL.

18"

ELEV. 1337.29

#6 @ 12"

COMPACTED TYPE "A" OR
"B" GRANULAR MATERIAL
PER SECTION 02300

SECTION Ⓑ
1/2" = 1'-0"
(BETWEEN CONSTRUCTION JOINTS)

Figure 13-32.   Steel reinforcing bar detail at wall-to-floor slab connection.
(Courtesy Lee-Pace Engineering, Inc.)

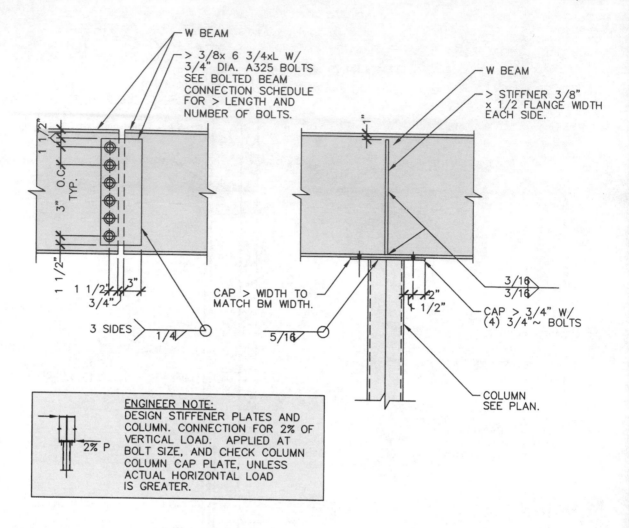

W BEAM

> 3/8x 6 3/4xL W/
3/4" DIA. A325 BOLTS
SEE BOLTED BEAM
CONNECTION SCHEDULE
FOR > LENGTH AND
NUMBER OF BOLTS.

W BEAM

> STIFFNER 3/8"
x 1/2 FLANGE WIDTH
EACH SIDE.

1 1/2"

3" O.C.
TYP.

1 1/2"

1 1/2"   3"
3/4"

CAP > WIDTH TO
MATCH BM WIDTH.

3 SIDES   1/4

5/16

1"

2"
1 1/2"

3/16
3/16

CAP > 3/4" W/
(4) 3/4"~ BOLTS

COLUMN
SEE PLAN.

ENGINEER NOTE:
DESIGN STIFFENER PLATES AND
COLUMN. CONNECTION FOR 2% OF
VERTICAL LOAD. APPLIED AT
BOLT SIZE, AND CHECK COLUMN
COLUMN CAP PLATE, UNLESS
ACTUAL HORIZONTAL LOAD
IS GREATER.

2% P

STEEL BEAM TO COLUMN
N.T.S.

Figure 13–33. Welded and bolted connection of steel beam to column.
(Courtesy Lee-Pace Engineering, Inc.)

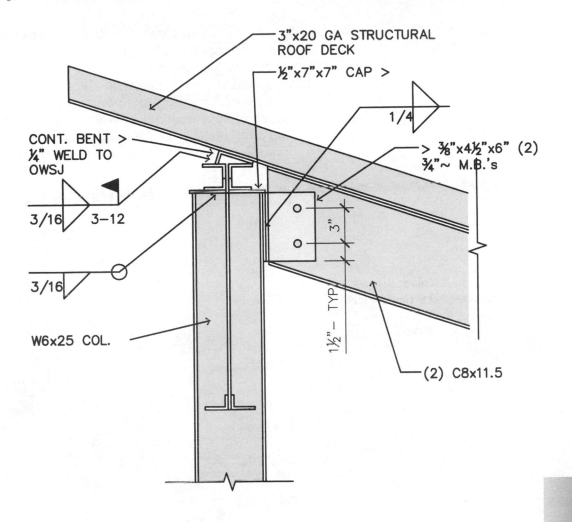

3"x20 GA STRUCTURAL
ROOF DECK

½"x7"x7" CAP >

1/4

CONT. BENT >
¼" WELD TO
OWSJ

> ⅜"x4½"x6" (2)
¾"~ M.B.'s

3/16   3-12

3/16

3"

1½" – TYP.

W6x25 COL.

(2) C8x11.5

CANOPY DETAIL
SCALE: 1" = 1'-0"

Figure 13-34.   Structural steel column connections at column and roof canopy.
(Courtesy Lee-Pace Engineering, Inc.)

Wood. Wood structural components can vary from stick framing details to large posts, columns, and beams. As with other structural details, the manner in which wood members are connected to each other and to other materials are most commonly indicated with local notes. Structural members are most commonly joined by a variety of steel connectors. These range from a basic plate to any shape of steel bent to accommodate the angles of the structural components. For example, notice the 3/8″ × 4½″ × 6″ connector in Figure 13–34, the steel angle bracket in Figure 13–35, and the hinge connector in Figure 13–37. A variety of wood structural details are shown in Figures 13–35 through 13–38.

Figure 13–35. Wood post, beam, and porch connection at concrete pier.
(Courtesy Lee-Pace Engineering, Inc.)

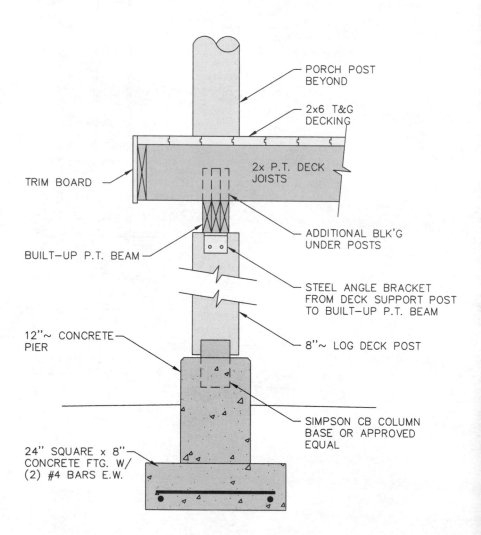

PORCH POST BEYOND

2x6 T&G DECKING

2x P.T. DECK JOISTS

TRIM BOARD

ADDITIONAL BLK'G UNDER POSTS

BUILT–UP P.T. BEAM

STEEL ANGLE BRACKET FROM DECK SUPPORT POST TO BUILT–UP P.T. BEAM

12″~ CONCRETE PIER

8″~ LOG DECK POST

SIMPSON CB COLUMN BASE OR APPROVED EQUAL

24″ SQUARE x 8″ CONCRETE FTG. W/ (2) #4 BARS E.W.

PORCH PIER CONNECTION
SCALE: 1″ = 1′–0″

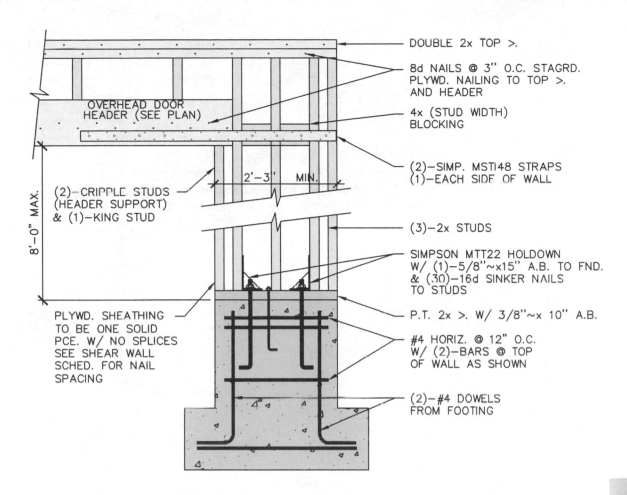

DOUBLE 2x TOP >.

8d NAILS @ 3" O.C. STAGRD. PLYWD. NAILING TO TOP >. AND HEADER

OVERHEAD DOOR HEADER (SEE PLAN)

4x (STUD WIDTH) BLOCKING

(2)—SIMP. MSTI48 STRAPS (1)—EACH SIDE OF WALL

(2)—CRIPPLE STUDS (HEADER SUPPORT) & (1)—KING STUD

2'–3' MIN.

8'–0" MAX.

(3)—2x STUDS

SIMPSON MTT22 HOLDOWN W/ (1)–5/8"~x15" A.B. TO FND. & (30)–16d SINKER NAILS TO STUDS

P.T. 2x >. W/ 3/8"~x 10" A.B.

PLYWD. SHEATHING TO BE ONE SOLID PCE. W/ NO SPLICES SEE SHEAR WALL SCHED. FOR NAIL SPACING

#4 HORIZ. @ 12" O.C. W/ (2)—BARS @ TOP OF WALL AS SHOWN

(2)—#4 DOWELS FROM FOOTING

LATERAL DETAIL
SCALE: 1" = 1'–0"

Figure 13–36. Overhead door header details, with connection to concrete footing.
(Courtesy Lee-Pace Engineering, Inc.)

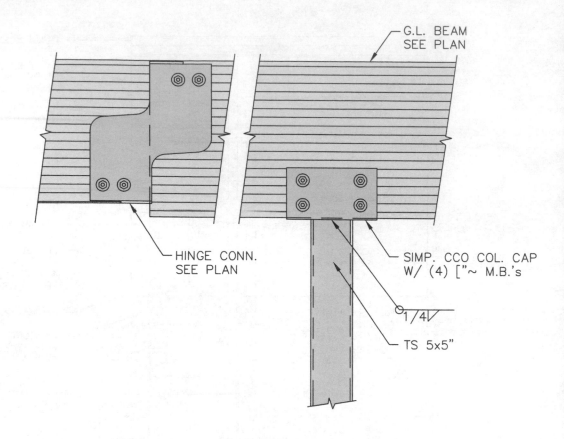

BEAM/BEAM COL. CONNECTION
SCALE: 1" = 1'-0"

Figure 13-37. Laminated beam connection and beam connection to steel column.
(Courtesy Lee-Pace Engineering, Inc.)

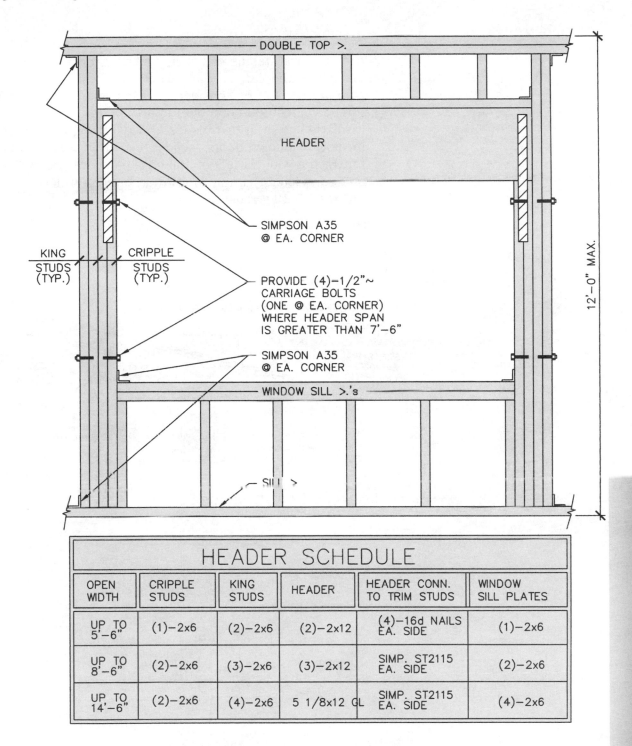

DOUBLE TOP >.

HEADER

SIMPSON A35
@ EA. CORNER

KING
STUDS
(TYP.)

CRIPPLE
STUDS
(TYP.)

PROVIDE (4)-1/2"~
CARRIAGE BOLTS
(ONE @ EA. CORNER)
WHERE HEADER SPAN
IS GREATER THAN 7'-6"

SIMPSON A35
@ EA. CORNER

WINDOW SILL >.'s

SILL >

12'-0" MAX.

HEADER SCHEDULE

OPEN WIDTH	CRIPPLE STUDS	KING STUDS	HEADER	HEADER CONN. TO TRIM STUDS	WINDOW SILL PLATES
UP TO 5'-6"	(1)-2x6	(2)-2x6	(2)-2x12	(4)-16d NAILS EA. SIDE	(1)-2x6
UP TO 8'-6"	(2)-2x6	(3)-2x6	(3)-2x12	SIMP. ST2115 EA. SIDE	(2)-2x6
UP TO 14'-6"	(2)-2x6	(4)-2x6	5 1/8x12 GL	SIMP. ST2115 EA. SIDE	(4)-2x6

TYP. OPENING FRAMING
SCALE: 1" = 1'-0"

Figure 13-38. Tabular dimension for typical header framing around an opening.
(Courtesy Lee-Pace Engineering, Inc.)

Architectural Details

Architectural details can include any aspect of the architectural discipline and can overlap structural details. Whereas structural components can be considered the skeleton of a building or structure, architectural components are all additional materials, from insulation to interior finishes and exterior treatments. This also includes windows, doors, facades, elevation views, and the manner in which a wide variety of building materials are applied, fastened, and connected. Some common architectural details are shown in Figures 13–39 through 13–41.

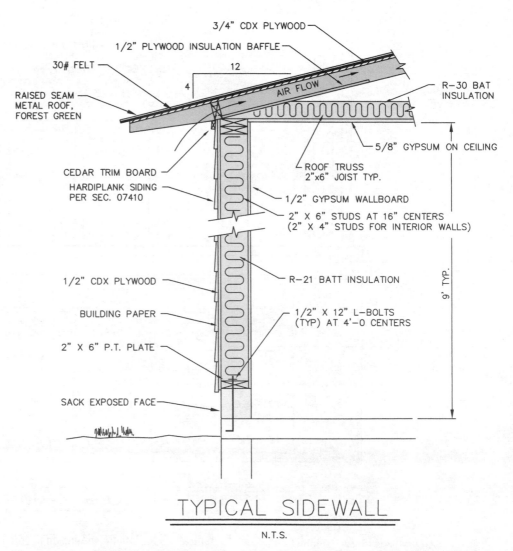

Figure 13–39. Section details of materials and installation in a typical sidewall for a residence. (Courtesy Lee-Pace Engineering, Inc.)

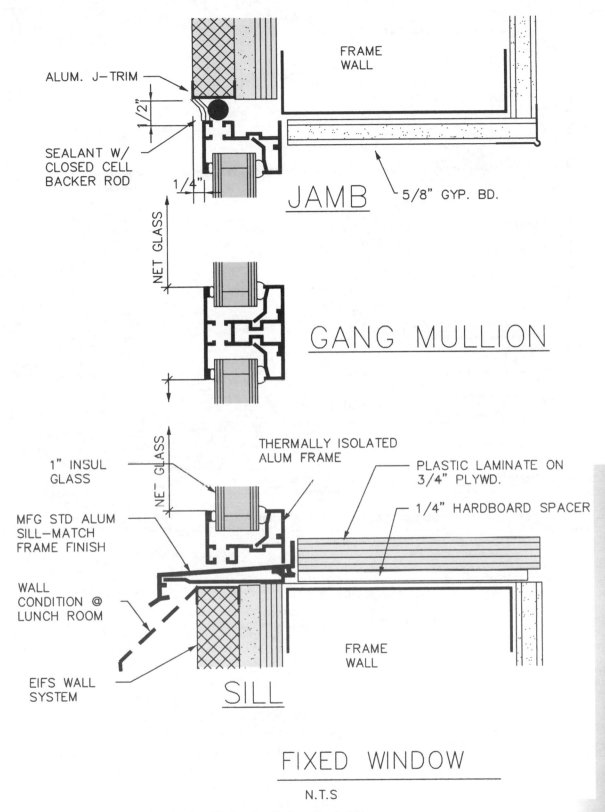

ALUM. J-TRIM

FRAME WALL

SEALANT W/ CLOSED CELL BACKER ROD

1/2"

1/4"

JAMB

5/8" GYP. BD.

NET GLASS

GANG MULLION

NET GLASS

1" INSUL GLASS

THERMALLY ISOLATED ALUM FRAME

PLASTIC LAMINATE ON 3/4" PLYWD.

1/4" HARDBOARD SPACER

MFG STD ALUM SILL-MATCH FRAME FINISH

WALL CONDITION @ LUNCH ROOM

FRAME WALL

EIFS WALL SYSTEM

SILL

FIXED WINDOW

N.T.S

Figure 13-40. **Aluminum framing installation details for a fixed window.**
(Courtesy Lee-Pace Engineering, Inc.)

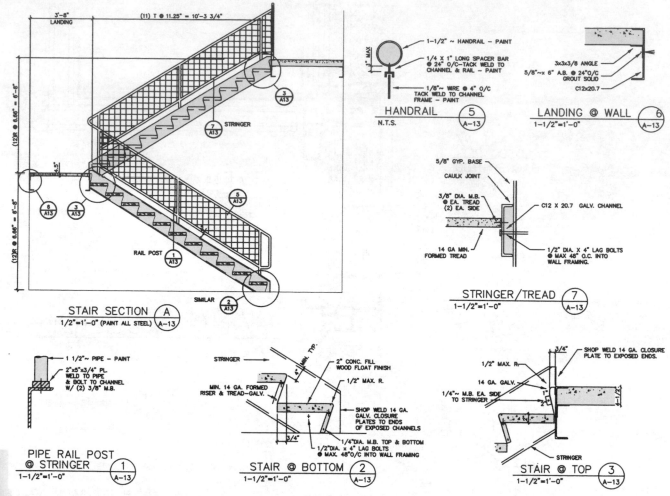

Figure 13-41. Section and fabrication details for a steel stair installation. (Courtesy Lee-Pace Engineering, Inc.)

Symbol Libraries

Detail drawings show multiple features, components, and symbols. Many of the geometrical shapes in a detail drawing may actually be individual drawings themselves. These smaller drawings can be referred to as *symbol drawings*. Therefore, a collection of symbols, compiled and archived for future use, is called a **symbol library**. The software terminology for these symbols may be *blocks* or *cells*. If you are using AutoCAD, you are familiar with the creation of blocks. Companies that use AutoCAD maintain symbol libraries that are either individual drawings (wblocks) or a single drawing file that contains symbols for a specific discipline.

Drafters and designers who are responsible for the creation and maintenance of drawings should make it a priority to become familiar with company standards regarding the creation, storage, and use of symbols and symbol libraries. Every company has different systems and standards. Therefore, it is imperative to learn these procedures early in your employment.

Many companies create a drawing component called a **legend**. This is usually an arrangement of symbols located on one side of the drawing. See Figure 13-42. It may also be large enough to occupy an entire drawing sheet. The legend can be altered depending on the scope of the project or the drawing discipline. The legend is primarily for easy interpretation of drawing symbols but may also act as a drawing tool for the drafter. Legend symbols can be copied and used in the drawing with relative ease. Again, consult your company standards for proper procedures.

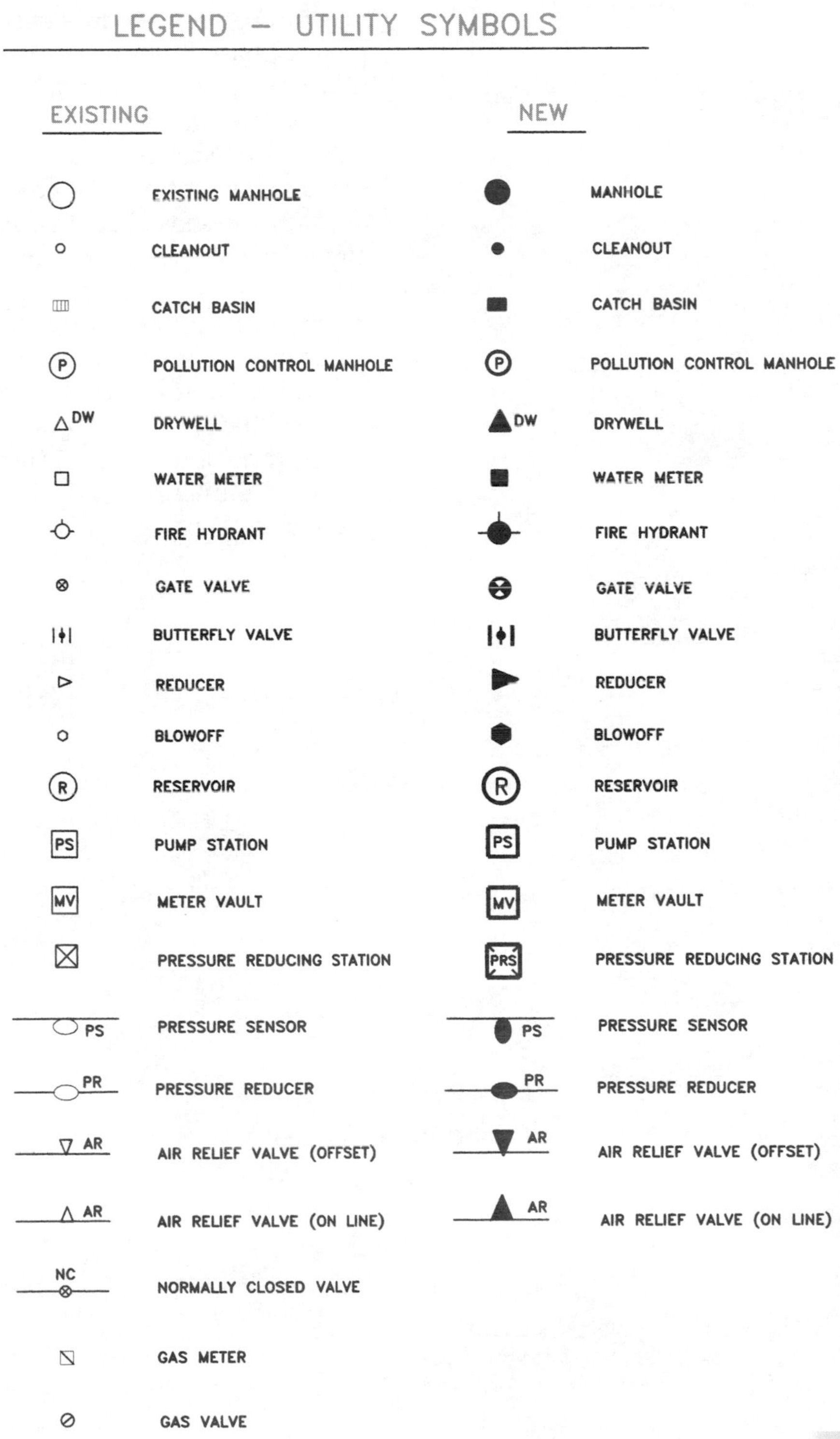

Figure 13-42. A legend is usually an arrangement of symbols located on one side of a drawing. This legend shows existing and new utility symbols.

LEGEND — UTILITY SYMBOLS

EXISTING		NEW	
○	EXISTING MANHOLE	●	MANHOLE
○	CLEANOUT	●	CLEANOUT
▥	CATCH BASIN	▬	CATCH BASIN
Ⓟ	POLLUTION CONTROL MANHOLE	Ⓟ	POLLUTION CONTROL MANHOLE
△ DW	DRYWELL	▲ DW	DRYWELL
□	WATER METER	◼	WATER METER
◇	FIRE HYDRANT	●	FIRE HYDRANT
⊗	GATE VALVE	⊗	GATE VALVE
❘♦❘	BUTTERFLY VALVE	❘♦❘	BUTTERFLY VALVE
▷	REDUCER	►	REDUCER
○	BLOWOFF	●	BLOWOFF
Ⓡ	RESERVOIR	Ⓡ	RESERVOIR
PS	PUMP STATION	PS	PUMP STATION
MV	METER VAULT	MV	METER VAULT
⊠	PRESSURE REDUCING STATION	PRS	PRESSURE REDUCING STATION
⬭ PS	PRESSURE SENSOR	● PS	PRESSURE SENSOR
⬭ PR	PRESSURE REDUCER	● PR	PRESSURE REDUCER
▽ AR	AIR RELIEF VALVE (OFFSET)	▼ AR	AIR RELIEF VALVE (OFFSET)
△ AR	AIR RELIEF VALVE (ON LINE)	▲ AR	AIR RELIEF VALVE (ON LINE)
NC ⊗	NORMALLY CLOSED VALVE		
◩	GAS METER		
⊘	GAS VALVE		

Checking Drawing Standards

Prior to the release of drawings for bids and/or construction permitting, it is important that they go through a final check for adherence to applicable standards. Standards checking is a procedure by which drawings are checked against a "base" drawing that contains up-to-date drawing, design, and construction standards for a specific discipline or trade. Software packages such as AutoCAD and MicroStation have routines that allow the user to put any drawing or set of drawings through a standards check before they are sent on to the next project phase. In order to accomplish this with the greatest amount of accuracy, it is important that drawing files designated as "standards drawings" be maintained. Civil engineering companies may have a wide variety of standards drawings on file for use with different drawing, design, and construction disciplines.

Software-based standards checking is straightforward and usually involves opening the drawing to be checked and opening the standards drawings to be used in the checking process. The software may automatically change items not up to standard or mark them for change by the CADD user.

The cleaner and more accurate drawings are when they are sent out for bids, permitting, or construction, the greater the potential for saving time and money. Therefore, as a civil drafter, it is imperative that you learn as much as possible about company standards and standards checking procedures.

TEST

Use Microsoft Word to open the file "Chapter 13 test" on the Student Web site.

13-1 Name at least six different disciplines with which a civil engineering firm may be involved.

13-2 What aspects of a project may be contracted out by a civil engineering firm to other engineering companies?

13-3 What are national and international organization standards? Name three organizations that maintain such standards.

13-4 What is a project specifications document, and what standards does it reflect?

13-5 What is a site plan?

13-6 What is the difference between a section and a cross section?

13-7 What is a profile?

13-8 What are the most important drawings for construction purposes?

13-9 If a detail drawing is not a typical construction standard, where is it normally shown?

13-10 Name four different disciplines that require detail drawings.

13-11 What is a symbol library?

13-12   What is the function of a legend?

13-13   What is standards checking?

STANDARD SIDEWALK RAMPS

Use Microsoft Word to open the file "Ch 13 sidewalk ramps" on the Student Web site.

Study the detail drawing titled "Standard Sidewalk Ramps with Planter Strip" in Figure T13–1 to answer the following questions.

1. What type of drawing is shown at the top?

2. How many sections are cut on this drawing?

3. What section shows the minimum ramp width?

4. What is the minimum ramp width?

5. What feature is located directly across the planter strip from the point of tangency?

6. What shapes are aligned on a square grid in the detectable warning area of the ramp?

7. What are the two grade slopes used on the ramp?

8. What standards must the sidewalk ramp meet?

9. What are the slopes for cut and fill at the inside of the curve on the ramps?

10. What drawing is to be referred to for sidewalk widths, planter strip widths, and sidewalk panel dimensions?

11. What compressive strength should the concrete have?

12. What note should be referred to for details on a typical scored joint?

PROBLEMS

P13-1   Redraw the street section in Figure 13–6 using the following information:

- The finished drawing should be plotted on a B-size sheet. Determine the appropriate scale for plotting purposes and for text height.
- Construct the drawing using accurate dimensions. Street width is 12′ from centerline. Planter strip is 5.50′ wide.
- Angle of repose for cut is 1 1/2:1.
- Thicknesses of road bed materials can be exaggerated.

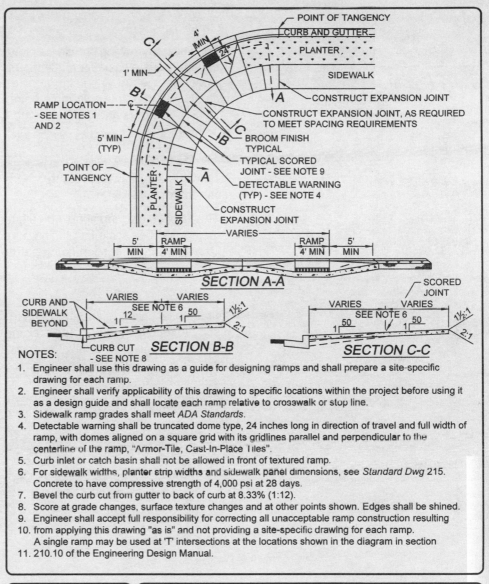

SECTION A-A

SECTION B-B

SECTION C-C

NOTES:
1. Engineer shall use this drawing as a guide for designing ramps and shall prepare a site-specific drawing for each ramp.
2. Engineer shall verify applicability of this drawing to specific locations within the project before using it as a design guide and shall locate each ramp relative to crosswalk or stop line.
3. Sidewalk ramp grades shall meet *ADA Standards*.
4. Detectable warning shall be truncated dome type, 24 inches long in direction of travel and full width of ramp, with domes aligned on a square grid with its gridlines parallel and perpendicular to the centerline of the ramp, "Armor-Tile, Cast-In-Place Tiles".
5. Curb inlet or catch basin shall not be allowed in front of textured ramp.
6. For sidewalk widths, planter strip widths and sidewalk panel dimensions, see *Standard Dwg* 215. Concrete to have compressive strength of 4,000 psi at 28 days.
7. Bevel the curb cut from gutter to back of curb at 8.33% (1:12).
8. Score at grade changes, surface texture changes and at other points shown. Edges shall be shined.
9. Engineer shall accept full responsibility for correcting all unacceptable ramp construction resulting
10. from applying this drawing "as is" and not providing a site-specific drawing for each ramp. A single ramp may be used at 'T' intersections at the locations shown in the diagram in section
11. 210.10 of the Engineering Design Manual.

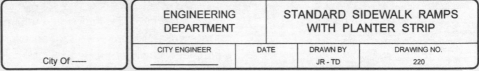

City Of ----	ENGINEERING DEPARTMENT		STANDARD SIDEWALK RAMPS WITH PLANTER STRIP	
	CITY ENGINEER	DATE	DRAWN BY JR - TD	DRAWING NO. 220

Figure T13-1.

P13-2 Redraw the street section in Figure 13–10 using the following information:

- The finished drawing should be plotted on a B-size sheet. Determine the appropriate scale for plotting purposes and for text height.
- Construct the drawing using accurate dimensions. Street width is 12′ from centerline. Planter strip is 8.5′ wide.
- Thicknesses of road bed materials can be exaggerated.

P13-3   Redraw the manhole detail from Figure 13–15 using the following
         information:

         ▪ The finished drawing should be plotted on an A-size sheet. Determine
           the appropriate scale for plotting purposes and for text height.
         ▪ Construct the drawing using accurate dimensions. Choose a
           dimension for the two variable-height dimensions on the right side.
         ▪ Include all notes and details. Number all general notes, if desired.

P13-4   Redraw the footing/wall detail from Figure 13–30 using the following
         information:

         ▪ The finished drawing should be plotted on an A-size sheet. Determine
           the appropriate scale for plotting purposes and for text height.
         ▪ Use appropriate section/hatch patterns.

P13-5   Contact local civil engineering firms in order to complete this problem.
         Assemble a collection of detail drawings for a variety of disciplines.
         Create a storage and retrieval system that allows all students or
         employees to access the files. Print a document that contains a list of
         all details, arranged by discipline. Include file name and path, plotting
         scale, file size, and any other information deemed appropriate.

P13-6   Create a library of as many civil engineering symbols as you can find.
         See Figure 13–42 for an example. Use all resources available to you,
         such as local companies, CD files in this text, Internet sources, and
         local and national professional organizations. Arrange the symbols
         according to disciplines and create a storage and retrieval system that
         allows all students or employees to access the files.

P13-7   Create a legend of civil engineering symbols for use on discipline-specific
         drawings. See Figure 13–42 for an example. Place the symbol legend on
         a template drawing that is used for each discipline. If you use AutoCAD
         blocks to create the legend, they can be copied directly from the legend
         for use on the drawing.

Introduction to Geographic Information Systems (GIS)

Learning Objectives

After completing this chapter, you will be able to:

- Answer questions related to GIS technology.
- Describe differences between CADD and GIS systems.
- Name the parcel-based GIS applications.
- Describe topology.
- Show a soil map in raster GIS format.
- Answer questions related to GPS technology.

Key Terms

Geographic information systems (GIS)
Tabular data
Spatial data
Attribute data
Spreadsheet
Desktop
Graphical user interface (GUI)
Georelational data model
Relational database management systems (RDBMS)
Topology
Vector
Raster
Parcel-based application
Demographic analysis
Geocoding
Facilities management
Modeling
Viewshed determination
Hypermedia
Global positioning system (GPS)

This chapter introduces and describes geographic information systems (GIS). It further presents information about GIS applications, training, and trends.

The topics covered include:

- Introduction to GIS
- Related disciplines
- GIS concepts
- GIS components
- Data formats
- GIS applications
- GIS industry
- Trends in GIS
- Introduction to GPS

Introduction

The National Center for Geographic Information & Analysis (NCGIA, **www.ncgia.ucsb.edu**) describes a GIS as "a computerized database management system for capture, storage, retrieval, analysis, and display of spatial data." Figure 14–1 shows how a GIS stores multiple layers of reality.

GIS software provides a set of tools for solving spatial problems by working with spatial and attribute data. *Spatial data* describes a feature's location, and *attribute data* describes the characteristics of the feature.

Figure 14–2 shows an example of a GIS application used in the forestry industry to document and manage stands of timber located in a specific area. This example contains *graphic data* and a map (Figure 14–2), as well as *tabular data* (Table 14–1). The map provides the spatial data, which in this example is the location of three distinct forest types. The table lists the attribute data, which in this figure

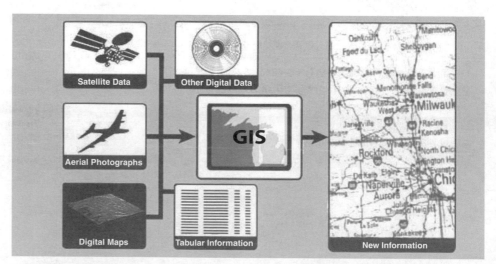

Figure 14–1.   A demonstration of how data integration is the linking of information in different forms through a GIS.

(Courtesy U.S. Geological Survey, Geographic Information Systems (GIS) Poster, **www.egsc.usgs.gov/isb/pubs/ gis_poster/**)

Figure 14-2. An example of a GIS application used in the forestry industry to document and manage stands of timber located in a specific area. This example contains graphic data as a map. The map provides the spatial data, which in this example is the location of three distinct forest types. The attribute data is found in Table 14-1.

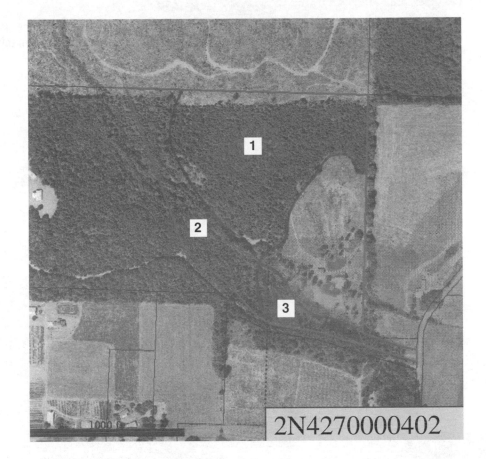

includes information regarding the size, identification, type, age, and harvest date of each forest area. Notice how the spatial data and attribute data can be correlated to effectively understand the characteristics of each stand of timber. Study the three portions of the map and table to further understand the GIS shown in Figure 14-2 and Table 14-1. An additional discussion of spatial data and attribute data is provided later in this chapter.

GIS is the geographical equivalent of a spreadsheet because it provides answers to "What if" questions that have spatial dimensions. A spreadsheet is used for number-relatd information processing that is displayed in table format. The difference between a GIS program and a spreadsheet program is that a GIS, program can also display the table data graphically. Although many other computer programs can use spatial data (for example, AutoCAD and statistical packages), only GIS programs have the ability to perform spatial operations.

GIS technology allows workers to function more efficiently and effectively. GIS software provides better decisions based on better information.

Another example of a GIS application is tracking employees within a company by name, address, employment date, and schedule. If the location of each employee's home is associated with a point on a map, then it could be determined which employees are candidates for carpooling or ride sharing. The GIS program can display this information graphically so that employees can see the relationship between their locations and the company's location.

Table 14-1. This table lists the attribute data, which includes information regarding the size, identification, type, age, and harvest date of each forest area. Notice how the spatial data in Figure 14-2 and attribute data in this figure can be correlated to effectively understand the characteristics of each stand of timber.

Stand Number	1	2	3
Acreage	17 acres	9 acres	3 acres
Forest type	Conifer	Conifer	Conifer
Elevation	280–400 feet	280–400 feet	280–400 feet
Slope	20–30%	20–60%	60%
Aspect	East	East and north	East
Tree species mix	Douglas fir	Douglas fir/western red cedar/alder/big leaf maple/vine maple	Western red cedar/ Douglas fir
Site index (50 years)	125	125	125
100 (years)	175	175	175
Site class	2	2	2
Age	25 years	20 years	~40 years
Average DBH	8 inch	10 inch	12 inch
Average density	330 trees/ac	294 trees/ac	258 trees/ac
Basal area/Ac	~115 sq. ft	~160 sq.ft	~203 sq.ft
Stocking level	92%	160%	~100%
Total stand volume	~2677.cu.ft	~2560.cu.ft	~3354.cu.ft
Growth rate	5–6 rings/inch	5–6 rings/inch	6 rings/inch
Incremental diam.	~1.7 inch in 5 years	~1.7 inch in 5 years	~1.5 inch in 5 years
Growth	~3.4 inch in 10 years	~3.4 inch in 10 years	~3 inches in 5 years
Projected growth at current rate	In 5 years: • Average stand DBH ~10″ • Average ht ~70′ In 10 years: • Average stand DBH ~12″ • Average ht ~80′	In 5 years: • Average stand DBH ~12″ • Average ht ~75–80′ In 10 years: • Average stand DBH ~14″ • Average ht ~85–90′	In 5 years: • Average stand DBH ~13.5″ • Average ht ~66.5′ In 10 years: • Average stand DBH ~15″ • Average ht ~104′
Inventory data	See attached	See attached	See attached
Understory vegetation	Trailing blackberry, bracken fern, sword fern, snowberry, Oregon-grape, salal, red huckleberry, rose	Vine maple, training blackberry, salal, Oregon-grape, red huckleberry	Sword fern, bracken fern, training, blackberry
Stand history	Clear cut and replanted about 25 years ago	Clear-cut and replanted about 20 years ago	Selectively logged about 20 years ago, left the cedar

History

In 1960, Canada became the first nation to develop a national GIS database. This GIS database gave Canada the ability to conduct nationwide geographical analysis. The New York Department of Natural Resources developed the first state GIS in 1975 around an inventory of its land use and vegetation. The next states to develop GIS programs were Minnesota, Maryland, and Texas.

During the 1960s, GIS programs focused on complex mathematics and were proprietary, expensive, and slow. During the 1970s, the focus shifted to data conversion and justification of the high cost of that conversion.

Software matured in the 1980s, and the performance of workstations and personal computers increased rapidly. This increase in performance prompted an annual growth rate of over 35 percent and an explosion in the number of GIS systems. These systems focused on integrating existing databases, data quality (or "fitness for use"), applications, and enhanced graphic capabilities.

Desktop mapping with GIS increased in the early 1990s. Software developers began to improve the user friendliness of GIS software. The term **desktop** refers to the use of personal computers (PC) for these applications.

GIS Software and Hardware

GIS users have migrated from mainframes and minicomputers to workstations and personal computers. The increased power and reduced price of personal computers, coupled with the availability of larger mass storage devices (such as CDs and optical disks), allow users to meet their needs with PC-based GIS. The shift to PC-based GIS has increased the number of GIS users because more organizations are able to afford GIS technology. In addition, more GIS are being networked, and users are producing higher-quality color output.

This section provides general information about GIS software manufacturer products. Much of the information is taken from the related Web sites. The information provided is intended as an introduction only. For more information, refer to the Web sites referenced with each product. This discussion is not intended to promote or endorse any of the products represented. Other GIS software products are available. Do an Internet search using key words such as *geographic information systems*, *GIS*, or *GIS software* to find additional products.

Caliper Corporation

Caliper (**www.caliper.com**) is a developer of GIS products such as Maptitude GIS for Windows and TransCAD transportation planning software.

Environmental Systems Research Institute, Inc.

Environmental Systems Research Institute, Inc., commonly known as ESRI (**www.esri.com**), produces a line of GIS products. ArcGIS is an integrated family of GIS software products for building a complete GIS. The ArcGIS framework allows you to use GIS wherever it is needed. ArcView is a GIS software product used for visualizing, managing, creating, and analyzing geographic data.

Manifold Systems

Manifold Systems (**www.manifold.net**) provides GIS products available in several versions, providing integration of raster images, vector drawings, terrain surfaces, terrain visualization, full programming capability, and a Web server.

MapInfo Corporation

MapInfo (**www.mapinfo.com**) offers a wide selection of software products, including desktop solutions, MapInfo Professional, and programmable tools.

GIS Training

Due to the dynamic nature of GIS, ongoing training and education are essential. While training on specific GIS software is invaluable, a good understanding of GIS concepts is equally important.

Two primary education tracks train users. One is for those who want to develop the technology itself, such as computer programmers. The second is for those who want to apply GIS within a particular discipline, such as soil scientists.

Related GIS Disciplines

GIS is an "enabling technology" because of the assistance it offers to the many disciplines that use spatial data. A GIS brings these disciplines together by emphasizing analysis, modeling, and integration. GIS often claims to be the science of spatial information, and it functions as a tool that integrates a variety of data.

Each of the following disciplines provides some of the techniques that comprise GIS:

- Geography: Provides techniques for spatial analysis.
- Cartography: Focuses on map design and data display.
- Remote sensing: Provides image analysis and data input.
- Photogrammetry: Calculates measurements from aerial photos.
- Civil engineering: Applies GIS in transportation and urban design.

- **Geodesy:** Furnishes highly accurate positional control for data.
- **Surveying:** Supplies positional data on natural and human-made objects.
- **Statistics:** Provides techniques for data analysis.
- **Mathematics:** Provides geometry and design theory.
- **Project management:** Develops, organizes, and coordinates the variety of tasks necessary to complete a project.
- **Computer science:** May provide any or all of the following: programming for GIS software application development, techniques for hardware and network support, database administration needed for spatial data management, and methods of data entry and display.

Third-Party Applications

The toolbox design of GIS software lends itself to specialized third-party applications. The number and diversity of these applications increase as divergent businesses adopt GIS technology. The term *toolbox* refers to computer software tools such as menus, toolbars, palettes, and dialog boxes.

Third-party applications include those for exploring for natural resources, dispatching emergency services, and evaluating the impact of global warming. GIS may either provide the input data or serve as the user-friendly front end for these applications.

GIS Trends

Desktop GIS makes mapping possible for those who have no formal training in cartography but who work with geographical data. Cartographers have valid concerns about the quality of output that these users produce. On the other hand, more people are able to use GIS; in and of itself, this will increase the acceptance of GIS.

Desktop Mapping

As the GIS industry matures, desktop mapping is a natural evolution. *Desktop mapping* software makes a PC-based GIS easier to use than mainstream GIS software. Desktop mapping has a graphical user interface that conforms to the Microsoft Windows standard. A graphical user interface (GUI) is the manner in which information and options are displayed by the software. One of the most common features of the Microsoft Windows GUI is the dialog box. A *dialog box* is accessed by a command or an option in the software. A dialog box may contain a variety of information that you pick for use. The use of dialog boxes saves time and increases productivity by reducing the amount of typing you must do. The GUI provides the casual GIS user access to spatial databases and the ability to easily produce maps, charts, and graphs. Desktop mapping has quickly become the most common GIS system in use today.

GIS Concepts

As previously discussed, geographical information has two related parts: spatial and attribute data. Spatial and attribute data are related by a common item that has a unique value. This relationship is called the **georelational data model**.

The georelational data model offers a consistent framework for analyzing spatial data. By putting maps and other kinds of spatial information into digital form, GIS allows users to manipulate and display geographical knowledge in new and exciting ways.

Spatial Data

From 80 to 90 percent of the information that utilities, planners, engineers, and governments use relates to locations on the earth.

GIS programs store spatial data as one of three primary feature types: points, lines, and polygons. Power poles, maintenance covers, and wells are examples of point features. Street centerlines, power lines, and contours are line features. Parcels, soils, and census tracts are polygon features. Other feature types that are designed for specific GIS applications include routes, regions, and voxels:

- **Routes:** Linear features used by the transportation industry.
- **Regions:** Can be overlapping or separate polygons. One example of a region could be a map of the earth with all the countries shown. The United States is displayed as separate polygons because the continental United States is separated from Alaska and Hawaii. Another example might be overlapping polygons, as in the mineral extraction industry, where different types of minerals may be in regions that are connected or overlapping.
- **Voxels:** Three-dimensional polygons used by model flow of air and water.

A GIS makes connections between activities based on location. A connection can suggest new insights and explanations. For example, GIS can link toxic waste records with school locations through geographic proximity.

Attribute Data

The term *attribute* can have a variety of related definitions. For example, an attribute is used to refer to text information on a CADD drawing. An attribute is also a characteristic or property of an object, such as weight, size, or color. An example of a characteristic of a GIS might be described by characters, images, numbers, values, and CADD drawings. Attributes are commonly stored in tabular format and linked to a feature. For example, the attributes of water wells in an area can list locations, depths, and gallons per minute produced from each well. When you hear reference to attribute data, this is data that relates to a specific location. In GIS applications, attribute data is linked in the GIS to spatial data that defines the location.

GIS programs use **relational database management systems (RDBMS)**. An RDBMS relates information from different files. Each related file contains one data item that is the same. RDBMS software programs store data in a manner that allows tables to be joined together by linking on a common item of data. This common item of data is called a *key*. In general, a *database management system* (DBMS) is a collection of programs that let you store, modify, and extract information from a database. A database (DB) is an electronic filing system that provides a collection of information organized for a computer program to rapidly select desired pieces of data. Requests for information from a database are made in the form of a *query*. A query is basically a question that allows you to find the desired information in the database. An example of a query in a forestry database might be Select All Species Where = "White Pine" and Age > 30. This query requests all records of forest stands with white pine trees older than 30 years. Most DBMS, allow you to output information in a report with graphs and charts.

Topology

Topology is a branch of mathematics that deals with relationships among geometric objects. Topology defines and manages relationships such as connectivity, adjacency, and contiguity. These relationships are intuitively obvious to humans but difficult for a computer to determine.

Topology explicitly defines boundaries for a computer. Further, topology is used to identify editing errors, perform polygon overlays, and conduct network analysis.

For example, if you build line topology on a street base, all lines know where they connect and how they relate to each other. This allows you to find the best route from one point to another on your street base. Topology adds spatial intelligence to points, lines, and polygons. Each polygon knows the X and Y coordinates of the beginning and ending points of the lines defining it. All connecting lines must have the same X and Y coordinates when building topology. When using CADD, it is very important to have lines meet perfectly by using features such as object snaps found in AutoCAD.

GIS and CADD

GIS and CADD are complementary technologies. Both systems use a digital data model to enter, store, query, and display information; with both, the user interacts by using screen menus and commands.

Comparisons Between GIS and CADD

- GIS data is in a database; CADD data is in the graphics.
- GIS data structures make use of topology; CADD data structures do not make use of topology.
- GIS coordinates are georeferenced; CADD coordinates are geometrically referenced.

- GIS databases have mapping accuracy; CADD drawings have engineering accuracy.
- GIS represents the world as it exists; CADD designs and drafts human-made and natural objects.

GIS Components

Data Analysis

Spatial analysis permits synthesis and data display in new and creative ways, using spatial and attribute queries.

Spatial queries act on points, lines, and polygons. The following are examples:

- **Point-in-polygon:** Locates points that are within polygons. (See Figure 14–3).
- **Polygon overlay:** Generates new polygons from two or more existing polygons.
- **Buffering:** Creates new polygons around a set of points, lines, or other polygons.
- **Nearest-neighbor:** Identifies features that are closest to another feature.
- **Network analysis:** Performs flow analysis, determines routing, or orders stops.

Figure 14–3. **Point-in-polygon is an example of a spatial analysis.** (Courtesy of NCGIA, University of California at Santa Barbara, www.ncgia.ucsb.edu)

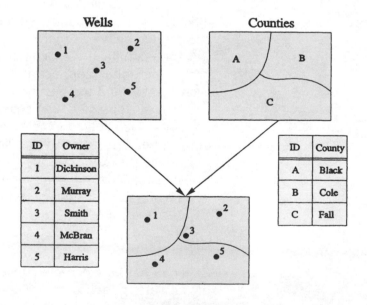

Attribute queries act on the features' attributes. The following are examples:

- **Extracting:**   Reselects a subset from existing features.
- **Generalizing:**   Combines polygon features based on similar attributes.

Data Display

Maps communicate geographical information in a clearly understood and easily interpreted format. GIS maps allow relationships between different types of data to be clearly seen.

GIS programs do not have any cartographic intelligence that can guide operators in the choice of map symbols and other graphic effects. The programs have tools to symbolize maps and draw lines, titles, legends, text, and scale bars.

User Interface

Today most software developers are using Windows-like environments. The design of these environments determines how easily and efficiently the end users perform tasks. The design becomes more important as software vendors develop new markets—such as banking and real estate—where the software is operated by non-GIS employees.

The term *user interface* refers to the way you and the computer communicate with each other to get the work done. The user interface includes what you see on the screen, the keys you have to push to get things done, and any other devices, such as a mouse, you use to control the computer. The term *desktop* is the background on your screen when you are using Windows or another GUI. The term relates to the idea that your computer screen is like the top of your desk.

For GIS software developers, the user interface is receiving more attention because it may reduce the amount of time necessary to learn the GIS program, provide quicker access to the data, and permit the casual user to make maps easily. Intuitive user interfaces and desktop applications enable people in specialized fields to use GIS as a resource at their desktops without needing hours of intensive training and study in GIS.

Data Formats

Spatial data can be stored in two formats, **vector** and **raster**. Each format has advantages based on the application and environment.

Vector Format

The most common format for storing spatial data (points, lines, and polygons) is vector. All CADD programs use the vector data format. Figure 14–4 shows the vector format.

Figure 14-4.   A vector format GIS.
(Courtesy of NCGIA, University of California at
Santa Barbara, www.ncgia.ucsb.edu)

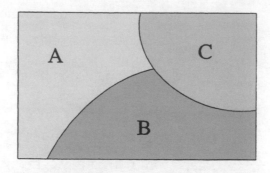

Figure 14-5.   A raster format GIS.
(Courtesy of NCGIA, University of California at
Santa Barbara), www.negia.ucsb.edu)

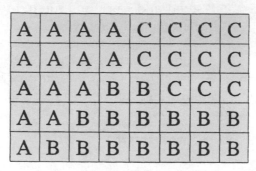

Vector formats work best with data that has well-defined boundaries: parcels, street right-of-ways, political boundaries, and other human-made artificial boundaries.

The vector format provides greater accuracy and resolution than raster format. Vector format can also store data in a minimum amount of disk space.

Raster Format

The raster format consists of an array of cells, sometimes called *grids* or *pixels* (picture elements). Each cell references a row and column, and it contains a letter or number representing the type or value of the attribute being mapped. Figure 14-5 shows the raster format.

Raster formats work best with features that are continuous and that change their characteristics gradually over distance—such as soils, vegetation, and wildlife habitat.

Scanned images and remote sensing data, including aerial and space photographs and satellite imagery, use the raster format. Electrostatic plotters produce maps in a raster format, at a resolution that makes the lines appear smooth.

Spatial analysis is easier to perform with a raster format. Unlike the vector format (which calculates line intersections), the raster system evaluates the values contained within each overlying cell.

Two principal disadvantages of raster formats are the large amounts of storage space required to hold the data and the lack of accuracy when using large-scale maps.

Format Conversions

Rasterization is the conversion of vector data to raster. This process is relatively easy as shown in Figure 14-6. *Vectorization* is converting raster data to vector. Vectorization computer software allows you to

Figure 14–6.   **Creating a raster GIS from a vector GIS.**
(Courtesy of NCGIA, University of California at Santa Barbara, www.ncgia.ucsb.edu)

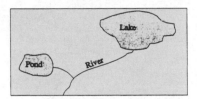

Reality - Hydrography

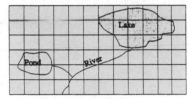

Reality overlaid with a grid

0	0	0	0	0	0	0	1	1	1	0	0
0	0	0	0	0	0	1	1	1	1	1	0
0	0	0	0	0	0	0	1	1	1	0	0
0	1	1	0	0	0	2	2	0	0	0	0
0	1	1	2	2	2	0	0	0	0	0	0
0	0	0	2	0	0	0	0	0	0	0	0

0 = No Water Feature
1 = Water Body
2 = River

Resulting raster

set the desired variables in the conversion process to suit the intended purpose. You can change the variables so that the vector outputs are designed specifically for the project. For example, a wolf biologist may want to set different parameters than a biologist studying mice when generating habitat polygons from a raster image. Detail and accuracy in the change of habitat from grassland to woodland may be more significant in the research of the mice.

As scanning and remote sensing become popular methods of building and updating GIS databases, GIS software packages have included the capability to convert between raster and vector formats.

GIS Applications

Parcel-Based Applications

Land use planning is the most common GIS application because of GIS's ability to perform "what if" scenarios.

Some other **parcel-based applications** include processing building permits, assessing taxes, inventorying vacant land, and adjusting school enrollment. Figure 14–7 shows a parcel-based map.

Natural Resource–Based Applications

Some of the first GIS applications were in forestry. Private timber companies use GIS programs to assist with planning and managing timber ownership, to plan harvest rotations, and to inventory timber and soil types.

Figure 14-7. **Tax lots and street right-of-ways in a parcel-based map.**
(Courtesy of Metro, Portland, Oregon)

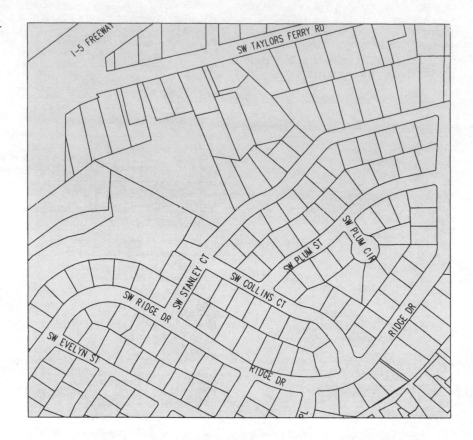

Other GIS applications include identifying wildlife habitats, analyzing environmental impacts, estimating earthquake impacts, and monitoring surface water pollution.

The oil and gas industries use GIS extensively to identify and develop new prospects for exploration. They also use GIS to manage their current lease holdings and pipeline and production facilities.

Civil Engineering–Based Applications

Civil engineers use GIS to provide a spatial context for efficiently managing their infrastructure, such as water and sewer systems, bridges, roads, airports, and solid waste facilities. GIS assists engineers in siting public and private developments by providing information about the potential impacts of the proposed development.

Some other engineering and public work applications include monitoring pavement conditions, tracking street lighting, siting landfills, and designing transit corridors.

Demographic Analysis

The 2000 U.S. Census (**www.census.gov**) provides a wealth of geographically referenced socioeconomic and demographic data. Governments use this demographic analysis data to support the provision of services. Businesses use census data in daily decision-making processes. GIS programs can use census data to conduct demographic analysis.

Using GIS to redistrict is an example of demographic analysis. Other examples include forecasting population and employment, identifying crime patterns, analyzing retail market potential, and siting branch locations.

Street Network–Based Applications

In preparation for the 1990 census, the Bureau of the Census developed a major national database called the Topological Integrated Geographic Encoding and Referencing (TIGER) files.

TIGER is the first comprehensive digital street map of the United States. TIGER's features include all streets and railroads, significant hydrographic features, Native American reservations, military bases, and political boundaries.

Some street-based applications that use GIS technology include planning of new highways, routing of local delivery services, and scheduling of long-distance freight haulers.

Geocoding

Geocoding is the process of displaying a spatial component such as an address, an *XY* coordinate, or a latitude and longitude, as a geographic location. Geocoding is possible with software and a street-based network that includes attributes describing the address range information within its attribute table for that street segment.

Facilities Management

Utilities—water companies, wastewater, gas, electric, and telecommunications—have been leaders in using GIS (called automated mapping and facilities management [AM/FM] systems).

Examples of facilities management include siting of transmission facilities, relicensing of hydroelectric projects, routing of meter readers, and tracking of energy use.

Modeling

One of the most powerful uses of GIS is modeling. Current applications include modeling of solid waste flow, projection of urban growth patterns, and anticipation of the spread of oil spills.

GIS complements other computer-based models that deal with georeferenced data such as economics, transportation, deforestation, and agricultural productivity. GIS provides input data for the model and then displays the model's output. An example is the solid waste flow model used by Metro in Portland, Oregon, shown in Figure 14–8.

3D Analysis

Identifying all locations that can be seen from a specific site is called viewshed determination. This is difficult with traditional map analysis methods but relatively easy and accurate with GIS.

Choices in Waste Flow
Solid Waste Simulation Model

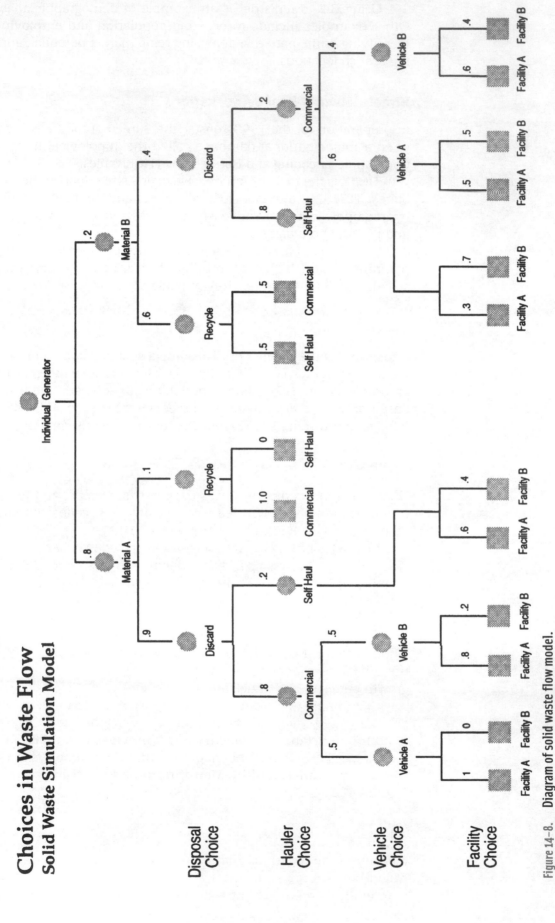

Figure 14–8. Diagram of solid waste flow model.
(Courtesy of Metro, Portland, Oregon, www.metro-regional.org)

Figure 14–9.   A 3D GIS.

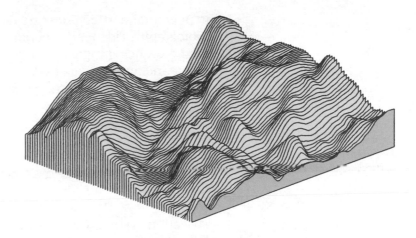

Viewing proposed impacts, such as tree harvesting or commercial development, helps avoid unsightly mistakes. Figure 14–9 shows the 3D perspective.

Although the lines between mainstream GIS and desktop mapping may be vague, several key features are found in most desktop mapping software packages. These features include:

- Reliance on the mouse as the primary method of interacting with the software.
- Ability to easily import maps, charts, graphs, and tables into other software packages.
- Quick access to spatial data.
- Simplified tools for display of spatial data.
- Large data packages bundled with the product.

Desktop mapping software comes bundled with several hundred gigabytes of data. This data can encompass the entire United States, with data layers such as counties, cities, roads, rivers, and other distinguishing features. The purchaser generally has the option to purchase, at a minimal cost, additional data such as demographics, lifestyle data, traffic counts for major highways, and weather-related data.

GIS development software programs, such as Arc/Info, are very different from desktop GIS applications. Arc/Info is like a helicopter that requires a skilled pilot to move it quickly and to utilize its many options. In this environment, you can build a mapping layer or coverage by digitizing, cleaning line work, building topology, and adding attribute information associated with graphics. In comparison, desktop GIS are like bicycles with training wheels. They are designed to seek and view information created in the larger GIS. No matter what your field of study, desktop GIS allows you to use GIS as a resource at your desktop with little training. It may take a little longer to use, but the average user finds it preferable.

Hypermedia

Hypermedia is a system for referencing and retrieving different forms of digital data. It is becoming more integrated with GIS. Some examples of the digital data used by GIS include satellite images, architectural and engineering drawings, survey information, aerial photography, video, and sound.

Referencing digital data geographically allows the end user to access and analyze data in new ways. This analysis reveals new associations and reveals existing relationships.

Introduction to GPS*

The **global positioning system (GPS)** was developed by the U.S. Department of Defense (DOD) as a worldwid, satellite-based radio-navigation system. Currently, the constellation consists of 24 operational satellites orbiting about 11,000 miles above the earth. There can be more than 24 operational satellites as new ones are launched to replace older satellites. There are also base stations located around the world that measure signals from satellites, sending data back to the satellites and then to the receivers. In April 1995, the U.S. Air Force Space Command officially declared the GPS satellite constellation as having met the requirement for *full operational capability (FOC)*, which means the system has been fully tested and is operational. GPS is one of the most exciting breakthroughs of modern technology.

GPS has two primary functions: to provide accurate geodetic locations and to provide precise time. Initially, GPS was developed as a military system; however, the United States has made GPS available to civilian users who own GPS receivers, at no charge. GPS is used in many civilian applications for navigation and recording of geodetic locations. Applications include aerospace, emergency rescue, intelligent vehicle systems (IVS), telecommunications, seismic research, land surveying, oil exploration, and more.

GPS Basics—How a Position Is Determined

GPS has three parts:

1. **Space segment:** The 24 satellites broadcasting signals travel at the speed of light. These signals include positional information from the satellites and precise time.

2. **Control segment:** Five ground stations around the world monitor the positions and health of the satellites. A healthy satellite is in its proper orbit.

3. **User segment:** GPS receivers and antennas receive the satellite signals. Some GPS receivers are now available in chip size and are integrated in small handheld systems. More accurate mapping-grade and survey-grade systems are equipped in backpacks and/or tripod-style configurations.

---

*Courtesy, in part, of Richard Ash, Global Mapping Technology, Corvallis, Oregon.

Using a basic principle from algebra, a GPS receiver calculates the distance between itself and a given satellite by determining the amount of time a signal travels from satellite to receiver:

Distance	=	Rate	×	Time
From satellite to receiver	=	Speed of light	×	Determined by receiver

The receiver measures the travel time from four satellites to the receiver to precisely triangulate and determine a position. Receivers and positioning methods that can more accurately determine the travel time yield more accurate results.

This *position* is commonly generated by the receiver as a latitude, longitude, and altitude (LLA) coordinate. An example of a GPS position in LLA might appear as:

Lat: 44 32 45.56 N
Lon: 123 14 22.16 W
Alt: 100 Feet

How Satellites and Base Stations Work Together

There are two controlling elements to the GPS: the satellites and the base stations. The satellites are referred to as the *space segment*, and the base stations are called the *control segment*. There are 24 or more satellites, as previously discussed, and there is a master control station located at Schriever Air Force Base (formerly Falcon AFB) in Colorado, as well as four monitoring stations located throughout the world. The base stations measure signals that are developed into orbital models for each satellite. The models compute exact orbital data and clock corrections for each satellite. The master control station uploads the orbital and clock data to the satellites. The satellites then send the necessary orbital data to GPS receivers over radio signals. Figure 14–10 demonstrates how the signal is sent from the satellite to the base station, back to the satellite, and then to the GPS receiver.

GPS Errors, Differential Correction, and GPS Accuracy

Prior to May 2000, the United States intentionally degraded the GPS signals, adding as much as 50 m of random error to independent GPS positions. This degradation, known as *selective availability* (SA), was implemented for military security purposes.

Although the removal of SA makes independent GPS positions much more accurate than previously available, other natural errors, such as atmospheric signal delays and satellite and receiver clock drift, still contribute relatively large errors, to the signal time and thus positions calculated by receivers. Independent GPS receivers can therefore tell your location anywhere on or above the earth to within about 15 to 40 m. The results can vary with equipment and the quality of the satellite constellation.

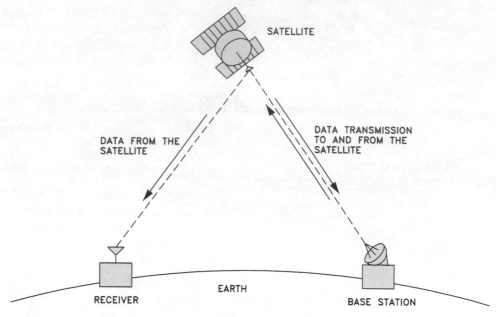

Figure 14-10. How satellites and base stations work together.

Although GPS receivers are very convenient for course precision and recreational applications such as boating, hiking, and hunting, an error range of 15 to 40 m is not acceptable for mapping applications, and it is useless for surveying requirements. However, with a process called *differential GPS*, or *differential correction*, higher accuracy is possible, typically to less than 5 m; and with survey-grade GPS equipment, accuracy is possible to 1 cm or less. Differential GPS is accomplished using two GPS receivers and mathematically comparing the satellite information collected. The information collected from one GPS receiver, called the *rover*, is compared with that collected at the same time by another proximally located GPS receiver at a known, fixed location called the *base station*.

GPS Systems Used for GIS and Mapping

GPS provides precise coordinate addresses. By themselves, GPS coordinates offer very limited information. However, by combining GPS and GIS data, you can create powerful and informative databases indexed by the positions determined by the GPS receiver.

A GIS consists of computers, software, data, and tools for analyzing features on the earth as related to their geography. GIS allows you to make models and decisions based on the where (geographic) and the what (information).

Following are some examples of how GPS and GIS are used in various industries:

- **Commerce:** A department store chain considering a new site can use GIS to analyze the demographics of potential customers in various communities.
- **Utility:** A utility company can inventory an electrical distribution system, knowing what customers are affected by downed power lines or blown transformers.

- **Agriculture:** Farmers use GIS to evaluate the effects of soil, water, and fertilizers in improving yields. Forestry companies evaluate the potential board feet and value of a future stand of trees, as well as possible effects of disease from pests.
- **Biological Research:** A wildlife biologist can study the effects of deer populations on sustainability of reintroducing wolves to a certain geographical habitat.

Professionals in these industries need to know what something is and where that something is located. GPS lends itself very well to GIS by providing accurate positions that geographically index the GIS databases. A typical GIS database is characterized by the following information:

- **Feature name:** The name or description of the object of interest, such as a store, utility pole, or tree.
- **Feature type:** Points, lines, or areas.
- **Feature attributes:** One or more key variables that you want to know about the feature.
- **Values:** The actual answers you provide for the attribute variables.
- **Geographical position:** A spatial address linked to this feature that tells you its precise location on the earth. A common spatial address system is provided in LLA.

A point feature has a single LLA address that defines its location. Line and area features have two or more coordinates connected together to define a consecutive series of locations. For example, the following is a GPS/GIS record collected by a GPS/GIS system:

Feature Name	Feature Type	Feature Attributes	Values	Geographic Position (collected by GPS)
Tree	Point	Tree ID # Species Health Rating Maintenance	12005 Oak 75 Remove Lower Limbs	Lat: 44 32 45.56N Lon: 123 14 22.16W Alt: 100 feet
Sidewalk	Line	Surface Material Condition	Asphalt Repair Required	Lat1: 40 48 1.61N Lon1: 124 8 59.03W Alt1: 28.24 feet Lat2: 40 48 1.34N Lon2: 124 8 58.56W Alt2: 28.68 feet Lat3: 40 48 1.06N Lon3: 124 8 58.1W Alt3: 28.86 feet

GPS/GIS systems offer a very effective way to inventory and describe features. GPS enables users to precisely locate these features, while GIS describes these positions in detail. In selecting a

GPS receiver for GIS applications, it is important to differentiate GPS/GIS systems from other types of GPS receivers. The following table shows basic types of GPS receivers and key features of GPS/GIS grade systems.

Basic Types of GPS Receivers and Key Features of GPS/GIS Resource-Grade Systems:

Receiver Type	Recreational	GPS/GIS Resource Grade	Survey Grade Systems
Uncorrected accuracy	15–40 m (2 RMS*)	15–40 m (2 RMS*)	15–40 m (2 RMS*)
Accuracy after applying differential correction	Generally, differential correction is not available in recreational units.	Basically two classes: A) 1–5 m (2 RMS*) B) Some < 1 m (2 RMS*)	1 cm + 1 ppm** (2 RMS*)
Feature types	Points only	Points, lines, polygons. Lines and polygons are digitized in the field.	Points, lines, polygons
GIS collection and export	No	Feature, attribute, value lists supported. Standard GIS and CADD software formats supported for export.	Varies with model, but some systems support full GIS capability found in GPS/GISs grade systems.
Applications	Course navigation and recreation (hiking, fishing, etc.)	Resource mapping and GIS data collection inventories.	Surveying
Typical cost	$200–$1000	$2000–$10,000	$32,000–$60,000

*RMS = Root mean square describes statistical confidence. 2 RMS refers to 95% confidence.

**ppm = parts per million. The abbreviation ppm refers to the degradation of accuracy as the distance between the base station receiver and data collection receiver (rover) is extended.

TEST

Part I

Use Microsoft Word to open the file "Chapter 14 test" on the Student Web site.

14-1 Why is GIS considered an enabling technology?

14-2 What is the most common GIS application?

14-3 Considering all the GIS systems in use today, what type of GIS system is the most common?

14-4 Describe three types of spatial queries.

14-5 List four GIS applications.

14-6 List three disciplines that use GIS.

Part II

14-7 What happens to data if it is converted from a raster format to a vector format?

14-8 What is the term for conversion of vector data to raster data?

14-9 Describe how a raster GIS stores data. Give three examples of the types of features where the raster format works best.

14-10 Describe two advantages of a vector GIS. Give three examples of the types of features where the vector format works best.

14-11 List two advantages of a well-designed GIS interface.

14-12 Fill in the blanks: _____ _____ permits synthesis and data display in new and creative ways, using spatial and attribute queries.

14-13 Fill in the blank: A _____ relates spatial data to attribute data.

14-14 What is the type of analysis that topology permits?

14-15 Give four examples of spatial data that civil engineers regularly use.

14-16 What type of database management system is used by GIS software?

14-17 Provide two reasons why GIS users have moved from mainframes and minicomputers to personal computers.

14-18 Define *desktop mapping*.

Part III

14-19 What does GPS stand for?

14-20 What organization developed GPS?

14-21 For what purpose was GPS developed?

14-22 Identify the two primary functions of GPS.

14-23 Briefly describe each of the following parts of the GPS:

Space segment

Control segment

User segment

14-24 How does a GPS receiver determine a position?

14-25 What does LLA stand for?

14-26 What does the LLA have to do with a GPS position?

14-27 Identify at least two factors that reduce the accuracy of a GPS receiver.

14-28 Give the typical amount of error for each of the following applications:

Recreational applications

Differential correction

Survey-grade GPS

14-29 Briefly explain the importance of combining GPS and GIS.

14-30 Give an example of GPS/GIS used in the commerce industry.

14-31 Give an example of GPS/GIS used in the utility industry.

14–32   Give an example of GPS/GIS used in the agriculture industry.

14–33   Give an example of GPS/GIS used in biological research.

14–34   Describe each of the five characteristics of a GIS database listed below:

Feature name

Feature type

Feature attribute

Values

Geographical position

PROBLEMS

P14–1   In your own words, describe three differences between CADD and GIS systems.

P14–2   Name three parcel-based GIS applications.

P14–3   Describe topology in your own words.

P14–4   Why would the raster format not be acceptable for storing parcel information?

P14–5   Show a soil map in raster GIS format with at least three different soil types.

The Chain

From the rope of ancient Egypt's rope stretchers came the *chain* and the steel tape. Whereas the steel tape, seen in Figure A–1, normally stretches to 100 ft, the old *Gunter chain* measures 66 ft. Chains of 20 m lengths, termed *land chains* because of their use in land surveys, are also popular and convenient.

The use and measurements of a chain or tape are shown in Figure A–2. Hubs or markers of some sort are placed at each point where a reading is to be made. When chain measurements must be made on a slope, the process is often referred to as *breaking chain*, (see Figure A–3). Most chaining prior to the use of EDM involved tape and *plumb bobs*.

Figure A–1. Steel tape used to measure distance.
(Courtesy of Sokkia)

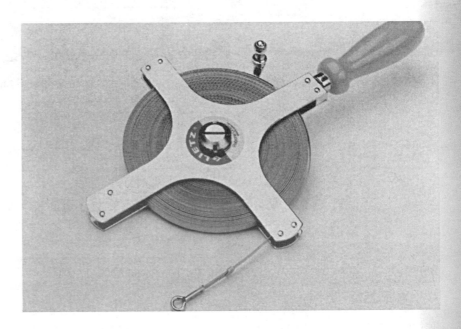

Figure A–2. Measuring distance with a chain or steel tape.

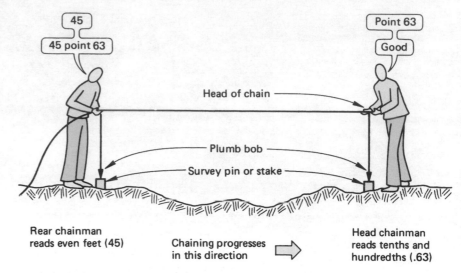

45

45 point 63

Point 63

Good

Head of chain

Plumb bob

Survey pin or stake

Rear chainman
reads even feet (45)

Chaining progresses
in this direction

Head chainman
reads tenths and
hundredths (.63)

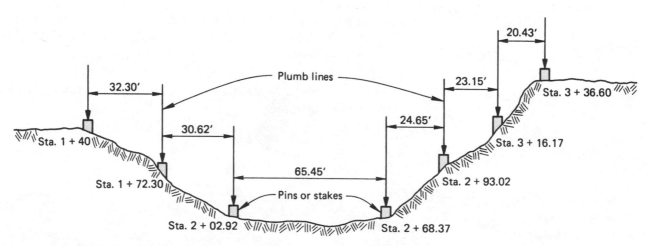

20.43'

23.15'

32.30'

Plumb lines

Sta. 3 + 36.60

24.65'

30.62'

Sta. 1 + 40

Sta. 3 + 16.17

65.45'

Sta. 1 + 72.30

Sta. 2 + 93.02

Pins or stakes

Sta. 2 + 02.92

Sta. 2 + 68.37

Figure A–3. "Breaking chain" on sloping terrain. Chain must be horizontal for each measurement.

Distance by Stadia

The Greeks used the word *stadium* (plural *stadia*) when referring to a unit of length. This unit was 600 Greek feet, which translates to 606 ft 9 in. in the English System. This unit of length was used when laying out distances in athletic contests. We now use the term to refer to a type of distance measuring that uses a rod and an instrument with crosshairs.

The *Philadelphia rod* is 7 ft long, extends to 12 or 13 ft, and is graduated to hundreths of a foot, but it can be read to thousandths. Distances are normally read only to hundreths. Elevations can be read to thousandths. Figure A–4 illustrates the stadia method of distance measurement, which is based on optics. The space between two horizontal crosshairs in the instrument is read by subtracting the bottom number from the top number and multiplying by 100. This gives a fairly accurate distance—one that is sufficient for low-order surveys (those requiring a lower degree of precision).

Figure A-4. Measuring distance by "stadia theory."

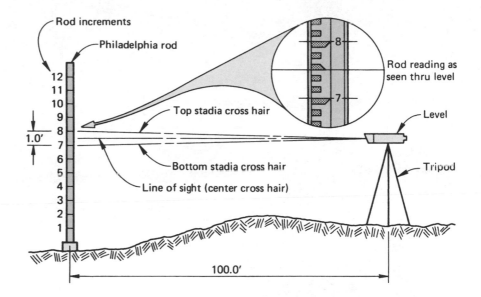

Contour Map Profiles Using Traditional Methods

Prior to the advent of powerful CADD software, a contour map profile was constructed if a profile leveling survey (discussed in the next section) had not yet been conducted. The only resource needed for a contour map profile is the map itself.

Map Layout

A straight line should be drawn on a contour map where the profile is to be made, as shown in Figure B–1. The line between points *A* and *B* may be a proposed road or sewer line, and it may be at an angle other than horizontal on your drawing board. For ease of projection, turn the map so that the profile line is horizontal and aligned with the horizontal scale of your drafting machine. A clean sheet of paper can then be placed directly below the profile line and used to construct the cross section (see Figure B–2).

Profile Construction

The horizontal scale of a profile is always the same as that of the map because the profile is projected from the map. The vertical scale may be exaggerated to give a clear picture of the shape of the land. The amount of exaggeration depends on the relief of the map, the scale of the map, and the purpose of the profile.

Figure B–1. **Profile to be cut along line *AB*.**

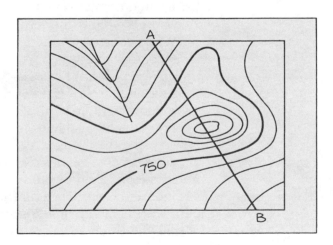

Figure B–2. Correct relationship of
map, drawing paper, and drafting
machine for profile construction.

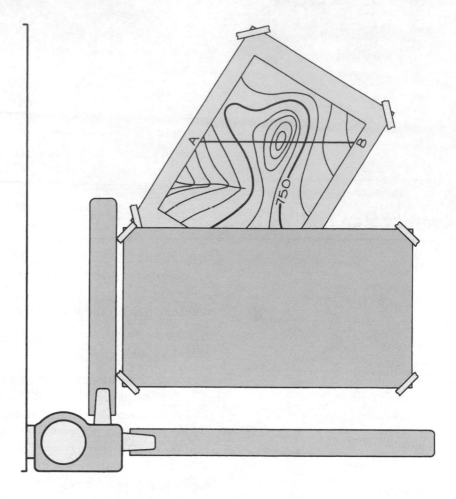

The length of a profile is established by projecting endpoints *A*
and *B* to the paper. The height of the profile depends first on the
amount of relief between points *A* and *B*. Find the lowest and highest contours that line *AB* crosses and subtract to determine the total
amount of elevation to be shown in the profile. This enables you to
establish a vertical scale to fit the paper and best show the relief.

The vertical scale of a profile is exaggerated to show the elevation
differences. In most cases, if you used the horizontal scale for the vertical, there would appear to be little change in elevation. Choose a vertical scale that fits the space allotted for the drawing or use the 10:1 ratio
that is often used in civil engineering. For example, if the horizontal
scale is 1 in. = 100 ft, the vertical scale would be 1 in. = 10 ft.

When constructing the vertical profile scale, provide an additional contour interval above and below the extreme points of the
profile. Also notice in Figure B–3 that the elevations are labeled along
one side, and the scales are written by the profile. The vertical scale
is sometimes written vertically near the elevation values.

Project horizontal lines from the vertical scale values across the
drawing, and then project all points from the map where the profile
line crosses contour lines. Notice in Figure B–3 that a point on the
profile is established where vertical and horizontal lines of the same
elevation intersect. Once all these points are established, connect
them with a smooth line. A sectioning symbol or shading is used to
indicate the ground that is cross sectioned.

Figure B-3.   **Layout and construction of a map profile.**

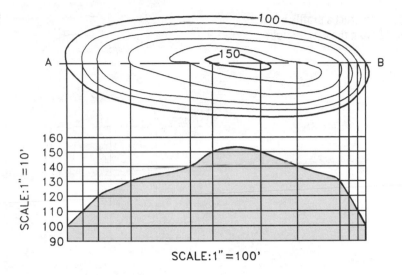

Figure B-4.   **Profile construction of a curved line. Measure distances on *AB* and establish them on straight line *AB*′.**

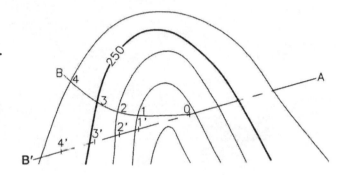

Profiles of Curved Lines

Layout of a profile from a straight line is simple, but plotting a profile from a curved line involves an additional step. Before the profile can be drawn, curved line *AB* must be established along a related straight line, *AB*′. This can be done with dividers, a compass, or an engineer's scale (see Figure B-4). Label the new points on line *AB*′ to avoid any confusion. Note that the straight line distance 0–1 is transferred to 0–1′, 1–2 is transferred to 1′–2′, and so on.

From this point, creating the profile is the same as it is for a straight line. Be certain that you project the actual contour crossings from point *A* to 0 and the newly established points, 1′ to 4′, from 0 to *B*′. See Figure B-5 for the proper method of projection.

The previous method was used to create a profile directly from a map using no surveyed topographic data. A more accurate traditional method could be used if surveying data is available. A list of station points along the map profile would be combined with contour elevations to create the profile. For example, a station value (distance) is recorded at the first contour crossed, and then the next station value (distance from the first station) is recorded at the next contour crossed. These points could then be plotted on a profile grid like the one shown in Figure B-3.

Figure B–5. Construct a profile of the curved line *AB* from the new straight line *AB'*.

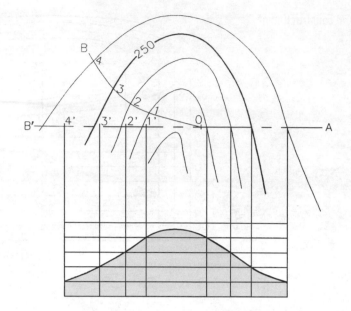

A civil drafter may need to enlarge contour maps to show greater cultural detail or to define the topography with additional contour lines. Other than the photographic process or using a scaling command in a CADD system, the grid system is the best drafting method to use when manually enlarging (or reducing) a map.

Grid Layout

First, a grid must be drawn on the existing map. The size of the grid squares depends on the complexity of the map and the amount of detail you wish to show. You may be instructed to enlarge the map to twice its present size, or a scale for the new map may be specified. If you draw the grid on the existing map with 1/4-in. squares and want to double the size, the grid for your new map is drawn with 1/2-in. squares. Suppose that the scale of the original map is 1 in. = 1000 ft and the new map is to be 1 in. = 250 ft. If you draw the grid on the original using 1/4-in. squares, the new grid is then drawn using 1-in. squares—four times the size.

The map in Figure C–1 must be enlarged to twice its size and has been overlaid with a 1/4-in. grid. Notice, too, that the vertical and horizontal grids have been numbered to avoid confusion when transferring points. Keep in mind that when a linear measurement is doubled, the area of that map is increased four times the original size. The appearance of Figure C–2 illustrates this point.

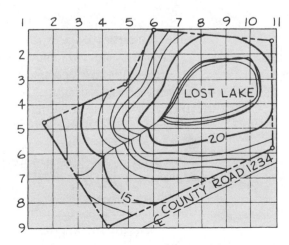

Figure C–1. A grid drawn over an original map.

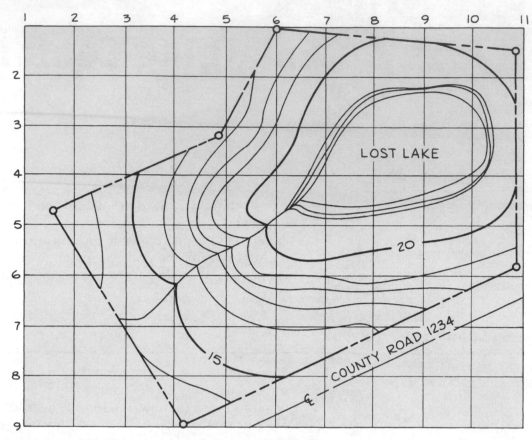

Figure C–2.   **The enlarged map uses the same number of gird lines, but the dimensions of the squares are doubled.**

The grid for the new map is constructed using the same number of squares as the original and is labeled the same. The only difference is its size (see Figure C–2). The squares now measure 1/2 in.

Map Construction

Map features can now be transferred from the original to the enlargement by eye, or by using an engineer's scale or proportional dividers. Measurements provide the greatest degree of accuracy, but a drafter soon realizes that "eyeballing" features on or near grid intersections may be accurate enough for a purposes of a map.

The two grids that you draw should be exactly the same, as should the labeling you use to identify the vertical and horizontal grid lines. Compare Figure C–1 and C–2. The process of transferring from the original to the enlargement is relatively simple. Choose one square and measure or estimate where features touch or cross the grid lines of that square. Transfer that measurement to the same square on the enlarged grid, remembering, of course, to increase its size proportionately.

The grid enlargement method can produce accurate maps, provided that the drafter establishes a proper coordinate system, uses good measuring techniques, and avoids unnecessary "artistic license."

Glossary

Aeronautical chart A special map used as an aid in air travel, indicating important features of land, such as mountains and outstanding landmarks.

Aerotriangulation A procedure that incorporates a GPS antenna mounted and locked over a camera on the fuselage of an airplane to create aerial photos linked to accurate location data.

Angle of repose The slope of cut and fill from the road, expressed in feet of horizontal run to feet of vertical rise.

Attribute data Data that refers to text information on a CADD drawing. An attribute is also a characteristic or property of an object, such as weight, size, or color. Attributes are commonly stored in tabular format and linked to a feature. For example, the attributes of water wells in an area can list locations, depths, and gallons per minute produced from each well. In GIS applications, attribute data is linked in the GIS to spatial data that defines the location. Attribute data describes the characteristics of the data.

Azimuth A horizontal direction measured in degrees from 0 to 360. Usually measured from north.

Backsight (B.S.) The rod or target location from which a measurement is made that is located in the opposite direction of the survey.

Base line A principal parallel used in establishing the rectangular system of land description.

Base station Also called a reference station, a receiver that is set up on a known location specifically to collect data for differentially correcting rover files. A base station calculates the error for each satellite and, through differential correction, improves the accuracy of GPS positions collected at unknown locations by a roving GPS receiver.

Bearing The direction of a line with respect to the quadrants of a compass, starting from north or south.

Bench mark A reference or data point from which surveys can begin. These are often brass caps mounted in concrete. Temporary bench marks may be iron pipes or spikes used for small surveys.

Borrow pit An area from which quantities of earth are excavated to construct embankments and fills.

Cadastral map A large-scale map depicting features in a city or town.

Computer-aided design (CAD) The use of a wide range of computer-based tools that assist in the design profession. CAD is also referred to as computer-aided drafting.

Computer-aided design and drafting (CADD) A process that involves use of a computer program for design and drafting applications. CADD is used in all industry design and drafting fields covered throughout this textbook, and it is demonstrated in two-dimensional (2D) and three-dimensional (3D) representations. CADD is used to create information, in graphic form, and it is also used to design and store other forms of information, such as engineering analysis, cost calculations, and material lists.

Computer-aided drafting (CAD)   Drafting accomplished with the use of a computer and one of any number of software packages that converts information given by the user into graphics. Also see *computer-aided design*.

CADD symbol   A symbol created for use in a CADD system.

Cartography   The art of making maps and charts.

Cesspool   A holding tank used to break down and distribute waste materials to an area of earth.

Chain   A measurement tool composed of links originally 66 ft in length. Steel tapes of 100 ft long are often referred to as chains.

Chord   A straight line connecting the endpoints of an arc.

Civil drafting   Drafting that is performed for civil engineering projects. See also *civil engineering*.

Civil engineering   A discipline concerned with the planning of bridges, roads, dams, canals, pipelines, and various municipal projects.

Civil engineer's scale   A scale made up of multiples of 10 that is typically used in civil drafting.

Civil engineering–based application   A specialized GIS that provides spatial context for efficiently managing infrastructure, such as water, sewer, bridges, airports, and solid waste facilities.

Closed traverse   A survey in which the lines close on the point of beginning or on another control point. Most often used for land surveys.

COGO (coordinate geometry)   A method of creating drawings with CAD that utilizes points or coordinates along with geometric angles and survey lengths and bearings.

Combined sewerage outlet (CSO)   A sewer system in which storm drains combine with the sanitary sewer and flow to a sewerage treatment plant.

Concave slope   A slope that flattens toward the bottom.

Concrete masonry units (CMUs)   Concrete building blocks.

Connecting traverse   A survey that closes on a data or control point other than the point of beginning.

Construction survey   A localized survey in which building lines, elevations of fills, excavations, foundations, and floors are established and checked.

Contour interval   The vertical elevation difference between contour lines.

Contour line   A line used to connect points of equal elevation.

Control point survey   A survey to determine the elevation of important points in a plot of land. These points are plotted on a map, and contour lines can then be drawn to connect them.

Control segment   Five GPS ground stations around the world, which monitor the positions and health of satellites.

Convex slope   A slope that develops a steeper gradient as it progresses.

Cross section   A profile or section cut through the land to show the shape or relief of the ground. Technically, a cross section is cut perpendicular, or across, the alignment of a horizontal feature such as a highway, street, canal, utility trench, or runway.

Cube corner prism   A reflecting prism that is a corner cut off of a cube of glass. This type of prism can be slightly out of alignment with the EDM and still provide an accurate measurement.

Culture symbol   A map symbol representing works of people.

Curve length   The length of a highway curve from beginning to end, measured along the centerline.

Cut and fill   A road construction term that describes the quantities of earth removed from hillsides and filled into low spots.

Data analysis   A computer program process that uses spatial analysis and attribute queries to synthesize and display data.

Deflection angle   In surveying, an angle that veers to the right or left of a straight line, often the centerline of a highway, power line, etc.

Degree (°)   A unit of angular measure.

Degree of curve   The angle of a chord (from the preceding one) that connects station points along the centerline of a highway curve.

Delta angle   The central or included angle of a highway curve.

Demographic analysis   GIS analysis related to the study of population statistics, changes, and trends.

Departure   The distance a property line extends in the east–west direction.

Desktop   The background on a computer screen when you are using Windows or an other graphical user interface.

Differential correction   Use of either GPS positions collected simultaneously from a base station (located on a known position) or real-time correction measure broadcasts to increase the accuracy of position information.

Differential leveling   A type of leveling that begins at a point of known elevation and works toward points whose elevations are unknown.

Digital elevation model (DEM)   A two- or three-dimensional map that has been digitally recorded and produced using a grid of elevation points. DEMs can describe a variety of land surfaces, including the earth surface, vegetation covering the earth, and underground water aquifers. The type of DEM that provides information about the earth's surface is referred to as a digital terrain model (DTM), though the terms DEM and DTM are often used interchangeably.

Digital terrain model (DTM)   A map that shows elevation changes in land forms. The map appears three-dimensional and is created with the use of point files derived from field survey data.

Digitizing   A method of transferring data from paper-based drawings to CADD. It is done with a digitizer and a mouse or puck. The information is entered by picking points off the existing drawing with the puck.

Dimensions   The size and location of features on a drawing. Civil drawings are generally dimensioned in feet (') and inches ("), such as 25'-60", or in decimal feet, such as 25.5'. Metric drawings are typically dimensioned in millimeters (mm) or meters (m).

Direction   The angular relationship of one line to another.

Distance meter   A surveying instrument that employs electronic signals such as lasers and infrared to accurately measure distances between the surveying instrument and a prism or prism array mounted on a tripod. Often termed an EDM (electronic distance meter). An EDM is most often built into the electronic total station.

Drag-and-drop   A feature that allows you to perform tasks by moving your cursor over the top of an icon in a folder or menu source. The icon represents a document, drawing, folder, or other application. After you press and hold the pick button on your pointing device, you drag the cursor to the desired folder or drawing and release the pick button. The selected content is added to your current drawing or chosen file.

Drawing interchange format (DXF)   An industry standard format that can be used to exchange drawing information between one CAD software package or model and another.

Drawing scale   Sizing of a drawing so the object represented can be illustrated clearly on standard sheet sizes. Civil drawings are generally scaled in increments of several feet to 1 in., such as 1 in. equals 100 ft. Drawings created with CADD are drawn full scale and plotted to a specific scale. Civil drawings typically use architectural and civil scales.

Architectural drawings are representations of buildings and use scales such as $1/4'' = 1'\text{-}0''$, and $1/8'' = 1'\text{-}0''$. Some of the smallest scale drawings are in the civil engineering field. A small-scale drawing shows a large area, while a large-scale drawing shows a small area. These drawings represent areas of land measured in feet or miles, and some of the scales used are $1'' = 10'$, $1'' = 20'$, $1'' = 50'$, and $1'' = 100'$.

Dynamic symbol   A normal symbol that has parameters and actions assigned to objects within the symbol.

Earthwork   Quantities of earth either excavated from areas or filled into low spots.

Easement   A legal right-of-way given by a property owner to allow others access to or over the property. An easement can be for access to and from another property, for utilities, or for other uses. When used for utilities, an easement is called a *utility easement*, which is generally a portion of land shared by a property owner and a public agency that contains a public utility, such as electrical power, telephone, or a sewer line.

Effluent   Wastewater that leaves a septic tank.

Electronic distance meter (EDM)   See *distance meter*.

Electronic total station   See *total station*.

Elevation   Altitude or height above sea level.

Engineering map   A map that provides detailed information on construction projects, including locations and dimensions of all structures, roads, parking, drainage ways, sewers, and other utilities.

Engineer's scale   A tool used by a drafting technician to accurately measure distances on a map.

Equator   A line that circles the earth at 0° latitude.

Ergonomics   The study of a worker's relationship to physical and psychological environments.

Error of closure   The amount of error found in a traverse that does not close.

Ethics   Rules and principles that define right and wrong conduct. A code of ethics is a formal document that states organizational values and the rules and principles that employees are expected to follow.

Facilities management   GIS applications related to utilities.

Field   Any open area that surrounds the main views or plans displayed on a drawing.

File organization   A drawing file organization in the U.S. National CAD Standard that covers drawing units, file naming, and sheet identification.

Font   All the uppercase and lowercase letters and numerals of a particular typeface design.

Foresight (F.S.)   A rod location in surveying from which an elevation and/or location reading is taken. The foresight becomes the next instrument setup point because the survey moves in the direction of the foresight.

Frequency   The interval along the horizontal alignment at which angle-of-repose projections are calculated.

Full operational capability (FOC)   The state in which the GPS system has been fully tested and is operational.

General notes   Notes that apply to an entire drawing.

Geocoding   The process of displaying a spatial component such as an address, an *xy* coordinate, or latitude and longitude, as a geographical location.

Geodetic survey   A survey in which the process of triangulation is used to account for the curvature of the earth.

Geographical maps   Small-scale maps depicting large areas of the earth.

Geographic information system (GIS)   A database or an inventory of many different types of information that can be accessed and combined according to particular needs. The inventory can include features such as topography, city streets, utility pipelines, transmission lines, and land use, among others.

Geographic north   See *true north*.

Geological map   A map that describes the location, type, and extent of geological features such as rock formations and edges of earth movement.

Georelational data model   The relationship between spatial and attribute data in a GIS system. By putting maps and other kinds of spatial information into digital form, GIS allows for the manipulation and display of geographical knowledge.

Geostationary orbit.   See *geosynchronous* (satellite).

Geosynchronous (satellite)   A satellite traveling in an orbit 22,300 mi (35,900 km) above the equator. At this altitude, the satellite rotates around the earth in 24 hours, thus matching the eath's rotation. Therefore, the satellite always remains in the same spot over the earth

Global navigation satellite system (GNSS)   A generic term for any system of satellites that provide global coverage for geographical positioning. See *global positioning system (GPS)*.

Global positioning system (GPS)   Developed by the U.S. government, a worldwide, satellite-based, radio-navigation system.

Grade   An established elevation of the ground or of a road surface.

Graphical user interface (GUI)   The manner in which information and options are displayed by computer software.

Graphic scale   A scale resembling a small ruler in the legend or margin of a map.

Great survey   A survey of each large portion of the public domain. It takes on as much as it can use of one parallel of latitude and one meridian of longitude.

Grid azimuth   A direction established for a rectangular survey system so the north–south grids of the survey are used as the reference, or zero line.

Grid north (GN)   The location of north in a grid mapping system.

Grid survey   A plot of land divided into a grid, with elevations established at each grid intersection. Contour maps can be drawn from grid survey field notes.

Grid system   A system used to establish points of reference for features of the earth's surface when preparing map drawings.

Hard copy   A physical drawing produced on paper or some other media by a printer or plotter.

Hydrologic map   A map depicting boundaries of major river basins.

Hypermedia   A system to reference and retrieve different forms of digital data.

Index contour   Every fifth line on a contour map. The index contour is a thicker line weight and is normally labeled with an elevation value.

Intellectual property   A product of company or personal work that is often the result of years of research, engineering, and development.

Intelligence   See *parametric solid modeling (PSM)*.

Interfluve   An area of higher elevation, such as a ridge, that separates streams.

Interior angle   The angle between two sides of a closed or loop traverse measured inside the traverse. Also known as an included angle.

Intermediate contour   The four thin contour lines between index lines. These lines are not normally labeled.

Intermediate foresight   A separate elevation taken in addition to the run of levels for information purposes. Its accuracy cannot be readily checked.

International date line   The earth's 180° meridian.

Internet   A worldwide network of computers connected to one another through telecommunication lines or satellites.

Interpolation   The insertion of missing values between numbers that are given; an educated guess.

Intranet   A computer network, based on Internet technology, that is designed to meet the internal needs for sharing information within a single organization or company.

Invert elevation   The bottom inside elevation of a pipe.

Land survey   A survey that locates property corners and boundary lines; usually a closed traverse.

Latitude   An angle measured from the point at the center of the earth. Imaginary lines that run parallel around the earth, east–west.

Layer   A logical grouping of data, such as transparent overlays of drawing information. Layers allow for details of a design or different drafting information to be separated. Layers are generally of different colors and have their own names. Layers can be kept together, or individual layers can be turned on or off as needed.

Legend   An area on the map that provides general information such as scale, title, and special symbols.

Length of curve   See *curve length*.

Level   A surveying instrument used to measure and transfer elevations. Occasionally used for distance measurements.

Leveling   The process of finding elevation points using a level instrument and a measuring tool such as a Philadelphia rod. The leveling process usually begins at a known elevation in order to determine the elevation of other points or objects.

Line standards   The type of lines and line thickness commonly used in civil drafting.

Line work   Refers to the placement and correct use of lines, shapes, and symbols on a drawing. Typically, line work represents the majority of information on a plan or map.

Local attraction   Any local influence that causes a magnetic needle to deflect away from the magnetic meridian.

Longitude   Imaginary lines that connect the north and south poles.

Loop traverse   A closed traverse that returns and "closes" on the point of beginning.

Lot and block   A method that describes land by referring to a recorded plat, lot number, county, and state.

Magnetic azimuth   A direction measured with magnetic north as the zero line.

Magnetic declination   The horizontal angle between the magnetic meridian and the true meridian.

Magnetic meridian   The meridian indicated by the needle of a magnetic compass.

Magnetic north (MN)   The direction a compass north arrow points.

Manhole   Also sometimes referred to as a maintenance hole, an underground structure used for maintenance access or for making connections to underground utilities and other services, including sewers, telephone, electricity, storm drains, and gas. A manhole is protected by a manhole cover, which is a metal or concrete cover designed to prevent accidental or unauthorized access to the manhole. The manhole cover is the round steel or cast iron plate that you typically see in streets and roads.

Map   A graphic representation of part of or the entire earth's surface, drawn to scale on a plane surface.

Map scale An aid in estimating distances.

Mean sea level (MSL) The average of high and low tides taken over an extended period of time.

Meridian A line of longitude.

Metes and bounds A method of describing and locating property by measurements from a known starting point.

Metric scale See *drawing scale*.

Military map Any map with information of military importance.

Mil A unit of angular measure. One mil equals 1/6400 of the circumference of a circle.

Minutes (') One-sixtieth of 1 degree. See also *degree*.

Model A CADD term that refers to the individual elements that make up a final drawing, such as the property lines, buildings, utilities, dimensions, and various drawing features.

Model file The file or files containing a CADD model. See also *model* .

Mylar The trade name of plastic media used as a base for drawings in the drafting industry. Also known as polyester film.

Nautical chart A special map used as an aid in water navigation, providing information such as water depth, bridge clearance, and overhead cables.

NAVSTAR GPS A satellite constellation of 24 operational satellites, with 5 satellites available as spares, operated and maintained by the U.S. Air Force for use by global positioning systems worldwide.

Numerical scale The proportion between the length of a line on a map and the corresponding length on the earth's surface.

Open traverse A survey that does not return to the point of beginning and does not have to end on a control point.

Parameter See *parametric solid modeling (PSM)*.

Parametric modeling Modeling with high-level software in which the user must enter specific data about the object being designed, such as a new highway alignment, and then the software creates the design in a 3D model. Parametric modeling software contains rules, or *constraints*, that govern how a component is structured.

Parametric solid modeling (PSM) Modeling that involves the development of solid models containing parameters, which are controls, constraints, and checks that allow you to easily and effectively make changes and updates. This means that when you describe the size, shape, and location of model geometry using specific parameters, you can easily modify those specifications to explore alternative design options. The parametric concept is also referred to as intelligence because parametric modeling occurs as a result of a software program's ability to store and manage model information.

Parcel-based application Any of a number of GIS applications related to land use planning, processing of building permits, tax assessment, inventorying of vacant land, and school enrollment adjustment.

Percent of grade The angular slope of a road. A 1 percent grade rises 1 ft vertically for every 100 ft of horizontal distance. A 100 percent grade is a 45° angle.

Philadelphia rod An instrument used for measuring elevations. It is 7 ft long, can extend to 12 or 13 ft, and is graduated to hundredths of a foot, but it can be read to thousandths.

Photogrammetric map A map made using aerial photographs. These photos are accurately scaled and transferred to the map drawing.

Photogrammetric survey A survey in which aerial photographs are taken in several overlapping flights. A photogrammetric survey becomes the "field notes" from which maps can be created.

Plan   A drawing that shows the detailed construction information looking down from above and can display buildings, roads, curbs, walks, and subsurface construction features such as sewers and utilities. The building outline on one side of the plan is the same building identified in the site area.

Plan and profile   A drawing composed of a plan view and profile view (usually located directly below the plan). This type of drawing is often created for projects such as highways, sewer and water lines, street improvements, etc.

Plane survey   A survey conducted as if the earth were flat. Curvature of the earth is not considered; therefore, plane geometry and plane trigonometry are used.

Planning map   A map used by planners that can be based on a variety of map types overlaid with information, such as zoning boundaries, urban growth boundaries, or population density.

Plat   A map of a piece of land. Also referred to as a plot plan or site plan. A plat is commonly considered to be a group of sites.

Plot plan   Also referred to as a site plan, a legal document that contains an accurate drawing and a written legal description of a piece of land.

Plumb bob   A pointed weight with a line attached to the top that is used in locating surveying instruments directly over a point or station. In chaining, a plumb bob is used to locate exact distance measurements directly over a station point.

Plunge   To flip an instrument or turn it over on its transverse axis.

Point of beginning   The point at which a survey begins.

Point of curve   The point at which a highway curve begins.

Point of intersection   The point at which two straight lines (bearings) intersect. Commonly used in highway centerline layout.

Point of reverse curve   The point at which one curve ends and the next curve begins. See also *reverse curve*.

Point of tangency   The point at the end of a curve.

Polygon   A closed figure with any number of straight-line segment sides but with no fewer than three sides. A regular polygon has equal-length sides and equal internal angles.

Position   The latitude, longitude, and altitude of a point.

Prime meridian   The imaginary line connecting the north and south poles and passing through Greenwich, England; represents 0° longitude.

Principal meridian   A meridian used as a basis for establishing a reference line for the origin of the rectangular system.

Profile   An outline of a cross section of the earth.

Prolongation   The extension of the preceding line of a survey beyond the current station point.

Quadrangle map   A type of cadastral map that shows the division of land into grids known as sections. See also *cadastral map*.

Quadrant   One of the four 90° quadrants of the compass circle: north–east, northwest, southeast, and southwest.

Radial survey   A survey in which control points are established by a method called *radiation*, in which measurements are taken from a survey instrument located at a central point, called a *transit station*. From this point, a series of angular and distance measurements called *side shots* are made to specific points.

Radius curve   The radius (measured in feet or meters) of a highway curve.

Range   A fixed distance between two points, such as between a starting and an ending waypoint or a satellite and a GPS receiver.

Raster   An image or a display composed of colored dots, or "bits." A raster image has no scale or numerical values such as length or elevation.

Raster format   A data format that consists of an array of cells, sometimes called grids or pixels (picture elements). Each cell references a row and column, and it contains a number representing the type of value of the attribute being mapped.

Rasterization   The conversion of vector data to raster data.

Raw data file   A file that is created in a survey instrument as field data is collected. This file contains all the measurements and calculations, known as "observations," and can be used to create a digital terrain model.

Rectangular system   A land legal description system that uses base lines and meridians in an arrangement of rows and blocks called townships. Each township is 6 miles square and is divided by rows and tiers creating a checkerboard of 36 squares called sections. Each section can be further divided, establishing a format for property identification.

Relief   Variations in the shape and elevation of land. Hills and valleys shown on a map constitute "local relief."

Representative fraction   The proportion between the length of a line on a map and the corresponding length on the earth's surface. See also *numerical scale*.

Reverse curve   An S curve that contains no straight sections between curves. See also *point of reverse curve*.

Rod   A square-shaped pole graduated to hundredths of a foot that is used to measure elevations and distances when viewed through a level or transit.

Route survey   An open traverse used to map linear features such as highways, pipelines, and power lines. A route survey does not have to close on itself or end on a control point.

Saddle   A low spot between two hills or mountain peaks.

Scale factor   A numerical value used in the proper scaling of text, dimension objects such as dimension text and arrowheads or slashes, and the size of model limits.

Scanner   A device that allows information to be transferred from paper-based drawings to CAD drawings. It is moved over the existing drawing and "reads" two-dimensional lines, converting them to data that can be read by the CAD system.

Seconds (″)   One-sixtieth of a minute. See also *degree*.

Section   A division of the rectangular system. A section is 1 mile square, containing 640 acres. In drawing terminology, a section cuts through something partially or completely to view it from the side.

Selective availability (SA)   Errors in data and satellite-clock dithering deliberately induced by the Department of Defense to restrict full GPS accuracy to authorized users, typically the U.S. military.

Septic tank   A concrete or steel tank used for sewage disposal that disperses wastewater to a system of underground lines and into the earth.

Sheet   In CADD, the layout that brings the model files together to create the composite drawing. It includes the border and title block.

Site plan   A plot plan with a building construction project shown, dimensioned, and located. A site plan includes the proposed building and other features, such as driveways, walks, and utilities. See also *plot plan*.

Soft copy   The computer software version of the drawing that you see on the computer screen, or the actual data file.

Space segment   The 24 satellites of the GPS system broadcasting signals that travel at the speed of light.

Spatial data   Data that describes a feature location.

Specific notes   Also known as local notes, notes that relate to specific features or instructions within a drawing.

Spreadsheet A program used for number-related information processing that is displayed in a table format.

Stadia A type of distance measurement that uses a level and a rod. Also a Greek term referring to a unit of length equal to 606 feet, 9 inches.

Standards checking A procedure by which drawings are checked against a "base" drawing that contains up-to-date drawing, design, and construction standards for a specific discipline or trade.

State plane coordinate (SPC) system A grid system that has known and precise coordinates in relation to the three-dimensional earth. It allows portions of the earth to be drawn accurately in two dimensions.

Stations Arbitrary points established in a survey usually located 100 ft apart. An instrument setup point is often referred to as a station.

Statute mile An international standard distance, intended as a permanent rule. A statute mile has 5,280 ft.

Stereo pair Aerial photos that have overlapping images and are placed under a stereoscope for 3D viewing.

Stereoscope A device that allows the viewer to see elevations in aerial photographs by viewing two identical photographs side by side.

Subdivision A parcel of land divided into small plats usually used for building sites.

Supplementary contour An additional contour line used when the normal contour interval is too large to clearly illustrate significant topographic features on land that has a gentle slope.

Surveyor's compass A compass used in mapping to calculate the direction of a line. The reading is usually a bearing or an included angle.

Symbol library A collection of symbols compiled and archived for future use.

Tabular data Information placed in table format.

Template A pattern of a standard or commonly used feature or features that are created once and then used on following drawings. A collection of symbols in a symbol library could be called a template. If you create a base drawing that contains standard components, values, settings, and borders and title blocks, it is referred to as a *template drawing*.

Template drawing See *template*.

Terrain The shape and lay of the land.

Text The words on a drawing when created using CADD or lettering when using manual drafting methods.

Text style A text style gives height, width, angle, and other characteristics of a text font.

Theodolite A precise surveying instrument that is used to measure angles, distances, and elevations.

Title block A block of information found on a drawing, usually in the lower-right corner or along the right edge.

Topographic map A map that represents the surface features of a region.

Topographic survey A survey that locates and describes features on the land, both natural and artificial. Often accomplished through the use of aerial photography.

Topography The science of representing surface features of a region on maps and charts.

Topology A branch of mathematics that deals with relationships among geometric objects.

Total station An electronic surveying instrument that measures horizontal and vertical angles, combined with distance measurement. Also referred to as an *electronic total station*.

Township A division of the rectangular system. A township is 6 miles square.

Transit line   The centerline of a linear survey (highway, pipeline, etc.).

Traverse   Any line surveyed across a parcel of land and a series of such lines connecting a number of points. A closed traverse is a polygon.

Triangulated irregular network (TIN)   A network of triangles that CADD software ccreates by connecting surveyed ground points. Each triangle represents a face on the surface, and the elevations of the corners of the face are known quantities.

Triangulation   The process of using a series of intersecting triangles as a reference in geodetic surveys. Some sides of these triangles may be hundreds of miles long and cross political boundaries.

True azimuth   A horizontal angle measured using true north as the reference line.

True north (TN)   The location of the north pole, also called geographic north, geographic meridian, and true meridian.

Turning point   A temporary bench mark (often a long screwdriver, stone, or anything stable) used as a pivot for a rod. The turning point can be both a backsight and a foresight for the rod.

Uniform drawing system   An eight-module system created by the Construction Specifications Institute (CSI) for organizing and presenting building design information.

Uniform slope theory   A theory that involves the equal spacing of contours between known points. This theory assumes that the slope of the ground between two elevation points is a straight line.

User interface   The way you and the computer communicate with each other to get the work done. The user interface includes what you see on the screen, the keys you have to press to get things done, and any other devices, such as the mouse you use to control the computer.

User segment   The user's portion of GPS including receivers and antennas.

Utilities   Service items to a home, business, or industry, such as electrical, gas, phone, or TV cable.

Vector   (1) A point or geometric feature that has a numerical location value. The endpoints of a line are vectors. The center of a circle is a vector. (2) The most common format for storing special data such as points, lines, and polygons in a computer. All computer-aided drafting programs use the vector data format.

Vellum   Transparent paper used in the drafting industry.

Verbal scale   A map scale expressed in the number of inches to the mile.

Vertical curve   The shape of a linear feature such as a road or highway (in profile) as it crests a hill or creates a sag in a valley or depression.

Vertical scale   The map scale given to a profile view showing vertical (elevation) relationships of features on and below the ground surface (grade). The vertical scale is often exaggerated to give a clear picture of the shape of the land. On plan and profile drawings, the vertical scale is often 10 times greater than the horizontal scale. For example, if the plan is $1'' = 50'$, then the vertical scale of the profile is $1'' = 5'$.

Vicinity map   A map showing a project site in relation to the surrounding area. This map provides information for access to the site.

Water features   Map features representing water, such as lakes, rivers, streams, and intermittent waters.

World Wide Web (WWW)   An interface for the Internet. See also *Internet*.

Abbreviations

AB	Anchor bolt
ABDN	Abandon
ABV	Above
AC	Asbestos cement, Asphaltic concrete
ACI	American Concrete Institute
ADJ	Adjacent, Adjustable
AHR	Anchor
AISC	American Institute of Steel Construction
ANSI	American National Standards Institute
APPROX	Approximate
ASPH	Asphalt
B & S	Bell and Spigot
BETW	Between
BKGD	Background
BL	Base line
BLDG	Building
BLT	Bolt
BLW	Bellow
BM	Beam, bench mark
BOT	Bottom
BRG	Bearing
BSMT	Basement
B/U	Built up
BV	Butterfll valve
BVC	Begin vertical curve
C TO C	Center to center
CB	Catch basin
CCP	Concrete cylinder pipe
CFM	Cubic feet per minute
CFS	Cubic feet per second
CI	Cast iron
CISP	Cast iron soil pipe
CJ	Construction joint
CLG	Ceiling
CLR	Clear, clearance
CMP	Corrugated metal pipe
CMU	Concrete masonry units
CO	Cleanout
COL	Column
CONC	Concrete
CONN	Connection

CONST	Construction
CONT	Contiune, continuous
CSO	Combined sewerage outlet
CSP	Concrete sewer pipe
CTR	Center
CYL	Cylinder
D	Degree of curve
D or DR	Drain
DIA	Diameter
DIAG	Diagonal
DIR	Direction
DIST	Distance
DN	Down
DTM	Digital terrain model
DWG	Drawing
EA	Each
EDM	Electronic distance meter
EF	Each face
EL or ELEV	Elevation
EOP	Edge of pavement
EQL SP	Equally spaced
EQPT	Equipment
EVC	End vertical curve
EW	Each Way
EXP	Expansion
EXP JT	Expansion joint
EXST	Existing
EXT	Exterior, extension
FCO	Floor cleanout
FD	Floor drain
FDN	Foundation
FG	Finish grade
FL	Floor, floor line, flow
FLL	Flow line
FOC	Face of concrete
FPM	Feet per minute
FPS	Feet per second
FS	Foresight
FTG	Footing
GN	Grid north
GND	Ground
GNSS	Global navigation satellite system
GPM	Gallons per minute
GPS	Gallons per second

GPS	Global positioning system		PSIG	Pounds per square inch, gauge
GR or GRD	Grade		PT	Point of tangency
GTV	Gate valve		PVC	Polyvinyl chloride
GVL	Gravel		PVMT	Pavement
HB	Hose bibb		R	Radius curve
HD	Hub drain		RC	Reinforced concrete
HDR	Header		RCP	Reinforced concrete pipe
HGT	Height		RD	Rain drain, roof drain
HI	Height of the instrument		REINF	Reinforce
HORIZ	Horizontal		REPL	Replace
ID	Inside diameter		REQD	Required
IE	Invert elevation		RMV	Remove
IF	Inside face		RW	Right-of-way
IFS	Intermediate foresight		SCHED	Schedule
IN	Inch		SECT	Section
INFL	Influent		SH	Sheet
INSTL	Installation		SPEC	Specification
INTR	Interior		SQ	Square
INVT	Invert		STA	Station
JT	Joint		STL	Steel
L	Length of Curve		STR	Straight
LATL	Lateral		STRUCT	Structure
LONG	Longitudinal		SUBMG	Submerged
MATL	Material		SYMM	Symmetrical
MAX	Maximum		T & B	Top and bottom
MH	Manhole		T & G	Tongue and groove
MIN	Minimum		TBM	Temporary bench mark
MISC	Miscellaneous		TC	Top of concrete
MN	Magnetic north		TD	Tangent distance
MON	Monument		TEMP	Temporary
MSL	Mean sea level		TF	Top face
NA	Not applicable		THK	Thick
NTS	Not to Scale		THKNS	Thickness
O TO O	Out ot out		TIN	Triangulated irregular network
OC	On center		TN	True north
OD	Outside diameter		TO	Top of
OF	Outside face		TOC	Top of curb
OPNG	Opening		TP	Turning point
OPP	Opposite		TRANSV	Transverse
ORIG	Original		TST	Top of steel
PC	Point of curve		TW	Top of wall
PI	Point of intersection		TYP	Typical
PL	Plate, property line		UTM	Universal transverse mercator
PLG	Piling		VC	Vertical curve
POB	Point of beginning		VERT	Vertical
PP	Piping		W/	With
PRC	Point of reverse curve		W/O	Without
PRCST	Precast		WP	Working point
PRESS	Pressure		WS	Water surface, waterstop, welded steel
PRV	Pressure reducing valve			

Index